P. K. DAS

# ANTI-BRIBERY AND ANTI-CORRUPTION LAWS IN INDIA

P.K. DAS

# ANTI-BRIBERY AND ANTI-CORRUPTION LAWS IN INDIA

Revised by

Editorial Board
Thakkar Law House (Whitesmann)

SECOND EDITION 2024

WHITESMANN PUBLISHING

First Edition 2019
Second Edition 2024



ISBN: 978-81-19725-86-1

**Published by:**
**WHITESMANN™**
**Vijay Thakkar**
**Thakkar Law House**
**Delhi -** 121-122, Rajendra Market, Near Telephone Exchange,
Opp. Tishazari Court Gate No. 3, Delhi - 110054
Mob. # 9818411155 | Ph. : 011-41824421, 42544595, 45530268
011-20833563
**Branch Office:**
**Faridabad -** 3 C/122, N.I.T. Faridabad, Haryana - 121001
Ph. : 0129-4899004, 4899453
E-mail : thakkarlawhouse@gmail.com
Website : www.whitesmann.com
www.thakkarlawhouse.com



Printed & Bound in India.

# PREFACE

*"Power tends to corrupt, and absolute power corrupts absolutely. Great men are almost bad men...".*

Lord Acton, British Catholic Historian, Politician and Writer in his letter to an Anglican Bishop.

In India or elsewhere in the globe the corruption prevails in the sphere of administration and those who are in the wheel of power or those are in the link of power practice. Always the people in every corner in the world who are victims of such practice including their governments shout against it. Many a time the contemporary governments try to eradicate these corrupt practice by their effort through their executives and anti-corruption bodies etc. and also by making the anti-corruption laws at centre or in State levels.

In British India just in the same year of its independence the first anti-corruption law viz The Prevention of Corruption Act, 1947 had been enacted. But this Act became obsolete and The Prevention of Corruption Act, 1988 repealed the above Act to deal with such menace and this Act was amended from time to time to tackle such practice and the very latest Amending Act was in Monsoon Session of Parliament in 2018 (16 of 2018) with effect from 26th July 2018.Besides India has more than 18 enactments against corruption. All these laws are given in this Book. The most important and the foremost Acts are The Lokpal and Lokayuktas Act of 2013, The Foreign Contribution (Regulation ) Act, 2010, The Black Money (Undisclosed Foreign Income and Assets) and Imposition of Tax Act, 2015 and The Fugitive Economic Offenders Act, 2018 etc. These Laws were enacted in lieu of the fight of government and the people of India against corruption and against black money etc.

It is also the fact that the Indian judiciary always try to punish the offenders of such practice whenever the case comes to its Bench. But on the contrary it applies its juristic mind to acquit the innocent public servants while trying these cases on the ground of humanistic approach, its cause and concern of human rights and good conscience. A separate Part on acquittal of innocent public servants who had been acquitted by the Supreme Court from corruption charges has been given for the reference of our esteem readers.

On the above grounds this Book has been prepared by including A to Z anti-bribery and anti-corruption laws and it is hoped that this Book can be helpful for the Bench, Bar, Public Servants, Law Libraries, Anti-corruption Bureaus both at centre and in States including Special Courts in the States and the people who are interested in this subject.

**New Delhi**
**14th May, 2019**

**P.K. DAS**
**email: pkumardaslawyer@gmail.com**

# CONTENTS



# PART - 1

# ANTI-BRIBERY AND ANTI-CORRUPTION LAWS IN INDIA

# THE PREVENTION OF CORRUPTION ACT, 1988

## CHAPTER I

## PRELIMINARY



## CHAPTER II

## APPOINTMENT OF SPECIAL JUDGES



## CHAPTER III

## OFFENCES AND PENALTIES

CHAPTER IV

**INVESTIGATION INTO CASES UNDER THE ACT**



CHAPTER IVA

**ATTACHMENT AND FORFEITURE OF PROPERTY**



CHAPTER V

**SANCTION FOR PROSECUTION AND OTHER MISCELLANEOUS PROVISIONS**



# THE CENTRAL VIGILANCE COMMISSION ACT, 2003

CHAPTER I

**PRELIMINARY**

## CHAPTER II

## THE CENTRAL VIGILANCE COMMISSION



## CHAPTER III

## FUNCTIONS AND POWERS OF THE CENTRAL VIGILANCE COMMISSION



## CHAPTER IV

## EXPENSES AND ANNUAL REPORT



## CHAPTER V

## MISCELLANEOUS

## THE COMMISSIONS OF INQUIRY ACT, 1952

## THE CRIMINAL LAW (AMENDMENT) ORDINANCE, 1944



## THE DELHI SPECIAL POLICE ESTABLISHMENT ACT, 1946

## THE DEPARTMENTAL INQUIRIES (ENFORCEMENT OF ATTENDANCE OF WITNESSES AND PRODUCTION OF DOCUMENTS) ACT, 1972



## THE FOREIGN CONTRIBUTION (REGULATION) ACT, 2010

CHAPTER I

**PRELIMINARY**



CHAPTER II

**REGULATION OF FOREIGN CONTRIBUTION AND FOREIGN HOSPITALITY**

CHAPTER III

**REGISTRATION**



CHAPTER IV

**ACCOUNTS, INTIMATION, AUDIT AND DISPOSAL OF ASSETS, ETC.**



CHAPTER V

**INSPECTION, SEARCH AND SEIZURE**

## CHAPTER VI
## ADJUDICATION



## CHAPTER VII
## APPEAL AND REVISION



## CHAPTER VIII
## OFFENCES AND PENALTIES



## CHAPTER IX
## MISCELLANEOUS

# THE FUGITIVE ECONOMIC OFFENDERS ACT, 2018

## CHAPTER I

## PRELIMINARY



## CHAPTER II

## DECLARATION OF FUGITIVE ECONOMIC OFFENDERS AND CONFISCATION OF PROPERTY



## CHAPTER III

## MISCELLANEOUS

# THE RIGHT TO INFORMATION ACT, 2005

## CHAPTER I
## PRELIMINARY



## CHAPTER II
## RIGHT TO INFORMATION AND OBLIGATIONS OF PUBLIC AUTHORITIES



## CHAPTER III
## THE CENTRAL INFORMATION COMMISSION



## CHAPTER IV
## THE STATE INFORMATION COMMISSION

## CHAPTER V

## POWERS AND FUNCTIONS OF THE INFORMATION COMMISSIONS, APPEAL AND PENALTIES



## CHAPTER VI

## MISCELLANEOUS



# THE SPECIAL COURT (TRIAL OF OFFENCES RELATING TO TRANSACTIONS IN SECURITIES) ACT, 1992

## THE WHISTLE BLOWERS PROTECTION ACT, 2014

CHAPTER I

**PRELIMINARY**



CHAPTER II

**PUBLIC INTEREST DISCLOSURE**



CHAPTER III

**INQUIRY IN RELATION TO PUBLIC INTEREST DISCLOSURE**



CHAPTER IV

**POWERS OF COMPETENT AUTHORITY**

CHAPTER V

**PROTECTION TO THE PERSONS MAKING DISCLOSURE**



CHAPTER VI

**OFFENCES AND PENALTIES**



CHAPTER VII

**MISCELLANEOUS**



# THE PREVENTION OF CORRUPTION ACT, 1947

## THE PROHIBITION OF BENAMI PROPERTY TRANSACTIONS ACT, 1988

CHAPTER I

**PRELIMINARY**



CHAPTER II

**PROHIBITION OF BENAMI TRANSACTIONS**



CHAPTER III

**AUTHORITIES**

CHAPTER VI

**SPECIAL COURTS**



CHAPTER VII

**OFFENCES AND PROSECUTION**



CHAPTER VIII

**MISCELLANEOUS**

# THE BLACK MONEY (UNDISCLOSED FOREIGN INCOME AND ASSETS) AND IMPOSITION OF TAX ACT, 2015

CHAPTER I

**PRELIMINARY**



CHAPTER II

**BASIS OF CHARGE**



CHAPTER III

**TAX MANAGEMENT**

CHAPTER IV

**PENALTIES**

CHAPTER VII

**GENERAL PROVISIONS**



## THE LOKPAL AND LOKAYUKTAS ACT, 2013

PART I

**PRELIMINARY**

## PART II

## LOKPAL FOR THE UNION

### CHAPTER I

### DEFINITIONS



### CHAPTER II

### ESTABLISHMENT OF LOKPAL



### CHAPTER III

### INQUIRY WING



### CHAPTER IV

### PROSECUTION WING



### CHAPTER V

### EXPENSES OF LOKPAL TO BE CHARGED ON CONSOLIDATED FUND OF INDIA



### CHAPTER VI

### JURISDICTION IN RESPECT OF INQUIRY

PART III

ESTABLISHMENT OF THE LOKAYUKTA



## RELEVANT PROVISIONS OF THE CENTRAL CIVIL SERVICES (CONDUCT) RULES, 1964



## RELEVANT PROVISIONS OF THE ALL INDIA SERVICES (CONDUCT) RULES, 1968

# RELEVANT PROVISIONS OF TIIE CENTRAL CIVIL SERVICES (CLASSIFICATION, CONTROL AND APPEAL) RULES, 1965

## PART - 2
## ACQUITTAL OF PUBLIC SERVANTS FROM CORRUPTION CHARGES BY SUPREME COURT

## ACQUITTAL OF PUBLIC SERVANTS BY SUPREME COURT FROM CORRUPTION CHARGES

# TABLE OF CASES

## A

## M

**T**

# PART - 1

# ANTI-BRIBERY AND ANTI-CORRUPTION LAWS IN INDIA

# THE PREVENTION OF CORRUPTION ACT, 1988

(49 of 1988)

[*9th September, 1988*]

*An Act to consolidate and amend the law relating to the prevention of corruption and for matters connected therewith.*

BE it enacted by Parliament in the Thirty-ninth Year of the Republic of India as follows:—

## CHAPTER I

## PRELIMINARY

**1. Short title and extent.**—(1) This Act may be called the Prevention of Corruption Act, 1988.

(2) It extends to the whole of India [1][***] and it applies also to all citizens of India outside India.

### COMMENTS

**(i) Question of Prospective and Retrospective nature of an Act**

The well settled principle of law is that a substantive provision unless specifically provided for or otherwise intended by the Parliament should be interpreted to be a prospective operation. The legal principle or the rule of law is also that all statutes should be presumed to have only a prospective operation.

*Jawahar Singh v. State of NCT of Delhi,* AIR 2009 SC 2391; *Sukhdev Singh v. State of Haryana,* (2013) 2 SCC 212.

**(ii) When an amendment should be retrospective**

If a particular amending act is clarification in nature, it would be a retrospective amendment.

*Vishal Agarwal v. Chhattisgarh State Electricity Board,* (2014) 1 Supreme Today 326.

**(iii) Principle of interpretation of penal provisions**

The penal provisions, particular with harder punishments ought to be construed strictly. The principle of substantive compliance would be applicable in the cases, where the language of the provision strictly or by necessary implication, admits of such compliance.

*Kishan Chand v. State of Haryana,* 2014 Cr. L.J. 841.

**(iv) Principle of interpretation of negative words**

The negative words are rarely held to be directory. The grammertic meaning affords to better guide to ascertain the intention of the legislative intent.

*Ashraf Khan v. State of Gujarat,* (2012) 11 SCC 606.

**(v) Interpretation of provisions of special and general laws**

The general law must be held the special provisions if there is a special procedure contained in the special Act.

*State of N.C.T. of Delhi v. Narendra,* (2014) 1 Supreme Today 181.

**2. Definitions.**—In this Act, unless the context otherwise requires,—

(a) "election" means any election, by whatever means held under any law for the purpose of selecting members of Parliament or of any Legislature, local authority or other public authority;

---

1. The words "except the State of Jammu and Kashmir" stood omitted by the Jammu and Kashmir Reorganisation Act, 2019 (34 of 2019), Sections 95, 96 and the Fifth Schedule (Table-1) (w.e.f. October 31, 2019).

[1][(aa) "prescribed" means prescribed by rules made under this Act and the expression "prescribe" shall be construed accordingly;]

(b) "public duty" means a duty in the discharge of which the State, the public or the community at large has an interest;

*Explanation.*—In this clause "State" includes a corporation established by or under a Central, Provincial or State Act, or an authority or a body owned or controlled or aided by the Government or a Government company as defined in section 617 of the Companies Act, 1956 (1 of 1956);

(c) "public servant" means—

(i) any person in the service or pay of the Government or remunerated by the Government by fees or commission for the performance of any public duty;

(ii) any person in the service or pay of a local authority;

(iii) any person in the service or pay of a corporation established by or under a Central, Provincial or State Act, or an authority or a body owned or controlled or aided by the Government or a Government company as defined in section 617 of the Companies Act, 1956 (1 of 1956);

(iv) any Judge, including any person empowered by law to discharge, whether by himself or as a member of any body of persons, any adjudicatory functions;

(v) any person authorised by a court of justice to perform any duty, in connection with the administration of justice, including a liquidator, receiver or commissioner appointed by such court;

(vi) any arbitrator or other person to whom any cause or matter has been referred for decision or report by a court of justice or by a competent public authority;

(vii) any person who holds an office by virtue of which he is empowered to prepare, publish, maintain or revise an electoral roll or to conduct an election or part of an election;

(viii) any person who holds an office by virtue of which he is authorised or required to perform any public duty;

(ix) any person who is the president, secretary or other office-bearer of a registered co-operative society engaged in agriculture, industry, trade or banking, receiving or having received any financial aid from the Central Government or a State Government or from any corporation established by or under a Central, Provincial or State Act, or any authority or body owned or controlled or aided by the Government or a Government company as defined in section 617 of the Companies Act, 1956 (1 of 1956);

(x) any person who is a chairman, member or employee of any Service Commission or Board, by whatever name called, or a member of any selection committee appointed by such Commission or Board

1. Inst. by Act 16 of 2018, Section 2(i) (w.e.f. July 26, 2018, according to S.O. 3664(E), dt. July 26, 2018).

for the conduct of any examination or making any selection on behalf of such Commission or Board;

(xi) any person who is a Vice-Chancellor or member of any governing body, professor, reader, lecturer or any other teacher or employee, by whatever designation called, of any University and any person whose services have been availed of by a University or any other public authority in connection with holding or conducting examinations;

(xii) any person who is an office-bearer or an employee of an educational, scientific, social, cultural or other institution, in whatever manner established, receiving or having received any financial assistance from the Central Government or any State Government, or local or other public authority.

*Explanation 1.*—Persons falling under any of the above sub-clauses are public servants, whether appointed by the Government or not.

*Explanation 2.*—Wherever the words "public servant" occur, they shall be understood of every person who is in actual possession of the situation of a public servant, whatever legal defect there may be in his right to hold that situation.

[1][(d) "undue advantage" means any gratification whatever, other than legal remuneration.

*Explanation.*—For the purposes of this clause,—

(a) the word "gratification" is not limited to pecuniary gratifications or to gratifications estimable in money;

(b) the expression "legal remuneration" is not restricted to remuneration paid to a public servant, but includes all remuneration which he is permitted by the Government or the organisation, which he serves, to receive.]

## COMMENTS

**(i) When a word is not defined**

If a particular words is not defined in the Act, the definition given in another statute is also its dictionary meaning can be given for deciding the matter.

*Wichha Sugar Company Ltd. v. Tarai Chinni Mill Mazdoor Union*, (2014) 1 Supreme Today, 169.

**(ii) Definition of Public Servant under Section 21 of IPC and under Section 2 of 1988 Act**

The words "Public Servant" defined under Section 21 of Indian Penal Code is no relevance under the Prevention of Corruption Act of 1988.

*State of M.P. v. Pravakar Rao*, 2002 SCC (Cri.) 1831.

**(iii) Scope of the words "Public Servant"**

The working of the Act justifies that claims made in the Statement of Objects and Reasons of the Act envisages widening of the scope of the expression to public servant. "Because it is given a prime position in the Act. Hence it is no longer

1. Inst. by Act 16 of 2018, Section 2(ii) (w.e.f. July 26, 2018, according to S.O. 3664(E), dt. July 26, 2018).

necessary to refer to Section 21 of IPC for the purpose of interpretation of the words of public servant".

**(iv) Public duty**

A duty assigned to a public servant is public duty provided that it is not illegal or against public policy. The duty may have been assigned by a statute or by the administrative order.

*Duttatraya Narayana Patil v. State of Maharashtra*, AIR 1975 SC 1685: 1975 Cr.L.R. (SC) 355.

## CHAPTER II
## APPOINTMENT OF SPECIAL JUDGES

**3. Power to appoint special Judges.**—(1) The Central Government or the State Government may, by notification in the Official Gazette, appoint as many special Judges as may be necessary for such area or areas or for such case or group of cases as may be specified in the notification to try the following offences, namely:—

(a) any offence punishable under this Act; and

(b) any conspiracy to commit or any attempt to commit or any abetment of any of the offences specified in clause (a).

(2) A person shall not be qualified for appointment as a special Judge under this Act unless he is or has been a Sessions Judge or an Additional Sessions Judge or an Assistant Sessions Judge under the Code of Criminal Procedure, 1973 (2 of 1974).

**4. Cases triable by special Judges.**—(1) Notwithstanding anything contained in the Code of Criminal Procedure, 1973 (2 of 1974), or in any other law for the time being in force, the offences specified in sub-section (1) of section 3 shall be tried by special Judges only.

(2) Every offence specified in sub-section (1) of section 3 shall be tried by the special Judge for the area within which it was committed, or, as the case may be, by the special Judge appointed for the case, or where there are more special Judges than one for such area, by such one of them as may be specified in this behalf by the Central Government.

(3) When trying any case, a special Judge may also try any offence, other than an offence specified in section 3, with which the accused may, under the Code of Criminal Procedure, 1973 (2 of 1974), be charged at the same trial.

[1][(4) Notwithstanding anything contained in the Code of Criminal Procedure, 1973 (2 of 1974), the trial of an offence shall be held, as far as practicable, on day-to-day basis and an endeavour shall be made to ensure that the said trial is concluded within a period of two years:

Provided that where the trial is not concluded within the said period, the special Judge shall record the reasons for not having done so:

---

1. Subst. by Act 16 of 2018, Section 3, for Sub-s. 4 (w.e.f. July 26, 2018, according to S.O. 3664(E), dt. July 26, 2018). Sub-s. (4), prior to subst., ran as under:

"(4) Notwithstanding anything contained in the Code of Criminal Procedure, 1973 (2 of 1974), a special Judge shall, as far as practicable, hold the trial of an offence on day-to-day basis.".

Provided further that the said period may be extended by such further period, for reasons to be recorded in writing but not exceeding six months at a time; so, however, that the said period together with such extended period shall not exceed ordinarily four years in aggregate.]

**5. Procedure and powers of special Judge.**—(1) A special Judge may take cognizance of offences without the accused being committed to him for trial and, in trying the accused persons, shall follow the procedure prescribed by the Code of Criminal Procedure, 1973 (2 of 1974), for the trial of warrant cases by the Magistrates.

(2) A special Judge may, with a view to obtaining the evidence of any person supposed to have been directly or indirectly concerned in, or privy to, an offence, tender a pardon to such person on condition of his making a full and true disclosure of the whole circumstances within his knowledge relating to the offence and to every other person concerned, whether as principal or abettor, in the commission thereof and any pardon so tendered shall, for the purposes of sub-sections (1) to (5) of section 308 of the Code of Criminal Procedure, 1973 (2 of 1974), be deemed to have been tendered under section 307 of that Code.

(3) Save as provided in sub-section (1) or sub-section (2), the provisions of the Code of Criminal Procedure, 1973 (2 of 1974), shall, so far as they are not inconsistent with this Act, apply to the proceedings before a special Judge; and for the purposes of the said provisions, the Court of the special Judge shall be deemed to be a Court of Session and the person conducting a prosecution before a special Judge shall be deemed to be a public prosecutor.

(4) In particular and without prejudice to the generality of the provisions contained in sub-section (3), the provisions of sections 326 and 475 of the Code of Criminal Procedure, 1973 (2 of 1974), shall, so far as may be, apply to the proceedings before a special Judge and for the purposes of the said provisions, a special Judge shall be deemed to be a Magistrate.

(5) A special Judge may pass upon any person convicted by him any sentence authorised by law for the punishment of the offence of which such person is convicted.

(6) A special Judge, while trying an offence punishable under this Act, shall exercise all the powers and functions exercisable by a District Judge under the Criminal Law Amendment Ordinance, 1944 (Ord. 38 of 1944).

### COMMENTS

#### Grounds for Sustainability of Discharge of Accused Persons by Special Judge

Since, the High Court has not assigned any reason at all as to why it found error with the order of the learned Trial Court discharging appellants herein, a valuable right which accrued in favour of the appellants of being discharged, has been taken away without assigning any reasons, in pursuance whereof, the discharge of the appellants, can be sustained, where (i) by the order dated October 7, 2015, the learned Special Judge had directed that charges be framed against five accused for the offences punishable under Section 120- B of the Indian Penal Code, 1860, read with Sections 13(2) and 13(1)(d) of The Act of 1988, and Sections 420, 465, 468 and 471 of the Indian Penal Code, (ii) the learned Special Judge had further directed that the charges be framed against some of the accused under Section 13(2) read with Section 13(1)(d) of The Act of 1988, as well as Sections 420, 465, 468 and 471 of The Code of 1860, and (iii) insofar as the present appellants are concerned, the learned Special Judge had discharged the accused persons.

*S. K. Tongia v. Central Bureau of Investigation*, MANU/SC/0955/2022.

**6. Power to try summarily.**—(1) Where a special Judge tries any offence specified in sub-section (1) of section 3, alleged to have been committed by a public servant in relation to the contravention of any special order referred to in sub-section (1) of section 12A of the Essential Commodities Act, 1955 (10 of 1955) or of an order referred to in clause (a) of sub-section (2) of that section, then, notwithstanding anything contained in sub-section (1) of section 5 of this Act or section 260 of the Code of Criminal Procedure, 1973 (2 of 1974), the special Judge shall try the offence in a summary way, and the provisions of sections 262 to 265 (both inclusive) of the said Code shall, as far as may be, apply to such trial:

Provided that, in the case of any conviction in a summary trial under this section, it shall be lawful for the special Judge to pass a sentence of imprisonment for a term not exceeding one year:

Provided further that when at the commencement of, or in the course of, a summary trial under this section, it appears to the special Judge that the nature of the case is such that a sentence of imprisonment for a term exceeding one year may have to be passed or that it is, for any other reason, undesirable to try the case summarily, the special Judge shall, after hearing the parties, record an order to that effect and thereafter recall any witnesses who may have been examined and proceed to hear or re-hear the case in accordance with the procedure prescribed by the said Code for the trial of warrant cases by Magistrates.

(2) Notwithstanding anything to the contrary contained in this Act or in the Code of Criminal Procedure, 1973 (2 of 1974), there shall be no appeal by a convicted person in any case tried summarily under this section in which the special Judge passes a sentence of imprisonment not exceeding one month, and of fine not exceeding two thousand rupees whether or not any order under section 452 of the said Code is made in addition to such sentence, but an appeal shall lie where any sentence in excess of the aforesaid limits is passed by the special Judge.

## CHAPTER III

## OFFENCES AND PENALTIES

[1][**7. Offence relating to public servant being bribed.**—Any public servant who,—

(a) obtain or accepts or attempts to obtain from any person, an undue advantage, with the intention to perform or cause performance of public

1. Subst. by Act 16 of 2018, Section 4, for Section 7 (w.e.f. July 26, 2018, according to S.O. 3664(E), dt. July 26, 2018). Previously Section 7 stood amended by Act 1 of 2014, Section 58 and the Schedule (w.e.f. January 16, 2014, according to S.O. 119(E), dt. January 16, 2014). Section 7, prior to subst., ran as under:

"*7. Public servant taking gratification other than legal remuneration in respect of an official act.*—Whoever, being, or expecting to be a public servant, accepts or obtains or agrees to accept or attempts to obtain from any person, for himself or for any other person, any

*Contd. on next page...*

duty improperly or dishonestly or to forbear or cause forbearance to perform such duty either by himself or by another public servant; or

(b) obtain or accepts or attempts to obtain, an undue advantage from any person as a reward for the improper or dishonest performance of a public duty or for forbearing to perform such duty either by himself or another public servant; or

(c) performs or induces another public servant to perform improperly or dishonestly a public duty or to forbear performance of such duty in anticipation of or in consequence of accepting an undue advantage from any person,

shall be punishable, with imprisonment for a term which shall not be less than three years but which may extend to seven years and shall also be liable to fine.

*Explanation 1.*—For the purpose of this section, the obtaining, accepting, or the attempting to obtain an undue advantage shall itself constitute an offence even if the performance of a public duty by public servant, is not or has been improper.

*Illustration*

A public servant, 'S' asks a person, 'P' to give him an amount of five thousand rupees to process his routine ration card application on time. 'S' is guilty of an offence under this section.

*Explanation 2.*—For the purpose of this section, -

(i) the expressions "obtain" or "accept" or "attempts to obtain" shall cover cases where a person being a public servant, obtain or "accepts" or

---

*...contd. from previous page*

gratification whatever, other than legal remuneration, as a motive or reward for doing or forbearing to do any official act or for showing or forbearing to show, in the exercise of his official functions, favour or disfavour to any person or for rendering or attempting to render any service or disservice to any person, with the Central Government or any State Government or Parliament or the Legislature of any State or with any local authority, corporation or Government company referred to in clause (c) of section 2, or with any public servant, whether named or otherwise, shall be punishable with imprisonment which shall be not less than three years but which may extend to seven years and shall also be liable to fine.

*Explanations.*—(a) "Expecting to be a public servant". If a person not expecting to be in office obtains a gratification by deceiving others into a belief that he is about to be in office, and that he will then serve them, he may be guilty of cheating, but he is not guilty of the offence defined in this section.

(b) "Gratification". The word "gratification" is not restricted to pecuniary gratifications or to gratifications estimable in money.

(c) "Legal remuneration". The words "legal remuneration" are not restricted to remuneration which a public servant can lawfully demand, but include all remuneration which he is permitted by the Government or the organisation, which he serves, to accept.

(d) "A motive or reward for doing". A person who receives a gratification as a motive or reward for doing what he does not intend or is not in a position to do, or has not done, comes within this expression.

(e) Where a public servant induces a person erroneously to believe that his influence with the Government has obtained a title for that person and thus induces that person to give the public servant, money or any other gratification as a reward for this service, the public servant has committed an offence under this section.".

**attempts to obtain, any undue advantage for himself or for another person, by abusing his position as a public servant or by using his personal influence over another public servant; or by any other corrupt or illegal means;**

**(ii) it shall be immaterial whether such person being a public servant obtains or accepts, or attempts to obtain the undue advantage directly or through a third party.]**

## COMMENTS

**Basis of Requirement for Sustaining Prosecution for Offence under Provision**

The basis requirement for sustaining a prosecution for the offence under Sections 7 and 13(1)(d) of The Act of 1988, is that on the date of the commission of the offence, the accused should be a 'public servant' as defined under Section 2(c) of The Act of 1988.

*A. Duraisamy v. State*, MANU/TN/6518/2022.

**(i) Acceptance of bribe : Presumption**

When it is established that accused was possessing the bribe money, it is for accused to explain that how the bribe money has been received by him.

*State of Gujarat v. Navinbhai Chandrakant Joshi*, (2018) 9 SCC 242: AIR 2018 SC 3345.

**(ii) Provisions under Sections 7 and 13**

The prosecution has legal obligation to prove the twin requirements of demand and acceptance of bribe money by accused. The proving of one alone but not to other is not sufficient to buckle the accused.

*Dasrath Singh Chandan v. Central Bureau of Investigation*, AIR 2018 SC 4720: (2018) 10 JT 8.

**(iii) Reduction of sentence**

On the ground of age of accused and case being above 23 years the court reduced sentence of 3 years to 1 year.

*K. Mani v. Inspector of Police, CBI, Kochi*, 2018 All SCR (Cri.) 511.

**7A. Taking undue advantage to influence public servant by corrupt or illegal means or by exercise of personal influence.**—Whoever accepts or obtain or attempts to obtain from another person for himself or for any other person any undue advantage as a motive or reward to induce a public servant, by corrupt or illegal means or by exercise of his personal influence to perform or to cause performance of a public duty improperly or dishonestly or to forbear or to cause to forbear such public duty by such public servant or by another public servant, shall be punishable with imprisonment for a term which shall not be less than three years but which may extend to seven years and shall also be liable to fine.

[1]**[8. Offence relating to bribing of a public servant.**—(1) Any person who gives or promises to give an undue advantage to another person or persons, with intention—

1. Subst. by Act 16 of 2018, Section 4, for Section 8 (w.e.f. July 26, 2018, according to S.O. 3664(E), dt. July 26, 2018). Previously Section 8 stood amended by Act 1 of 2014, Section 58 and the Schedule (w.e.f. January 16, 2014, according to S.O. 119(E), dt. January 16, 2014). Section 8, prior to subst., ran as under:

   "*8. Taking gratification, in order, by corrupt or illegal means, to influence public servant.*— Whoever accepts or obtains, or agrees to accept, or attempts to obtain, from any person, for

*Contd. on next page...*

(i) to induce a public servant to perform improperly a public duty; or

(ii) to reward such public servant for the improper performance of public duty;

shall be punishable with imprisonment for a term which may extend to seven years or with fine or with both:

Provide that the provisions of this section shall not apply where a person is compelled to give such undue advantage:

Provide further that the person so compelled shall report the matter to the law enforcement authority or investigating agency within a period of seven days from the date of giving such undue advantage:

Provide also that when the offence under this section has been committed by commercial organisation, such commercial organisation shall be publishable with fine.

*Illustration*—A person, 'P' gives a public servant, 'S' an amount of ten thousand rupees to ensure that he is granted a license, over all the other bidders. 'P' is guilty of an offence under this sub-section.

*Explanation.*—It shall be immaterial whether the person to whom an undue advantage is given or promised to be given is the same person as the person who is to perform, or has performed, the public duty concerned, and, it shall also be immaterial whether such undue advantage is given or promised to be given by the person directly or through a third party.

(2) Nothing in sub-section (1) shall apply to a person, if that person, after informing a law enforcement authority or investigating agency, gives or promises to give any undue advantage to another person in order to assist such law enforcement authority or investigating agency in its investigation of the offence alleged against the [1][latter].]

## COMMENT

**Appeal against conviction**

Though the receiver of money may not be the public servant, the prosecution has to establish by convincing evidence that amount must have been received for inducing the public servant for doing something by that public servant in his official capacity. In absence of convincing evidence to show that appellant had received money from complainant to induce public servant to work in his favour.

*Babji v. State of Andhra Pradesh*, AIR 2018 SC 3831: (2018) 10 SCALE 201.

---

*...contd. from previous page...*

himself or for any other person, any gratification whatever as a motive or reward for inducing, by corrupt or illegal means, any public servant, whether named or otherwise, to do or to forbear to do any official act, or in the exercise of the official functions of such public servant to show favour or disfavour to any person, or to render or attempt to render any service or disservice to any person with the Central Government or any State Government or Parliament or the Legislature of any State or with any local authority, corporation or Government company referred to in clause (c) of section 2, or with any public servant, whether named or otherwise, shall be punishable with imprisonment for a term which shall be not less than three years but which may extend to seven years and shall also be liable to fine.".

1. Corrected by Corrigenda, dt. August 1, 2018, for "later".

[1][9. **Offence relating to bribing a public servant by a commercial organisation.**—(1) Where an offence under this Act has been committed by a commercial organisation, such organisation shall be punishable with fine, if any person associated with such commercial organisation gives or promises to give any undue advantage to a public servant intending—

(a) to obtain or retain business for such commercial organisation; or

(b) to obtain or retain an advantage in the conduct of business for such commercial organisation:

Provided that it shall be a defence for the commercial organisation to prove that it had in place adequate procedures in compliance of such guidelines as may be prescribed to prevent persons associated with it from undertaking such conduct.

(2) For the purposes of this section, a person is said to give or promise to give any undue advantage to a public servant, if he is alleged to have committed the offence under section 8, whether or not such person has been prosecuted for such offence.

(3) For the purposes of section 8 and this section,—

(a) "commercial organisation" means—

(i) a body which is incorporated in India and which carries on a business, whether in India or outside India;

(ii) any other body which is incorporated outside India and which carries on a business, or part of a business, in any part of India;

(iii) a partnership firm or any association of persons formed in India and which carries on a business whether in India or outside India; or

(iv) any other partnership or association of persons which is formed outside India and which carries on a business, or part of a business, in any part of India;

(b) "business" includes a trade or profession or providing service;

(c) a person is said to be associated with the commercial organisation, if such person performs services for or on behalf of the commercial organisation irrespective of any promise to give or giving of any undue advantage which constitutes an offence under sub-section (1).

1. Subst. by Act 16 of 2018, Section 4, for Section 9 (w.e.f. July 26, 2018, according to S.O. 3664(E), dt. July 26, 2018). Previously Section 9 stood amended by Act 1 of 2014, Section 58 and the Schedule (w.e.f. January 16, 2014, according to S.O. 119(E), dt. January 16, 2014). Section 9, prior to subst., ran as under:

"9. *Taking gratification, for exercise of personal influence with public servant.*—Whoever accepts or obtains or agrees to accept or attempts to obtain, from any person, for himself or for any other person, any gratification whatever, as a motive or reward for inducing, by the exercise of personal influence, any public servant whether named or otherwise to do or to forbear to do any official act, or in the exercise of the official functions of such public servant to show favour or disfavour to any person, or to render or attempt to render any service or disservice to any person with the Central Government or any State Government or Parliament or the Legislature of any State or with any local authority, corporation or Government company referred to in clause (c) of section 2, or with any public servant, whether named or otherwise, shall be punishable with imprisonment for a term which shall be not less than three years but which may extend to seven years and shall also be liable to fine.".

*Explanation 1.*—The capacity in which the person performs services for or on behalf of the commercial organisation shall not matter irrespective of whether such person is employee or agent or subsidiary of such commercial organisation.

*Explanation 2.*—Whether or not the person is a person who performs services for or on behalf of the commercial organisation is to be determined by reference to all the relevant circumstances and not merely by reference to the nature of the relationship between such person and the commercial organisation.

*Explanation 3.*—If the person is an employee of the commercial organisation, it shall be presumed unless the contrary is proved that such person is a person who has performed services for or on behalf of the commercial organisation.

(4) Notwithstanding anything contained in the Code of Criminal Procedure, 1973 (2 of 1974), the offence under sections 7A, 8 and this section shall be cognizable.

(5) The Central Government shall, in consultation with the concerned stakeholders, including departments and with a view to preventing persons associated with commercial organisations from bribing any person, being a public servant, prescribe such guidelines as may be considered necessary which can be put in place for compliance by such organisations.]

[1][**10. Person in charge of commercial organisation to be guilty of offence.**— Where an offence under section 9 is committed by a commercial organisation, and such offence is proved in the court to have been committed with the consent or connivance of any director, manager, secretary or other officer shall be of the commercial organisation, such director, manager, secretary or other officer shall be guilty of the offence and shall be liable to be proceeded against and shall be punishable with imprisonment for a term which shall not be less than three years but which may extend to seven years and shall also be liable to fine.

*Explanation.*—For the purposes of this section, "director", in relation to a firm means a partner in the firm.]

**11. Public servant obtaining [2][undue advantage], without consideration from person concerned in proceeding or business transacted by such public servant.**—Whoever, being a public servant, accepts or obtains [3][***] or attempts to obtain for himself, or for any other person, any [4][undue advantage] without

1. Subst. by Act 16 of 2018, Section 4, for Section 10 (w.e.f. July 26, 2018, according to S.O. 3664(E), dt. July 26, 2018). Previously Section 9 stood amended by Act 1 of 2014, Section 58 and the Schedule (w.e.f. January 16, 2014, according to S.O. 119(E), dt. January 16, 2014). Section 9, prior to subst., ran as under:

   "10. *Punishment for abetment by public servant of offences defined in section 8 or 9.*—Whoever, being a public servant, in respect of whom either of the offences defined in section 8 or section 9 is committed, abets the offence, whether or not that offence is committed in consequence of that abetment, shall be punishable with imprisonment for a term which shall be not less than six months but which may extend to five years and shall also be liable to fine.".
2. Subst. by Act 16 of 2018, Section 5(i), for "valuable thing" (w.e.f. July 26, 2018, according to S.O. 3664(E), dt. July 26, 2018).
3. The words "or agrees to accept" stood omitted by Act 16 of 2018, Section 5(ii) (w.e.f. July 26, 2018, according to S.O. 3664(E), dt. July 26, 2018).
4. Subst. by Act 16 of 2018, Section 5(iii), for "valuable thing" (w.e.f. July 26, 2018, according to S.O. 3664(E), dt. July 26, 2018).

consideration, or for a consideration which he knows to be inadequate, from any person whom he knows to have been, or to be, or to be likely to be concerned in any proceeding or business transacted or about to be transacted by such public servant, or having any connection with the [1][official functions or public duty] of himself or of any public servant to whom he is subordinate, or from any person whom he knows to be interested in or related to the person so concerned, shall be punishable with imprisonment for a term which shall be not less than six months but which extend to five years and shall also be liable to fine.

[2][**12. Punishment for abetment of offences.**—Whoever abets any offence punishable under this Act, whether or not that offence is committed in consequence of that abetment, shall be punishable with imprisonment for a term which [3][shall not be] less than three years, out which may extend to seven years and shall also be liable to fine.]

**13. Criminal misconduct by a public servant.**—[4][(1) A public servant is said to commit the offence of criminal misconduct,—

(a) if he dishonestly or fraudulently misappropriates or otherwise converts for his own use any property entrusted to him or any property under

1. Subst. by Act 16 of 2018, Section 5(iv), for "official functions" (w.e.f. July 26, 2018, according to S.O. 3664(E), dt. July 26, 2018).
2. Subst. by Act 16 of 2018, Section 6, for Section 12 (w.e.f. July 26, 2018, according to S.O. 3664(E), dt. July 26, 2018). Previously Section 12 stood amended by Act 1 of 2014, Section 58 and Schedule (w.e.f. January 16, 2014, according to S.O. 119(E), dt. January 16, 2014). Section 12, prior to subst., ran as under:

   "*12. Punishment for abetment of offences defined in section 7 or 11.*—Whoever abets any offence punishable under section 7 or section 11 whether or not that offence is committed in consequence of that abetment, shall be punishable with imprisonment for a term which shall be not less than three years but which may extend to seven years and shall also be liable to fine.".
3. Corrected by Corrigenda, dt. August 1, 2018, for "shall be not".
4. Subst. by Act 16 of 2018, Section 7, for Sub-s. (1) (w.e.f. July 26, 2018, according to S.O. 3664(E), dt. July 26, 2018). Sub-s. (1), prior to subst., ran as under:

   "(1) A public servant is said to commit the offence of criminal misconduct,—

   (a) if he habitually accepts or obtains or agrees to accept or attempts to obtain from any person for himself or for any other person any gratification other than legal remuneration as a motive or reward such as is mentioned in Section 7; or

   (b) if he habitually accepts or obtains or agrees to accept or attempts to obtain for himself or for any other person, any valuable thing without consideration or for a consideration which he knows to be inadequate from any person whom he knows to have been, or to be, or to be likely to be concerned in any proceeding or business transacted or about to be transacted by him, or having any connection with the official functions of himself or of any public servant to whom he is subordinate, or from any person whom he knows to be interested in or related to the person so concerned; or

   (c) if he dishonestly or fraudulently misappropriates or otherwise converts for his own use any property entrusted to him or under his control as a public servant or allows any other person so to do; or

   (d) if he,—

      (i) by corrupt or illegal means, obtains for himself or for any other person any valuable thing or pecuniary advantage; or

      (ii) by abusing his position as a public servant, obtains for himself or for any other person any valuable thing or pecuniary advantage; or

*Contd. on next page...*

his control as a public servant or allows any other person so to do; or

(b) if he intentionally enriches himself illicitly during the period of his office.

*Explanation 1.*—A person shall be presumed to have intentionally enriched himself illicitly if he or any person on his behalf, is in possession of or has, at any time during the period of his office, been in possession of pecuniary resources or property disproportionate to his known sources of income which the public servant cannot satisfactorily account for.

*Explanation 2.*—The expression "known sources of income" means income received from any lawful sources."

(2) Any public servant who commits criminal misconduct shall be punishable with imprisonment for a term which shall be not less than [1][four years] but which may extend to [2][ten years] and shall also be liable to fine.

## COMMENTS

**Grounds for Absence of Ingredients *Prima Facie* in Criminal Case *Inter Alia* under Provision**

In the instant case the ingredients of the alleged offences are not *prima facie* made out against appellant herein, in view that (i) during the investigation, no incriminating material or money was seized from the house of the appellant, (ii) it is not a case where allegations of illegal gratification or disproportionate assets have been successfully found by prosecution against the appellant, and (iii) when the Income Tax Department had assessed the block income tax return for seven years, the Department recorded a refund Rs. 8843 to the appellant after detailed scrutiny of the records, where (a) the application for discharge filed by the appellant under the provision of Section 239 of Code of Criminal Procedure, 1973, in connection with Special Case No. 02 of 2011 (criminal case), has been dismissed by learned Special Judge, Anti-Corruption Bureau, the (b) the criminal case was registered against the appellant and others for commission of offences under Sections 109, 409, 420, 467, 471, 477A and 120B of Indian Penal Code, 1860, and under Section 13(1)(c) and 13(1)(d) read with Section 13(2) of The Act of 1988.

*Pushpendra Kumar Sinha v. State of Jharkhand,* AIR2022SC3983: MANU/SC/1036/2022.

---

*...contd. from previous page*

(iii) while holding office as a public servant, obtains for any person any valuable thing or pecuniary advantage without any public interest; or

(e) if he or any person on his behalf, is in possession or has, at any time during the period of his office, been in possession for which the public servant cannot satisfactorily account, of pecuniary resources or property disproportionate to his known sources of income.

*Explanation.*—For the purposes of this section, "known sources of income" means income received from any lawful source and such receipt has been intimated in accordance with the provisions of any law, rules or orders for the time being applicable to a public servant.".

1. Subst. by Act 1 of 2014, Section 58 and the Schedule, for "one year" (w.e.f. January 16, 2014, according to S.O. 119(E), dt. January 16, 2014).
2. Subst. by Act 1 of 2014, Section 58 and the Schedule, for "seven years" (w.e.f. January 16, 2014, according to S.O. 119(E), dt. January 16, 2014).

**Grounds for Non-sustainability of Conviction under Provision**

The conviction of appellant herein under Section 13(1)(d)(ii) read with Section 15 of The Act of 1988, is totally unsustainable, in view that (i) the appellant did not have any role to play in either the sanctioning of the money or making of payment, (ii) in the investigation, the Investigating Officer had not found any criminal intent, (iii) and for an offence punishable under Section 13(1)(d)(ii) read with Section 15 of The Act of 1988, it is necessary to establish that a public servant has attempted to obtain for himself or for any other person any valuable thing or pecuniary advantage, where (a) the learned Special Judge, Prevention of Corruption Act No. 1, Jaipur, has convicted the appellant for the offences punishable Section 13(1)(d)(ii) read with Section 15 of The Act of 1988, and Section 477A of Indian Penal Code, 1860, and has sentenced the appellant to suffer rigorous imprisonment for one year and a fine of Rs. 5000/- each for both the offences.

*Shiv Kumar Sharma v. State of Rajasthan*, MANU/SC/0995/2022.

**(i) Conviction based on voluntary confession**

The conviction can be based on a voluntary confession but the rule of prudence requires that wherever possible it should be corroborated by independent evidence.

*Ram Lal v. State of Himachal Pradesh*, AIR 2018 SC 4616: (2018) 9 JT 428.

**(ii) Sanction for prosecution**

Unless there is failure of justice on account of error, omission or irregularity in grant of sanction for prosecution the proceedings under the Act cannot be vitiated.

*State of Mizoram v. Dr. C. Sangnghina*, (2018) 10 JT 524: AIR 2018 SC 5342.

[1][**14. Punishment for habitual offender.**—Whoever convicted of an offence under this Act subsequently commits an offence punishable under this Act, shall be punishable with imprisonment for a term which [2][shall not be] less than five years but which may extend to ten years and shall also be liable to fine.]

**15. Punishment for attempt.**—Whoever attempts to commit an offence referred to in [3][clause (a)] of sub-section (1) of section 13 shall be punishable with imprisonment for a term [4][which shall not be less than two years but which may extend to five years] and with fine.

**16. Matters to be taken into consideration for fixing fine.**—Where a sentence of fine is imposed under [5][section 7 or section 8 or section 9 or section

1. Subst. by Act 16 of 2018, Section 8, for Section 14 (w.e.f. July 26, 2018, according to S.O. 3664(E), dt. July 26, 2018). Previously Section 14 stood amended by Act 1 of 2014, Section 58 and the Schedule (w.e.f. January 16, 2014, according to S.O. 119(E), dt. January 16, 2014). Section 14, prior to subst., ran as under:

   "*14. Habitual committing of offence under sections 8, 9 and 12.*—Whoever habitually commits,—

   (a) an offence punishable under section 8 or section 9; or

   (b) an offence punishable under section 12,

   shall be punishable with imprisonment for a term which shall be not less than five years but which may extend to ten years and shall also be liable to fine.".
2. Corrected by Corrigenda, dt. August 1, 2018, for "shall be not".
3. Subst. by Act 16 of 2018, Section 9, for "clause (c) or clause (d)" (w.e.f. July 26, 2018, according to S.O. 3664(E), dt. July 26, 2018).
4. Subst. by Act 1 of 2014, Section 58 and the Schedule, for "which may extend to three years" (w.e.f. January 16, 2014, according to S.O. 119(E), dt. January 16, 2014).
5. Subst. by Act 16 of 2018, Section 10(a), for "sub-section (2) of section 13 or section 14" (w.e.f. July 26, 2018, according to S.O. 3664(E), dt. July 26, 2018).

10 or section 11 or sub-section (2) of section 13 or section 14 or section 15], the court in fixing the amount of the fine shall take into consideration the amount or the value of the property, if any, which the accused person has obtained by committing the offence or where the conviction is for an offence referred to in [1][clause (b)] of sub-section (1) of section 13, the pecuniary resources or property referred to in that clause for which the accused person is unable to account satisfactorily.

## CHAPTER IV

## INVESTIGATION INTO CASES UNDER THE ACT

**17. Persons authorised to investigate.**—Notwithstanding anything contained in the Code of Criminal Procedure, 1973 (2 of 1974), no police officer below the rank,—

(a) in the case of the Delhi Special Police Establishment, of an Inspector of Police;

(b) in the metropolitan areas of Bombay, Calcutta, Madras and Ahmedabad and in any other metropolitan area notified as such under sub-section (1) of section 8 of the Code of Criminal Procedure, 1973 (2 of 1974), of an Assistant Commissioner of Police;

(c) elsewhere, of a Deputy Superintendent of Police or a police officer of equivalent rank,

shall investigate any offence punishable under this Act without the order of a Metropolitan Magistrate or a Magistrate of the first class, as the case may be, or make any arrest therefor without a warrant:

Provided that if a police officer not below the rank of an Inspector of Police is authorised by the State Government in this behalf by general or special order, he may also investigate any such offence without the order of a Metropolitan Magistrate or a Magistrate of the first class, as the case may be, or make arrest therefor without a warrant:

Provided further that an offence referred to in [2][clause (b) of sub-section (1)] of section 13 shall not be investigated without the older of a police officer not below the rank of a Superintendent of Police.

### COMMENT

**Necessity by Police Officer of Rank of Authorizing Any Investigation**

A police officer of the rank of Superintendent of Police (SP) must authorize any investigation into an offence alleged to have been committed under Section 13(1)(e) of The Act of 1988, flowing from Section 17 of The Act of 1988.

*Zakir Abdul Mirajkar v. State of Maharashtra and Ors.*, MANU/SC/1041/2022.

[3]**[17A. Enquiry or Inquiry or investigation of offences relatable to recommendations made or decision taken by public servant in discharge**

1. Subst. by Act 16 of 2018, Section 10(b), for "clause (e)" (w.e.f. July 26, 2018, according to S.O. 3664(E), dt. July 26, 2018).
2. Subst. by Act 16 of 2018, Section 11, for "clause (e) of sub-section (1)" (w.e.f. July 26, 2018, according to S.O. 3664(E), dt. July 26, 2018).
3. Inst. by Act 16 of 2018, Section 12 (w.e.f. July 26, 2018, according to S.O. 3664(E), dt. July 26, 2018) as corrected by the Corrigenda, dt. August 1, 2018.

**of official functions or duties.**—No police officer shall conduct any enquiry or inquiry or investigation into any offence alleged to have been committed by a public servant under this Act, where the alleged offence is relatable to any recommendation made or decision taken by such public servant in discharge of his official functions or duties, without the previous approval-

(a) in the case of a person who is or was employed, at the time when the offence was alleged to have been committed, in connection with the affairs of the Union, of that Government;

(b) in the case of a person who is or was employed, at the time when the offence was alleged to have been committed, in connection with the affairs of a State, of that Government;

(c) in the case of any other person, of the authority competent to remove him from his office, at the time when the offence was alleged to have been committed:

Provided that no such approval shall be necessary for cases involving arrest of a person on the spot on the charge of accepting or attempting to accept any undue advantage for himself or for any other person:

Provided further that the concerned authority shall convey its decision under this section within a period of three months, which may, for reasons to be recorded in writing by such authority, be extended by a further period of one month.

**STATE AMENDMENT**

**Union Territory of Jammu and Kashmir.—**

In its application to the Union Terrtory of Jammu and Kashmir, after Section 17A, insert the following Section, namely:—

"*17B. Establishment of Anti-Corruption Bureau for the Union territory of Jammu and Kashmir.*—(1) Notwithstanding anything contained in this Act, the Government of Union territory of Jammu and Kashmir shall, by notification in the Official Gazette, establish a Bureau for investigation of offences under this Act under the name of 'Anti-Corruption Bureau'.

(2) The Bureau shall consist of the Director and such other officers and staff subordinate to him as the Government of Union territory of Jammu and Kashmir may from time to time think fit to appoint.

(3) The qualification of officers (other than the Director) shall be such as may be prescribed by the Government of Union territory of Jammu and Kashmir:

Provided that till qualification of officers (other than the Director) is prescribed by the Government of Union territory of Jammu and Kashmir, the rules notified by the Government in this regard under the Prevention of Corruption Act, Samvat, 2006 (now repealed) shall continue to govern the qualification of such officers.

(4) The Director and the officers and staff subordinate to him shall hold office for such term and on such conditions as the Government of Union territory of Jammu and Kashmir may from time to time determine?

*Explanation.*—The Anti-Corruption Bureau established under the Prevention of Corruption Act, Samvat, 2006 (now repealed) shall deemed to be Anti-Corruption Bureau established under the provisions of this Act, as if the same has been established under the provisions of this Act and any reference to the Anti-Corruption Bureau in any law, order, notification or rules in force in the Union Territory of Jammu and Kashmir shall be construed to mean the Anti-Corruption Bureau established under the provisions of this Act.

*17C. Powers of attachment of property.*—(1) If an officer (not below the rank of Deputy Superintendent of Police) of the Anti-Corruption Bureau, investigating an offence committed under this Act, has reason to believe that any property in relation to which an investigation is being conducted has been acquired by resorting to such acts of omission and commission which constitute an offence of 'criminal misconduct' as defined under section 5, he shall, with the prior approval in writing of the Director of the Anti-Corruption Bureau, make an order seizing such property and, where it is not practicable to seize such property, make an order of attachment directing that such property shall not be transferred or otherwise dealt with, except with the prior permission of the officer making such order or of the Designated Authority to be notified by the Government of Union territory of Jammu and Kashmir before whom the properties seized or attached are produced and a copy of such order shall be served on the person concerned:

Provided that the Investigating Officer may, at any stage of investigation after registration of F.I.R. in respect of any case under the Act where he has reason to believe that such property is likely to be transferred or otherwise dealt with to defeat the prosecution of the case direct that such property shall not be transferred or dealt with for such period, not exceeding ninety days, as may be specified in the order except with the prior approval of the Designated Authority.

*Explanation.*—For the purposes of this section, "attachment" shall include temporarily assuming the custody, possession and/or control of such property.

(2) The Investigating officer shall inform the Designated Authority, within forty eight hours, of the seizure or attachment of such property together with a report of the circumstances occasioning the seizure or attachment of such property, as the case may be.

(3) It shall be open to the Designated Authority before whom the seized or attached properties are produced either to confirm or revoke the order of seizure or attachment so issued within [thirty days]:

Provided that an opportunity of being heard shall be afforded to the Investigating Officer and the person whose property is being attached or seized before making any order under this sub-section:

Provided further that till disposal of the case the Designated Authority shall ensure the safety and protection of such property.

(4) In the case of immovable property attached by the Investigating Officer, it shall be deemed to have been produced before the Designated Authority, when the Investigating Officer notifies his report and places it at the disposal of the Designated Authority.

(5) Any person aggrieved by an order under the proviso to sub-section (1) may apply to the Designated Authority for grant of permission to transfer or otherwise deal with such property.

(6) The Designated Authority may either grant, or refuse to grant, the permission to the applicant.

(7) The Designated Authority, acting under the provisions of this Act, shall have all the powers of a civil court required for making a full and fair enquiry into the matter before it.

*17D. Appeal against the order of Designated Authority.*—(1) Any person aggrieved by an order made by the Designated Authority under sub-section (3) or sub-section (5) of section 17C may prefer an appeal, within one month from the date of receipt of the order, to the Special Judge and the Special Court may either confirm the order of attachment of property or seizure so made or revoke such order and release the property or pass such order as it may deem just and proper within a period of sixty days.

(2) Where any property is seized or attached under section 17C and the Special Court is satisfied about such seizure or attachment, it may order forfeiture of such property, whether or not the person from whose possession it is seized or attached is prosecuted in the Special Court for an offence under this Act.

(3) It shall be competent for the Special Court to make an order in respect of property seized or attached,—

(a) directing it to be sold if it is a perishable property and the provisions of section 459 of the Code of Criminal Procedure, 1973 (2 of 1974) shall, as nearly as may be practicable, apply to the net proceeds of such sale;

(b) nominating any officer of the Government, in the case of any other property, to perform the function of the Administrator of such property subject to such conditions as may be specified by the Special Court.

*17E. Issue of show-cause notice before forfeiture of the property.*—No order under sub-section (2) of section 17D shall be made by the Special Court—

(a) unless the person holding or in possession of such property is given a notice in writing informing him of the grounds on which it is proposed to forfeit such property and such person is given an opportunity of making a representation in writing within such reasonable time as may be specified in the notice against the grounds of forfeiture and is also given a reasonable opportunity of being heard in the matter;

(b) if the person holding or in possession of such property establishes that he is a *bona fide* transferee of such property for value without knowing that such property has been so acquired.

*17F. Appeal.*—(1) Any person aggrieved by order of the Special Court under section 17D may within one month from the date of the receipt of such order, appeal to the High Court of Jammu and Kashmir.

(2) Where any order under section 17D is modified or annulled by the High Court or where in a prosecution instituted for the contravention of the provisions of this Act, the person against whom an order of the special court has been made is acquitted, such property shall be returned to him and in either case if it is not possible for any reason to return the forfeited property, such person shall be paid the price therefor as if the property had been sold to the Government with reasonable interest calculated from the date of seizure of the property and such price shall be determined in the manner prescribed.

*17G. Order of forfeiture not to interfere with other punishments.*—The order of forfeiture made under this Act by the Special Court, shall not prevent the infliction of any other punishment to which the person affected thereby is liable under this Act.

[According to the Jammu and Kashmir Reorganisation (Adaptation of Central Laws) Order, 2020 (w.e.f. March 18, 2020), S.O. 1123(E), dt. March 18, 2020, published in the Gazette of India, Extraordinary, Part II, Section 3(ii), No. 1016, dt. March 18, 2020].

**18. Power to inspect bankers' books.**—If from information received or otherwise, a police officer has reason to suspect the commission of an offence which he is empowered to investigate under section 17 and considers that for the purpose of investigation or inquiry into such offence, it is necessary to inspect any bankers' books, then, notwithstanding anything contained in any law for the time being in force, he may inspect any bankers' books in so far as they relate to the accounts of the persons suspected to have committed that offence or of any other person suspected to be holding money on behalf of such person, and take or cause to be taken certified copies of the relevant entries therefrom, and the bank concerned shall be bound to assist the police officer in the exercise of his powers under this section:

Provided that no power under this section in relation to the accounts of any person shall be exercised by a police officer below the rank of a Superintendent of Police, unless he is specially authorised in this behalf by a police officer of or above the rank of a superintendent of Police.

*Explanation*.—In this section, the expressions "bank" and "bankers' books" shall have the meanings respectively assigned to them in the Bankers' Books Evidence Act, 1891 (18 of 1891).

## [1][CHAPTER IVA
## ATTACHMENT AND FORFEITURE OF PROPERTY

**18A. Provisions of Criminal Law Amendment Ordinance, 1944 to apply to attachment under this Act.**—(1) Save as otherwise provided under the Prevention of Money Laundering Act, 2002 (15 of 2003), the provisions of the Criminal Law Amendment Ordinance, 1944 (Ord. 38 of 1944) shall, as far as may be, apply to the attachment, administration of attached property and execution of order of attachment or confiscation of money or property procured by means of an offence under this Act.

(2) For the purposes of this Act, the provisions of the Criminal Law Amendment Ordinance, 1944 (Ord. 38 of 1944) shall have effect, subject to the modification that the references to "District Judge" shall be construed as references to "Special Judge".]

## CHAPTER V
## SANCTION FOR PROSECUTION AND OTHER MISCELLANEOUS PROVISIONS

**19. Previous sanction necessary for prosecution.**—(1) No court shall take cognizance of an offence punishable under [2][section 7, 11, 13 and 15] alleged to have been committed by a public servant, except with the previous sanction [3][save as otherwise provided in the Lokpal and Lokayuktas Act, 2013 (1 of 2014)]—

1. Inst. by Act 16 of 2018, Section 13 (w.e.f. July 26, 2018, according to S.O. 3664(E), dt. July 26, 2018).
2. Subst. by Act 16 of 2018, Section 14(i), for "sections 7, 10, 11, 13 and 15" (w.e.f. July 26, 2018, according to S.O. 3664(E), dt. July 26, 2018).
3. Inst. by Act 1 of 2014, Section 58 and Schedule, (w.e.f. January 16, 2014, according to S.O. 119(E), dt. January 16, 2014).

(a) in the case of a person [1][who is employed, or as the case may be, was at the time of commission of the alleged offence employed] in connection with the affairs of the Union and is not removable from his office save by or with the sanction of the Central Government, of that Government;

(b) in the case of a person [2][who is employed, or as the case may be, was at the time of commission of the alleged offence employed] in connection with the affairs of a State and is not removable from his office save by or with the sanction of the State Government, of that Government;

(c) in the case of any other person, of the authority competent to remove him from his office.

[3][Provided that no request can be made, by a person other than a police officer or an officer of an investigation agency or other law enforcement authority, to the appropriate Government or competent authority, as the case may be, for the previous sanction of such Government or authority for taking cognizance by the court of any of the offences specified in this sub-section, unless—

(i) such person has filed a complaint in a competent court about the alleged offences for which the public servant is sought to be prosecuted; and

(ii) the court has not dismissed the complaint under section 203 of the Code of Criminal Procedure, 1973 (2 of 1974) and directed the complainant to obtain the sanction for prosecution against the public servant for further proceeding:

Provided further that in the case of request from the person other than a police officer or an officer of an investigation agency or other law enforcement authority, the appropriate Government or competent authority shall not accord sanction to prosecute a public servant without providing an opportunity of being heard to the concerned public servant:

Provided also that the appropriate Government or any competent authority shall, after the receipt of the proposal requiring sanction for prosecution of a public servant under this sub-section, endeavour to convey the decision on such proposal within a period of three months from the date of its receipt:

Provided also that in case where, for the purpose of grant of sanction for prosecution, legal consultation is required, such period may, for the reasons to be recorded in writing, be extended by a further period of one month:

Provided also that the Central Government may, for the purpose of sanction for prosecution of a public servant, [4][presecribe] such guidelines as it considers necessary.

1. Subst. by Act 16 of 2018, Section 14(ii), for "who is employed" (w.e.f. July 26, 2018, according to S.O. 3664(E), dt. July 26, 2018).
2. Subst. by Act 16 of 2018, Section 14(iii), for "who is employed" (w.e.f. July 26, 2018, according to S.O. 3664(E), dt. July 26, 2018).
3. Inst. by Act 16 of 2018, Section 14(iv) (w.e.f. July 26, 2018, according to S.O. 3664(E), dt. July 26, 2018).
4. Corrected by Corrigenda, dt. August 1, 2018, for "presecribe".

*Explanation.*—For the purposes of sub-section (1), the expression "public servant" includes such person—

(a) who has ceased to hold the office during which the offence is alleged to have been committed; or

(b) who has ceased to hold the office during which the offence is alleged to have been committed and is holding an office other than the office during which the offence is alleged to have been committed.]

(2) Where for any reason whatsoever any doubt arises as to whether the previous sanction as required under sub-section (1) should be given by the Central Government or the State Government or any other authority, such sanction shall be given by that Government or authority which would have been competent to remove the public servant from his office at the time when the offence was alleged to have been committed.

(3) Notwithstanding anything contained in the code of Criminal Procedure, 1973 (2 of 1974),—

(a) no finding, sentence or order passed by a special Judge shall be reversed or altered by a Court in appeal, confirmation or revision on the ground of the absence of, or any error, omission or irregularity in, the sanction required under sub-section (1), unless in the opinion of that court, a failure of justice has in fact been occasioned thereby;

(b) no court shall stay the proceedings under this Act on the ground of any error, omission or irregularity in the sanction granted by the authority, unless it is satisfied that such error, omission or irregularity has resulted in a failure of justice;

(c) no court shall stay the proceedings under this Act on any other ground and no court shall exercise the powers of revision in relation to any interlocutory order passed in any inquiry, trial, appeal or other proceedings.

(4) In determining under sub-section (3) whether the absence of, or any error, omission or irregularity in, such sanction has occasioned or resulted in a failure of justice the court shall have regard to the fact whether the objection could and should have been raised at any earlier stage in the proceedings.

*Explanation.*—For the purposes of this section,—

(a) error includes competency of the authority to grant sanction;

(b) a sanction required for prosecution includes reference to any requirement that the prosecution shall be at the instance of a specified authority or with the sanction of a specified person or any requirement of a similar nature.

**COMMENT**

**Framing of Charge**

The order of framing of charges may not be held to be purely a interlocutory order and can in a given situation be interfered with under Section 397 or Section 482 of the Criminal Procedure Code, 1973.

*Asian Resurfacing of Road Agency Pvt. Ltd. v. Central Bureau of Investigation,* AIR 2018 SC 2039: (2018) 248 DLT 244.

[1][20. **Presumption where public servant accepts any undue advantage.**—Where, in any trial of an offence punishable under section 7 or under section 11, it is proved that a public servant accused of an offence has accepted or obtained or attempted to obtain for himself, or for any other person, any undue advantage from any person, it shall be presumed, unless the contrary is proved, that he accepted or obtained and attempted to obtain that undue advantage, as a motive or reward under section 7 for performing or to cause performance of a public duty improperly or dishonestly either by himself or by another public servant or, as the case may be, any undue advantage without consideration or for a consideration which he knows to be inadequate under section 11.]

## COMMENTS

**(i) Presumption of acceptance of bribe**

The presumption raised under Section 20 of the Act for offence under Section 7 of the said Act is rebuttable presumption.

*State of Gujarat v. Navinbhai Chandrakant Joshi*, (2018) 9 SCALE 34: AIR 2018 SC 3345: 2018 Cr.L.J. 3733.

**(ii) Presumption under the Section**

When sub-section (1) of Section 20 deals with legal presumption, it is to be understood as *in terrorem i.e.* in the tone of a command that it has to be presumed that the accused accepted the gratification as a motive or reward for doing or forbearing to do any official act etc., if the condition envisaged in the former part of the section is satisfied. The only condition for drawing such a legal presumption under Section 20 is that during trial it should be proved that the accused has accepted or agreed to accept any gratification. The section does not say that the said condition should be satisfied through direct evidence. As only requirement is that it must be proved that the accused has accepted or agreed to accept gratification. The direct evidence is

---

1. Subst. by Act 16 of 2018, Section 15, for Section 20 (w.e.f. July 26, 2018, according to S.O. 3664(E), dt. July 26, 2018). Section 20, prior to subst., ran as under:

"20. *Presumption where public servant accepts gratification other than legal remuneration.*—(1) Where, in any trial of an offence punishable under section 7 or section 11 or clause (a) or clause (b) of sub-section (1) of section 13 it is proved that an accused person has accepted or obtained or has agreed to accept or attempted to obtain for himself, or for any other person, any gratification (other than legal remuneration) or any valuable thing from any person, it shall be presumed, unless the contrary is proved, that he accepted or obtained or agreed to accept or attempted to obtain that gratification or that valuable thing, as the case may be, as a motive or reward such as is mentioned in section 7 or, as the case may be, without consideration or for a consideration which he knows to be inadequate.

(2) Where in any trial of an offence punishable under section 12 or under clause (b) of section 14, it is proved that any gratification (other than legal remuneration) or any valuable thing has been given or offered to be given or attempted to be given by an accused person, it shall be presumed, unless the contrary is proved, that he gave or offered to give or attempted to give that gratification or that valuable thing, as the case may be, as a motive or reward such as is mentioned in section 7, or as the case may be, without consideration or for a consideration which he knows to be inadequate.

(3) Notwithstanding anything contained in sub-sections (1) and (2), the court may decline to draw the presumption referred to in either of the said sub-sections, if the gratification or thing aforesaid is, in its opinion, so trivial that no interference of corruption may fairly be drawn.".

one of the modes through which a fact can be proved. But that is not the only mode envisaged in the Evidence Act.

*M. Narsingha Rao v. State of Andhra Pradesh*, (2001) 1 SCC 691; *See* also *Neeraj Dutta v. State (Govt. of NCT of Delhi)*, (2009) 3 SCALE 818: (2019) 3 JT 16.

**21. Accused person to be a competent witness.**—Any person charged with an offence punishable under this Act, shall be a competent witness for the defence and may give evidence on oath in disproof of the charges made against him or any person charged together with him at the same trial:

Provided that—

(a) he shall not be called as a witness except at his own request;

(b) his failure to give evidence shall not be made the subject of any comment by the prosecution or give rise to any presumption against himself or any person charged together with him at the same trial;

(c) he shall not be asked, and if asked shall not be required to answer, any question tending to show that he has committed or been convicted of any offence other than the offence with which he is charged, or is of bad character, unless—

(i) the proof that he has committed or been convicted of such offence is admissible evidence to that he is guilty of the offence with which he is charged, or

(ii) he has personally or by his pleader asked any question of any witness for the prosecution with a view to establish his own good character, or has given evidence of his good character, or the nature or conduct of the defence is such as to involve imputations on the character of the prosecutor or of any witness for the prosecution, or

(iii) he has given evidence against any other person charged with the same offence.

**22. The Code of Criminal Procedure, 1973 to apply subject to certain modifications.**—The provisions of the Code of Criminal Procedure, 1973 (2 of 1974), shall in their application to any proceeding in relation to an offence punishable under this Act have effect as if,—

(a) in sub-section (1) of section 243, for the words "The accused shall then be called upon", the words "The accused shall then be required to give in writing at once or within such time as the Court may allow, a list of the persons (if any) whom he proposes to examine as his witnesses and of the documents (if any) on which he proposes to rely and he shall then be called upon" had been substituted;

(b) in sub-section (2) of section 309, after the third proviso, the following proviso had been inserted, namely:—

"Provided also that the proceeding shall not be adjourned or postponed merely on the ground that an application under section 397 has been made by a party to the proceeding.";

(c) after sub-section (2) of section 317, the following sub-section had been inserted, namely:—

"(3) Notwithstanding anything contained in sub-section (1) or sub-section (2), the Judge may, if he thinks fit and for reasons to be recorded by him, proceed with inquiry or trial in the absence of the accused or his pleader and record the evidence of any witness subject to the right of the accused to recall the witness for cross-examination.";

(d) in sub-section (1) of section 397, before the *Explanation*, the following proviso had been inserted, namely:—

"Provided that where the powers under this section are exercised by a Court on an application made by a party to such proceedings, the Court shall not ordinarily call for the record of the proceedings:—

(a) without giving the other party an opportunity of showing cause why the record should not be called for; or

(b) if it is satisfied that an examination of the record of the proceedings may be made from the certified copies.".

**23. Particulars in a charge in relation to an offence under [1][section 13(1)(a)].**— Notwithstanding anything contained in the Code of Criminal Procedure, 1973 (2 of 1974), when an accused is charged with an offence under [2][clause (a)] of sub-section (1) of section 13, it shall be sufficient to describe in the charge the property in respect of which the offence is alleged to have been committed and the dates between which the offence is alleged to have been committed, without specifying particular items or exact dates, and the charge so framed shall be deemed to be a charge of one offence within the meaning of section 219 of the said Code:

Provided that the time included between the first and last of such dates shall not exceed one year.

[3]**[24. Statement by bribe given not to subject him to prosecution.**— [*Repealed. by the Prevention of Corruption (Amendment) Act, 2018 (16 of 2018), Section 17 (w.e.f. July 26, 2018, according to S.O. 3664(E), dt. July 26, 2018.*]]

**25. Military, Naval and Air Force or other law not to be affected.**—(1) Nothing in this Act shall affect the jurisdiction exercisable by, or the procedure applicable to, any court or other authority under the Army Act, 1950 (45 of 1950), the Air Force Act, 1950 (46 of 1950), the Navy Act, 1957 (62 of 1957), the Border Security Force Act, 1968 (47 of 1968), the Coast Guard Act, 1978 (30 of 1978) and the National Security Guard Act, 1986 (47 of 1986).

1. Subst. by Act 16 of 2018, Section 16(a), for "section 13(1)(c)" (w.e.f. July 26, 2018, according to S.O. 3664(E), dt. July 26, 2018).
2. Subst. by Act 16 of 2018, Section 16(b), for "clause (c)" (w.e.f. July 26, 2018, according to S.O. 3664(E), dt. July 26, 2018).
3. Section 24, prior to omission, ran as under:

"*24. Statement by bribe giver not to subject him to prosecution.*—Notwithstanding anything contained in any law for the time being in force, a statement made by a person in any proceeding against a public servant for an offence under sections 7 to 11 or under section 13 or section 15, that he offered or agreed to offer any gratification (other than legal remuneration) or any valuable thing to the public servant, shall not subject such person to a prosecution under section 12.".

(2) For the removal of doubts, it is hereby declared that for the purposes of any such law as is referred to in sub-section (1), the court of a special Judge shall be deemed to be a court of ordinary criminal justice.

**26. Special Judges appointed under Act 46 of 1952 to be special Judges appointed under this Act.**—Every special Judge appointed under the Criminal Law Amendment Act, 1952 for any area or areas and is holding office on the commencement of this Act shall be deemed to be a special Judge appointed under section 3 of this Act for that area or areas and, accordingly, on and from such commencement, every such Judge shall continue to deal with all the proceedings pending before him on such commencement in accordance with the provisions of this Act.

**STATE AMENDMENT**

**West Bengal.**—

In its application to the State of West Bengal, after Section 26, insert the following section, namely:—

"*26-A. Judges appointed to preside over Special Courts under West Bengal Act 21 of 1949 to be deemed to be special Judges appointed under this Act.*—(1) Every Judge appointed to preside over a Special Court under the West Bengal Criminal Law Amendment (Special Courts) Act, 1949 (West Bengal Act 21 of 1949) for any area or areas and holding office on the commencement of this Act shall be deemed to be a special Judge appointed under section 3 of this Act for that area or areas and, accordingly, on and from such commencement every such Judge shall continue to deal with all the proceedings pending before him on such commencement in accordance with the provisions of this Act.

(2) Every Judge appointed to preside over a Special Court under the West Bengal Criminal Law Amendment (Special Courts) Act, 1949, for any area or areas, holding office on any date after the commencement of this Act but before the commencement of the Prevention of Corruption (West Bengal Amendment) Act, 1994 (hereinafter referred to as the said date) and purporting to act under the provisions of this Act, shall be deemed to be a Special Judge appointed under section 3 of this Act for that area or areas and, accordingly, on and from the said date, every such Judge shall continue to deal with all the proceedings pending before him on the said date in accordance with the provisions of this Act."

[According to West Bengal Act 56 of 1994, Section 3.]

**27. Appeal and revision.**—Subject to the provisions of this Act, the High Court may exercise, so far as they may be applicable, all the powers of appeal and revision conferred by the Code of Criminal Procedure, 1973 (2 of 1974) on a High Court as if the court of special Judge were a Court of Session trying cases within the local limits of the High Court.

**28. Act to be in addition to any other law.**—The provisions of this Act shall be in addition to, and not in derogation of, any other law for the time being in force, and nothing contained herein shall exempt any public servant from any proceeding which might, apart from this Act, be instituted against him.

**29. Amendment of the Ordinance 38 of 1944.**—In the Criminal Law Amendment Ordinance, 1944,—

(a) in sub-section (1) of section 3, sub-section (1) of sector 9, clause (a) of section 10, sub-section (1) of section 11 and sub-section (1) of section 13, for the words "State Government", wherever they occur, the words "State Government or, as the case may be, the Central Government" shall be substituted;

(b) in section 10, in clause (a), for the words " three months", the words "one year" shall be substituted;

(c) in the Schedule,—

(i) paragraph 1 shall be omitted;

(ii) in paragraphs 2 and 4,—

(a) after the words "a local authority", the words and figures "or a corporation established by or under a Central, Provincial or State Act, or an authority or a body owned or controlled or aided by Government or a Government company as defined in section 617 of the Companies Act, 1956 (1 of 1956) or a society aided by such corporation, authority body or Government company" shall be inserted;

(b) after the words "or authority", the words "or corporation or body or Government company or society" shall be inserted;

(iii) for paragraph 4A, the following paragraph shall be substituted, namely:—

"4A. An offence punishable under the Prevention of Corruption Act, 1988.";

(iv) in paragraph 5, for the words and figures "items 2, 3 and 4", the words, figures and letter "items 2, 3, 4 and 4A" shall be substituted.

[1][**29A. Power to make rules.**—(1) The Central Government may, by notification in the Official Gazette, make rules for carrying out the provisions of this Act.

(2) In particular, and without prejudice to the generality of the foregoing power, such rules may provide for all or any of the following matters, namely:—

(a) guidelines which can be put in place by commercial organisation under section 9;

(b) guidelines for sanction of prosecution under sub-section (1) of section 29;

(c) any other matter which is required to be, or may be, prescribed.

(3) Every rule made under this Act, shall be laid, as soon as may be after it is made, before each House of Parliament, while it is in session, for a total period of thirty days which may be comprised in one session or in two or more successive sessions, and if, before the expiry of the session immediately following the session or the successive sessions aforesaid, both Houses agree in making any modification in the rule, or both Houses agree that the rule should not be made, the rule shall thereafter have effect only in such modified from or be of no effect, as the case may be; so, however,

1. Inst. by Act 16 of 2018, Section 18 (w.e.f. July 26, 2018, according to S.O. 3664(E), dt. July 26, 2018).

that any such modification or annulment shall be without prejudice to the validity of anything previously done under that rule.]

**30. Repeal and saving.**—(1) The Prevention of Corruption Act, 1947 (2 of 1947) and the Criminal Law Amendment Act, 1952 (46 of 1952) are hereby repealed.

(2) Notwithstanding such repeal, but without prejudice to the application of section 6 of the General Clauses Act, 1897 (10 of 1897), anything done or any action taken or purported to have been done or taken under or in pursuance of the Acts so repealed shall, insofar as it is not inconsistent with the provisions of this Act, be deemed to have been done or taken under or in pursuance of the corresponding provision of this Act.

[1]**31. Omission of certain sections of Act 45 of 1860.**—Sections 161 to 165A (both inclusive) of the Indian Penal Code, 1860 (45 of 1860) shall be omitted, and section 6 of the General Clauses Act, 1897 (10 of 1897), shall apply to such omission as if the said sections had been repealed by a Central Act.

---

1. Repealed by Act 30 of 2001, Section 2 and First Schedule (w.e.f. September 3, 2001).

# THE CENTRAL VIGILANCE COMMISSION ACT, 2003

(45 of 2003)

[*11th September, 2003*]

*An Act to provide for the constitution of a Central Vigilance Commission to inquire or cause inquiries to be conducted into offences alleged to have been committed under the Prevention of Corruption Act, 1988 by certain categories of public servants of the Central Government, corporations established by or under any Central Act, Government companies, societies and local authorities owned or controlled by the Central Government and for matters connected therewith or incidental thereto.*

BE it enacted by Parliament in the Fifty-fourth Year of the Republic of India as follows:—

## CHAPTER I
## PRELIMINARY

**1. Short title.** —This Act may be called the Central Vigilance Commission Act, 2003.

### COMMENT

The salient features of the Act are to be found in Section 4 of the Act which mandates that the appointment of the Central Vigilance Commissioner and the Vigilance Commissioners shall be made by the President on the recommendation of a Committee consisting of Prime Minister, Minister of Home Affairs not the leader of the Opposition in the Lok Sabha.

*Alok Kumar Verma v. Union of India*, (2019) 1 SCALE 257: AIR 2019 SC 438.

**2. Definitions.**—In this Act, unless the context otherwise requires,—

(a) "Central Vigilance Commissioner" means the Central Vigilance Commissioner appointed under sub-section (1) of section 4;

(b) "Commission" means the Central Vigilance Commission constituted under sub-section (1) of section 3;

(c) "Delhi Special Police Establishment" means the Delhi Special Police Establishment constituted under sub-section (1) of section 2 of the Delhi Special Police Establishment Act, 1946 (25 of 2016);

(d) "Government company" means a Government company within the meaning of the Companies Act, 1956 (1 of 1956);

[1][(da) "Lokpal" means the Lokpal established under sub-section (1) of section 3 of the Lokpal and Lokayuktas Act, 2013 (1 of 2014);]

(e) "prescribed" means prescribed by rules made under this Act;

(f) "Vigilance Commissioner" means a Vigilance Commissioner appointed under sub-section (1) of section 4.

## CHAPTER II
## THE CENTRAL VIGILANCE COMMISSION

**3. Constitution of Central Vigilance Commission.**—(1) There shall be constituted a body to be known as the Central Vigilance Commission to

1. Inst. by Act 1 of 2014, Section 58 and the Schedule, Part V (w.e.f. January 16, 2014) according to S.O. 119(E), dt. January 16, 2014.

exercise the powers conferred upon, and to perform the functions assigned to it under this Act and the Central Vigilance Commission constituted under sub-section (1) of section 3 of the Central Vigilance Commission Ordinance, 1999 (Ord. 4 of 1999) which ceased to operate, and continued under the Government of India in the Ministry of Personnel, Public Grievances and Pensions (Department of Personnel and Training) Resolution No. 371/20/99-AVD. III, dated the 4th April, 1999 as amended *vide* Resolution of even number, dated the 13th August, 2002 shall be deemed to be the Commission constituted under this Act.

(2) The Commission shall consist of—

(a) a Central Vigilance Commissioner — Chairperson;

(b) not more than two Vigilance Commissioners — Members.

(3) The Central Vigilance Commissioner and the Vigilance Commissioners shall be appointed from amongst persons—

(a) who have been or are in an All-India Service or in any civil service of the Union or in a civil post under the Union having knowledge and experience in the matters relating to vigilance, policy making and administration including police administration; or

(b) who have held office or are holding office in a corporation established by or under any Central Act or a Government company owned or controlled by the Central Government and persons who have expertise and experience in finance including insurance and banking, law, vigilance and investigations:

Provided that, from amongst the Central Vigilance Commissioner and the Vigilance Commissioners, not more than two persons shall belong to the category of persons referred to either in clause (a) or clause (b).

(4) The Central Government shall appoint a Secretary to the Commission on such terms and conditions as it deems fit to exercise such powers and discharge such duties as the Commission may by regulations specify in this behalf.

(5) The Central Vigilance Commissioner, the other Vigilance Commissioners and the Secretary to the Commission appointed under the Central Vigilance Commission Ordinance, 1999 (Ord. 4 of 1999) or the Resolution of the Government of India in the Ministry of Personnel, Public Grievances and Pensions (Department of Personnel and Training) Resolution No. 371/20/99-AVD. III, dated the 4th April, 1999 as amended *vide* Resolution of even number, dated the 13th August, 2002 shall be deemed to have been appointed under this Act on the same terms and conditions including the term of office subject to which they were so appointed under the said Ordinance or the Resolution, as the case may be.

*Explanation.*—For the purposes of this sub-section, the expression "term of office" shall be construed as the term of office with effect from the date the Central Vigilance Commissioner or any Vigilance Commissioner has entered upon his office and continued as such under this Act.

(6) The headquarters of the Commission shall be at New Delhi.

**COMMENT**

**Appoint as Vigilance Commissioner**

The competency and integrity of institution of Vigilance Commission requires to be ensured by the Government. The personal integrity of individual also becomes relevant as it has correlation with institution's integrity.

*Common Cause (A. Registered Society) v. Union of India,* (2018) 8 SCALE 433: (2018) 9 SCC 382; *See* also *Centre for Public Interest Litigation v. Union of India,* AIR 2011 SC 1267: (2011) 3 SLR 390.

**4. Appointment of Central Vigilance Commissioner and Vigilance Commissioners.**—(1) The Central Vigilance Commissioner and the Vigilance Commissioners shall be appointed by the President by warrant under his hand and seal:

Provided that every appointment under this sub-section shall be made after obtaining the recommendation of a Committee consisting of—

(a) the Prime Minister — Chairperson;

(b) the Minister of Home Affairs — Member;

(c) the Leader of the Opposition in the House of the People — Member.

*Explanation.*—For the purposes of this sub-section, "the Leader of the Opposition in the House of the People" shall, when no such Leader has been so recognized, include the Leader of the single largest group in opposition of the Government in the House of the People.

(2) No appointment of a Central Vigilance Commissioner or a Vigilance Commissioner shall be invalid merely by reason of any vacancy in the Committee.

**5. Terms and other conditions of service of Central Vigilance Commissioner.**—(1) Subject to the provisions of sub-sections (3) and (4), the Central Vigilance Commissioner shall hold office for a term of four years from the date on which he enters upon his office or till he attains the age of sixty-five years, whichever is earlier. The Central Vigilance Commissioner, on ceasing to hold the office, shall be ineligible for reappointment in the Commission.

(2) Subject to the provisions of sub-sections (3) and (4), every Vigilance Commissioner shall hold office for a term of four years from the date on which he enters upon his office or till he attains the age of sixty-five years, whichever is earlier:

Provided that every Vigilance Commissioner, on ceasing to hold the office, shall be eligible for appointment as the Central Vigilance Commissioner in the manner specified in sub-section (1) of section 4:

Provided further that the term of the Vigilance Commissioner, if appointed as the Central Vigilance Commissioner, shall not be more than four years in aggregate as the Vigilance Commissioner and the Central Vigilance Commissioner.

(3) The Central Vigilance Commissioner or a Vigilance Commissioner shall, before he enters upon his office, make and subscribe before the President, or

some other person appointed in that behalf by him, an oath or affirmation according to the form set out for the purpose in Schedule to this Act.

(4) The Central Vigilance Commissioner or a Vigilance Commissioner may, by writing under his hand addressed to the President, resign his office.

(5) The Central Vigilance Commissioner or a Vigilance Commissioner may be removed from his office in the manner provided in section 6.

(6) On ceasing to hold office, the Central Vigilance Commissioner and every other Vigilance Commissioner shall be ineligible for—

(a) any diplomatic assignment, appointment as administrator of a Union territory and such other assignment or appointment which is required by law to be made by the President by warrant under his hand and seal;

(b) further employment to any office of profit under the Government of India or the Government of a State.

(7) The salary and allowances payable to and the other conditions of service of—

(a) the Central Vigilance Commissioner shall be the same as those of the Chairman of the Union Public Service Commission;

(b) the Vigilance Commissioner shall be the same as those of a Member of the Union Public Service Commission:

Provided that if the Central Vigilance Commissioner or any Vigilance Commissioner is, at the time of his appointment, in receipt of a pension (other than a disability or wound pension) in respect of any previous service under the Government of India or under the Government of a State, his salary in respect of the service as the Central Vigilance Commissioner or any Vigilance Commissioner shall be reduced by the amount of that pension including any portion of pension which was commuted and pension equivalent of other forms of retirement benefits excluding pension equivalent of retirement gratuity:

Provided further that if the Central Vigilance Commissioner or any Vigilance Commissioner is, at the time of his appointment, in receipt of retirement benefits in respect of any previous service rendered in a corporation established by or under any Central Act or a Government company owned or controlled by the Central Government, his salary in respect of the service as the Central Vigilance Commissioner or, as the case may be, the Vigilance Commissioner shall be reduced by the amount of pension equivalent to the retirement benefits:

Provided also that the salary, allowances and pension payable to, and the other conditions of service of, the Central Vigilance Commissioner or any Vigilance Commissioner shall not be varied to his disadvantage after his appointment.

**6. Removal of Central Vigilance Commissioner and Vigilance Commissioner.**—(1) Subject to the provisions of sub-section (3), the Central Vigilance Commissioner or any Vigilance Commissioner shall be removed from his office only by order of the President on the ground of proved misbehaviour or incapacity after the Supreme Court, on a reference made to it by the President, has, on inquiry, reported that the Central Vigilance

Commissioner or any Vigilance Commissioner, as the case may be, ought on such ground be removed.

(2) The President may suspend from office, and if deem necessary prohibit also from attending the office during inquiry, the Central Vigilance Commissioner or any Vigilance Commissioner in respect of whom a reference has been made to the Supreme Court under sub-section (1) until the President has passed orders on receipt of the report of the Supreme Court on such reference.

(3) Notwithstanding anything contained in sub-section (1), the President may by order remove from office the Central Vigilance Commissioner or any Vigilance Commissioner if the Central Vigilance Commissioner or such Vigilance Commissioner, as the case may be,—

(a) is adjudged an insolvent; or

(b) has been convicted of an offence which, in the opinion of the Central Government, involves moral turpitude; or

(c) engages during his term of office in any paid employment outside the duties of his office; or

(d) is, in the opinion of the President, unfit to continue in office by reason of infirmity of mind or body; or

(e) has acquired such financial or other interest as is likely to affect prejudicially his functions as a Central Vigilance Commissioner or a Vigilance Commissioner.

(4) If the Central Vigilance Commissioner or any Vigilance Commissioner is or becomes in any way, concerned or interested in any contract or agreement made by or on behalf of the Government of India or participates in any way in the profit thereof or in any benefit or emolument arising therefrom otherwise than as a member and in common with the other members of an incorporated company, he shall, for the purposes of sub-section (1), be deemed to be guilty of misbehaviour.

### COMMENT

**Removal of the Vigilance Commissioner**

Section 6 of the Act contemplates the removal of Central Vigilance Commissioner not a Vigilance Commissioner only by the Order of the President on the ground of proved misbehaviour or incapacity as may be found by the Supreme Court of India on a reference being made by the President to the Supreme Court.

*Alok Kumar Verma v. Union of India*, AIR 2019 SC 438: (2019) 1 SCALE 257.

**7. Power to make rules by Central Government for staff.**—The Central Government may, in consultation with the Commission, make rules with respect to the number of members of the staff of the Commission and their conditions of service.

## CHAPTER III

## FUNCTIONS AND POWERS OF THE CENTRAL VIGILANCE COMMISSION

**8. Functions and powers of Central Vigilance Commission.**—(1) The functions and powers of the Commission shall be to—

(a) exercise superintendence over the functioning of the Delhi Special Police Establishment in so far as it relates to the investigation of offences alleged to have been committed under the Prevention of Corruption Act, 1988 (49 of 1988) or an offence with which a public servant specified in sub-section (2) may, under the Code of Criminal Procedure, 1973 (2 of 1974), be charged at the same trial;

(b) give directions to the Delhi Special Police Establishment for the purpose of discharging the responsibility entrusted to it under sub-section (1) of section 4 of the Delhi Special Police Establishment Act, 1946 (25 of 1946):

Provided that while exercising the powers of superintendence under clause (a) or giving directions under this clause, the Commission shall not exercise powers in such a manner so as to require the Delhi Special Police Establishment to investigate or dispose of any case in a particular manner;

(c) inquire or cause an inquiry or investigation to be made on a reference made by the Central Government wherein it is alleged that a public servant being an employee of the Central Government or a corporation established by or under any Central Act, Government company, society and any local authority owned or controlled by that Government, has committed an offence under the Prevention of Corruption Act, 1988 (49 of 1988) or an offence with which a public servant may, under the Code of Criminal Procedure, 1973 (2 of 1974), be charged at the same trial;

(d) inquire or cause an inquiry or investigation to be made into any complaint against any official belonging to such category of officials specified in sub-section (2) wherein it is alleged that he has committed an offence under the Prevention of Corruption Act, 1988 (49 of 1988) and an offence with which a public servant specified in sub-section (2) may, under the Code of Criminal Procedure, 1973 (2 of 1974), be charged at the same trial;

(e) review the progress of investigations conducted by the Delhi Special Police Establishment into offences alleged to have been committed under the Prevention of Corruption Act, 1988 (49 of 1988) or the public servant may, under the Code of Criminal Procedure, 1973 (2 of 1974), be charged at the same trial;

(f) review the progress of applications pending with the competent authorities for sanction of prosecution under the Prevention of Corruption Act, 1988 (49 of 1988);

(g) tender advice to the Central Government, corporations established by or under any Central Act, Government companies, societies and local authorities owned or controlled by the Central Government on such matters as may be referred to it by that Government, said Government companies, societies and local authorities owned or controlled by the Central Government or otherwise;

(h) exercise superintendence over the vigilance administration of the various Ministries of the Central Government or corporations established by or under any Central Act, Government companies, societies and local authorities owned or controlled by that Government:

Provided that nothing contained in this clause shall be deemed to authorize the Commission to exercise superintendence over the vigilance administration in a manner not consistent with the directions relating to vigilance matters issued by the Government and to confer power upon the Commission to issue directions relating to any policy matters:

(2) The persons referred to in clause (d) of sub-section (1) are as follows:—

(a) members of All-India Services serving in connection with the affairs of the Union and Group 'A' officers of the Central Government;

(b) such level of officers of the corporations established by or under any Central Act, Government companies, societies and other local authorities, owned or controlled by the Central Government, as that Government may, by notification in the Official Gazette, specify in this behalf:

Provided that till such time a notification is issued under this clause, all officers of the said corporations, companies, societies and local authorities shall be deemed to be the persons referred to in clause (d) of sub-section (1).

[1][(c) on a reference made by the Lokpal under the proviso to sub-section (1) of section 20 of the Lokpal and Lokayuktas Act, 2013 (1 of 2014), the persons referred to in clause (d) of sub-section (1) shall also include—

(i) members of Group B, Group C and Group D services of the Central Government;

(ii) such level of officials or staff of the corporations established by or under any Central Act, Government companies, societies and other local authorities, owned or controlled by the Central Government, as that Government may, by notification in the Official Gazette, specify in this behalf:

Provided that till such time a notification is issued under this clause, all officials or staff of the said corporations, companies, societies and local authorities shall be deemed to be the persons referred in clause (d) of sub-section (1).]

## COMMENT

**Parameters of entertaining P.I.L.**

The matter should be of great public importance if the Public Interest Litigation is to be entertained. It should be the petitioner's *bona fide* effort to agitate such matter before the court.

*Centre for Public Interest Litigation v. Union of India,* (2011) 1 SCC 560: 2011 AIR (SCW) 157.

1. Inst. by Act 1 of 2014, Section 58 and the Schedule, Part V (w.e.f. January 16, 2014) according to S.O. 119(E), dt. January 16, 2014.

[1][**8A. Action on preliminary inquiry in relation to public servants.**—(1) Where, after the conclusion of the preliminary inquiry relating to corruption of public servants belonging to Group C and Group D officials of the Central Government, the findings of the Commission disclose, after giving an opportunity of being heard to the public servant, a *prima facie* violation of conduct rules relating to corruption under the Prevention of Corruption Act, 1988 (49 of 1988) by such public servant, the Commission shall proceed with one or more of the following actions, namely:—

(a) cause an investigation by any agency or the Delhi Special Police Establishment, as the case may be;

(b) initiation of the disciplinary proceedings or any other appropriate action against the concerned public servant by the competent authority;

(c) closure of the proceedings against the public servant and to proceed against the complainant under section 46 of the Lokpal and Lokayuktas Act, 2013 (1 of 2014).

(2) Every preliminary inquiry referred to in sub-section (1) shall ordinarily be completed within a period of ninety days and for reasons to be recorded in writing, within a further period of ninety days from the date of receipt of the complaint.]

[1][**8B. Action on investigation in relation to public servants.**—(1) In case the Commission decides to proceed to investigate into the complaint under clause (a) of sub-section (1) of section 8A, it shall direct any agency (including the Delhi Special Police Establishment) to carry out the investigation as expeditiously as possible and complete the investigation within a period of six months from the date of its order and submit the investigation report containing its findings to the Commission:

Provided that the Commission may extend the said period by a further period of six months for the reasons to be recorded in writing.

(2) Notwithstanding anything contained in section 173 of the Code of Criminal Procedure, 1973 (2 of 1974), any agency (including the Delhi Special Police Establishment) shall, in respect of cases referred to it by the Commission, submit the investigation report to the Commission.

(3) The Commission shall consider every report received by it under sub-section (2) from any agency (including the Delhi Special Police Establishment) and may decide as to—

(a) file charge-sheet or closure report before the Special Court against the public servant;

(b) initiate the departmental proceedings or any other appropriate action against the concerned public servant by the competent authority.]

**9. Proceedings of Commission.**—(1) The proceedings of the Commission shall be conducted at its headquarters.

1 Inst. by Act 1 of 2014, Section 58 and the Schedule, Part V (w.e.f. January 16, 2014) according to S.O. 119(E), dt. January 16, 2014.

(2) The Commission may, by unanimous decision, regulate the procedure for transaction of its business as also allocation of its business amongst the Central Vigilance Commissioner and other Vigilance Commissioners.

(3) Save as provided in sub-section (2), all business of the Commission shall, as far as possible, be transacted unanimously.

(4) Subject to the provisions of sub-section (3), if the Central Vigilance Commissioner and other Vigilance Commissioners differ in opinion on any matter, such matter shall be decided according to the opinion of the majority.

(5) The Central Vigilance Commissioner, or, if for any reason he is unable to attend any meeting of the Commission, the senior-most Vigilance Commissioner present at the meeting, shall preside at the meeting.

(6) No act or proceeding of the Commission shall be invalid merely by reason of—

(a) any vacancy in, or any defect in the constitution of, the Commission; or

(b) any defect in the appointment of a person acting as the Central Vigilance Commissioner or as a Vigilance Commissioner; or

(c) any irregularity in the procedure of the Commission not affecting the merits of the case.

**10. Vigilance Commissioner to act as Central Vigilance Commissioner in certain circumstances.**—(1) In the event of the occurrence of any vacancy in the office of the Central Vigilance Commissioner by reason of his death, resignation or otherwise, the President may, by notification, authorise one of the Vigilance Commissioners to act as the Central Vigilance Commissioner until the appointment of a new Central Vigilance Commissioner to fill such vacancy.

(2) When the Central Vigilance Commissioner is unable to discharge his functions owing to absence on leave or otherwise, such one of the Vigilance Commissioners as the President may, by notification, authorise in this behalf, shall discharge the functions of the Central Vigilance Commissioner until the date on which the Central Vigilance Commissioner resumes his duties.

**11. Power relating to inquiries.**—The Commission shall, while conducting any [1][inquiry referred to in clauses (c) and (d) of sub-section (1) of section 8], have all the powers of a civil court trying a suit under the Code of Civil Procedure, 1908 (5 of 1908) and in particular, in respect of the following matters, namely:—

(a) summoning and enforcing the attendance of any person from any part of India and examining him on oath;

(b) requiring the discovery and production of any document;

(c) receiving evidence on affidavits;

(d) requisitioning any public record or copy thereof from any court or office;

1. Subst. by G.S.R. 654(E), dt. September 28, 2004, for "inquiry referred to in clauses (b) and (c) of sub-section (1) of section 8" (w.e.f. October 1, 2004).

(e) issuing commissions for the examination of witnesses or other documents; and

(f) any other matter which may be prescribed.

[1][**11A. Director of Inquiry for making preliminary inquiry.**—(1) There shall be a Director of Inquiry, not below the rank of Joint Secretary to the Government of India, who shall be appointed by the Central Government for conducting preliminary inquiries referred to the Commission by the Lokpal.

(2) The Central Government shall provide the Director of Inquiry such officers and employees as may be required for the discharge of his functions under this Act.]

**12. Proceedings before Commission to be judicial proceedings.**—The Commission shall be deemed to be a civil court for the purposes of section 195 and Chapter XXVI of the Code of Criminal Procedure, 1973 (2 of 1974) and every proceeding before the Commission shall be deemed to be a judicial proceeding within the meaning of sections 193 and 228 and for the purposes of section 196 of the Indian Penal Code (45 of 1860).

## CHAPTER IV

## EXPENSES AND ANNUAL REPORT

**13. Expenses of Commission to be charged on the Consolidated Fund of India.**—The expenses of the Commission, including any salaries, allowances and pensions payable to or in respect of the Central Vigilance Commissioner, the Vigilance Commissioners, Secretary and the staff of the Commission, shall be charged on the Consolidated Fund of India.

**14. Annual report.**—(1) It shall be the duty of the Commission to present annually to the President a report as to the work done by the Commission within six months of the close of the year under report.

(2) The report referred to in sub-section (1) shall contain a separate part on the functioning of the Delhi Special Police Establishment in so far as it relates to sub-section (1) of section 4 of the Delhi Special Police Establishment Act, 1946 (25 of 1946).

(3) On receipt of such report, the President shall cause the same to be laid before each House of Parliament.

## CHAPTER V

## MISCELLANEOUS

**15. Protection of action taken in good faith.**—No suit, prosecution or other legal proceeding shall lie against the Commission, the Central Vigilance Commissioner, any Vigilance Commissioner, the Secretary or against any staff of the Commission in respect of anything which is in good faith done or intended to be done under this Act.

**16. Central Vigilance Commissioner, Vigilance Commissioner and staff to be public servants.**—The Central Vigilance Commissioner, every

1. Inst. by Act 1 of 2014, Section 58 and the Schedule, Part V (w.e.f. January 16, 2014) according to 119(E), dt. January 16, 2014.

Vigilance Commissioner, the Secretary and every staff of the Commission shall be deemed to be a public servant within the meaning of section 21 of the Indian Penal Code (45 of 1860).

**17. Report of any inquiry made on reference by Commission to be forwarded to that Commission.**—(1) The report of the inquiry undertaken by any agency on a reference made by the Commission shall be forwarded to the Commission.

(2) The Commission shall, on receipt of such report and after taking into consideration any other factors relevant thereto, advise the Central Government and corporations established by or under any Central Act, Government companies, societies and local authorities owned or controlled by that Government, as the case may be, as to the further course of action.

(3) The Central Government and the corporations established by or under any Central Act, Government companies, societies and other local authorities owned or controlled by that Government, as the case may be, shall consider the advice of the Commission and take appropriate action:

Provided that where the Central Government, any corporation established by or under any Central Act, Government company, society or local authority owned or controlled by the Central Government, as the case may be, does not agree with the advice of the Commission, it shall, for reasons to be recorded in writing, communicate the same to the Commission.

**18. Power to call for information.**—The Commission may call for reports, returns and statements from the Central Government or corporations established by or under any Central Act, Government companies, societies and other local authorities owned or controlled by that Government so as to enable it to exercise general supervision over the vigilance and anti-corruption work in that Government and in the said corporations, Government companies, societies and local authorities.

**19. Consultation with Commission in certain matters.**—The Central Government shall, in making any rules or regulations governing the vigilance or disciplinary matters relating to persons appointed to public services and posts in connection with the affairs of the Union or to members of the All-India Services, consult the Commission.

**20. Power to make rules.**—(1) The Central Government may, by notification in the Official Gazette, make rules for the purpose of carrying out the provisions of this Act.

(2) In particular, and without prejudice to the generality of the foregoing power, such rules may provide for all or any of the following matters, namely:—

(a) the number of members of the staff and their conditions of service under section 7;

(b) any other power of the civil court to be prescribed under clause (f) of section 11; and

(c) any other matter which is required to be, or may be, prescribed.

**21. Power to make regulations.**—(1) The Commission may, with the previous approval of the Central Government, by notification in the Official

Gazette, make regulations not inconsistent with this Act and the rules made thereunder to provide for all matters for which provision is expedient for the purposes of giving effect to the provisions of this Act.

(2) In particular, and without prejudice to the generality of the foregoing power, such regulations may provide for all or any of the following matters, namely:—

(a) the duties and the powers of the Secretary under sub-section (4) of section 3; and

(b) the procedure to be followed by the Commission under sub-section (2) of section 9.

**22. Notification, rule, etc., to be laid before Parliament.**—Every notification issued under clause (b) of sub-section (2) of section 8 and every rule made by the Central Government and every regulation made by the Commission under this Act shall be laid, as soon as may be after it is issued or made, before each House of Parliament, while it is in session, for a total period of thirty days which may be comprised in one session or in two or more successive sessions, and if, before the expiry of the session immediately following the session or the successive sessions aforesaid, both Houses agree in making any modification in the notification or the rule or the regulation, or both Houses agree that the notification or the rule or the regulation should not be made, the notification or the rule or the regulation shall thereafter have effect only in such modified form or be of no effect, as the case may be; so, however, that any such modification or annulment shall be without prejudice to the validity of anything previously done under that notification or rule or regulation.

**23. Power to remove difficulties.**—(1) If any difficulty arises in giving effect to the provisions of this Act, the Central Government may, by order, not inconsistent with the provisions of this Act, remove the difficulty:

Provided that no such order shall be made after the expiry of a period of two years from the date of commencement of this Act.

(2) Every order made under this section shall, as soon as may be after it is made, be laid before each House of Parliament.

**24. Provisions relating to existing Vigilance Commission.**—With effect from the constitution of the Commission under sub-section (1) of section 3, the Central Vigilance Commission set up by the Resolution of Government of India in the Ministry of Home Affairs No. 24/7/64-ADV, dated the 11th February, 1964 (hereinafter referred to in this section as the existing Vigilance Commission) shall, insofar as its functions are not inconsistent with the provisions of this Act, continue to discharge the said functions and—

(a) all actions and decisions taken by the Vigilance Commission insofar as such actions and decisions are relatable to the functions of the Commission constituted under this Act shall be deemed to have been taken by the Commission;

(b) all proceedings pending before the Vigilance Commission, insofar as such proceedings relate to the functions of the Commission, shall be deemed to be transferred to the Commission and shall be dealt with in accordance with the provisions of this Act;

(c) the employees of the Vigilance Commission shall be deemed to have become the employees of the Commission on the same terms and conditions;

(d) all the assets and liabilities of the Vigilance Commission shall be transferred to the Commission.

**25. Appointments, etc., of officers of Directorate of Enforcement.—** Notwithstanding anything contained in the Foreign Exchange Management Act, 1999 (42 of 1999) or any other law for the time being in force,—

(a) the Central Government shall appoint a Director of Enforcement in the Directorate of Enforcement in the Ministry of Finance on the recommendation of the Committee consisting of—

(i) the Central Vigilance Commissioner — Chairperson;

(ii) Vigilance Commissioners — Members;

(iii) Secretary to the Government of India in-charge of the Ministry of Home Affairs in the Central Government — Member;

(iv) Secretary to the Government of India in-charge of the Ministry of Personnel in the Central Government — Member;

(v) Secretary to the Government of India in-charge of the Department of Revenue, Ministry of Finance in the Central Government — Member;

(b) while making a recommendation, the Committee shall take into consideration the integrity and experience of the officers eligible for appointment;

(c) no person below the rank of Additional Secretary to the Government of India shall be eligible for appointment as a Director of Enforcement;

(d) a Director of Enforcement shall continue to hold office for a period of not less than two years from the date on which he assumes office;

[1][Provided that the period for which the Director of Enforcement holds the office on his initial appointment may, in public interest, on the recommendation of the Committee under clause (a) and for the reasons to be recorded in writing, be extended up to one year at a time:

Provided further that no such extension shall be granted after the completion of a period of five years in total including the period mentioned in the initial appointment;]

(e) a Director of Enforcement shall not be transferred except with the previous consent of the Committee referred to in clause (a);

(f) the Committee referred to in clause (a) shall, in consultation with the Director of Enforcement, recommend officers for appointment to the posts above the level of the Deputy Director of Enforcement

1. Inst. by Act 46 of 2021, Section 2 (w.e.f. November 14, 2021).

and also recommend the extension or curtailment of the tenure of such officers in the Directorate of Enforcement;

(g) on receipt of the recommendation under clause (f), the Central Government shall pass such orders as it thinks fit to give effect to the said recommendation.

**26. Amendment of Act 25 of 1946.**—In the Delhi Special Police Establishment Act, 1946.—

(a) after section 1, the following section shall be inserted, namely:—

"1A. Interpretation section.—Words and expressions used herein and not defined but defined in the Central Vigilance Commission Act, 2003, shall have the meanings, respectively, assigned to them in that Act.";

(b) for section 4, the following sections shall be substituted, namely:—

"4. *Superintendence and administration of Special Police Establishment.*—(1) The superintendence of the Delhi Special Police Establishment in so far as it relates to investigation of offences alleged to have been committed under the Prevention of Corruption Act, 1988 (49 of 1988), shall vest in the Commission.

(2) Save as otherwise provided in sub-section (1), the superintendence of the said police establishment in all other matters shall vest in the Central Government.

(3) The administration of the said police establishment shall vest in an officer appointed in this behalf by the Central Government (hereinafter referred to as the Director) who shall exercise in respect of that police establishment such of the powers exercisable by an Inspector-General of Police in respect of the police force in a State as the Central Government may specify in this behalf.

4A. *Committee for appointment of Director.*—(1) The Central Government shall appoint the Director on the recommendation of the Committee consisting of—

(a) the Central Vigilance Commissioner — Chairperson;

(b) Vigilance Commissioners — Members;

(c) Secretary to the Government of India in-charge of the Ministry of Home Affairs in the Central Government — Member;

(d) Secretary (Coordination and Public Grievances) in the Cabinet Secretariat — Member.

(2) While making any recommendation under sub-section (1), the Committee shall take into consideration the views of the outgoing Director.

(3) The Committee shall recommend a panel of officers—

(a) on the basis of seniority, integrity and experience in the investigation of anti-corruption cases; and

(b) chosen from amongst officers belonging to the Indian Police Service constituted under the All-India Services Act, 1951 (61 of 1951),

for being considered for appointment as the Director.

*4B. Terms and conditions of service of Director*—(1) The Director shall, notwithstanding anything to the contrary contained in the rules relating to his conditions of service, continue to hold office for a period of not less than two years from the date on which he assumes office.

(2) The Director shall not be transferred except with the previous consent of the Committee referred to in sub-section (1) of section 4A.

*4C. Appointment for posts of Superintendent of Police and above, extension and curtailment of their tenure, etc.*—(1) The Committee referred to in section 4A shall, after consulting the Director, recommend officers for appointment to the posts of the level of Superintendent of Police and above and also recommend the extension or curtailment of the tenure of such officers in the Delhi Special Police Establishment.

(2) On receipt of the recommendation under sub-section (1), the Central Government shall pass such orders as it thinks fit to give effect to the said recommendation.";

(c) after section 6, the following section shall be inserted, namely:—

"*6A. Approval of Central Government to conduct inquiry or investigation.*—(1) The Delhi Special Police Establishment shall not conduct any inquiry or investigation into any offence alleged to have been committed under the Prevention of Corruption Act, 1988 (49 of 1988) except with the previous approval of the Central Government where such allegation relates to—

(a) the employees of the Central Government of the level of Joint Secretary and above; and

(b) such officers as are appointed by the Central Government in corporations established by or under any Central Act, Government companies, societies and local authorities owned or controlled by that Government.

(2) Notwithstanding anything contained in sub-section (1), no such approval shall be necessary for cases involving arrest of a person on the spot on the charge of accepting or attempting to accept any gratification other than legal remuneration referred to in clause (c) of the *Explanation* to section 7 of the Prevention of Corruption Act, 1988 (49 of 1988).".

## COMMENT

**Appoint of Director of C.B.I.**

The Director of Central Bureau of Investigation is considered to be a superior post. It is only a tenure post. The seniority alone cannot be a criteria but merit would play a decisive role which has to be determined with relevant considerations like integrity and experience in investigating anti-corruption cases.

*Union of India v. C. Dinakar, I.P.S.*, (2014) 5 JT 345.

**27. Repeal and saving.**—(1) The Government of India in the Ministry of Personnel, Public Grievances and Pensions (Department of Personnel and Training) Resolution No. 371/20/99-AVD. III, dated the 4th April, 1999 as amended *vide* Resolution of even number, dated the 13th August, 2002 is hereby repealed.

(2) Notwithstanding such repeal and the cesser of operation of the Central Vigilance Commission Ordinance, 1999 (Ord. 4 of 1999), anything done or any action taken under the said Resolution and the said Ordinance including the appointments made and other actions taken or anything done or any action taken or any appointment made under the Delhi Special Police Establishment Act, 1946 (25 of 1946) and the Foreign Exchange Regulation Act, 1973 (46 of 1973) as amended by the said Ordinance shall be deemed to have been made or done or taken under this Act or the Delhi Special Police Establishment Act, 1946 and the Foreign Exchange Regulation Act, 1973 as if the amendments made in those Acts by this Act were in force at all material times.

## THE SCHEDULE

[*See* section 5(3)]

## FORM OF OATH OR AFFIRMATION TO BE MADE BY THE CENTRAL VIGILANCE COMMISSIONER OR VIGILANCE COMMISSIONER

"I, A.B., having been appointed Central Vigilance Commissioner (or Vigilance Commissioner) of the Central Vigilance Commission do $\frac{\text{swear in the name of God}}{\text{solemnly affirm}}$ that I will bear true faith and allegiance to the Constitution of India as by law established, that I will uphold the sovereignty and integrity of India, that I will duly and faithfully and to the best of my ability, knowledge and judgment perform the duties of my office without fear or favour, affection or ill-will and that I will uphold the constitution and the laws.".

# THE COMMISSIONS OF INQUIRY ACT, 1952

(60 of 1952)[1]

[*14th August, 1952*]

*An Act to provide for the appointment of Commissions of Inquiry and for vesting such Commissions with certain powers.*

BE it enacted by Parliament as follows:—

**1. Short title, extent and commencement.**—(1) This Act may be called the Commissions of Inquiry Act, 1952.

[2][(2) It extends to the whole of India:

[3][***]

(3) It shall come into force on such date[4] as the Central Government may, by notification in the Official Gazette, appoint.

**2. Definitions.**—In this Act, unless the context otherwise requires,—

(a) "appropriate Government" means—

(i) the Central Government, in relation to a Commission appointed by it to make an inquiry into any matter relatable to any of the entries enumerated in List I or List II or List III in the Seventh Schedule to the Constitution; and

(ii) the State Government, in relation to a Commission appointed by it to make an inquiry into any matter relatable to any of the entries enumerated in List II or List III in the Seventh Schedule to the Constitution:

[5][***]

(b) "Commission" means a Commission of Inquiry appointed under section 3;

(c) "prescribed" means prescribed by rules made under this Act.

---

1. This Act stood extended to—
Goa, Daman and Diu by Regulation 12 of 1962, Section 3 and Schedule (w.e.f. February 1, 1965).
Dadra and Nagar Haveli (w.e.f. July 1, 1965) by Regulation 6 of 1963, Section 2 and Schedule I.
Pondicherry (w.e.f. October 1, 1963) by Regulation 7 of 1963, Section 3 and Schedule I.
2. Subst. by Act 79 of 1971, Section 2, for Sub-s. (2).
3. The proviso stood omitted by Act 34 of 2019, Section 95 and the Fifth Schedule (w.e.f. October 31, 2019). Prior to omission, ran as under:
Provided that it shall apply to the State of Jammu and Kashmir only insofar as it relates to inquiries pertaining to matters relatable to any of the entries enumerated in List I or List III in the Seventh Schedule to the Constitution as applicable to that State.
4. Enforced from October 1, 1952, according to S.R.O. 1670, dt. the September 30, 1952, refer to Gazette of India, Extraordinary, Part II, Section 3, pg. 861.
This Act, stood amended by Act 79 of 1971, enforced from the State of Jammu & Kashmir on March 6, 1972 and in the districts of Kohima and Mokokchung in the State of Nagaland on Feburary15, 1972, according to notification No. 954(E), dt. March 4, 1972 and 74(E), dt. February, 1972 respectively, issued under Section 15 of Act 79 of 1971.
5. The Proviso stood omitted by the Jammu and Kashmir Reorganization (Adaptation of Central Laws) Order, 2020, according to notification No. S.O. 1123(E) dt. (March 18, 2020) and according to Union Territory of Ladakh Reorganisation (Adaptation of Central Laws) Order, 2020, Notification No. S.O. 3774(E), dt. (October 23, 2020).

**[2A. [Construction of references to laws not in force in the State of Jammu and Kashmir*.**—*Omitted by the Jammu and Kashmir Reorganisations (Adaptation of Central Laws) Order, 2020, according to notification No. S.O. 1123(E), dt. (March 18, 2020) and according to Union Territory of Ladakh Reorganisation (Adaptation of Central Laws) Order, 2020, Notification No. S.O. 3774(E), dt. (October 23, 2020).*]

**3. Appointment of Commission.**—(1) [1][Save as otherwise provided in the Lokpal and Lokayuktas Act, 2013, the appropriate Government may], if it is of opinion that it is necessary so to do, and shall if a resolution in this behalf is passed by [2][each House of Parliament or, as the case may be, the Legislature of the State], by notification in the Official Gazette, appoint a Commission of Inquiry for the purpose of making an inquiry into any definite matter of public importance and performing such functions and within such time as may be specified in the notification, and the Commission so appointed shall make the inquiry and perform the functions accordingly:

Provided that where any such Commission has been appointed to inquire into any matter—

(a) by the Central Government, no State Government shall, except with the approval of the Central Government, appoint another Commission to inquire into the same matter for so long as the Commission appointed by the Central Government is functioning;

(b) by a State Government, the Central Government shall not appoint another Commission to inquire into the same matter for so long as the Commission appointed by the State Government is functioning, unless the Central Government is of opinion that the scope of the inquiry should be extended to two or more States.

(2) The Commission may consist of one or more members appointed by the appropriate Government, and where the Commission consists of more than one member, one of them may be appointed as the Chairman thereof.

[3][(3) The appropriate Government may, at any stage of an inquiry by the Commission fill any vacancy which may have arisen in the office of a member of the Commission (whether consisting of one or more than one member).

(4) The appropriate Government shall cause to be laid before [3][each House of Parliament or, as the case may be, the Legislature of the State], the report, if any, of the Commission on the inquiry made by the Commission under sub-section (1) together with a memorandum of the action taken thereon, within a period of six months of the submission of the report by the Commission to the appropriate Government.]

[4][***]

---

* According to Notification No. S.O. 3912 (E), dt. October 30, 2019, this Act is made applicable to the Union territory of Jammu and Kashmir and the Union territory of Ladakh.

1. Subst. by Act 1 of 2014, Section 58 and Schedule, Part I, for "The appropriate Government may" (w.e.f. January 16, 2014), according S.O. 119(E), dt. January 16, 2014.
2. Subst. by Act 19 of 1990, Section 2, for certain words.
3. Inst. by Act 79 of 1971, Section 5.
4. Sub-s. (5) and (6) stood omitted by Act 19 of 1990, Section 2.

## COMMENT

**Formation of Inquiry Commission**

While enlarging scope of enquiry the addition of references to the Commission in absence of substantial material cannot be done.

*State of Madhya Pradesh v. Arjun Singh*, (1993) 1 SCC 51: (1992) 3 SCALE 155.

**4. Powers of Commission.**—The Commission shall have the powers of a civil court, while trying a suit under the Code of Civil Procedure, 1908 (5 of 1908), in respect of the following matters, namely:—

(a) [1][summoning and enforcing the attendance of any person from any part of India] and examining him on oath;

(b) requiring the discovery and production of any document;

(c) receiving evidence on affidavits;

(d) requisitioning any public record or copy thereof from any court or office;

(e) issuing commissions for the examination of witnesses or documents;

(f) any other matter which may be prescribed.

**5. Additional powers of Commission.**—(1) Where the appropriate Government is of opinion that, having regard to the nature of the inquiry to be made and other circumstances of the case, all or any of the provisions of sub-section (2) or sub-section (3) or sub-section (4) or sub-section (5) should be made applicable to a Commission, the appropriate Government may, by notification in the Official Gazette, direct that all or such of the said provisions as may be specified in the notification shall apply to that Commission and on the issue of such a notification, the said provisions shall apply accordingly.

(2) The Commission shall have power to require any person, subject to any privilege which may be claimed by that person under any law for the time being in force, to furnish information on such points or matters as, in the opinion of the Commission, may be useful for, or relevant to, the subject matter of the inquiry [2][and any person so required shall be deemed to be legally bound to furnish such information within the meaning of section 176 and section 177 of the Indian Penal Code (45 of 1860)].

(3) The Commission or any officer, not below the rank of a Gazetted Officer, specially authorised in this behalf by the Commission may enter any building or place where the Commission has reason to believe that any books of account or other documents relating to the subject-matter of the inquiry may be found, and may seize any books of account or documents or take extracts or copies therefrom, subject to the provisions of section 102 and section 103 of the Code of Criminal Procedure, 1898 (5 of 1898), in so far as they may be applicable.

(4) The Commission shall be deemed to be a civil court and when any offence as is described in section 175, section 178, section 179, section 180 or section 228 of the Indian Penal Code (45 of 1860) is committed in the view or presence of the Commission, the Commission may, after recording the facts constituting the offence and the statement of the accused as provided

1. Subst. by Act 79 of 1971, Section 6, for certain words.
2. Inst. by Act 79 of 1971, Section 7.

for in the Code of Criminal Procedure, 1898 (5 of 1898), forward the case to a magistrate having jurisdiction to try the same and the magistrate to whom any such case is forwarded shall proceed to hear the complaint against the accused as if the case had been forwarded to him under section 482 of the Code of Criminal Procedure, 1898 (5 of 1898).

(5) Any proceeding before the Commission shall be deemed to be a judicial proceeding within the meaning of sections 193 and 228 of the Indian Penal Code (45 of 1860).

## COMMENT

**Commission of Enquiry is not a court**

The Commission of Enquiry is not a court for the purpose of section 195 of the Code of Criminal Procedure.

*Baliram Waman Hiray v. Justice B. Lentin*, (1988) 4 SCC 419: (1988) 4 JT 265

[1][**5A. Power of Commission to utilise the services of certain officers and investigation agencies for conducting investigation pertaining to inquiry.**—(1) The Commission may, for the purpose of conducting any investigation pertaining to the inquiry, utilise the services,—

(a) in the case of a Commission appointed by the Central Government, of any officer or investigation agency of the Central Government or any State Government with the concurrence of the Central Government or the State Government, as the case may be; or

(b) in the case of a Commission appointed by the State Government, of any officer or investigation agency of the State Government or Central Government with the concurrence of the State Government or the Central Government, as the case may be.

(2) For the purpose of investigating into any matter pertaining to the inquiry, any officer or agency whose services are utilised under sub-section (1) may, subject to the direction and control of the Commission,—

(a) summon and enforce the attendance of any person and examine him;

(b) require the discovery and production of any document; and

(c) requisition any public record or copy thereof from any office.

(3) The provisions of section 6 shall apply in relation to any statement made by a person before any officer or agency whose services are utilised under sub-section (1) as they apply in relation to any statement made by a person in the course of giving evidence before the Commission.

(4) The officer or agency, whose services are utilised under sub-section (1), shall investigate into any matter pertaining to the inquiry and submit a report thereon (hereafter in this section referred to as the investigation report) to the Commission within such period as may be specified by the Commission in this behalf.

(5) The Commission shall satisfy itself about the correctness of the facts stated and the conclusions, if any, arrived at in the investigation report

1. Inst. by Act 79 of 1971, Section 8 (w.e.f. December 30, 1971).

submitted to it under sub-section (4), and for this purpose the Commission may make such inquiry (including the examination of the person or persons who conducted or assisted in the investigation) as it thinks fit.]

[1][**5B. Power of Commission to appoint assessors.**—The Commission may, for the purpose of conducting any inquiry, appoint persons having special knowledge of any matter connected with the inquiry as assessors, to assist and advise the Commission in the inquiry and the assessors shall be entitled to such travelling and other expenses as may be prescribed.]

**6. Statements made by persons to the Commission.**—No statement made by a person in the course of giving evidence before the Commission shall subject him to, or be used against him in, any civil or criminal proceeding except a prosecution for giving false evidence by such statement:

Provided that the statement—

(a) is made in reply to a question which he is required by the Commission to answer, or

(b) is relevant to the subject matter of the inquiry.

[2][**6A. Persons not obliged to disclose secret process of manufacture of goods in certain cases.**—Except in cases where a Commission is expressly required to inquire into the process of manufacture of any goods, nothing in this Act shall be deemed to compel any person giving evidence before the Commission to disclose any secret process of manufacture thereof.]

[3][**7. Commission to cease to exist when so notified.**—(1) The appropriate Government may, by notification in the Official Gazette, declare that—

(a) a Commission (other than a Commission appointed in pursuance of a resolution passed by [4][each House of Parliament or, as the case may be, the Legislature of the State] shall cease to exist, if it is of opinion that the continued existence of the Commission is unnecessary;

(b) a Commission appointed in pursuance of a resolution passed by [4][each House of Parliament or, as the case may be, the Legislature of the State] shall cease to exist if a resolution for the discontinuance of the Commission is passed by [4][each House of Parliament or, as the case may be, the Legislature of the State].

(2) Every notification issued under sub-section (1) shall specify the date from which the Commission shall cease to exist and on the issue of such notification, the Commission shall cease to exist with effect from the date specified therein.]

**8. Procedure to be followed by the Commission.**—The Commission shall, subject to any rules that may be made in this behalf, have power to regulate its own procedure (including the fixing of places and times of its sittings and deciding whether to sit in public or in private) [5][***].

1. Inst. by Act 63 of 1988, Section 2.
2. Inst. by Act 79 of 1971, Section 9.
3. Subst. by Act 79 of 1971 Section 10, for Section 7.
4. Subst. by Act 19 of 1990 Section 3, for certain words.
5. Certain words stood omitted by Act 79 of 1971, Section 11.

[1][**8A. Inquiry not to be interrupted by reason of vacancy or change in the constitution of the Commission.**—(1) Where the Commission consists of two or more members, it may act notwithstanding the absence of the Chairman or any other member or any vacancy among its members.

(2) Where during the course of an inquiry before a Commission, a change has taken place in the constitution of the Commission by reason of any vacancy having, been filled or by any other reason, it shall not be necessary for the Commission to commence the inquiry a fresh and the inquiry may be continued from the stage at which the change took place.

**COMMENT**

**Single Member Enquiry Commission**

The reconstitution by replacement or substitution of existing member cannot be permissible and can be obviously beyond the competency of State Government.

*State of Madhya Pradesh v. Ajay Singh*, (1993) 1 SCC 302: (1992) 3 SCALE 45.

**8B. Persons likely to be prejudicially affected to be heard.**—If, at any stage of the inquiry, the Commission,—

(a) considers it necessary to inquire into the conduct of any person; or

(b) is of opinion that the reputation of any person is likely to be prejudicially affected by the inquiry,

the Commission shall give to that person a reasonable opportunity of being heard in the inquiry and to produce evidence in his defence:

Provided that nothing in this section shall apply where the credit of a witness is being impeached.

**8C. Right of cross-examination and representation by legal practitioner.**—The appropriate Government, every person referred to in section 8B and, with the permission of the Commission, any other person whose evidence is recorded by the Commission,—

(a) may cross-examine a witness other than a witness produced by it or him;

(b) may address the Commission; and

(c) may be represented before the Commission by a legal practitioner or, with the permission of the Commission, by any other person.]

**9. Protection of action taken in good faith.**—No suit or other legal proceeding shall lie against the appropriate Government, the Commission or any member thereof, or any person acting under the direction either of the appropriate Government or of the Commission in respect of anything which is in good faith done or intended to be done in pursuance of this Act or of any rules or orders made thereunder or in respect of the publication, by or under the authority of the appropriate Government or the Commission, of any report, paper or proceedings.

**10. Members, etc., to be public servants.**—Every member of the Commission and every officer appointed or authorised by the Commission

1. Inst. by Act 79 of 1971, Section 12.

in exercise of functions under this Act shall be deemed to be a public servant within the meaning of section 21 of the Indian Penal Code (45 of 1860).

[1][**10A. Penalty for acts calculated to bring the Commission or any member thereof into disrepute.**—(1) If any person, by words either spoken or intended to be read, makes or publishes any statement or does any other act, which is calculated to bring the Commission or any member thereof into disrepute, he shall be punishable with simple imprisonment for a term which may extend to six months, or with fine, or with both.

[2][(2) Notwithstanding anything contained in the Code of Criminal Procedure, 1973 (2 of 1974), when an offence under sub-section (1) is alleged to have been committed, the High Court may take cognizance of such offence, without the case being committed to it, upon a complaint in writing, made by a member of a Commission or an officer of the Commission authorised by it in this behalf.

(3) Every complaint referred to it in sub-section (2) shall set forth the facts which constitute the offence alleged, the nature of such offence and such other particulars as are reasonably sufficient to give notice to the accused of the offence alleged to have been committed by him.

(4) No High Court shall take cognizance of an offence under sub-section (1) unless the complaint is made within six months from the date on which the offence is alleged to have been committed.

(5) A High Court taking cognizance of an offence under sub-section (1) shall try the case in accordance with the procedure for the trial of warrant cases instituted otherwise than on a police report before a court of a Magistrate:

Provided that the personal attendance of a member of a Commission as a complainant or otherwise is not required in such trial.

(6) Notwithstanding anything contained in the Code of Criminal Procedure, 1973 (2 of 1974) an appeal shall lie as a matter of right from any judgment of the High Court to the Supreme Court, both on facts and on law.

(7) Every appeal to the Supreme Court under sub-section (6) shall be preferred within a period of thirty days from the date of the judgment appealed from:

Provided that the Supreme Court may entertain an appeal after the expiry of the said period of thirty days if it is satisfied that the appellant had sufficient cause for not preferring the appeal within the period of thirty days.]]

**11. Act to apply to other inquiring authorities in certain cases.**—Where any authority (by whatever name called), other than a Commission appointed under section 3, has been or is set up under any resolution or order of the appropriate Government for the purpose of making an inquiry into any definite matter of public importance and that Government is of opinion that all or any of the provisions of this Act should be made

1. Inst. by Act 79 of 1971, Section 13.
2. Subst. by Act 63 of 1988, Section 3, for Sub-s. (2).

applicable to that authority, that Government may, subject to the prohibition contained in the proviso to sub section (1) of section 3, by notification in the Official Gazette, direct that the said provisions of this Act shall apply to that authority, and on the issue of such a notification, that authority shall be deemed to be a Commission appointed under section 3 for the purposes of this Act.

**12. Power to make rules.**—(1) The appropriate Government may, by notification in the Official Gazette, make rules to carry out the purposes of this Act.

(2) In particular, and without prejudice to the generality of the foregoing power, such rules may provide for all or any of the following matters, namely:—

(a) the term of office and the conditions of service of the members of the Commission;

(b) the manner in which inquiries may be held under this Act and the procedure to be followed by the Commission in respect of the proceedings before it;

(c) the powers of civil court which may be vested in the Commission;

[1][(cc) the travelling and other expenses payable to assessors appointed under section 5B, and to person summoned by the Commission to give evidence or to produce documents before it;]

(d) any other matter which has to be, or may be, prescribed.

[2][(3) Every rule made by the Central Government under this section shall be laid, as soon as may be after it is made, before each House of Parliament while it is in session for a total period of thirty days which may be comprised in one session or [3][in two or more successive sessions, and if, before the expiry of the session immediately following the session or the successive sessions aforesaid], both Houses agree in making any modification in the rule or both Houses agree that the rule should not be made, the rule shall thereafter have effect only in such modified form or be of no effect, as the case may be; so, however, that any such modification or annulment shall be without prejudice to the validity of anything previously done under that rule.]

[4][(4) Every rule made by the State Government under this section shall be laid, as soon as may be after it is made, before the State Legislature.]

---

1. Inst. by Act 63 of 1988, Section 4
2. Inst. by Act 79 of 1971, Section 14.
3. Subst. by Act 4 of 1986, Section 2 and the Schedule, for certain words (w.e.f. May 15, 1986).
4. Inst. by Act 4 of 1986, Section 2 and the Schedule (w.e.f. May 15, 1986).

# THE CRIMINAL LAW (AMENDMENT) ORDINANCE, 1944

(38 of 1944)

[*23rd August, 1944*]

*An Ordinance to prevent the disposal or concealment of property procured by means of certain offence.*

*Whereas an emergency has arisen which makes it necessary to provide for preventing the disposal or concealment of money or other property procured by means of certain offences punishable under the Indian Penal Code.*

*Now, therefore, in exercise of the powers conferred by section 72 of the Government of India Act, as set out in the Ninth Schedule to the Government of India Act, 1935, the Governor-General is pleased to make the promulgate the following Ordinance:—*

**1. Short title, extent and commencement.**—(1) This Ordinance may be called The Criminal Law (Amendment) Ordinance, 1944.

[1][(2) It extends to the whole of India except the State of Jammu and Kashmir* and applies also to citizens of India outside India].

[2][(3) It shall come into force at once.]

**2. Interpretation.**—(1) In this Ordinance, "Scheduled offence" means an offence specified in the Schedule to this Ordinance.

[3][(2) For the purpose of this Ordinance, the date of the termination of criminal proceeding shall be deemed to be—

(a) where such proceeding are taken to the Supreme Court in appeal, whether on the certificate of a High Court or otherwise, the date on which the Supreme Court passes its final orders in such appeal; or

(b) where such proceedings are taken to the High Court and orders are passed thereon and

(i) no application for a certificate for leave to appeal to the Supreme Court is made to the High Court, the day immediately following the expiry of ninety days from the date on which the High Court passes its final order;

(ii) an application for a certificate for leave to appeal to the Supreme Court has been refused by the High Court, the day immediately following the expiry of sixty days from the date of the refusal of the certificate;

(iii) a certificate for leave to appeal to the Supreme Court has been granted by the High Court, but no appeal is lodged in the

1. Subst. by the Part B State (Laws) Act, 1951 (3 of 1951), Section 3 and Schedule (w.e.f. April 1, 1951).

* This Act is made applicable to the Union territory of Jammu and Kashmir and the Union territory of Ladakh by the Jammu and Kashmir Reorganisation (Removal of Difficulties) Order, 2019 according to Notification No. S.O. 3912(E), dt. October 30, 2019.

2. Inst. by Act VI of 1945.

3. Subst. by the Criminal Law (Amendment) Act, 1959 (41 of 1959), Section 2 (w.r.e.f. January 26, 1950).

Supreme Court, the day immediately following the expiry of thirty days from the date of the order granting the certificate; or

(c) where such proceedings are not taken to the High Court, the day immediately following the expiry of sixty days from the date of the last judgment or order of a Criminal Court in the Proceedings.]

(3) The functions of a District Judge under this Ordinance shall in Presidency Towns be exercised by the Chief Judge of the Small Cause Court.

**3. Application for attachment of property.**—(1) Where the [1][State Government or, as the case may be, the Central Government], has reason to believe that any person has committed (whether after the commencement of this Ordinance or not) any scheduled offence, the [1][State Government or, as the case may be, the Central Government] may, whether or not any Court has taken cognizance of the offence, authorise the making of an application to the District Judge within the local limits of whose jurisdiction the said person/ordinarily resides or carries on business, for the attachment under this Ordinance, of the money or other property which the [1][State Government or, as the case may be, the Central Government] believes the said person to have procured by means of the offence, or if such money or property cannot for any reason be attached or other property of the said person of value as nearly as may be equivalent to that of the aforesaid money or other property.

(2) The provisions of Order XXVII of the First Schedule to the Code of Civil Procedure, 1908 (5 of 1908), shall apply to proceedings for an order of attachment under this Ordinance as they apply to suits by the Government.

(3) An application under sub-section (1) shall be accompanied by one or more affidavits, stating the grounds on which the belief that the said person has committed any scheduled offence is founded, and the amount of money or value of other property believed to have been procured by means of the offence. The application shall also furnish—

(a) any information available as to the location for the time being of any such money or other property, and shall, if necessary, give particulars, including the estimated value, of other property of the said person;

(b) the names and addresses of any other persons believed to have or to be likely to claim, any interest or title in the property of the said person.

**4. *Ad interim* attachment.**—(1) Upon receipt of an application under section 3, the District Judge shall, unless for reasons to be recorded in writing he is of the opinion that there exist no *prima facie* grounds for believe that the person in respect of whom the application is made has committed any scheduled offence or that he has procured thereby any money or other property, pass without delay an *ad interim* order attaching the money or other property alleged to have been so procured, or if it transpires that

1. Subst. by the Prevention of Corruption Act, 1988 (49 of 1988), Section 29(a), for "State Government" (w.e.f. September 9,1988). Previously stood amended by A.O., 1950.

such money or other property is not available for attachment of such other property of the said person of equivalent value as the District Judge may think fit:

Provided that the District Judge may if he thinks fit before passing such order, and shall, before refusing to pass such order examine the person or persons making the affidavit accompanying the application.

(2) At the same time as he passes an order under sub-section (1), the District Judge shall issue to the person whose money or other property is being attached a notice accompanied by copies of the order, the application and affidavits and of the evidence, if any recorded, calling upon him to show cause on a date to be specified in the notice why the order of attachment should not be made absolute.

(3) The District Judge shall also issue notices, accompanied by copies of the documents accompanying the notice under sub-section (2) to all persons represented to him as having or being likely to claim, any interest or title in the property of the person to whom notice is issued under the said sub-section calling upon each such person to appear on the same date as that specified in the notice under the said sub-section and make objection if he so desires to the attachment of the property or any portion thereof on the ground that he has an interest in such property or portion thereof.

(4) Any person claiming an interest in the attached property or any portion thereof may, notwithstanding that no notice has been served upon him under this section make an objection as aforesaid to the District Judge at any time before an order is passed under sub-section (1) or sub-section (3), as the case may be, of section 5.

**5. Investigation of objections to attachment.**—(1) If no cause is shown and no objections are made under section 4 on or before the specified date, the District Judge shall forthwith pass an order making the *ad interim* order of attachment absolute.

(2) If cause is shown or any objections are made as aforesaid, the District Judge shall proceed to investigate the same, and in so doing, as regards the examination of the parties and in all other respects he shall, subject to the provisions of this Ordinance, follow the procedure and exercise all the powers of a Court in hearing a suit under the Code of Civil Procedure, 1908 (5 of 1908), and any person making an objection under section 4 shall be required to adduce evidence to show that at the date of the attachment he had some interest in the property attached.

(3) After investigation under sub-section (2), the District Judge shall pass an order either making the *ad interim* order of attachment absolute or varying it by releasing a portion of the property from attachment or withdrawing the order:

Provided that the District Judge shall not—

(a) release from attachment any interest which he is satisfied that the person believed to have committed a scheduled offence has in the property, unless he is also satisfied that there will remain under attachment an amount of the said person's property of value not less than that of the property believed to have been procured by the said person by means of the offence, or

(b) withdraw the order of attachment unless he is satisfied that the said person has not by means of the offence procured any money or other property.

**6. Attachment of property of *mala fide* transferees.**—(1) Where the assets available for attachment of a person believed to have committed scheduled offence are found to be less than the amount or value which he is believed to have procured by means of such offence, and where the District Judge is satisfied by affidavit or otherwise, that there is reasonable cause for believing that the said person has, after the date on which the offence is alleged to have been committed, transferred (whether after the commencement of this Ordinance or not) any of his property otherwise than in good faith and for consideration, the District Judge may by notice, require any transferee of such property (whether or not he received the property directly from the said person) to appear on the date to be specified in the notice and show cause why so much of the transferee's property as is equivalent to the proper value of property transferred should not be attached.

(2) Where the said transferee does not appear and show cause on the specified date, or where after investigation in the manner provided in sub-section (2) of section 6, the District Judge is satisfied that the transfer of the property to the said transferee was not in good faith and for consideration, the District Judge shall order the attachment of so much of the said transferee's property as is in the opinion of the District Judge equivalent to the proper value of the property, transferred.

**7. Execution of orders of attachment.**—An order of attachment of property under this Ordinance shall be carried into effect so far as may be practicable in the manner provided in the Code of Civil Procedure, 1908 (5 of 1908) for the attachment of property in execution of a decree.

**8. Security in lieu of attachment.**—Any person whose property has been or is about to be attached under this Ordinance may at any time apply to the District Judge to be permitted to give security in lieu of such attachment and where the security offered and given is in the opinion of the District Judge satisfactory and sufficient, he may withdraw or, as the case may be, refrain from passing, the order of attachment.

**9. Administration of attached property.**—(1) The District Judge may, on the application of any person interested in any property attached under this Ordinance and after giving the agent of the [1][State Government or, as the case may be, the Central Government] an opportunity of being heard, make such orders as the District Judge considers just and reasonable for—

(a) providing from such of the attached property as the applicant claims an interest in, such sums as may be reasonably necessary for the maintenance of the applicant and of his family and for the expenses connected with the defence of the applicant where

1. Subst. by the Prevention of Corruption Act, 1988 (49 of 1988), Section 29(a), for "State Government" (w.e.f. September 9, 1988).

criminal proceedings have been instituted against him in any Court for a scheduled offence;

(b) safe guarding so far as may be practicable the interests of any business affected by the attachment, and in particular, the interest of any partners in such business.

(2) Where it appears to the District Judge to be just and convenient, he may by order appoint a receiver to manage any property attached under this Ordinance in accordance with such instructions as the District Judge may from time to time think fit to give and where a receiver is so appointed, the provisions of rules 2, 3, 4 and 5 of Order XL of the First Schedule to the Code of Civil Procedure, 1908 (5 of 1908), shall be applicable.

[1][**9A. Administration of attached property where Court ordering attachment has ceased to exercise jurisdiction of India.**—Where any property has been attached under this Ordinance by order of a District Judge made before the 15th day of August, 1947, and such District Judge has after that date ceased to exercise jurisdiction in the territories to which this Ordinance extends; that order of attachment shall be deemed to be an order made by the District Judge within the local limits of whose jurisdiction the Court taking cognizance of the scheduled offence is situate, and all functions of the District Judge under this Ordinance in regard to the attached property shall be exercised by that District Judge.]

**10. Duration of attachment**—An order of attachment of property under this Ordinance shall, unless it is withdrawn earlier in accordance with the provisions of this Ordinance, continue in force

(a) where no Court has taken cognizance of the alleged scheduled offence at the time when the order is applied for, [2][one year] from the date of the order under sub-section (1) of section 4 or sub-section (2) of section 6 as the case may be, unless cognizance of such offence is in the meantime so taken or unless the District Judge on application by the agent of the [3][State Government or, as the case may be, the Central Government] thinks it proper and just that the period should be extended and passes an order accordingly; or

(b) where a Court has taken cognizance of the alleged scheduled offence whether, before or after the time when the order was applied for until orders are passed by the District Judge in accordance with the provisions of this Ordinance after the termination of the criminal proceedings.

**11. Appeals.**—(1) The [3][State Government or, as the case may be, the Central Government] or any person who has shown cause under section 4 or section 6 or has made an objection under section 4 or has made an application under section 8 or section 9, if aggrieved by any order of the

1. Inst. by Act XIV of 1950.
2. Subst. by the Prevention of Corruption Act, 1988 (49 of 1988), Section 29(b), for "three months" (w.e.f. September 9, 1988).
3. Subst. by the Prevention of Corruption Act, 1988 (49 of 1988), Section 29(a), for "State Government" (w.e.f. September 9, 1988).

District Judge under any of the foregoing provisions of this Ordinance, may appeal to the High Court within thirty days from the date on which the order complained against was passed.

(2) Upon any appeal under this section the High Court may, after giving such parties, as it thinks proper, an opportunity of being heard, pass such orders as it thinks fit.

(3) Until an appeal under this section is finally disposed of by the High Court no Court shall, otherwise than in accordance with the provisions of section 8 or section 13, order the withdrawal or suspension of any order of attachment to which the appeal relates.

**12. Criminal Courts to evaluate property procured by scheduled offences.**—(1) Where before judgment is pronounced in any criminal trial for a scheduled offence it is represented to the Court that an order of attachment of property has been passed under this Ordinance in connection with such offence, the Court shall, if it is convicting the accused, record a finding as to the amount of money or value of other property procured by the accused by means of the offence.

(2) In any appeal or revisional proceedings against such conviction, the appellate or revisional Court shall, unless it sets aside the conviction, either confirm such finding or modify it in such manner as it thinks proper.

(3) In any appeal or revisional proceedings against an order of acquittal passed in a trial such as is referred to in sub-section (1), the appellate or revisional Court, if it convicts the accused, shall record a finding such as is referred to in that sub-section.

[1][(4) Where the accused is convicted of a scheduled offence other than one specified in Item I of the Schedule to this Ordinance and where it appears that the offence has caused loss to more than one Government referred to in the said Schedule or local authority the finding referred to in this section shall indicate the amount of loss sustained by each such Government or local authority.]

[1][(5) Where the accused is convicted at the same trial of one or more offences specified in Item I of the Schedule to this Ordinance and of one or more offences specified in any of the other items of the said schedule, the finding referred to in this section shall indicate separately the amount procured by means of the two classes of offences.]

**13. Disposal of attached property upon termination of criminal proceedings.**—(1) Upon the termination of any criminal proceedings for any scheduled offence in respect of which any order of attachment of property has been made under this Ordinance or security given in lieu thereof, the agent of the [2][State Government or, as the case may be, the Central Government] shall without delay inform the District Judge, and shall where criminal proceedings have been taken in any Court, furnish the District Judge with a copy of the judgment or order of the trying Court

1. Subst. by Ord. XIV of 1945.
2. Subst. by the Prevention of Corruption Act, 1988 (49 of 1988), Section 29(a), for "State Government" (w.e.f. September 9, 1988).

and with copies of the judgments or orders, if any, of the appellate or revisional Courts thereon.

(2) Where it is reported to the District Judge under sub-section (1) that cognizance of the alleged scheduled offence has not been taken or where the final judgment or order of the Criminal Court is one of acquittal, the District Judge shall forthwith withdraw any orders of attachment of property made in connection with the offence, or where security has been given in lieu of such attachment, order such security to be returned.

(3) Where the final judgment or order of the Criminal Courts is one of conviction the District Judge shall order that from the property of the convicted person attached under this Ordinance or out of the security given in lieu of such attachment, there shall be forfeited to Government such amount or value as is found in the final judgment or order of the Criminal Courts in pursuance of section 12 to have been procured by the convicted person by means of the offence together with the costs of attachment as determined by the District Judge and where the final judgment or order of the Criminal Courts has imposed or upheld a sentence of fine on the said person (whether alone or in conjunction with any other punishment), the District Judge may order, without prejudice to any other mode of recovery, that the said fine shall be recovered from the residue of the said attached property or of the security given in lieu of attachment.

(4) Where the amounts ordered to be forfeited or recovered under sub-section (3) exceed the value of the property of the convicted person attached, and where the property of any transferee of the convicted person has been attached under section 6, the District Judge shall order that the balance of the amount ordered to be forfeited under sub-section (3) together with the costs of attachment of the transferee's property is determined by the District Judge shall be forfeited to Government from the attached property of the transferee or out of the security given in lieu of such attachment; and the District Judge may order, without prejudice to any other mode of recovery, that any fine referred to in sub-section (3) or any portion thereof not recovered under that sub-section shall be recovered from the attached property of the transferee or out of security given in lieu of such attachment.

(5) If any property remains under attachment in respect of any scheduled offence of any security given in lieu of such attachment remains with the District Judge after his orders under sub-section (3) and (4) have been carried into effect the order of attachment in respect of such property remaining shall be forthwith withdrawn or as the case may be the remainder of the security returned, under the orders of the District Judge.

[1][(6) Every sum ordered to be forfeited under this section in connection with any scheduled offence other than one specified in item I of the Schedule to this Ordinance shall, after deduction of the costs of attachment as determined by the District Judge, be credited to the Government being a Government referred to in the said Schedule or local authority to which the offence has caused loss or where there is more than one such

1. Subst. by A.O. 1950.

Government or local authority, the sum shall after such deduction as aforesaid, be distributed among them in proportion to the loss sustained by each.]

**14. Bar to other proceedings.**—Save as provided in section 11 and notwithstanding anything contained in any other law,—

(a) no suit or other legal proceeding shall be maintainable in any Court—

(i) in respect of any property ordered to be forfeited under section 13 or which has been taken in recovery of fine in pursuance of an order under that section, or

(ii) while any other property is attached under this Ordinance, in respect of such other property—

by any person upon whom a notice has been served under section 4 or section 6 or who has made an objection under sub-section (4) of section 4; and

(b) no Court shall, in any legal proceedings or otherwise pass any decree or order, other than a final decree in a suit by a person not being a person referred to in clause (a), which shall have the effect of nullifying or affecting in any way any subsisting order of attachment of property under this Ordinance, or the right of the District Judge to hold security in lieu of any such order of attachment.

**15. Protection of action taken.**—No suit, prosecution or other legal proceedings shall lie against any person for anything in good faith done or intended to be done in pursuance of this Ordinance.

## THE SCHEDULE

(*See* Section 2)

## OFFENCES IN CONNECTION WITH WHICH PROPERTY IS LIABLE TO BE ATTACHED

[1][***]

2. An offence punishable under section 406 or section 408 or section 409 of the Indian Penal Code (45 of 1860), where the property in respect of which the offence is committed is property entrusted by His Majesty's Government in the United Kingdom or in any part of His Majestry's dominions or the Central or a [2][State] Government or a department of any such Government or a local authority [3][or a Corporation established by or under a Central, provincial or State Act, or an authority or a body owned or controlled or aided by Government or a Government company as defined in section 617 of the Companies Act, 1956 (1 of 1956), or a society aided by such corporation, authority, body or Government company] or a person acting on behalf of

1. Paragraph 1 stood omitted by the Prevention of Corruption Act, 1988 (49 of 1988), Section 29(c)(i) (w.e.f. September 9, 1988).
2. Subst. by the A.O. 1950.
3. Inst. by the Prvention of Corruption Act, 1988 (49 of 1988), Section 29(c)(ii)(a) (w.e.f. September 9, 1988).

any such Government or department or authority [1][or corporation or body or Government Company or Society.]

3. An offence punishable under section 411 or section 414 of the Indian Penal Code (45 of 1860), where the stolen property in respect of which the offence is committed is property such as is described in the proceeding item and in respect of which an offence punishable under section 406 or [2][section 408] or section 409 of the said Code has been committed.

4. An offence punishable under section 417 or section 420 of the Indian Penal Code (45 of 1860), where the person deceived is His Majesty's Government in the United Kingdom or in any part of His Majesty's dominions for the Central or a [3][State] Government or a department of any such Government or a local authority [4][or a corporation established by or under a Central, Provincial or State Act, or an authority or a body owned or controlled or aided by Government or a Government company as defined in section 617 of the Companies Act, 1956 (1 of 1956) or a society aided by such corporation, authority, body or Government Company] or a person acting on behalf of any such Government or department or authority [4][or corporation or body or Government company or society.]

[5][4A. An offence punishable under the Prevention of Corruption Act, 1988 (49 of 1988).]

5. Any conspiracy to commit or any attempt to commit or any abetment or any of the offences specified in [6][items 2, 3, 4 and 4A.]

---

1. Inst. by the Prevention of Corruption Act, 1988 (49 of 1988), Section 29(c)(ii)(a) (w.e.f. September 9, 1988).
2. Added by Ord. XIV of 1945.
3. Subst. by the A.O. 1950.
4. Inst. by the Prevention of Corruption Act, 1988 (49 of 1988), Section 29(c)(ii)(b) (w.e.f. September 9, 1988).
5. Subst. by the Prevention of Corruption Act, 1988 (49 of 1988), Section 29(c)(iii), for Paragraph 4A (w.e.f. September 9, 1988).
6. Subst. by the Prevention of Corruption Act, 1988 (49 of 1988), Section 29(c)(iv), for "items 2, 3 and 4" (w.e.f. September 9, 1988).

# THE DELHI SPECIAL POLICE ESTABLISHMENT ACT, 1946

(25 of 1946)[1]

[*19th November, 1946*]

*An Act to make provision for the constitution of a special police force* [1]*[in Delhi for the investigation of certain offences in* [2]*[the Union territories]] for the superintendence and administration of the said force and for the extension to other areas* [3]*[***] of the powers and jurisdiction of members of the said force in regard to the investigation of the said offences.*

WHEREAS it is necessary to constitute a special police force [1][in Delhi for the investigation of certain offences in [2][the Union territories]] and to make provision for the superintendence and administration of the said force and for the extension to other area [3][***] of the powers and jurisdiction of the members of the said force in regard to the investigation of the said offences;

It is hereby enacted as follows:—

**1. Short title and extent.**—(1) This Act may be called the Delhi Special Police Establishment Act, 1946.

(2) It extends to [4][the whole of India], [5][***].

[6]**[1A. Interpretation section.**— Words and expressions used herein and not defined but defined in the Central Vigilance Commission Act, 2003 (45 of 2003), shall have the meanings, respectively, assigned to them in that Act.]

**2. Constitution and powers of special police establishment.**—(1) Notwithstanding anything in the Police Act, 1861 (5 of 1861), the Central Government may constitute a special police force to be called the Delhi Special Police Establishment [7][***] for the investigation [8][in any [9][Union territory]] of offences notified under section 3.

(2) Subject to any orders which the Central Government may make in this behalf, members of the said police establishment shall have throughout

1. Subst. by Act 26 of 1952, Section 2, for "for the State of Delhi for the investigation of certain offences committed in connection with matters concerning Departments of the Central Government" (w.e.f. March 6, 1952).
2. Subst. by the A.O. 1956, for "Part C States".
3. The words "in the States" stood omitted by Act 3 of 1951, Section 3 and the Schedule (w.e.f. April 1, 1951).
4. Subst. by the A.O. 1950, for "all the Provinces of India".
5. The words "except the State of Jammu and Kashmir" stood omitted by Act 62 of 1956, Section 2 and the Schedule (w.e.f. November 1, 1956). Previously the words "except the State of Jammu and Kashmir" were subst. by the Part B States (Laws) Act, 1951 (3 of 1951), Section 3 and Schedule, for "except in Part B States" (w.e.f. April 1, 1951).
6. Inst. by Act 45 of 2003, Section 26 (w.e.f. September 11, 2003).
7. The words "for the State of Delhi" stood omitted by Act 26 of 1952, Section 3 (w.e.f. March 6, 1952).
8. Subst. by Act 26 of 1952, Section 3, for "any Part C States" (w.e.f. March 6, 1952).
9. Subst. by the A.O. 1956, for "Part C States".

[1][any [2][Union territory]], in relation to the investigation of such offences and arrest of persons concerned in such offences, all the powers, duties, privileges and liabilities which police officers of [3][that Union territory] have in connection with the investigation of offences committed therein.

(3) Any member of the said police establishment of or above the rank of Sub-Inspector may, subject to any orders which the Central Government may make in this behalf, exercise in [4][any [2][Union territory]] any of the powers of the officer in charge of a police station in the area in which he is for the time being and when so exercising such powers shall, subject to any such orders as aforesaid, be deemed to be an officer in charge of a police station discharging functions of such an officer within the limits of his station.

**3. Offences to be investigated by special police establishment.**—The Central Government may, by notification in the Official Gazette, specify the offences or classes of offences [5][***] which are to be investigated by the Delhi Special Police Establishment.

[6]**[4. Superintendence and administration of Special Police Establishment.**—(1) The superintendence of the Delhi Special Police Establishment in so far as it relates to investigation of offences alleged to have been committed under the Prevention of Corruption Act, 1988 (49 of 1988), shall vest in the Commission.

(2) Save as otherwise provided in sub-section (1), the superintendence of the said police establishment in all other matters shall vest in the Central Government.

(3) The administration of the said police establishment shall vest in an officer appointed in this behalf by the Central Government (hereinafter referred to as the Director) who shall exercise in respect of that police establishment such of the powers exercisable by an Inspector-General of Police in respect of the police force in a State as the Central Government may specify in this behalf.]

[7]**[4A. Committee for appointment of Director.**— [8][(1) The Central Government shall appoint the Director on the recommendation of the Committee consisting of—

1. Subst. by Act 26 of 1952, Section 3, for "the State of Delhi" (w.e.f. March 6, 1952).
2. Subst. by the A.O. 1956, for "Part C States".
3. Subst. by A.O. 1956, for "that State".
4. Subst. by Act 26 of 1952, Section 3, for "any Part C States" (w.e.f. March 6, 1952).
5. The words "committed in connection with matters concerning Departments of the Central Government" stood omitted by Act 26 of 1952, Section 4 (w.e.f. March 6, 1952).
6. Subst. by Act 45 of 2003, Section 26, for Section 4 (w.e.f. September 11, 2003).
7. Subst. by Act 45 of 2003, Section 26, for Section 4 (w.e.f. September 11, 2003).
8. Subst. by Act 1 of 2014, Section 58 and the Schedule, for Sub-s. (1) (w.e.f. January 16, 2014, according to S.O. 119(E), dt. January 16, 2014). Previously Sub-s. (1) was amended by Act 20 of 2006, Section 2 (w.e.f. April 6, 2006). Sub-s. (1), prior to subst., ran as under:

   "(1) The Central Government shall appoint the Director on the recommendation of the Committee consisting of:—

*Contd. on next page...*

(a) the Prime Minister — Chairperson;

[1][(b) the Leader of Opposition recognised as such in the House of the People or where there is no such Leader of Opposition, then the Leader of the single largest Opposition Party in that House — Member;]

(c) the Chief Justice of India or Judge of the Supreme Court nominated by him — Member.]

[2][(2) No appointment of a Director shall be invalid merely by reason of any vacancy or absence of a Member in the Committee.]

(3) The Committee shall recommend a panel of officers—

(a) on the basis of seniority, integrity and experience in the investigation of anti-corruption cases; and

(b) chosen from amongst officers belonging to the Indian Police Service constituted under the All-India Services Act, 1951 (61 of 1951),

for being considered for appointment as the Director.

[3][**4B. Terms and conditions of service of Director.**—(1) The Director shall, notwithstanding anything to the contrary contained in the rules relating to his conditions of service, continue to hold office for a period of not less than two years from the date on which he assumes office.]

[4][Provided that the period for which the Director holds the office on his initial appointment may, in public interest, on the recommendation of the Committee under sub-section (1) of section 4A and for the reasons to be recorded in writing, Be extended up to one year at a time :

Provided further that no such extension shall be granted after the completion of a period of five years in total including the period mentioned in the initial appointment.]

---

*Contd. from previous page...*

(a) the Central Vigilance Commissioner — Chairperson;
(b) Vigilance Commissioners — Members;
(c) Secretary to the Government of India in-charge of the Ministry of Home Affairs in the Central Government — Member;
(d) the Secretary to the Government of India in-charge of the Ministry or Department of the Central Government having administrative control of the Delhi Special Police Establishment — Member;".

1. Subst. by Act 28 of 2014, Section 2, for clause (b) (w.e.f. November 29, 2014). Clause (b), prior to subst., ran as under:

   "(b) the Leader of Opposition in the House of the People — Member;"

2. Inst. by Act 28 of 2014, Section 2 (w.e.f. November 29, 2014). Previously Sub-s. 2 was stood omitted by Act 1 of 2014, Section 58 and Schedule, Part II (w.e.f. January 16, 2014, according to S.O. 119(E), dt. January 16, 2014). Sub-s. (2), prior to omission by Act 1 of 2014, ran as under:

   "(2) While making any recommendation under Sub-s. (1), the Committee shall take into consideration the views of the outgoing Director.".

3. Section 4, 4A, 4B and 4C subst. by Act 45 of 2003, Section 26 for Section 4 (w.e.f. September 11, 2003).
4. Inst. by Act 45 of 2021, Section 2 (w.r.e.f. November 14, 2021).

(2) The Director shall not be transferred except with the previous consent of the Committee referred to in sub-section (1) of section 4A.

[1][**4BA. Director of Prosecution.**—(1) There shall be a Directorate of Prosecution headed by a Director who shall be an officer not below the rank of Joint Secretary to the Government of India, for conducting prosecution of cases under this Act.

(2) The Director of Prosecution shall function under the overall supervision and control of the Director.

(3) The Central Government shall appoint the Director of Prosecution on the recommendation of the Central Vigilance Commission.

(4) The Director of Prosecution shall notwithstanding anything to the contrary contained in the rules relating to hi conditions of service, continue to hold office for a period of not less than two years from the date on which he assumes office.]

[2][**4C. Appointment for posts of Superintendent of Police and above, extension and curtailment of their tenure, etc.**—[3][(1) The Central Government shall appoint officers to the posts of the level of Superintendent of Police and above except Director, and also recommend the extension or curtailment of the tenure of such officers in the Delhi Special Police Establishment, on the recommendation of a committee consisting of:—

(a) the Central Vigilance Commissioner —Chairperson;

(b) Vigilance Commissioners —Members;

(c) Secretary to the Government of India in Charge of the Ministry of Home —Members;

(d) Secretary to the Government of India in charge of the Department of Personnel —Members:

Provided that the Committee shall consult the Director before submitting its recommendation to the Central Government.]

(2) On receipt of the recommendation under sub-section (1), the Central Government shall pass such orders as it thinks fit to give effect to the said recommendation.]

**5. Extension of powers and jurisdiction of special police establishment to other areas.**—(1) The Central Government may by order extend to any area (including Railway areas) [4][in [5][a State, not being a Union territory]] the powers

1. Inst. by Act 1 of 2014, Section 58 and the Schedule, Part II (w.e.f. January 16, 2014, according to S.O. 119(E), dt. January 16, 2014).
2. Subst. by Act 45 of 2003, Section 26, for Section 4 (w.e.f. September 11, 2003).
3. Subst. by Act 1 of 2014, Section 58 and the Schedule, for Sub-s. (1) (w.e.f. January 16, 2014, according to S.O. 119(E), dt. January 16, 2014). Sub-s. (1), prior to subst., ran as under:

   "The Committee referred to in section 4A shall, after consulting the Director, recommend officers for appointment to the posts of the level of Superintendent of Police and above and also recommend the extension or curtailment of the tenure of such officers in the Delhi Special Police Establishment.".
4. Subst. by Act 26 of 1952, Section 5, for "in India outside the State of Delhi" (w.e.f. March 6, 1952).
5. Subst. by the A.O, 1956, for "a Part A State or a Part B State".

and jurisdiction of members of the Delhi Special Police Establishment for the investigation of any offences or classes of offences specified in a notification under section 3.

(2) When by an order under sub-section (1) the powers and jurisdiction of members of the said police establishment are extended to any such area, a member thereof may, subject to any orders which the Central Government may make in this behalf, discharge the functions of a police officer in that area and shall, while so discharging such functions, be deemed to be a member of the police force of that area and be vested with the powers, functions and privileges and be subject to the liabilities of a police officer belonging to that police force.

[1][(3) Where any such order under sub-section (1) is made relation to any area, then, without prejudice to the provisions of sub-section (2), any member of the Delhi Special Police Establishment of or above the rank of Sub-Inspector may, subject to any orders which the Central Government may make in this behalf, exercise the powers of the officer in charge of a police station in that area and when so exercising such powers, shall be deemed to be an officer in charge of a police station discharging the functions of such an officer within the limits of his station.]

**COMMENT**

**Investigation of offence by C.B.I.**

The Magistrate has power to order CBI to conduct investigation under Section 156(3) of Cr.P.C. The Power of High Court under Article 226 of the Constitution and Supreme Court under Article 32 or 142(1) of Constitution can be invoked, though sparingly for giving such direction to the CBI to investigate in certain cases.

*Central Bureau of Investigation v. State of Rajasthan*, (2001) 1 CRIMES 191: (2001) 3 SCC 333.

[2]**[6. Consent of State Government to exercise of powers and jurisdiction.**— Nothing contained in section 5 shall be deemed to enable any member of the Delhi Special Police Establishment to exercise powers and jurisdiction in any area in [3][a State, not being a Union territory or railway area], without the consent of the Government of that State.]

**COMMENT**

**Power of Supreme Court**

The Supreme Court has power to direct CBI inquiry without the consent of the State Government.

*Akhilesh Yadav v. Vishwanath Chaturvedi*, (2013) 2 SCC 1: (2013) 2 ALT 15.

*[4]**[6A. Approval of Central Government to conduct, inquiry or investigation.**—(1) The Delhi Special Police Establishment shall not conduct

1. Inst. by Act 40 of 1964, Section 5 (w.e.f. December 18, 1964).
2. Subst. by Act 26 of 1952, Section 6, for Section 6 (w.e.f. March 6, 1952).
3. Subst. by the A.O., 1956, for "a Part A State or a Part B State, not being a railway area".
4. Inst. by Act 45 of 2003, Section 26 (w.e.f. September 11, 2003).

* Section 6A(1) struck down by the Supreme Court in the case of *Dr. Subramanian Swamy v. Director, Central Bureau of Investigation & Anr.*, Writ Petition (Civil) No. 38 of 1997 and Writ Petition (Civil) No. 21 of 2004, refer to AIR 2014 SC 2140.

any inquiry or investigation into any offence alleged to have been committed under the Prevention of Corruption Act, 1988 (49 of 1988) except with the previous approval of the Central Government where such allegation relates to—

(a) the employees of the Central Government of the level of Joint Secretary and above; and

(b) such officers as are appointed by the Central Government in corporations established by or under any Central Act, Government companies, societies and local authorities owned or controlled by that Government.

(2) Notwithstanding anything contained in sub-section (1), no such approval shall be necessary for cases involving arrest of a person on the spot on the charge of accepting or attempting to accept any gratification other than legal remuneration referred to in clause (c) of the *Explanation* to section 7 of the Prevention of Corruption Act, 1988 (49 of 1988)].

**COMMENT**

**Approval of Central Government**

The approval of the Central Government is not necessary under Section 6A of the Delhi Special Police Establishment Act, 1946 in a matter whose the inquiry or investigation into under the Prevention of Corruption Act is being monitored by the Court.

*Manohar Lal Sharma v. The Principal Secretary*, (2014) 4 SCC 1: (2013) 15 SCALE 305.

**7. Repeal of Ordinance 22 of 1946.**—[*Repealed by the Repealing and Amending Act, 1950 (35 of 1950), Section 2 and Schedule I.*]

# THE DEPARTMENTAL INQUIRIES (ENFORCEMENT OF ATTENDANCE OF WITNESSES AND PRODUCTION OF DOCUMENTS) ACT, 1972

(18 of 1972)

[*31st May, 1972*]

*An Act to provide for the enforcement of attendance of witnesses and production of documents in certain departmental inquiries and for matters connected therewith or incidental thereto.*

BE it enacted by Parliament in the Twenty-third Year of the Republic of India as follows:—

**1. Short title and extent.**—(1) This Act may be called the Departmental Inquiries (Enforcement of Attendance of Witnesses and Production of Documents) Act, 1972.

(2) It extends to the whole of India except the State of Jammu and Kashmir*.

**2. Departmental inquiries to which the Act shall apply.**—The provisions of this Act shall apply to every departmental inquiry made in relation to—

(a) persons appointed to public services or posts in connection with the affairs of the Union;

(b) persons who, having been appointed to any public service or post in connection with the affairs of the Union, are in service or pay of,—

(i) any local authority in any Union territory,

(ii) any corporation established by or under a Central Act and owned or controlled by the Central Government,

(iii) any Government company within the meaning of section 617 of the Companies Act, 1956 (1 of 1956), in which not less than fifty-one per cent. of the paid-up share capital is held by the Central Government or any company which is a subsidiary of such Government company,

(iv) any society registered under the Societies Registration Act, 1860 (21 of 1860), which is subject to the control of the Central Government.

**3. Definitions.**—For the purposes of this Act,—

(a) "departmental inquiry" means an inquiry held under and in accordance with—

(i) any law made by Parliament or any rule made thereunder, or

* According to notification No. S.O. 3912(E), dt. October 30, 2019, this Act is made applicable to the Union territory of Jammu and Kashmir and the Union territory of Ladakh.

(ii) any rule made under the proviso to article 309, or continued under article 313, of the Constitution of India,

into any allegation of lack of integrity against any person to whom this Act applies;

(b) "inquiring authority" means an officer or authority appointed by the Central Government or by any officer or authority subordinate to that Government to hold a departmental inquiry and includes any officer or authority who is empowered by or under any law or rule for the time being in force to hold such inquiry;

(c) "lack of integrity" includes bribery or corruption.

**4. Power of Central Government to authorise the exercise of powers specified in section 5.**—(1) Where the Central Government is of opinion that for the purposes of any departmental inquiry it is necessary to summon as witnesses, or call for any document from, any class or category of persons, it may, by notification in the Official Gazette, authorise the inquiring authority to exercise the power specified in section 5 in relation to any person within such class or category and thereupon the inquiring authority may exercise such power at any stage of the departmental inquiry.

(2) The power conferred on the Central Government by sub-section (1) may also be exercised by such authority, not being an authority inferior to the appointing authority in relation to the person against whom the departmental inquiry is being held, as the Central Government may, by notification in the Official Gazette, specify in this behalf.

**5. Power of authorised inquiring authority to enforce attendance of witnesses and production of documents.**—(1) Every inquiring authority authorised under section 4 (hereafter referred to as the "authorised inquiring authority") shall have the same powers as are vested in a civil court under the Code of Civil Procedure, 1908 (5 of 1908), while trying a suit, in respect of the following matters, namely:—

(a) the summoning and enforcing the attendance of any witness and examining him on oath;

(b) requiring the discovery and production of any document or other material which is producible as evidence;

(c) the requisitioning of any public record from any court or office.

(2) Notwithstanding anything contained in sub-section (1), the authorised inquiring authority shall not compel the Reserve Bank of India, the State Bank of India, any subsidiary bank as defined in clause (k) of section 2 of the State Bank of India (Subsidiary Banks) Act, 1959 (38 of 1959), or any corresponding new bank constituted under section 3 of the Banking Companies (Acquisition and Transfer of Undertakings) Act, 1970 (5 of 1970),—

(a) to produce any books of account or other documents which the Reserve Bank of India, the State Bank of India, the subsidiary bank or the corresponding new bank claims to be of a confidential nature, or

(b) to make any such books or documents a part of the record of the proceedings of the departmental inquiry, or

(c) to give inspection of any such books or documents, if produced, to any party before it or to any other person.

(3) Every process issued by an authorised inquiring authority for the attendance of any witness or for the production of any document shall be served and executed through the District Judge within the local limits of whose jurisdiction the witness or other person, on whom the process is to be served or executed, voluntarily resides or carries on business or personally works for gain, and, for the purpose of taking any action for the disobedience of any such process, every such process shall be deemed to be a process issued by the District Judge.

(4) Every authorised inquiring authority making any departmental inquiry under this Act shall be deemed to be a civil court for the purposes of sections 480 and 482 of the Code of Criminal Procedure, 1898 (5 of 1898).

**6. Territorial limits in which powers specified in section 5 may be exercised.**—For the purpose of exercising the powers specified in section 5, the territorial jurisdiction of every authorised inquiring authority shall extend to the limits of the territory to which this Act extends.

**7. Power to make rules.**—(1) The Central Government may, by notification in the Official Gazette, make rules for the purpose of giving effect to the provisions of this Act.

(2) Every rule made by the Central Government under this section shall be laid, as soon as may be after it is made, before each House of Parliament while it is in session for a total period of thirty days which may be comprised in one session or in two or more successive sessions, and if, before the expiry of the session immediately following the session or the successive sessions aforesaid, both Houses agree in making any modification in the rule or both Houses agree that the rule should not be made, the rule shall thereafter have effect only in such modified form or be of no effect, as the case may be; so, however, that the modification or annulment shall be without prejudice to the validity of anything previously done under that rule.

# THE FOREIGN CONTRIBUTION (REGULATION) ACT, 2010

(42 of 2010)

[*26th September, 2010*]

*An Act to consolidate the law to regulate the acceptance and utilisation of foreign contribution or foreign hospitality by certain individuals or associations or companies and to prohibit acceptance and utilisation of foreign contribution or foreign hospitality for any activities detrimental to the national interest and for matters connected therewith or incidental thereto.*

BE it enacted by Parliament in the Sixty-first Year of the Republic of India as follows:—

## CHAPTER I

## PRELIMINARY

**1. Short title, extent, application and commencement.**—(1) This Act may be called the Foreign Contribution (Regulation) Act, 2010.

(2) It extends to the whole of India, and it shall also apply to—

(a) citizens of India outside India; and

(b) associate branches or subsidiaries, outside India, of companies or bodies corporate, registered or incorporated in India.

(3) It shall come into force on such date[1] as the Central Government may, by notification in the Official Gazette, appoint:

Provided that different dates may be appointed for different provisions of this Act and any reference in any such provision to the commencement of this Act shall be construed as a reference to the coming into force of that provision.

**2. Definitions.**—(1) In this Act, unless the context otherwise requires,—

(a) "association" means an association of individuals, whether incorporated or not, having an office in India and includes a society, whether registered under the Societies Registration Act, 1860 (21 of 1860), or not, and any other organisation, by whatever name called;

(b) "authorised person in foreign exchange" means an authorised person referred to in clause (c) of section 2 of the Foreign Exchange Management Act, 1999 (42 of 1999);

(c) "bank" means a banking company as referred to in clause (c) of section 5 of the Banking Regulation Act, 1949 (10 of 1949);

(d) "candidate for election" means a person who has duly nominated as a candidate for election to any Legislature;

1. May 1, 2011, according to notification No. S.O. 909(E), dt. April 29, 2011, refer to Gazette of India, Extraordinary, Part II, Section 3(ii).

(e) "certificate" means certificate of registration granted under sub-section (3) of section 12;

(f) "company" shall have the meaning assigned to it under clause (17) of section 2 of the Income-tax Act, 1961 (43 of 1961);

(g) "foreign company" means any company or association or body of individuals incorporated outside India and includes—

(i) a foreign company within the meaning of section 591 of the Companies Act, 1956 (1 of 1956);

(ii) a company which is a subsidiary of a foreign company;

(iii) the registered office or principal place of business of a foreign company referred to in sub-clause (i) or company referred to in sub-clause (ii);

(iv) a multi-national corporation.

*Explanation.*—For the purposes of this sub-clause, a corporation incorporated in a foreign country or territory shall be deemed to be a multi-national corporation if such corporation,—

(a) has a subsidiary or a branch or a place of business in two or more countries or territories; or

(b) carries on business, or otherwise operates, in two or more countries or territories;

(h) "foreign contribution" means the donation, delivery or transfer made by any foreign source,—

(i) of any article, not being an article given to a person as a gift for his personal use, if the market value, in India, of such article, on the date of such gift, is not more than such sum as may be specified from time to time, by the Central Government by the rules made by it in this behalf;

(ii) of any currency, whether Indian or foreign;

(iii) of any security as defined in clause (h) of section 2 of the Securities Contracts (Regulation) Act, 1956 (42 of 1956) and includes any foreign security as defined in clause (o) of section 2 of the Foreign Exchange Management Act, 1999 (42 of 1999).

*Explanation 1.*—A donation, delivery or transfer of any article, currency or foreign security referred to in this clause by any person who has received it from any foreign source, either directly or through one or more persons, shall also be deemed to be foreign contribution within the meaning of this clause.

*Explanation* 2.—The interest accrued on the foreign contribution deposited in any bank referred to in sub-section (1) of section 17 or any other income derived from the foreign contribution or interest thereon shall also be deemed to be foreign contribution within the meaning of this clause.

*Explanation* 3.—Any amount received, by any person from any foreign source in India, by way of fee (including fees charged by an educational institution in India from foreign student) or towards cost in lieu of goods or services rendered by such person in the ordinary course of his business, trade or commerce whether within India or outside India or any contribution received from an agent of a foreign source towards such fee or cost shall be excluded from the definition of foreign contribution within the meaning of this clause;

(i) "foreign hospitality" means any offer, not being a purely casual one, made in cash or kind by a foreign source for providing a person with the costs of travel to any foreign country or territory or with free boarding, lodging, transport or medical treatment;

(j) "foreign source" includes,—

(i) the Government of any foreign country or territory and any agency of such Government;

(ii) any international agency, not being the United Nations or any of its specialised agencies, the World Bank, International Monetary Fund or such other agency as the Central Government may, by notification, specify in this behalf;

(iii) a foreign company;

(iv) a corporation, not being a foreign company, incorporated in a foreign country or territory;

(v) a multi-national corporation referred to in sub-clause (iv) of clause (g);

(vi) a company within the meaning of the Companies Act, 1956 (1 of 1956), and more than one-half of the nominal value of its share capital is held, either singly or in the aggregate, by one or more of the following, namely:—

(A) the Government of a foreign country or territory;

(B) the citizens of a foreign country or territory;

(C) corporations incorporated in a foreign country or territory;

(D) trusts, societies or other associations of individuals (whether incorporated or not), formed or registered in a foreign country or territory;

(E) foreign company;

[1][Provided that where the nominal value of share capital is within the limits specified for foreign investment under the Foreign Exchange Management Act, 1999 (42 of 1999), or the rules or regulations made thereunder, then, notwithstanding the nominal value of share capital of a company being more than one-half of such value at the time of making the contribution, such company shall not be a foreign source;]

(vii) a trade union in any foreign country or territory, whether or not registered in such foreign country or territory;

1. Inst. by Act 28 of 2016, Section 236 (w.r.e.f. August 5, 1976 according to the Act 13 of 2018, Section 220).

(viii) a foreign trust or a foreign foundation, by whatever name called, or such trust or foundation mainly financed by a foreign country or territory;

(ix) a society, club or other association of individuals formed or registered outside India;

(x) a citizen of a foreign country;

(k) "Legislature" means—

(A) either House of Parliament;

(B) the Legislative Assembly of a State, or in the case of a State having a Legislative Council, either House of the Legislature of that State;

(C) Legislative Assembly of a Union territory constituted under the Government of Union Territories Act, 1963 (20 of 1963);

(D) Legislative Assembly for the National Capital Territory of Delhi referred to in the Government of National Capital Territory of Delhi Act, 1991 (1 of 1992);

(E) Municipality as defined in clause (e) of article 243P of the Constitution;

(F) District Councils and Regional Councils in the States of Assam, Meghalaya, Tripura and Mizoram as provided in the Sixth Schedule to the Constitution;

(G) Panchayat as defined in clause (d) of article 243 of the Constitution; or

(H) any other elective body as may be notified by the Central Government;

(l) "notification" means notification published in the Official Gazette and the expression "notify" shall be construed accordingly;

(m) "person" includes—

(i) an individual;

(ii) a Hindu undivided family;

(iii) an association;

(iv) a company registered under section 25 of the Companies Act, 1956 (1 of 1956);

(n) "political party" means—

(i) an association or body of individual citizens of India—

(A) to be registered with the Election Commission of India as a political party under section 29A of the Representation of the People Act, 1951 (43 of 1951); or

(B) which has set up candidates for election to any Legislature, but is not so registered or deemed to be registered under the Election Symbols (Reservation and Allotment) Order, 1968;

(ii) a political party mentioned in column 2 of Table 1 and Table 2 to the notification of the Election Commission of India No. 56/J&K/02, dated the 8th August, 2002, as in force for the time being;

(o) "prescribed" means prescribed by rules made under this Act;

(p) "prescribed authority" means an authority specified as such by rules made by the Central Government under this Act;

(q) "registered newspaper" means a newspaper registered under the Press and Registration of Books Act, 1867 (25 of 1867);

(r) "relative" has the meaning assigned to it in clause (41) of section 2 of the Companies Act, 1956 (1 of 1956);

(s) "scheduled bank" shall have the meaning assigned to it under clause (e) of section 2 of the Reserve Bank of India Act, 1934 (2 of 1934);

(t) "subsidiary" and "associate" shall have the meanings, respectively assigned to them in the Companies Act, 1956 (1 of 1956);

(u) "trade union" means a trade union registered under the Trade Unions Act, 1926 (16 of 1926);

(2) Words and expressions used herein and not defined in this Act but defined in the Representation of the People Act, 1950 (43 of 1950) or the Representation of the People Act, 1951 (43 of 1951) or the Foreign Exchange Management Act, 1999 (42 of 1999) shall have the meanings respectively assigned to them in those Acts.

## CHAPTER II

## REGULATION OF FOREIGN CONTRIBUTION AND FOREIGN HOSPITALITY

**3. Prohibition to accept foreign contribution.**—(1) No foreign contribution shall be accepted by any—

(a) candidate for election;

(b) correspondent, columnist, cartoonist, editor, owner, printer or publisher of a registered newspaper;

[1][(c) public servant, Judge, Government servant or employee of any corporation or any other body controlled or owned by the Government;]

(d) member of any Legislature;

(e) political party or office-bearer thereof;

(f) organisation of a political nature as may be specified under sub-section (1) of section 5 by the Central Government;

(g) association or company engaged in the production or broadcast of audio news or audio visual news or current affairs programmes through any electronic mode, or any other electronic form as defined in clause (r) of sub-section (1) of section 2 of the Information

1. Subst. by Act 33 of 2020, Section 2, for clause (c) (w.e.f. September 29, 2020).

Technology Act, 2000 (21 of 2000) or any other mode of mass communication;

(h) correspondent or columnist, cartoonist, editor, owner of the association or company referred to in clause (g).

[1][*Explanation*.1—For the purpose of clause (c), "public servant" means a public servant as defined in section 21 of the Indian Penal Code (45 of 1860).

*Explanation* 2.—In clause (c) and section 6, the expression "corporation" means a corporation owned or controlled by the Government and includes a Government company as defined in clause (45) of section 2 of the Companies Act, 2013 (18 of 2013).]

(2) (a) No person, resident in India, and no citizen of India resident outside India, shall accept any foreign contribution, or acquire or agree to acquire any currency from a foreign source, on behalf of any political party, or any person referred to in sub-section (1), or both.

(b) No person, resident in India, shall deliver any currency, whether Indian or foreign, which has been accepted from any foreign source, to any person if he knows or has reasonable cause to believe that such other person intends, or is likely, to deliver such currency to any political party or any person referred to in sub-section (1), or both.

(c) No citizen of India resident outside India shall deliver any currency, whether Indian or foreign, which has been accepted from any foreign source, to—

(i) any political party or any person referred to in sub-section (1), or both; or

(ii) any other person, if he knows or has reasonable cause to believe that such other person intends, or is likely, to deliver such currency to a political party or to any person referred to in sub-section (1), or both.

(3) No person receiving any currency, whether Indian or foreign, from a foreign source on behalf of any person or class of persons, referred to in section 9, shall deliver such currency—

(a) to any person other than a person for which it was received, or

(b) to any other person, if he knows or has reasonable cause to believe that such other person intends, or is likely, to deliver such currency to a person other than the person for which such currency was received.

**4. Persons to whom section 3 shall not apply.**—Nothing contained in section 3 shall apply to the acceptance, by any person specified in that section, of any foreign contribution where such contribution is accepted by him, subject to the provisions of section 10,—

(a) by way of salary, wages or other remuneration due to him or to any group of persons working under him, from any foreign

1. *Explanation* subst. by Act 33 of 2020, Section. 2 (w.e.f. September 29, 2020).

source or by way of payment in the ordinary course of business transacted in India by such foreign source; or

(b) by way of payment, in the course of international trade or commerce, or in the ordinary course of business transacted by him outside India; or

(c) as an agent of a foreign source in relation to any transaction made by such foreign source with the Central Government or State Government; or

(d) by way of a gift or presentation made to him as a member of any Indian delegation, provided that such gift or present was accepted in accordance with the rules made by the Central Government with regard to the acceptance or retention of such gift or presentation; or

(e) from his relative; or

(f) by way of remittance received, in the ordinary course of business through any official channel, post office, or any authorised person in foreign exchange under the Foreign Exchange Management Act, 1999 (42 of 1999); or

(g) by way of any scholarship, stipend or any payment of like nature:

Provided that in case any foreign contribution received by any person specified under section 3, for any of the purposes other than those specified under this section, such contribution shall be deemed to have been accepted in contravention of the provisions of section 3.

**5. Procedure to notify an organisation of a political nature.**—(1) The Central Government may, having regard to the activities of the organisation or the ideology propagated by the organisation or the programme of the organisation or the association of the organisations with the activities of any political party, by an order published in the Official Gazette, specify such organisation as an organisation of a political nature not being a political party, referred to in clause (f) of sub-section (1) of section 3:

Provided that the Central Government may, by rules made by it, frame the guidelines specifying the ground or grounds on which an organisation shall be specified as an organisation of a political nature.

(2) Before making an order under sub-section (1), the Central Government shall give the organisation in respect of whom the order is proposed to be made, a notice in writing informing it of the ground or grounds, on which it is proposed to be specified as an organisation of political nature under that sub-section.

(3) The organisation to whom a notice has been served under sub-section (2), may, within a period of thirty days from the date of the notice, make a representation to the Central Government giving reasons for not specifying such organisation as an organisation under sub-section (1):

Provided that the Central Government may entertain the representation after the expiry of the said period of thirty days, if it is satisfied that the organisation was prevented by sufficient cause from making the representation within thirty days.

(4) The Central Government may, if it considers it appropriate, forward the representation referred to in sub-section (3) to any authority to report on such representation.

(5) The Central Government may, after considering the representation and the report of the authority referred to in sub-section (4), specify such organisation as an organisation of a political nature not being a political party and make an order under sub-section (1) accordingly.

(6) Every order under sub-section (1) shall be made within a period of one hundred and twenty days from the date of issue of notice under sub-section (2):

Provided that in case no order is made within the said period of one hundred and twenty days, the Central Government shall, after recording the reasons therefor, make an order under sub-section (1) within a period of sixty days from the expiry of the said period of one hundred and twenty days.

**6. Restriction on acceptance of foreign hospitality.**—No member of a Legislature or office-bearer of a political party or Judge or Government servant or employee of any corporation or any other body owned or controlled by the Government shall, while visiting any country or territory outside India, accept, except with the prior permission of the Central Government, any foreign hospitality:

Provided that it shall not be necessary to obtain any such permission for an emergent medical aid needed on account of sudden illness contracted during a visit outside India, but, where such foreign hospitality has been received, the person receiving such hospitality shall give, within one month from the date of receipt of such hospitality an intimation to the Central Government as to the receipt of such hospitality, and the source from which, and the manner in which, such hospitality was received by him.

[1][**7. Prohibition to transfer foreign contribution to other person.**—No person who—

(a) is registered and granted a certificate or has obtained prior permission under this Act; and

(b) receives any foreign contribution, shall transfer such foreign contribution to any other person.]

**COMMENT**

**Prohibition to transfer contribution**

Any person who receives foreign contribution as per provision of the Act, shall not transfer to other person unless that person is authorised to receive foreign contribution as per Rules made by the central government.

**8. Restriction to utilise foreign contribution for administrative purpose.**—(1) Every person, who is registered and granted a certificate or given prior permission under this Act and receives any foreign contribution,—

1. Subst. by Act 33 of 2020, Section. 3, for Section 7 (w.e.f. September 29, 2020).

(a) shall utilise such contribution for the purposes for which the contribution has been received:

Provided that any foreign contribution or any income arising out of it shall not be used for speculative business:

Provided further that the Central Government shall, by rules, specify the activities or business which shall be construed as speculative business for the purpose of this section;

(b) shall not defray as far as possible such sum, not exceeding [1][twenty per cent.] of such contribution, received in a financial year, to meet administrative expenses:

Provided that administrative expenses exceeding [1][twenty per cent.] of such contribution may be defrayed with prior approval of the Central Government.

(2) The Central Government may prescribe the elements which shall be included in the administrative expenses and the manner in which the administrative expenses referred to in sub-section (1) shall be calculated.

### COMMENT

**Utilization of foreign contribution**

The foreign contribution shall be utilized for the purpose for which it has been received and such contribution can be used for administrative expenses with 50% of such contribution received in a financial year, however, administrative expenses exceeding 50% of contribution to be defrayed with the prior approval of the central government.

**9. Power of Central Government to prohibit receipt of foreign contribution, etc., in certain cases.**—The Central Government may—

(a) prohibit any person or organisation, not specified in section 3, from accepting any foreign contribution;

(b) require any person or class of persons, not specified in section 6, to obtain prior permission of the Central Government before accepting any foreign hospitality;

(c) require any person or class of persons not specified in section 11, to furnish intimation within such time and in such manner as may be prescribed as to the amount of any foreign contribution received by such person or class of persons as the case may be, and the source from which and the manner in which such contribution was received and the purpose for which and the manner in which such foreign contribution .was utilised;

(d) without prejudice to the provisions of sub-section (1) of section 11, require any person or class of persons specified in that sub-section to obtain prior permission of the Central Government before accepting any foreign contribution;

(e) require any person or class of persons, not specified in section 6, to furnish intimation, within such time and in such manner as may be prescribed, as to the receipt of any foreign hospitality, the

1. Subst. by Act 33 of 2020, Section. 4, for "fifty per cent." (w.e.f. September 29, 2020).

source from which and the manner in which such hospitality was received:

Provided that no such prohibition or requirement shall be made unless the Central Government is satisfied that the acceptance of foreign contribution by such person or class of persons, as the case may be, or the acceptance of foreign hospitality by such person, is likely to affect prejudicially—

(i) the sovereignty and integrity of India; or

(ii) public interest; or

(iii) freedom or fairness of election to any Legislature; or

(iv) friendly relations with any foreign State; or

(v) harmony between religious, racial, social, linguistic or regional groups, castes or communities.

**10. Power to prohibit payment of currency received in contravention of the Act.**—Where the Central Government is satisfied, after making such inquiry as it may deem fit, that any person has in his custody or control any article or currency or security, whether Indian or foreign, which has been accepted by such person in contravention of any of the provisions of this Act, it may, by order in writing, prohibit such person from paying, delivering, transferring or otherwise dealing with, in any manner whatsoever, such article or currency or security save in accordance with the written orders of the Central Government and a copy of such order shall be served upon the person so prohibited in the prescribed manner, and thereupon the provisions of sub-sections (2), (3), (4) and (5) of section 7 of the Unlawful Activities (Prevention) Act, 1967 (37 of 1967) shall, so far as may be, apply to, or in relation to, such article or currency or security and references in the said sub-sections to moneys, securities or credits shall be construed as references to such article or currency or security.

## CHAPTER III
## REGISTRATION

**11. Registration of certain persons with Central Government.**—(1) Save as otherwise provided in this Act, no person having a definite cultural, economic, educational, religious or social programme shall accept foreign contribution unless such person obtains a certificate of registration from the Central Government:

Provided that any association registered with the Central Government under section 6 or granted prior permission under that section of the Foreign Contribution (Regulation) Act, 1976 (49 of 1976), as it stood immediately before the commencement of this Act, shall be deemed to have been registered or granted prior permission, as the case may be, under this Act and such registration shall be valid for a period of five years from the date on which this section comes into force.

(2) Every person referred to in sub-section (1) may, if it is not registered with the Central Government under that sub-section, accept any foreign contribution only after obtaining the prior permission of the Central Government

and such prior permission shall be valid for the specific purpose for which it is obtained and from the specific source:

[1][Provided that the Central Government, on the basis of any information or report, and after holding a summary inquiry, has reason to believe that a person who has been granted prior permission has contravened any of the provisions of this Act, it may, pending any further inquiry, direct that such person shall not utilise the unutilised foreign contribution or receive the remaining portion of foreign contribution which has not been received or, as the case may be, any additional foreign contribution, without prior approval of the Central Government:

Provided further that if the person referred to in sub-section (1) or in this sub-section has been found guilty] of violation of any of the provisions of this Act or the Foreign Contribution (Regulation) Act, 1976 (49 of 1976), the unutilised or unreceived amount of foreign contribution shall not be utilised or received, as the case may be, without the prior approval of the Central Government.

(3) Notwithstanding anything contained in this Act, the Central Government may, by notification in the Official Gazette, specify—

(i) the person or class of persons who shall obtain its prior permission before accepting the foreign contribution; or

(ii) the area or areas in which the foreign contribution shall be accepted and utilised with the prior permission of the Central Government; or

(iii) the purpose or purposes for which the foreign contribution shall be utilised with the prior permission of the Central Government; or

(iv) the source or sources from which the foreign contribution shall be accepted with the prior permission of the Central Government.

**12. Grant of certificate of registration.**—(1) An application by a person, referred to in section 11 for grant of certificate or giving prior permission, shall be made to the Central Government in such form and manner and along with such fee, as may be prescribed.

[2][(1A) Every person who makes an application under sub-section (1) shall be required to open "FCRA Account" in the manner specified in section 17 and mention details of such account in his application.]

(2) On receipt of an application under sub-section (1), the Central Government shall, by an order, if the application is not in the prescribed form or does not contain any of the particulars specified in that form, reject the application.

(3) If on receipt of an application for grant of certificate or giving prior permission and after making such inquiry as the Central Government deems fit, it is of the opinion that the conditions specified in sub-section (4)

1. Subst. by Act 33 of 2020, Section 5, for certain words (w.e.f. September 29, 2020).
2. Inst. by Act 33 of 2020, Section 6 (w.e.f. September 29, 2020).

are satisfied, it may, ordinarily within ninety days from the date of receipt of application under sub-section (1), register such person and grant him a certificate or give him prior permission, as the case may be, subject to such terms and conditions as may be prescribed:

Provided that in case the Central Government does not grant, within the said period of ninety days, a certificate or give prior permission, it shall communicate the reasons therefor to the applicant:

Provided further that a person shall not be eligible for grant of certificate or giving prior permission, if his certificate has been suspended and such suspension of certificate continues on the date of making application.

(4) The following shall be the conditions for the purposes of sub-section (3), namely:—

(a) the person making an application for registration or grant of prior permission under sub-section (1),—

(i) is not fictitious or *benami*;

(ii) has not been prosecuted or convicted for indulging in activities aimed at conversion through inducement or force, either directly or indirectly, from one religious faith to another;

(iii) has not been prosecuted or convicted for creating communal tension or disharmony in any specified district or any other part of the country;

(iv) has not been found guilty of diversion or mis-utilisation of its funds;

(v) is not engaged or likely to engage in propagation of sedition or advocate violent methods to achieve its ends;

(vi) is not likely to use the foreign contribution for personal gains or divert it for undesirable purposes;

(vii) has not contravened any of the provisions of this Act;

(viii) has not been prohibited from accepting foreign contribution;

(b) the person making an application for registration under sub-section (1) has undertaken reasonable activity in its chosen field for the benefit of the society for which the foreign contribution is proposed to be utilised;

(c) the person making an application for giving prior permission under sub-section (1) has prepared a reasonable project for the benefit of the society for which the foreign contribution is proposed to be utilised;

(d) in case the person being an individual, such individual has neither been convicted under any law for the time being in force nor any prosecution for any offence pending against him;

(e) in case the person being other than an individual, any of its directors or office bearers has neither been convicted under any law for the time being in force nor any prosecution for any offence is pending against him;

(f) the acceptance of foreign contribution by the person referred to in sub-section (1) is not likely to affect prejudicially—

(i) the sovereignty and integrity of India; or

(ii) the security, strategic, scientific or economic interest of the State; or

(iii) the public interest; or

(iv) freedom or fairness of election to any Legislature; or

(v) friendly relation with any foreign State; or

(vi) harmony between religious, racial, social, linguistic, regional groups, castes or communities;

(g) the acceptance of foreign contribution referred to in sub-section (1),—

(i) shall not lead to incitement of an offence;

(ii) shall not endanger the life or physical safety of any person.

(5) Where the Central Government refuses the grant of certificate or does not give prior permission, it shall record in its order the reasons therefor and furnish a copy thereof to the applicant:

Provided that the Central Government may not communicate the reasons for refusal for grant of certificate or for not giving prior permission to the applicant under this section in cases where there is no obligation to give any information or documents or records or papers under the Right to Information Act, 2005 (22 of 2005).

(6) The certificate granted under sub-section (3) shall be valid for a period of five years and the prior permission shall be valid for the specific purpose or specific amount of foreign contribution proposed to be received, as the case may be.

[1][**12A. Power of Central Government to require Aadhaar number, etc., as identification document.**—Notwithstanding anything contained in this Act, the Central Government may require that any person who seeks prior permission or prior approval under section 11, or makes an application for grant of certificate under section 12, or, as the case may be, for renewal of certificate under section 16, shall provide as identification document, the Aadhaar number of all its office bearers or Directors or other key functionaries, by whatever name called, issued under the Aadhaar (Targeted Delivery of Financial and Other Subsidies, Benefits and Services) Act, 2016 (18 of 2016), or a copy of the Passport or Overseas Citizen of India Card, in case of a foreigner.]

**13. Suspension of certificate.**—(1) Where the Central Government, for reasons to be recorded in writing, is satisfied that pending consideration of the question of cancelling the certificate on any of the grounds mentioned in sub-section (1) of section 14, it is necessary so to do, it may, by order in writing, suspend the certificate [2][for a period of one hundred and eighty

1. Inst. by Act 33 of 2020, Section 7 (w.e.f. September 29, 2020).
2. Subst. by Act 33 of 2020, Section 8, for "for such period not exceeding one hundred and eighty days as may be specified" (w.e.f. September 29, 2020).

days, or such further period, not exceeding one hundred and eighty days, as may be specified] in the order.

(2) Every person whose certificate has been suspended shall—

(a) not receive any foreign contribution during the period of suspension of certificate:

Provided that the Central Government, on an application made by such person, if it considers appropriate, allow receipt of any foreign contribution by such person on such terms and conditions as it may specify;

(b) utilise, in the prescribed manner, the foreign contribution in his custody with the prior approval of the Central Government.

**14. Cancellation of certificate.**—(1) The Central Government may, if it is satisfied after making such inquiry as it may deem fit, by an order, cancel the certificate if—

(a) the holder of the certificate has made a statement in, or in relation to, the application for the grant of registration or renewal thereof, which is incorrect or false; or

(b) the holder of the certificate has violated any of the terms and conditions of the certificate or renewal thereof; or

(c) in the opinion of the Central Government, it is necessary in the public interest to cancel the certificate; or

(d) the holder of certificate has violated any of the provisions of this Act or rules or order made thereunder; or

(e) if the holder of the certificate has not been engaged in any reasonable activity in its chosen field for the benefit of the society for two consecutive years or has become defunct.

(2) No order of cancellation of certificate under this section shall be made unless the person concerned has been given a reasonable opportunity of being heard.

(3) Any person whose certificate has been cancelled under this section shall not be eligible for registration or grant of prior permission for a period of three years from the date of cancellation of such certificate.

[1][**14A. Surrender of certificate.**—On a request being made in this behalf, the Central Government may permit any person to surrender the certificate granted under this Act, if, after making such inquiry as it deems fit, it is satisfied that such person has not contravened any of the provisions of this Act, and the management of foreign contribution and asset, if any, created out of such contribution has been vested in the authority as provided in sub-section (1) of section 15.]

**15. Management of foreign contribution of person whose certificate has been cancelled [2][or surrendered].**—(1) The foreign contribution and assets created out of the foreign contribution in the custody of every person

1. Inst. by Act 33 of 2020, Section 9 (w.e.f. September 29 2020).
2. Inst. by Act 33 of 2020, Section 10 (w.e.f. September 29, 2020).

whose certificate has been cancelled under section 14 [1][or surrendered under section 14A] shall vest in such authority as may be prescribed.

(2) The authority referred to in sub-section (1) may, if it considers necessary and in public interest, manage the activities of the person referred to in that sub-section for such period and in such manner, as the Central Government may direct and such authority may utilise the foreign contribution or dispose of the assets created out of it in case adequate funds are not available for running such activity.

(3) The authority referred to in sub-section (1) shall return the foreign contribution and the assets vested upon it under that sub-section to the person referred to in the said sub-section if such person is subsequently registered under this Act.

**16. Renewal of certificate.**—(1) Every person who has been granted a certificate under section 12 shall have such certificate renewed within six months before the expiry of the period of the certificate.

[2][Provided that the Central Government may, before renewing the certificate, make such inquiry, as it deems fit, to satisfy itself that such person has fulfilled all conditions specified in sub-section (4) of section 12.]

(2) The application for renewal of the certificate shall be made to the Central Government in such form and manner and accompanied by such fee as may be prescribed.

(3) The Central Government shall renew the certificate, ordinarily within ninety days from the date of receipt of application for renewal of certificate subject to such terms and conditions as it may deem fit and grant a certificate of renewal for a period of five years:

Provided that in case the Central Government does not renew the certificate within the said period of ninety days, it shall communicate the reasons therefor to the applicant:

Provided further that the Central Government may refuse to renew the certificate in case where a person has violated any of the provisions of this Act or rules made thereunder.

## CHAPTER IV

## ACCOUNTS, INTIMATION, AUDIT AND DISPOSAL OF ASSETS, ETC.

[3]**[17. Foreign contribution through scheduled bank.**—(1) Every person who has been granted certificate or prior permission under section 12 shall receive foreign contribution only in an account designated as "FCRA Account" by the bank, which shall be opened by him for the purpose of remittances of foreign contribution in such branch of the State Bank of India at New Delhi, as the Central Government may, by notification, specify in this behalf:

Provided that such person may also open another "FCRA Account" in any of the scheduled bank of his choice for the purpose of keeping or utilising

1. Inst. by Act 33 of 2020, Section 10 (w.e.f. September 29, 2020).
2. The proviso inst. by Act 33 of 2020, Section 11 (w.e.f. September 29, 2020).
3. Subst. by Act 33 of 2020, Section 12, for Section 17 (w.e.f. September 29, 2020).

the foreign contribution which has been received from his "FCRA Account" in the specified branch of State Bank of India at New Delhi:

Provided further that such person may also open one or more accounts in one or more scheduled banks of his choice to which he may transfer for utilising any foreign contribution received by him in his "FCRA Account" in the specified branch of the State Bank of India at New Delhi or kept by him in another "FCRA Account" in a scheduled bank of his choice:

Provided also that no funds other than foreign contribution shall be received or deposited in any such account.

(2) The specified branch of the State Bank of India at New Delhi or the branch of the scheduled bank where the person referred to in sub-section (1) has opened his foreign contribution account or the authorised person in foreign exchange, shall report to such authority as may be specified—

(a) the prescribed amount of foreign remittance;

(b) the source and manner in which the foreign remittance was received; and

(c) other particulars, in such form and manner as may be prescribed.]

**18. Intimation.**—(1) Every person who has been granted a certificate or given prior approval under this Act shall give, within such time and in such manner as may be prescribed, an intimation to the Central Government, and such other authority as may be specified by the Central Government, as to the amount of each foreign contribution received by it, the source from which and the manner in which such foreign contribution was received, and the purposes for which, and the manner in which such foreign contribution was utilised by him.

(2) Every person receiving foreign contribution shall submit a copy of a statement indicating therein the particulars of foreign contribution received duly certified by officer of the bank or authorised person in foreign exchange and furnish the same to the Central Government along with the intimation under sub-section (1).

**19. Maintenance of accounts.**—Every person who has been granted a certificate or given prior approval under this Act shall maintain, in such form and manner as may be prescribed,—

(a) an account of any foreign contribution received by him; and

(b) a record as to the manner in which such contribution has been utilised by him.

**20. Audit of accounts.**—Where any person who has been granted a certificate or given prior permission, fails to furnish any intimation under this Act within the time specified therefor or the intimation so furnished is not in accordance with law or if, after inspection of such intimation, the Central Government has any reasonable cause to believe that any provision of this Act has been, or is being, contravened, the Central Government may, by general or special order, authorise such gazetted officer, holding a Group A post under the Central Government or any other officer or authority or organisation, as it may think fit, to audit any books of account kept or maintained by such person and thereupon every such officer shall have the right to enter in or upon any premises at any reasonable hour, before sunset and after sunrise, for the purpose of auditing the said books of account:

Provided that any information obtained from such audit shall be kept confidential and shall not be disclosed except for the purposes of this Act.

**21. Intimation by candidate for election.**—Every candidate for election, who had received any foreign contribution, at any time within one hundred and eighty days immediately preceding the date on which he is duly nominated as such candidate, shall give, within such time and in such manner as may be prescribed, an intimation to the Central Government or prescribed authority or both as to the amount of foreign contribution received by him, the source from which, and the manner in which, such foreign contribution was received and the purposes for which and the manner in which such foreign contribution was utilised by him.

**22. Disposal of assets created out of foreign contribution.**—Where any person who was permitted to accept foreign contribution under this Act, ceases to exist or has become defunct, all the assets of such person shall be disposed of in accordance with the provisions contained in any law for the time being in force under which the person was registered or incorporated, and in the absence of any such law, the Central Government may, having regard to the nature of assets created out of foreign contribution received under this Act, by notification, specify that all such assets shall be disposed off by such authority, as it may specify, in such manner and procedure as may be prescribed.

## CHAPTER V
## INSPECTION, SEARCH AND SEIZURE

**23. Inspection of accounts or records.**—If the Central Government has, for any reason, to be recorded in writing, any ground to suspect that any provision of this Act has been or is being, contravened by—

(a) any political party; or

(b) any person; or

(c) any organisation; or

(d) any association,

it may, by general or special order, authorise such gazetted officer, holding a Group A post under the Central Government or such other officer or authority or organisation, as it may think fit (hereinafter referred to as the inspecting officer), to inspect any account or record maintained by such political party, person, organisation or association, as the case may be, and thereupon every such inspecting officer shall have the right to enter in or upon any premises at any reasonable hour, before sunset and after sunrise, for the purpose of inspecting the said account or record.

### COMMENT

If the registered person or person to whom prior permission has been granted, fails to furnish or the intimation given is not in accordance with law then accounts shall be inspected.

**24. Seizure of accounts or records.**—If, after inspection of an account or record referred to in section 23, the inspecting officer has any reasonable cause to believe that any provision of this Act or of any other law relating to foreign exchange has been, or is being, contravened, he may seize such account or record and produce the same before the court, authority or tribunal in which any proceeding is brought for such contravention:

Provided that the authorised officer shall return such account or record to the person from whom it was seized if no proceeding is brought within six months from the date of such seizure for the contravention disclosed by such account or record.

**25. Seizure of article or currency or security received in contravention of the Act.**—If any gazetted officer, authorised in this behalf by the Central Government by general or special order, has any reason to believe that any person has in his possession or control any article exceeding the value specified in sub-clause (i) of clause (h) of sub-section (1) of section 2 or currency or security whether Indian or foreign, in relation to which any provision of this Act has been or is being, contravened, he may seize such article or currency or security.

**26. Disposal of seized article or currency or security.**—(1) The Central Government, may, having regard to the value of article or currency or security, their vulnerability to theft or any relevant consideration, by notification, specify such article or currency or security which shall, as soon as may be after their seizure, be disposed of by such officer and in such manner, as the Central Government may, from time to time, determine after following the procedure hereinafter specified.

(2) The article or currency or security seized shall be forwarded without unnecessary delay to such officer as may be specified.

(3) Where any article or currency or security has been seized and forwarded to such officer, the officer referred to in sub-section (1), shall prepare an inventory of such article or currency or security containing such details relating to their description, value or such other identifying particulars as the officer referred to in that sub-section may consider relevant to the identity of the article or the currency or security and make an application to any Magistrate for the purposes of certifying the correctness of the inventory so prepared.

(4) Where an application is made under sub-section (2), the Magistrate shall, as soon as may be, allow the application.

(5) Notwithstanding anything contained in the Indian Evidence Act, 1872 (1 of 1872) or the Code of Criminal Procedure, 1973 (2 of 1974), every court trying an offence under this Act, shall treat the inventory, as certified by the Magistrate, as primary evidence in respect of such offence.

(6) Every officer acting under sub-section (3) shall forthwith report the seizure to the Court of Session or Assistant Sessions Judge having jurisdiction for adjudging the confiscation under section 29.

**27. Seizure to be made in accordance with Act 2 of 1974.**—The provisions of the Code of Criminal Procedure, 1973 (2 of 1974) shall apply in so far as they are not inconsistent with the provisions of this Act to all seizures made under this Act.

## CHAPTER VI
## ADJUDICATION

**28. Confiscation of article or currency or security obtained in contravention of the Act.**—Any article or currency or security which is seized under section 25 shall be liable to confiscation if such article or currency or security has been adjudged under section 29 to have been received or obtained in contravention of this Act.

**29. Adjudication of confiscation.**—(1) Any confiscation referred to in section 28 may be adjudged—

(a) without limit, by the Court of Session within the local limits of whose jurisdiction the seizure was made; and

(b) subject to such limits as may be prescribed, by such officer, not below the rank of an Assistant Sessions Judge, as the Central Government may, by notification in the Official Gazette, specify in this behalf.

(2) When an adjudication under sub-section (1) is concluded by the Court of Session or Assistant Sessions Judge, as the case may be, the Sessions Judge or Assistant Sessions Judge may make such order as he thinks fit for the disposal by confiscation or delivery of seized article or currency or security, as the case may be, to any person claiming to be entitled to possession thereof or otherwise, or which has been used for the commission of any offence under this Act.

**30. Procedure for confiscation.**—No order of adjudication of confiscation shall be made unless a reasonable opportunity of making a representation against such confiscation has been given to the person from whom any article or currency or security has been seized.

## CHAPTER VII
## APPEAL AND REVISION

**31. Appeal.**—(1) Any person aggrieved by any order made under section 29 may prefer an appeal,—

(a) where the order has been made by the Court of Session, to the High Court to which such Court is subordinate; or

(b) where the order has been made by any officer specified under clause (b) of sub-section (1) of section 29, to the Court of Session within the local limits of whose jurisdiction such order of adjudication of confiscation was made,

within one month from the date of communication to such person of the order:

Provided that the appellate court may, if it is satisfied that the appellant was prevented by sufficient cause from preferring the appeal within the said period of one month, allow such appeal to be preferred within a further period of one month, but not thereafter.

(2) Any organisation referred to in clause (f) of sub-section (1) of section 3, or any person or association referred to in section 6 or section 9, aggrieved

by an order made in pursuance of section 5 or by an order of the Central Government refusing to give permission under this Act, or by any order made by the Central Government under sub-section (2) or sub-section (4) of section 12, or sub-section (1) of section 14, as the case may be, may, within sixty days from the date of such order, prefer an appeal against such order to the High Court within the local limits of whose jurisdiction the appellant ordinarily resides or carries on business or personally works for gain, or, where the appellant is an organisation or association, the principal office of such organisation or association is located.

(3) Every appeal preferred under this section shall be deemed to be an appeal from an original decree and the provisions of Order XLI of the First Schedule to the Code of Civil Procedure, 1908 (5 of 1908), shall, as far as may be, apply thereto as they apply to an appeal from an original decree.

**32. Revision of orders by Central Government.**—(1) The Central Government may, either of its own motion or on an application for revision by the person registered under this Act, call for and examine the record of any proceeding under this Act in which any such order has been passed by it and may make such inquiry or cause such inquiry to be made and, subject to the provisions of this Act, may pass such order thereon as it thinks fit.

(2) The Central Government shall not of its own motion revise any order under this section if the order has been made more than one year previously.

(3) In the case of an application for revision under this section by the person referred to in sub-section (1), the application must be made within one year from the date on which the order in question was communicated to him or the date on which he otherwise came to know of it, whichever is earlier:

Provided that the Central Government may, if it is satisfied that such person was prevented by sufficient cause from making the application within that period, admit an application made after the expiry of that period.

(4) The Central Government shall not revise any order where an appeal against the order lies but has not been made and the time within which such appeal may be made has not expired or such person has not waived his right of appeal or an appeal has been filed under this Act.

(5) Every application by such person for revision under this section shall be accompanied by such fee, as may be prescribed.

*Explanation.*—An order by the Central Government declining to interfere shall, for the purposes of this section, be deemed not to be an order prejudicial to such person.

## CHAPTER VIII

## OFFENCES AND PENALTIES

**33. Making of false statement, declaration or delivering false accounts.**—Any person, subject to this Act, who knowingly,—

(a) gives false intimation under clause (c) of section 9 or section 18; or

(b) seeks prior permission or registration by means of fraud, false representation or concealment of material fact, shall, on conviction by a court, be liable to imprisonment for a term which may extend to six months or with fine or with both.

**34. Penalty for article or currency or security obtained in contravention of section 10.**—If any person, on whom any prohibitory order has been served under section 10, pays, delivers, transfers or otherwise deals with, in any manner whatsoever, any article or currency or security, whether Indian or foreign, in contravention of such prohibitory order, he shall be punished with imprisonment for a term which may extend to three years, or with fine, or with both; and notwithstanding anything contained in the Code of Criminal Procedure, 1973 (2 of 1974), the court trying such contravention may also impose on the person convicted an additional fine equivalent to the market value of the article or the amount of the currency or security in respect of which the prohibitory order has been contravened by him or such part thereof as the court may deem fit.

**35. Punishment for contravention of any provision of the Act.**—Whoever accepts, or assists any person, political party or organisation in accepting, any foreign contribution or any currency or security from a foreign source, in contravention of any provision of this Act or any rule or order made thereunder, shall be punished with imprisonment for a term which may extend to five years, or with fine, or with both.

**36. Power to impose additional fine where article or currency or security is not available for confiscation.**—Notwithstanding anything contained in the Code of Criminal Procedure, 1973 (2 of 1974), the court trying a person, who, in relation to any article or currency or security, whether Indian or foreign, does or omits to do any act which act or omission would render such article or currency or security liable to confiscation under this Act, may, in the event of the conviction of such person for the act or omission aforesaid, impose on such person a fine not exceeding five times the value of the article or currency or security or one thousand rupees, whichever is more, if such article or currency or security is not available for confiscation, and the fine so imposed shall be in addition to any other fine which may be imposed on such person under this Act.

**37. Penalty for offences where no separate punishment has been provided.**—Whoever fails to comply with any provision of this Act for which no separate penalty has been provided in this Act shall be punished with imprisonment for a term which may extend to one year, or with fine or with both.

**38. Prohibition of acceptance of foreign contribution.**—Notwithstanding anything contained in this Act, whoever, having been convicted of any offence under section 35 or section 37, in so far as such offence relates to the acceptance or utilisation of foreign contribution, is again convicted of such offence shall not accept any foreign contribution for a period of five years from the date of the subsequent conviction.

**39. Offences by companies.**—(1) Where an offence under this Act or any rule or order made thereunder has been committed by a company, every person who, at the time the offence was committed, was in charge of, and was responsible to, the company for the conduct of the business of the company, as well as the company, shall be deemed to be guilty of the offence and shall be liable to be proceeded against and punished accordingly:

Provided that nothing contained in this sub-section shall render such person liable to any punishment if he proves that the offence was committed without his knowledge or that he had exercised all due diligence to prevent the commission of such offence.

(2) Notwithstanding anything contained in sub-section (1), where an offence under this Act or any rule or order made thereunder has been committed by a company and it is proved that the offence has been committed with the consent or connivance of, or is attributable to any neglect on the part of, any director, manager, secretary or other officer of the company, such director, manager, secretary or other officer shall also be deemed to be guilty of that offence and shall be liable to be proceeded against and punished accordingly.

*Explanation.*—For the purposes of this section,—

(a) "company" means any body corporate and includes a firm, society, trade union or other association of individuals; and

(b) "director", in relation to a firm, society, trade union or other association of individuals, means a partner in the firm or a member of the governing body of such society, trade union or other association of individuals.

**40. Bar on prosecution of offences under the Act.**—No court shall take cognizance of any offence under this Act, except with the previous sanction of the Central Government or any officer authorised by that Government in this behalf.

***NOTIFICATION***

In exercise of the powers conferred by section 40 of the Foreign Contribution (Regulation) Act, 2010 (42 of 2010), the Central Government has authorised the following officers for according previous sanction as required under the said section, namely:—

(i) the Union Home Secretary in respect of offences investigated by the Central Bureau of Investigation;

(ii) the Home Secretary of the State Government concerned, in respect of offences investigated by the Investigating Agencies (Crime Branch) of the State Governments.

[According to S.O. 2445(E), dt. October 27, 2011, published in the Gazette of India, Extraordinary, Part II, Section 3(ii).]

**41. Compounding of certain offences.**—(1) Notwithstanding anything contained in the Code of Criminal Procedure, 1973 (2 of 1974), any offence punishable under this Act (whether committed by an individual or association or any officer or employee thereof), not being an offence punishable with imprisonment only, may, before the institution of any prosecution, be compounded by such officers or authorities and for such sums as the

Central Government may, by notification in the Official Gazette, specify in this behalf.

(2) Nothing in sub-section (1) shall apply to an offence committed by an individual or association or its officer or other employee within a period of three years from the date on which a similar offence committed by it or him was compounded under this section.

*Explanation*.—For the purposes of this section, any second or subsequent offence committed after the expiry of a period of three years from the date on which the offence was previously compounded, shall be deemed to be a first offence.

(3) Every officer or authority referred to in sub-section (1) shall exercise the powers to compound an offence, subject to the direction, control and supervision of the Central Government.

(4) Every application for the compounding of an offence shall be made to the officer or authority referred to in sub-section (1) in such form and manner along with such fee as may be prescribed.

(5) Where any offence is compounded before the institution of any prosecution, no prosecution shall be instituted in relation to such offence, against the offender in relation to whom the offence is so compounded.

(6) Every officer or authority referred to in sub-section (1), while dealing with a proposal for the compounding of an offence for a default in compliance with any provision of this Act which requires by an individual or association or its officer or other employee to obtain permission or file or register with, or deliver or send to, the Central Government or any prescribed authority any return, account or other document, may, direct, by order, if he or it thinks fit to do so, any individual or association or its officer or other employee to file or register with, such return, account or other document within such time as may be specified in the order.

## *NOTIFICATIONS*

In exercise of the powers conferred by sub-section (1) of section 41 of the Act, the Central Government hereby specifies that the following offences by any 'person' may, before the institution of any prosecution, be compounded for the payment of sums as penalty, as indicated against each of the offences under the Act:—

| Sl. No. | Nature of offence | Quantum of penalty |
|---|---|---|
| (i) | Acceptance of cheque or draft towards foreign contribution by a 'person' without registration or prior permission of the Central Government even in cases where the cheque or draft has not been deposited in a Bank by the 'person'. | Rs. 10,000/- or 2 per cent of the foreign contribution involved, whichever is higher. |
| (ii) | Acceptance of cheque or draft by a 'person' towards foreign contribution without registration or prior permission of the Central Government and depositing the same in a Bank notwithstanding non-utilisation of the amount of the foreign contribution. | Rs. 25,000/- or 3 per cent of the foreign contribution involved, whichever is higher. |

| | | |
|---|---|---|
| (iii) | Acceptance of foreign contribution by a 'person' without registration or prior permission of the Central Government and utilisation of the same notwithstanding any inquiry which revealed that the contribution received was not diverted towards any purpose other than the objectives or purpose for which the same was received, utilisation of the contribution was as per the objectives of receipt of the same and records of receipt and utilisation have been kept properly. | Rs. 1,00,000/- or 5 per cent of the foreign contribution involved, whichever is higher. |
| (iv) | Acceptance of foreign contribution in kind by a 'person' without registration or prior permission of the Central Government notwithstanding that nothing adverse was reported after inquiry. | Rs. 10,000/- or 2 per cent of the foreign contribution involved, whichever is higher. |

(2) In exercise of the powers conferred by sub-section (1) of section 41 of the Act, the Central Government hereby specifies that the Director or Deputy Secretary in charge of the FCRA Wing of the Foreigners Division in the Ministry of Home Affairs shall be the authority for exercising the powers for compounding of an offence under the Act.

[According to S.O. 1976(E), dt. August 26, 2011, published in the Gazette of India, Extraordinary, Part II, Section 3(ii), dt. August 26, 2011.]

In exercise of the powers conferred by sub-section (1) of section 41 read with section 35 of the Foreign Contribution (Regulation) Act, 2010 (42 of 2010) and rule 17 of the Foreign Contribution (Regulation) Rules, 2011 and in supersession of the notification of the Government of India in the Ministry of Home Affairs number S.O. 1070(E), dated the 26th April, 2013, published in the Gazette of India, Extraordinary, Part-II, Section 3, Sub-section (ii), except as respects things done or omitted to be done before such supersession, the Central Government hereby notifies that officer specified in column (4) of the table below, may, before institution of any prosecution under this Act, compound the offences specified in column (2), on payment of the amount specified in column (3), of the said table, namely:—

**TABLE**

| Sl. No. | Offence | Amount of Penalty | Officer competent for compounding |
|---|---|---|---|
| (1) | (2) | (3) | (4) |
| 1. | Non-furnishing of return upto three months after the 31st December every year | Penalty of two per cent of the amount of foreign contribution received during the financial year or ten thousand rupees, Whichever is less | The Director or the Deputy Secretary in Charge of the Foreign Contribution (Regulation) Act Wing of Foreign Division in the Ministry of Home Affairs |
| 2. | Non-furnishing of return after three months upto six months after the 31st December every year | Penalty of three per cent of the amount of foreign contribution received during the financial year or fifty thousand rupees, Whichever is less | The Director or the Deputy Secretary in Charge of the Foreign Contribution (Regulation) Act Wing of Foreign Division in the Ministry of Home Affairs |

| Sl. No. | Offence | Amount of Penalty | Officer competent for compounding |
|---|---|---|---|
| (1) | (2) | (3) | (4) |
| 3. | Non-furnishing of return after six months upto one year after the 31st December every year | Penalty of four per cent of the amount of foreign contribution received during the financial year or two Lakh rupees, Whichever is less | The Director or the Deputy Secretary in Charge of the Foreign Contribution (Regulation) Act Wing of Foreign Division in the Ministry of Home Affairs |
| 4. | Non-furnishing of return after one year upto two years after the 31st December every year | Penalty of five per cent of the amount of foreign contribution received during the financial year or five Lakh rupees, Whichever is less | The Director or the Deputy Secretary in Charge of the Foreign Contribution (Regulation) Act Wing of Foreign Division in the Ministry of Home Affairs |
| 5. | Non-furnishing of return after two years upto three years after the 31st December every year | Penalty of ten per cent of the amount of foreign contribution received during the financial year or ten Lakh rupees, Whichever is less | The Director or the Deputy Secretary in Charge of the Foreign Contribution (Regulation) Act Wing of Foreign Division in the Ministry of Home Affairs |

[According to S.O. 2133(E), dt. June 16, 2016, published in the Gazette of India, Extraordinary, Part II, Section 3(ii), No. 1521, dt. June 16, 2016.]

## CHAPTER IX
## MISCELLANEOUS

**42. Power to call for information or document.**—Any inspecting officer referred to in section 23 who is authorised in this behalf by the Central Government may, during the course of any inspection of any account or record maintained by any political party, person, organisation or association in connection with the contravention of any provision of this Act,—

(a) call for information from any person for the purpose of satisfying himself whether there has been any contravention of the provisions of this Act or rule or order made thereunder;

(b) require any person to produce or deliver any document or thing useful or relevant to such inspection;

(c) examine any person acquainted with the facts and circumstances of the case related to the inspection.

**43. Investigation into cases under the Act.**—Notwithstanding anything contained in the Code of Criminal Procedure, 1973 (2 of 1974), any offence punishable under this Act may also be investigated into by such authority as the Central Government may specify in this behalf and the authority so specified shall have all the powers which an officer-in-charge of a police station has while making an investigation into a cognizable offence.

**44. Returns by prescribed authority to Central Government.**—The prescribed authority shall furnish to the Central Government at such time and in such form and manner such returns and statements as may be prescribed.

**45. Protection of action taken in good faith.**—No suit or other legal proceedings shall lie against the Central Government or the authority referred to in section 44 or any of its officers in respect of any loss or damage caused or likely to be caused by anything which is in good faith done or intended to be done in pursuance of the provisions of this Act or, any rule or order made thereunder.

**46. Power of Central Government to give directions.**—The Central Government may give such directions as it may deem necessary to any other authority or any person or class of persons regarding the carrying into execution of the provisions of this Act.

**47. Delegation of powers.**—The Central Government may, by notification, direct that any of its powers or functions under this Act, except power to make rules under section 48, shall, in relation to such matters and subject to such conditions, if any, may be specified in the notification, be exercised or discharged also by such authority as may be specified.

**48. Power to make rules.**—(1) The Central Government may, by notification, make rules for carrying out the provisions of this Act.

(2) In particular, and without prejudice to the generality of the foregoing power, such rules may provide for all or any of the following matters, namely:—

(a) the value of the article which may be specified under sub-clause (i) of clause (h) of sub-section (1) of section 2;

(b) the authority which may be specified under clause (p) of sub-section (1) of section 2;

(c) acceptance or retention of gift or presentation under clause (d) of section 4;

(d) guidelines specifying the ground or grounds on which an organisation may be specified as an organisation of political nature under sub-section (1) of section 5;

(e) the activities or business which shall be construed as speculative business under the proviso to clause (a) of sub-section (1) of section 8;

(f) the elements and the manner in which the administrative expenses shall be calculated under sub-section (2) of section 8;

(g) the time within which and the manner in which any person or class of persons or an association may be required to furnish intimation regarding the amount of foreign contribution received under clause (c) of section 9;

(h) the time within which and the manner in which any person or class of persons may be required to furnish intimation regarding foreign hospitality under clause (e) of section 9;

(i) the manner in which the copy of the order of the Central Government shall be served upon any person under section 10;

(j) the form and manner in which the application for grant of certificate of registration or giving of prior permission under sub-section (1) of section 12;

(k) the fee to be accompanied by the application under sub-section (1) of section 12;

(l) the terms and conditions for granting a certificate or giving prior permission under clause (g) of sub-section (4) of section 12;

(m) the manner of utilising the foreign contribution under clause (b) of sub-section (2) of section 13;

(n) the authority with whom the foreign contribution to be vested under sub-section (1) of section 15;

(o) the period within which and the manner in which the foreign contribution shall be managed under sub-section (2) of section 15;

(p) the form and manner in which the application for a renewal of certificate of registration shall be made under sub-section (2) of section 16;

(q) the fee to be accompanied by the application for renewal of certificate under sub-section (2) of section 16;

(r) the prescribed amount of foreign remittance, the form and manner in which the foreign remittance received by every bank or authorised person in foreign exchange shall be reported under sub-section (2) of section 17;

(s) the time within which and the manner in which the person who has been granted certificate of registration or given prior permission under this Act shall give intimation under section 18;

(t) the form and manner in which account of any foreign contribution and the manner in which such contribution has been utilised shall be maintained under section 19;

(u) the time within which and the manner in which a candidate for election shall give intimation under section 21;

(v) the manner and procedure to be followed in disposing of the assets under section 22;

(w) the limits subject to which any confiscation may be adjudged under clause (b) of sub-section (1) of section 29;

(x) the fee to be accompanied along with every application for revision under sub-section (5) of section 32;

(y) the form and manner for making of an application for compounding of an offence and the fee therefor under sub-section (4) of section 41;

(z) the form and manner in which and the time within which returns and statements to be furnished by the prescribed authority under section 44;

(za) any other matter which is required to be, or may be, prescribed.

**49. Orders and rules to be laid before Parliament.**—Every order made under section 5 and every rule made by the Central Government under this Act shall be laid, as soon as may be after it is made, before each House of Parliament while it is in session for a total period of thirty days which may be comprised in one session or in two or more successive sessions, and if, before the expiry of the session immediately following the session or the successive sessions aforesaid, both Houses agree in making any modification in the order or rule or both Houses agree that the order or rule should not be made, the order or rule shall thereafter have effect only in such modified form or be of no effect, as the case may be; so, however, that any such modification or annulment shall be without prejudice to the validity of anything previously done under that order or rule.

**50. Power to exempt in certain cases.**—If the Central Government is of opinion that it is necessary or expedient in the interests of the general public so to do, it may, by order and subject to such conditions as may be specified in the order, exempt any person or association or organisation (not being a political party), or any individual (not being a candidate for election) from the operation of all or any of the provisions of this Act and may, as often as may be necessary, revoke or modify such order.

*NOTIFICATION*

In exercise of the powers conferred by section 50 of the Foreign Contribution (Regulation) Act, 2010 (42 of 2010), the Central Government hereby notifies that the international organisations specified below shall not be treated as foreign source for the purpose of the said Act, namely:—

(i) South Asian Association for Regional Cooperation Disaster Management Centre (SDMC);

(ii) Global Fund for Disaster Risk Reduction (GFDRR);

(iii) Asian Disaster Reduction Centre (ADRC); and

(iv) Asian Disaster Preparedness Centre (ADPC).

[According to S.O. 3210(E), dt. October 17, 2016, published in the Gazette of India, Extraordinary, Part II, Section 3(ii), No. 2477, dt. October 18, 2016.]

**51. Act not to apply to certain Government transactions.**—Nothing contained in this Act shall apply to any transaction between the Government of India and the Government of any foreign country or territory.

**52. Application of other laws not barred.**—The provisions of this Act shall be in addition to, and not in derogation of, the provisions of any other law for the time being in force.

**53. Power to remove difficulties.**—(1) If any difficulty arises in giving effect to the provisions of this Act, the Central Government may, by order, published in the Official Gazette, make such provisions not inconsistent with the provisions of this Act as may appear to be necessary for removing the difficulty:

Provided that no order shall be made under this section after the expiry of two years from the commencement of this Act.

(2) Every order made under this section shall be laid, as soon as may be after it is made, before each House of Parliament.

**54. Repeal and saving.**—(1) The Foreign Contribution (Regulation) Act, 1976 (49 of 1976) (hereafter referred to as the repealed Act) is hereby repealed.

(2) Notwithstanding such repeal,—

(a) anything done or any action taken or purported to have been done or taken under the repealed Act shall, in so far as it is not inconsistent with the provisions of this Act, be deemed to have been done or taken under the corresponding provisions of this Act;

(b) any organisation of a political nature, not being a political party, to whom the prior permission was granted under section 5 of the repealed Act, shall continue to be the organisation of a political nature, not being a political party, under clause (f) of sub-section (1) of section 3 of this Act, till such permission is withdrawn by the Central Government;

(c) permission to accept foreign hospitality granted under section 9 of the repealed Act shall be deemed to be the permission granted under section 6 of this Act until such permission is withdrawn by the Central Government;

(d) any association prohibited from accepting any foreign contribution under clause (a) of section 10 of the repealed Act, in so far as it is not inconsistent with the provisions of this Act, shall be deemed to be an association prohibited from accepting any foreign contribution under section 9 of this Act;

(e) permission obtained under clause (b) of section 10 of the repealed Act shall, in so far as it is not inconsistent with the provisions of this Act, be deemed to be the permission until such permission is withdrawn by the Central Government;

(f) any order issued under section 12 of the repealed Act shall be deemed to be an order issued under section 10 of this Act;

(g) any order issued under section 31 of the repealed Act exempting any association or any individual shall be deemed to be an order under section 50 of this Act till such order is varied or revoked.

(3) Save as provided in sub-section (2), mention of particular matters in that sub-section shall not be held to prejudice or affect the general application of section 6 of the General Clauses Act, 1897 (10 of 1897), with regard to the effect of repeal.

# THE FUGITIVE ECONOMIC OFFENDERS ACT, 2018[1]

(17 of 2018)

[*31st July, 2018*]

*An Act to provide for measures to deter fugitive economic offenders from evading the process of law in India by staying outside the jurisdiction of Indian courts, to preserve the sanctity of the rule of law in India and for matters connected therewith or incidental thereto.*

BE it enacted by Parliament in the Sixty-ninth Year of the Republic of India as follows:—

## CHAPTER I

## PRELIMINARY

**1. Short title, extent and commencement.**—(1) This Act may be called the Fugitive Economic Offenders Act, 2018.

(2) It extends to the whole of India.

(3) It shall be deemed to have come into force on the 21st day of April, 2018.

**2. Definitions.**—(1) In this Act, unless the context otherwise requires,—

(a) "Administrator" means an Administrator appointed under sub-section (1) of section 15;

(b) "*benami* property" and "*benami* transaction" shall have the same meanings as assigned to them under clauses (8) and (9) respectively of section 2 of the Prohibition of *Benami* Property Transactions Act, 1988 (45 of 1988);

(c) "contracting State" means any country or place outside India in respect of which arrangements have been made by the Central Government with the Government of such country through a treaty or otherwise;

(d) "Deputy Director" means the Deputy Director appointed under sub-section (1) of section 49 of the Prevention of Money-laundering Act, 2002 (15 of 2003);

(e) "Director" means the Director appointed under sub-section (1) of section 49 of the Prevention of Money-laundering Act, 2002 (15 of 2003);

(f) "fugitive economic offender" means any individual against whom a warrant for arrest in relation to a Scheduled Offence has been issued by any Court in India, who—

(i) has left India so as to avoid criminal prosecution; or

(ii) being abroad, refuses to return to India to face criminal prosecution;

1. Published in the Gazette of India, Extra., Part. II, Section 1, No. 29, dt. August 1, 2018.

(g) "key managerial personnel" shall have the same meaning as assigned to it in clause (51) of section 2 of the Companies Act, 2013 (18 of 2013);

(h) "notification" means a notification published in the Official Gazette and the expression "notify" shall be construed accordingly;

(i) "person" includes—

(i) an individual;

(ii) a Hindu Undivided Family;

(iii) a company;

(iv) a trust;

(v) a partnership;

(vi) a limited liability partnership;

(vii) an association of persons or a body of individuals, whether incorporated or not;

(viii) every artificial juridical person not falling within any of the preceding sub-clauses; and

(ix) any agency, office or branch owned or controlled by any of the above persons mentioned in the preceding sub-clauses;

(j) "prescribed" means prescribed by rules made under this Act;

(k) "proceeds of crime" means any property derived or obtained, directly or indirectly, by any person as a result of criminal activity relating to a Scheduled Offence, or the value of any such property, or where such property is taken or held outside the country, then the property equivalent in value held within the country or abroad;

(l) "Schedule" means the Schedule appended to this Act;

(m) "Scheduled Offence" means an offence specified in the Schedule, if the total value involved in such offence or offences is one hundred crore rupees or more;

(n) "Special Court" means a Court of Session designated as a Special Court under sub-section (1) of section 43 of the Prevention of Money-laundering Act, 2002 (15 of 2003).

(2) The words and expressions used and not defined in this Act but defined in the Prevention of Money-laundering Act, 2002 (15 of 2003) shall have the meanings respectively assigned to them in that Act.

## COMMENT

**Fugitive economic offender**

A fugitive economic offender has been defined as a person against whom an arrest warrant has been issued for committing any offence listed in the Schedule of the Act. Further :

(i) he has left the country for avoiding prosecution;

(ii) refuses to return to face prosecution, etc.

**3. Application of Act.**—The provisions of this Act shall apply to any individual who is, or becomes, a fugitive economic offender on or after the date of coming into force of this Act.

## CHAPTER II

## DECLARATION OF FUGITIVE ECONOMIC OFFENDERS AND CONFISCATION OF PROPERTY

**4. Application for declaration of fugitive economic offender and procedure therefor.**—(1) Where the Director or any other officer not below the rank of Deputy Director authorised by the Director for the purposes of this section, has reason to believe (the reasons for such belief to be recorded in writing), on the basis of material in his possession, that any individual is a fugitive economic offender, he may file an application in such form and manner as may be prescribed in the Special Court that such individual may be declared as a fugitive economic offender.

(2) The application referred to in sub-section (1) shall contain—

(a) reasons for the belief that an individual is a fugitive economic offender;

(b) any information available as to the whereabouts of the fugitive economic offender;

(c) a list of properties or the value of such properties believed to be the proceeds of crime, including any such property outside India for which confiscation is sought;

(d) a list of properties or *benami* properties owned by the individual in India or abroad for which confiscation is sought; and

(e) a list of persons who may have an interest in any of the properties listed under clauses (c) and (d).

(3) The Authorities appointed for the purposes of the Prevention of Money-laundering Act, 2002 (15 of 2003) shall be the Authorities for the purposes of this Act.

### COMMENT

**Application for declaration of fugitive economic offender.**

A director or deputy director appointed under the Prevention of Money-Laundering Act, 2002 may file an application before a Special Court (designated under the 2002 Act) to declare a person as a economic fugitive offender.

**5. Attachment of property.**—(1) The Director or any other officer authorised by the Director, not below the rank of Deputy Director, may, with the permission of the Special Court, attach any property mentioned in the application under section 4 by an order in writing in such manner as may be prescribed.

(2) Notwithstanding anything contained in sub-section (1) or section 4, the Director or any other officer, not below the rank of Deputy Director, authorised by the Director, may, by an order in writing, at any time prior to the filing of the application under section 4, attach any property—

(a) for which there is a reason to believe that the property is proceeds of crime, or is a property or *benami* property owned by an individual who is a fugitive economic offender; and

(b) which is being or is likely to be dealt within a manner which may result in the property being unavailable for confiscation:

Provided that the Director or any other officer who provisionally attaches any property under this sub-section shall, within a period of thirty days from the date of such attachment, file an application under section 4 before the Special Court.

(3) The attachment of any property under this section shall continue for a period of one hundred and eighty days from the date of order of attachment or such other period as may be extended by the Special Court before the expiry of such period.

(4) Nothing in this section shall prevent the person interested in the enjoyment of the immovable property attached under sub-section (1) from such enjoyment.

*Explanation.*—For the purposes of this sub-section, the expression "person interested", in relation to any immovable property includes all persons claiming or entitled to claim any interest in the property.

**6. Powers of Director and other officers.**—The Director or any other officer shall, for the purposes of section 4, have the same powers as are vested in a civil court under the Code of Civil Procedure, 1908 (5 of 1908) while trying a suit in respect of the following matters, namely:—

(a) discovery and inspection;

(b) enforcing the attendance of any person, including any officer of a reporting entity and examining him on oath;

(c) compelling the production of records;

(d) receiving evidence on affidavits;

(e) issuing commissions for examination of witnesses and documents; and

(f) any other matter which may be prescribed.

**COMMENT**

**Power of Director etc.**

The Director or Deputy Director will have the powers vested in a civil court. These power include (i) entering a place on the belief that an individual is a fugitive economic offender and (ii) directing that a building be searched or documents be seized.

**7. Power of survey.**—(1) Notwithstanding anything contained in any other provisions of this Act, where a Director or any other officer authorised by the Director, on the basis of material in his possession, has reason to believe (the reasons for such belief to be recorded in writing), that an individual may be a fugitive economic offender, he may enter any place—

(i) within the limits of the area assigned to him; or

(ii) in respect of which he is authorised for the purposes of this section, by such other authority, who is assigned the area within which such place is situated.

(2) Where the Director or any other officer authorised by him, on the basis of material in his possession, has reason to believe (the reasons for such belief to be recorded in writing) that an individual may be a fugitive economic offender and it is necessary to enter any place as mentioned in sub-section (1), he may request any proprietor, employee or any other person who may be present at that time, to—

(a) afford him the necessary facility to inspect such records as he may require and which may be available at such place;

(b) afford him the necessary facility to check or verify the proceeds of crime or any transaction related to proceeds of crime which may be found therein; and

(c) furnish such information as he may require as to any matter which may be useful for, or relevant to any proceedings under this Act.

(3) The Director, or any other officer acting under this section may—

(i) place marks of identification on the records inspected by him and make or cause to be made extracts or copies therefrom;

(ii) make an inventory of any property checked or verified by him; and

(iii) record the statement of any person present at the property which may be useful for, or relevant to, any proceeding under this Act.

**8. Search and seizure.**—(1) Notwithstanding anything contained in any other law for the time being in force, where the Director or any other officer not below the rank of Deputy Director authorised by him for the purposes of this section, on the basis of information in his possession, has reason to believe (the reason for such belief to be recorded in writing) that any person—

(i) may be declared as a fugitive economic offender;

(ii) is in possession of any proceeds of crime;

(iii) is in possession of any records which may relate to proceeds of crime; or

(iv) is in possession of any property related to proceeds of crime,

then, subject to any rules made in this behalf, he may authorise any officer subordinate to him to—

(a) enter and search any building, place, vessel, vehicle or aircraft where he has reason to suspect that such records or proceeds of crime are kept;

(b) break open the lock of any door, box, locker, safe, almirah or other receptacle for exercising the powers conferred by clause (a) where the keys thereof are not available;

(c) seize any record or property found as a result of such search;

(d) place marks of identification on such record or property, if required or make or cause to be made extracts or copies therefrom;

(e) make a note or an inventory of such record or property; and

(f) examine on oath any person, who is found to be in possession or control of any record or property, in respect of all matters relevant for the purposes of any investigation under this Act.

(2) Where an authority, upon information obtained during survey under section 7, is satisfied that any evidence shall be or is likely to be concealed or tampered with, he may, for reasons to be recorded in writing, enter and search the building or place where such evidence is located and seize that evidence.

**9. Search of persons.**—Notwithstanding anything contained in any other law for the time being in force—

(a) if an authority, authorised in this behalf by the Central Government by general or special order, has reason to believe (the reason for such belief to be recorded in writing) that any person has secreted about his person or anything under his possession, ownership or control, any record or proceeds of crime which may be useful for or relevant to any proceedings under this Act, he may search that person and seize such record or property which may be useful for or relevant to any proceedings under this Act;

(b) where an authority is about to search any person, he shall, if such person so requires, take such person within twenty-four hours to the nearest Gazetted Officer, superior in rank to him, or a Magistrate:

Provided that the period of twenty-four hours shall exclude the time necessary for the journey undertaken to take such person to the nearest Gazetted Officer, superior in rank to him, or the Magistrate's Court;

(c) if the requisition under clause (b) is made, the authority shall not detain the person for more than twenty-four hours prior to taking him before the Gazetted Officer, superior in rank to him, or the Magistrate referred to in that clause:

Provided that the period of twenty-four hours shall exclude the time necessary for the journey from the place of detention to the office of the Gazetted Officer, superior in rank to him, or the Magistrate's Court;

(d) the Gazetted Officer or the Magistrate before whom any such person is brought shall, if he sees no reasonable ground for search, forthwith discharge such person but otherwise shall direct that search be made;

(e) before making the search under clause (a) or clause (d), the authority shall call upon two or more persons to attend and witness the search and the search shall be made in the presence of such persons;

(f) the authority shall prepare a list of record or property seized in the course of the search and obtain the signatures of the witnesses on the list;

(g) no female shall be searched by anyone except a female; and

(h) the authority shall record the statement of the person searched under clause (a) or clause (d) in respect of the records or proceeds of crime found or seized in the course of the search.

**10. Notice.**—(1) Where an application under section 4 has been duly filed, the Special Court shall issue a notice to an individual who is alleged to be a fugitive economic offender.

(2) The notice referred to in sub-section (1), shall also be issued to any other person who has any interest in the property mentioned in the application under sub-section (2) of section 4.

(3) A notice under sub-section (1) shall—

(a) require the individual to appear at a specified place and time not less than six weeks from the date of issue of such notice; and

(b) state that failure to appear on the specified place and time shall result in a declaration of the individual as a fugitive economic offender and confiscation of property under this Act.

(4) A notice under sub-section (1) shall be forwarded to such authority, as the Central Government may notify, for effecting service in a contracting State.

(5) The authority referred to in sub-section (4) shall make efforts to serve the notice within a period of two weeks in such manner as may be prescribed.

(6) A notice under sub-section (1) may also be served to the individual alleged to be a fugitive economic offender by electronic means to—

(a) his electronic mail address submitted in connection with an application for allotment of Permanent Account Number under section 139A of the Income-tax Act, 1961 (43 of 1961);

(b) his electronic mail address submitted in connection with an application for enrolment under section 3 of the Aadhaar (Targeted Delivery of Financial and Other Subsidies, Benefits and Services) Act, 2016 (18 of 2016); or

(c) any other electronic account as may be prescribed, belonging to the individual which is accessed by him over the internet, subject to the satisfaction of the Special Court that such account has been recently accessed by the individual and constitutes a reasonable method for communication of the notice to the individual.

**11. Procedure for hearing application.**—(1) Where any individual to whom notice has been issued under sub-section (1) of section 10 appears in person at the place and time specified in the notice, the Special Court may terminate the proceedings under this Act.

(2) Where any individual to whom notice has been issued under sub-section (1) of section 10 fails to appear at the place and time specified in the notice, but enters appearance through counsel, the Special Court may in its discretion give a period of one week to file a reply to the application under section 4.

(3) Where any individual to whom notice has been issued under sub-section (1) of section 10 fails to enter appearance either in person or through counsel, and the Special Court is satisfied—

(a) that service of notice has been effected on such party; or

(b) that notice could not be served in spite of best efforts because such individual has evaded service of notice,

it may, after recording reasons in writing, proceed to hear the application.

(4) The Special Court may also give any person to whom notice has been issued under sub-section (2) of section 10 a period of one week to file a reply to the application under section 4.

**12. Declaration of fugitive economic offender.**—(1) After hearing the application under section 4, if the Special Court is satisfied that an individual is a fugitive economic offender, it may, by an order, declare the individual as a fugitive economic offender for reasons to be recorded in writing.

(2) On a declaration under sub-section (1), the Special Court may order that any of the following properties stand confiscated to the Central Government—

(a) the proceeds of crime in India or abroad, whether or not such property is owned by the fugitive economic offender; and

(b) any other property or *benami* property in India or abroad, owned by the fugitive economic offender.

(3) The confiscation order of the Special Court shall, to the extent possible, identify the properties in India or abroad that constitute proceeds of crime which are to be confiscated and in case such properties cannot be identified, quantify the value of the proceeds of crime.

(4) The confiscation order of the Special Court shall separately list any other property owned by the fugitive economic offender in India which is to be confiscated.

(5) Where the Special Court has made an order for confiscation of any property under sub-section (2), and such property is in a contracting State, the Special Court may issue a letter of request to a Court or authority in the contracting State for execution of such order.

(6) Every letter of request to be transmitted to a contracting State under sub-section (5) shall be transmitted in such form and manner as the Central Government may, by notification, specify in this behalf.

(7) The Special Court may, while making the confiscation order, exempt from confiscation any property which is a proceed of crime in which any other person, other than the fugitive economic offender, has an interest if it is satisfied that such interest was acquired *bona fide* and without knowledge of the fact that the property was proceeds of crime.

(8) All the rights and title in the confiscated property shall, from the date of the confiscation order, vest in the Central Government, free from all encumbrances.

(9) Where on the conclusion of the proceedings, the Special Court finds that the individual is not a fugitive economic offender, the Special Court shall order release of property or record attached or seized under this Act to the person entitled to receive it.

(10) Where an order releasing the property has been made by the Special Court under sub-section (9), the Director or any other officer authorised by him in this behalf may withhold the release of any such property or record for a period of ninety days from the date of receipt of such order, if he is of the opinion that such property is relevant for the appeal proceedings under this Act.

**13. Supplementary application.**—(1) Where at any time after the institution of the application under section 4, any other property is discovered or identified which constitutes proceeds of crime or is property or *benami* property owned by the individual in India or abroad who is a fugitive economic offender liable to be confiscated under this Act, the Director or any other officer not below the rank of Deputy Director authorised by the Director for the purposes of this section, may file a supplementary application in the Special Court seeking confiscation of such properties.

(2) The provisions of sections 4 to 12 shall, as far as may be, apply in relation to such application as they apply in relation to an application under section 4.

**14. Power to disallow civil claims.**—Notwithstanding anything contained in any other law for the time being in force,—

(a) on a declaration of an individual as a fugitive economic offender, any Court or tribunal in India, in any civil proceeding before it, may, disallow such individual from putting forward or defending any civil claim; and

(b) any Court or tribunal in India in any civil proceeding before it, may, disallow any company or limited liability partnership from putting forward or defending any civil claim, if an individual filing the claim on behalf of the company or the limited liability partnership, or any promoter or key managerial personnel or majority shareholder of the company or an individual having a controlling interest in the limited liability partnership has been declared as a fugitive economic offender.

*Explanation.*—For the purposes of this section, the expressions—

(a) "company" means any body corporate and includes a firm, or other association of persons; and

(b) "limited liability partnership" shall have the same meaning as assigned to it in clause (n) of sub-section (1) of section 2 of the Limited Liability Partnership Act, 2008 (6 of 2009).

**15. Management of properties confiscated under this Act.**—(1) The Central Government may, by order published in the Official Gazette, appoint as many of its officers (not below the rank of a Joint Secretary to the Government of India) as it thinks fit, to perform the functions of an Administrator.

(2) The Administrator appointed under sub-section (1) shall receive and manage the property in relation to which an order has been made under sub-section (2) of section 12 in such manner and subject to such conditions as may be prescribed.

(3) The Administrator shall also take such measures, as the Central Government may direct, to dispose of the property which is vested in the Central Government under section 12:

Provided that the Central Government or the Administrator shall not dispose of any property for a period of ninety days from the date of the order under sub-section (2) of section 12.

## CHAPTER III

## MISCELLANEOUS

**16. Rules of evidence.**—(1) The burden of proof for establishing—

(a) that an individual is a fugitive economic offender; or

(b) that a property is the proceeds of crime or any other property in which the individual alleged to be a fugitive economic offender has an interest,

shall be on the Director or the person authorised by the Director to file the application under section 4.

(2) Notwithstanding anything contained in any other law for the time being in force, where any person referred to in sub-section (2) of section 10 claims that any interest in any property was acquired *bona fide* and without knowledge of the fact that, such property constitutes proceeds of crime, the burden of proving such fact shall lie upon him.

(3) The standard of proof applicable to the determination of facts by the Special Court under this Act shall be preponderance of probabilities.

**17. Appeal.**—(1) An appeal shall lie from any judgment or order, not being an interlocutory order, of a Special Court to the High Court both on facts and on law.

(2) Every appeal under this section shall be preferred within a period of thirty days from the date of the judgment or order appealed from:

Provided that the High Court may entertain an appeal after the expiry of the said period of thirty days, if it is satisfied that the appellant had sufficient cause for not preferring the appeal within the period of thirty days:

Provided further that no appeal shall be entertained after the expiry of period of ninety days.

**18. Bar of jurisdiction.**—No civil court shall have jurisdiction to entertain any suit or proceeding in respect of any matter which the Special Court is empowered by or under this Act to determine and no injunction shall be granted by any court or other authority in respect of any action taken or to be taken in pursuance of any power conferred by or under this Act.

**19. Protection of action taken in good faith.**—No suit, prosecution or other legal proceeding shall lie against the Central Government or Presiding

Officer of the Special Court or Director or Deputy Director or any other officer authorised by the Director for anything which is in good faith done or intended to be done under this Act or any rule made thereunder.

**20. Power of Central Government to amend Schedule.**—(1) The Central Government may, having regard to the objects of this Act, and if it considers necessary or expedient so to do, by notification add to, or as the case may be, omit from the Schedule any offences specified therein.

(2) Every such notification shall, as soon as after it is issued, be laid before each House of Parliament.

**21. Overriding effect.**—The provisions of this Act shall have effect, notwithstanding anything inconsistent therewith contained in any other law for the time being in force.

**22. Application of other laws not barred.**—The provisions of this Act shall be in addition to and not in derogation of any other law for the time being in force.

**23. Power to make rules.**—(1) The Central Government may, by notification in the Official Gazette, make rules for carrying out the provisions of this Act.

(2) In particular, and without prejudice to generality of the foregoing power, such rules may provide for all or any of the following matters, namely:—

(a) the form and manner of filing application under sub-section (1) of section 4;

(b) the manner of attachment of property under sub-section (1) of section 5;

(c) other matters under clause (f) of section 6;

(d) the procedure for conducting search and seizure under section 8;

(e) the manner in which the notice shall be served under sub-section (5) of section 10;

(f) any other electronic account under clause (c) of sub-section (6) of section 10;

(g) the manner and conditions subject to which the Administrator shall receive and manage the property confiscated under sub-section (2) of section 15; and

(h) any other matter which is required to be, or may be, prescribed or in respect of which provision is to be made by rules.

**24. Laying of rules before Parliament.**—Every rule made under this Act shall be laid, as soon as may be after it is made, before each House of Parliament, while it is in session, for a total period of thirty days which may be comprised in one session or in two or more successive sessions, and if, before the expiry of the session immediately following the session or the successive sessions aforesaid, both Houses agree in making any modification in the rule or both Houses agree that the rule should not be made, the rule shall thereafter have effect only in such modified form or be of no effect, as the case may be; so, however, that any such modification or annulment shall be without prejudice to the validity of anything previously done under that rule.

**25. Power to remove difficulties.**—(1) If any difficulty arises in giving effect to the provisions of this Act, the Central Government may, by order, published in the Official Gazette, make such provisions not inconsistent with the provisions of this Act as may appear to be necessary for removing the difficulty:

Provided that no order shall be made under this section after the expiry of five years from the date of commencement of this Act.

(2) Every order made under this section shall be laid, as soon as may be after it is made, before each House of Parliament.

**26. Repeal and saving.**—(1) The Fugitive Economic Offenders Ordinance, 2018 (Ord. 1 of 2018), is hereby repealed.

(2) Notwithstanding such repeal, anything done or any action taken under the said Ordinance, shall be deemed to have been done or taken under this Act.

## THE SCHEDULE

[*See* section 2(1) and (m)]

| Section | Description of offence |
|---|---|
| **I.** | **Offences under the Indian Penal Code, 1860 (45 of 1860)** |
| 120B read with any offence in this Schedule | Punishment of criminal conspiracy. |
| 255 | Counterfeiting Government stamp. |
| 257 | Making or selling instrument for counterfeiting Government stamp. |
| 258 | Sale of counterfeit Government stamp. |
| 259 | Having possession of counterfeit Government stamp. |
| 260 | Using as genuine a Government stamp known to be counterfeit. |
| 417 | Punishment for cheating. |
| 418 | Cheating with knowledge that wrongful loss may ensue to person whose interest offender is bound to protect. |
| 420 | Cheating and dishonestly inducing delivery of property. |
| 421 | Dishonest or fraudulent removal or concealment of property to prevent distribution among creditors. |
| 422 | Dishonestly or fraudulently preventing debt being available for creditors. |
| 423 | Dishonest or fraudulent execution of deed of transfer containing false statement of consideration. |
| 424 | Dishonest or fraudulent removal or concealment of property. |
| 467 | Forgery of valuable security, will, etc. |
| 471 | Using as genuine a forged [document or electronic record]. |
| 472 | Making or possessing counterfeit seal, etc., with intent to commit forgery punishable under section 467. |

| Section | Description of offence |
|---|---|
| 473 | Making or possessing counterfeit seal, etc., intent to commit forgery punishable otherwise. |
| 475 | Counterfeiting device or mark used for authenticating documents described in section 467, or possessing counterfeit marked material. |
| 476 | Counterfeiting device or mark used for authenticating documents other than those described in section 467, or possessing counterfeit marked material. |
| 481 | Using a false property mark. |
| 482 | Punishment for using a false property mark. |
| 483 | Counterfeiting a property mark used by another. |
| 484 | Counterfeiting a mark used by a public servant. |
| 485 | Making or possession of any instrument for counterfeiting a property mark. |
| 486 | Selling goods marked with a counterfeit property mark. |
| 487 | Making a false mark upon any receptacle containing goods. |
| 488 | Punishment for making use of any such false mark. |
| 489A | Counterfeiting currency notes or bank notes. |
| 489B | Using as genuine, forged or counterfeit currency notes or bank notes. |
| **II.** | **Offences under the Negotiable Instruments Act, 1881 (26 of 1881)** |
| 138 | Dishonour of cheque for insufficiency, etc., of funds in the account. |
| **III.** | **Offences under the Reserve Bank of India Act, 1934 (2 of 1934)** |
| 58B | Penalties. |
| **IV.** | **Offences under the Central Excise Act, 1944 (1 of 1944)** |
| Section 9 | Offences and Penalties. |
| **V.** | **Offences under the Customs Act, 1962 (52 of 1962)** |
| 135 | Evasion of duty or prohibitions. |
| **VI.** | **Offences under the Prohibition of *Benami* Property Transactions Act, 1988 (45 of 1988)** |
| 3 | Prohibition of *benami* transactions. |
| **VII.** | **Offences under the Prevention of Corruption Act, 1988 (49 of 1988)** |
| 7 | Public servant taking gratification other than legal remuneration in respect of an official act. |
| 8 | Taking gratification in order, by corrupt or illegal means, to influence public servant. |
| 9 | Taking gratification for exercise of personal influence with public servant. |
| 10 | Punishment for abetment by public servant of offences defined in section 8 or section 9 of the Prevention of Corruption Act, 1988. |
| 13 | Criminal misconduct by a public servant. |

| Section | Description of offence |
|---|---|
| **VIII. Offences under the Securities and Exchange Board of India Act, 1992 (15 of 1992)** | |
| 12A read with section 24 | Prohibition of manipulative and deceptive devices, insider trading and substantial acquisition of securities or control. |
| 24 | Offences for contravention of the provisions of the Act. |
| **IX. Offences under the Prevention of Money-laundering Act, 2002 (15 of 2003)** | |
| 3 | Offence of money-laundering. |
| 4 | Punishment for money-laundering. |
| **X. Offences under the Limited Liability Partnership Act, 2008 (6 of 2009)** | |
| Sub-section (2) of section 30 | Carrying on business with intent or purpose to defraud creditors of the Limited Liability Partnership or any other person or for any other fraudulent purpose. |
| **XI. Offences under the Foreign Contribution (Regulation) Act, 2010 (42 of 2010)** | |
| 34 | Penalty for article or currency or security obtained in contravention of section 10. |
| 35 | Punishment for contravention of any provision of the Act. |
| **XII. Offences under the Companies Act, 2013 (18 of 2013)** | |
| Sub-section (4) of section 42 of the Companies Act, 2013 read with section 24 of the Securities and Exchange Board of India Act, 1992 (15 of 1992) | Offer or invitation for subscription of securities on private placement. |
| 74 | Repayment of deposits, etc., accepted before commencement of the Companies Act, 2013. |
| 76A | Punishment for contravention of section 73 or section 76 of the Companies Act, 2013. |
| Second proviso to sub-section (4) of section 206 | Carrying on business of a company for a fraudulent or unlawful purpose. |
| Clause (b) of section 213 | Conducting the business of a company with intent to defraud its creditors, members or any other persons or otherwise for a fraudulent or unlawful purpose, or in a manner oppressive to any of its members or that the company was formed for any fraudulent or unlawful purpose. |
| 447 | Punishment for fraud. |
| 452 | Punishment for wrongful withholding of property. |

| Section | Description of offence |
|---|---|
| **XIII. Offences under the Black Money (Undisclosed Foreign Income and Assets) and Imposition of Tax Act, 2015 (22 of 2015)** | |
| 51 | Punishment for wilful attempt to evade tax. |
| **XIV. Offences under the Insolvency and Bankruptcy Code, 2016 (31 of 2016)** | |
| 69 | Punishment for transactions defrauding creditors. |
| **XV. Offences under the Central Goods and Services Tax Act, 2017 (12 of 2017)** | |
| Sub-section (5) of section 132 | Punishment for certain offences. |

# THE RIGHT TO INFORMATION ACT, 2005

(22 of 2005)

[*15th June, 2005*]

*An Act to provide for setting out the practical regime of right to information for citizens to secure access to information under the control of public authorities, in order to promote transparency and accountability in the working of every public authority, the constitution of a Central Information Commission and State Information Commissions and for matters connected therewith or incidental thereto.*

WHEREAS the Constitution of India has established democratic Republic;

AND WHEREAS democracy requires an informed citizenry and transparency of information which are vital to its functioning and also to contain corruption and to hold Governments are their instrumentalities accountable to the governed;

AND WHEREAS revelation of information in actual practice is likely to conflict with other public interests including efficient operations of the Governments, optimum use of limited fiscal resources and the preservation of confidentiality of sensitive information;

AND WHEREAS it is necessary to harmonise these conflicting interests while preserving the paramountcy of the democratic ideal;

NOW, THEREFORE, it is expedient to provide for furnishing certain information to citizens who desire to have it.

BE it enacted by Parliament in the Fifty-sixth Year of the Republic of India as follows:—

## CHAPTER I
## PRELIMINARY

**1. Short title, extent and commencement.**—(1) This Act may be called the Right to Information Act, 2005.

(2) It extends to the whole of India[1][***].

(3) The provisions of sub-section (1) of section 4, sub-sections (1) and (2) of section 5, sections 12, 13, 15, 16, 24 , 27 and 28 shall come into force at once, and the remaining provisions of this Act shall come into force on the one hundred and twentieth day of its enactment.

**2. Definitions.**—In this Act, unless the context otherwise requires,—

(a) "appropriate Government" means in relation to a public authority which is established, constituted, owned, controlled or substantially financed by funds provided directly or indirectly—

(i) by the Central Government or the Union territory administration, the Central Government;

(ii) by the State Government, the State Government;

1. The words "except the State of Jammu and Kashmir" stood omitted by Act 34 of 2019, Section 95 and the Fifth Schedule (w.e.f. October 31, 2019).

(b) "Central Information Commission" means the Central Information Commission constituted under sub-section (1) of section 12;

(c) "Central Public Information Officer" means the Central Public Information Officer designated under sub-section (1) and includes a Central Assistant Public Information Officer designated as such under sub-section (2) of section 5;

(d) "Chief Information Commissioner" and "Information Commissioner" mean the Chief Information Commissioner and Information Commissioner appointed under sub-section (3) of section 12;

(e) "competent authority" means—

(i) the Speaker in the case of the House of the People or the Legislative Assembly of a State or a Union territory having such Assembly and the Chairman in the case of the Council of States or Legislative Council of a State;

(ii) the Chief Justice of India in the case of the Supreme Court;

(iii) the Chief Justice of the High Court in the case of a High Court;

(iv) the President or the Governor, as the case may be, in the case of other authorities established or constituted by or under the Constitution;

(v) the administrator appointed under article 239 of the Constitution;

(f) "information" means any material in any form, including records, documents, memos, e-mails, opinions, advices, press releases, circulars, orders, logbooks, contracts, reports, papers, samples, models, data material held in any electronic form and information relating to any private body which can be accessed by a public authority under any other law for the time being in force;

(g) "prescribed" means prescribed by rules made under this Act by the appropriate Government or the competent authority, as the case may be;

(h) "public authority" means any authority or body or institution of self-government established or constituted—

(a) by or under the Constitution;

(b) by any other law made by Parliament;

(c) by any other law made by State Legislature;

(d) by notification issued or order made by the appropriate Government,

and includes any—

(i) body owned, controlled or substantially financed;

(ii) non-Government organisation substantially financed,

directly or indirectly by funds provided by the appropriate Government;

(i) "record" includes—

(a) any document, manuscript and file;

(b) any microfilm, microfiche and facsimile copy of a document;

(c) any reproduction of image or images embodied in such microfilm (whether enlarged or not); and

(d) any other material produced by a computer or any other device;

(j) "right to information" means the right to information accessible under this Act which is held by or under the control of any public authority and includes the right to—

(i) inspection of work, documents, records;

(ii) taking notes, extracts or certified copies of documents or records;

(iii) taking certified samples of material;

(iv) obtaining information in the form of diskettes, floppies, tapes, video cassettes or in any other electronic mode or through printouts where such information is stored in a computer or in any other device;

(k) "State Information Commission" means the State Information Commission constituted under sub-section (1) of section 15;

(l) "State Chief Information Commissioner" and "State Information Commissioner" mean the State Chief Information Commissioner and the State Information Commissioner appointed under sub-section (3) of section 15;

(m) "State Public Information Officer" means the State Public Information Officer designated under sub-section (1) and includes a State Assistant Public Information Officer designated as such under sub-section (2) of section 5;

(n) "third party" means a person other than the citizen making a request for information and includes a public authority.

**COMMENT**

**Meaning of right to information**

If the information called for falls in any of the categories specified under Section 8 or relates to organisation to which the Act itself does not apply in terms of Section 24 of the Act, the public authority can take such stand before Commission and can decline to furnish such information.

*Bihar Public Service Commission v. Saiyed Hussain Abbas Rizwi*, (2013) 1 MLJ 747.

## CHAPTER II
## RIGHT TO INFORMATION AND OBLIGATIONS OF PUBLIC AUTHORITIES

**3. Right to information.**—Subject to the provisions of this Act, all citizens shall have the right to information.

**4. Obligations of public authorities.**—(1) Every public authority shall—

(a) maintain all its records duly catalogued and indexed in a manner and the form which facilitates the right to information under this Act and ensure that all records that are appropriate to be computerised are, within a reasonable time and subject to availability of resources, computerised and connected through a network all over the country on different systems so that access to such records is facilitated;

(b) publish within one hundred and twenty days from the enactment of this Act,—

(i) the particulars of its organisation, functions and duties;

(ii) the powers and duties of its officers and employees;

(iii) the procedure followed in the decision making process, including channels of supervision and accountability;

(iv) the norms set by it for the discharge of its functions;

(v) the rules, regulations, instructions, manuals and records, held by it or under its control or used by its employees for discharging its functions;

(vi) a statement of the categories of documents that are held by it or under its control;

(vii) the particulars of any arrangement that exists for consultation with, or representation by, the members of the public in relation to the formulation of its policy or implementation thereof;

(viii) a statement of the boards, councils, committees and other bodies consisting of two or more persons constituted as its part or for the purpose of its advice, and as to whether meetings of those boards, councils, committees and other bodies are open to the public, or the minutes of such meetings are accessible for public;

(ix) a directory of its officers and employees;

(x) the monthly remuneration received by each of its officers and employees, including the system of compensation as provided in its regulations;

(xi) the budget allocated to each of its agency, indicating the particulars of all plans, proposed expenditures and reports on disbursements made;

(xii) the manner of execution of subsidy programmes, including the amounts allocated and the details of beneficiaries of such programmes;

(xiii) particulars of recipients of concessions, permits or authorisations granted by it;

(xiv) details in respect of the information, available to or held by it, reduced in an electronic form;

(xv) the particulars of facilities available to citizens for obtaining information, including the working hours of a library or reading room, if maintained for public use;

(xvi) the names, designations and other particulars of the Public Information Officers;

(xvii) such other information as may be prescribed;

and thereafter update these publications every year;

(c) publish all relevant facts while formulating important policies or announcing the decisions which affect public;

(d) provide reasons for its administrative or quasi-judicial decisions to affected persons.

(2) It shall be a constant endeavour of every public authority to take steps in accordance with the requirements of clause (b) of sub-section (1) to provide as much information *suo motu* to the public at regular intervals through various means of communications, including internet, so that the public have minimum resort to the use of this Act to obtain information.

(3) For the purposes of sub-section (1), every information shall be disseminated widely and in such form and manner which is easily accessible to the public.

(4) All materials shall be disseminated taking into consideration the cost effectiveness, local language and the most effective method of communication in that local area and the information should be easily accessible, to the extent possible in electronic format with the Central Public Information Officer or State Public Information Officer, as the case may be, available free or at such cost of the medium or the print cost price as may be prescribed.

*Explanation.*—For the purposes of sub-sections (3) and (4), "disseminated" means making known or communicated the information to the public through notice boards, newspapers, public announcements, media broadcasts, the internet or any other means, including inspection of offices of any public authority.

**5. Designation of Public Information Officers.**—(1) Every public authority shall, within one hundred days of the enactment of this Act, designate as many officers as the Central Public Information Officers or State Public Information Officers, as the case may be, in all administrative units or offices under it as may be necessary to provide information to persons requesting for the information under this Act.

(2) Without prejudice to the provisions of sub-section (1), every public authority shall designate an officer, within one hundred days of the enactment of this Act, at each sub-divisional level or other sub-district level as a Central Assistant Public Information Officer or a State Assistant Public Information Officer, as the case may be, to receive the applications for information or appeals under this Act for forwarding the same forthwith to the Central Public Information Officer or the State Public Information Officer or senior officer specified under sub-section (1) of section 19 or the Central Information Commission or the State Information Commission, as the case may be:

Provided that where an application for information or appeal is given to a Central Assistant Public Information Officer or a State Assistant Public Information Officer, as the case may be, a period of five days shall be added in computing the period for response specified under sub-section (1) of section 7.

(3) Every Central Public Information Officer or State Public Information Officer, as the case may be, shall deal with requests from persons seeking information and render reasonable assistance to the persons seeking such information.

(4) The Central Public Information Officer or State Public Information Officer, as the case may be, may seek the assistance of any other officer as he or she considers it necessary for the proper discharge of his or her duties.

(5) Any officer, whose assistance has been sought under sub-section (4), shall render all assistance to the Central Public Information Officer or State Public Information Officer, as the case may be, seeking his or her assistance and for the purposes of any contravention of the provisions of this Act, such other officer shall be treated as a Central Public Information Officer or State Public Information Officer, as the case may be.

**6. Request for obtaining information.**—(1) A person, who desires to obtain any information under this Act, shall make a request in writing or through electronic means in English or Hindi or in the official language of the area in which the application is being made, accompanying such fee as may be prescribed, to—

(a) the Central Public Information Officer or State Public Information Officer, as the case may be, of the concerned public authority;

(b) the Central Assistant Public Information Officer or State Assistant Public Information Officer, as the case may be,

specifying the particulars of the information sought by him or her:

Provided that where such request cannot be made in writing, the Central Public Information Officer or State Public Information Officer, as the case may be, shall render all reasonable assistance to the person making the request orally to reduce the same in writing.

(2) An applicant making request for information shall not be required to give any reason for requesting the information or any other personal details except those that may be necessary for contacting him.

(3) Where an application is made to a public authority requesting for an information,—

(i) which is held by another public authority; or

(ii) the subject matter of which is more closely connected with the functions of another public authority,

the public authority, to which such application is made, shall transfer the application or such part of it as may be appropriate to that other public authority and inform the applicant immediately about such transfer:

Provided that the transfer of an application pursuant to this sub-section shall be made as soon as practicable but in no case later than five days from the date of receipt of the application.

### COMMENT

**No reason for requesting information required**

There is no mandate on applicant to give any reason for requesting information. Anybody should be able to obtain information as long as it is part of public record of public authority. Even private documents submitted to public authorities, may under certain situations, form part of public record.

*Ferari Hotels Private Ltd. v. State Information Commissioner, Greater Mumbai,* (2019) 1 SCC 909.

**7. Disposal of request.**—(1) Subject to the proviso to sub-section (2) of section 5 or the proviso to sub-section (3) of section 6, the Central Public Information Officer or State Public Information Officer, as the case may be, on receipt of a request under section 6 shall, as expeditiously as possible, and in any case within thirty days of the receipt of the request, either provide the information on payment of such fee as may be prescribed or reject the request for any of the reasons specified in sections 8 and 9:

Provided that where the information sought for concerns the life or liberty of a person, the same shall be provided within forty-eight hours of the receipt of the request.

(2) If the Central Public Information Officer or State Public Information Officer, as the case may be, fails to give decision on the request for information within the period specified under sub-section (1), the Central Public Information Officer or State Public Information Officer, as the case may be, shall be deemed to have refused the request.

(3) Where a decision is taken to provide the information on payment of any further fee representing the cost of providing the information, the Central Public Information Officer or State Public Information Officer, as the case may be, shall send an intimation to the person making the request, giving—

(a) the details of further fees representing the cost of providing the information as determined by him, together with the calculations made to arrive at the amount in accordance with fee prescribed under sub-section (1), requesting him to deposit that fees, and the period intervening between the despatch of the said intimation and payment of fees shall be excluded for the purpose of calculating the period of thirty days referred to in that sub-section;

(b) information concerning his or her right with respect to review the decision as to the amount of fees charged or the form of access provided, including the particulars of the appellate authority, time limit, process and any other forms.

(4) Where access to the record or a part thereof is required to be provided under this Act and the person to whom access is to be provided is sensorily disabled, the Central Public Information Officer or State Public Information Officer, as the case may be, shall provide assistance to enable access to the information, including providing such assistance as may be appropriate for the inspection.

(5) Where access to information is to be provided in the printed or in any electronic format, the applicant shall, subject to the provisions of sub-section (6), pay such fee as may be prescribed:

Provided that the fee prescribed under sub-section (1) of section 6 and sub-sections (1) and (5) of section 7 shall be reasonable and no such fee shall be charged from the persons who are of below poverty line as may be determined by the appropriate Government.

(6) Notwithstanding anything contained in sub-section (5), the person making request for the information shall be provided the information free of charge where a public authority fails to comply with the time limits specified in sub-section (1).

(7) Before taking any decision under sub-section (1), the Central Public Information Officer or State Public Information Officer, as the case may be, shall take into consideration the representation made by a third party under section 11.

(8) Where a request has been rejected under sub-section (1), the Central Public Information Officer or State Public Information Officer, as the case may be, shall communicate to the person making the request,—

(i) the reasons for such rejection;

(ii) the period within which an appeal against such rejection may be preferred; and

(iii) the particulars of the appellate authority.

(9) An information shall ordinarily be provided in the form in which it is sought unless it would disproportionately divert the resources of the public authority or would be detrimental to the safety or preservation of the record in question.

**8. Exemption from disclosure of information.**—(1) Notwithstanding anything contained in this Act, there shall be no obligation to give any citizen,—

(a) information, disclosure of which would prejudicially affect the sovereignty and integrity of India, the security, strategic, scientific or economic interests of the State, relation with foreign State or lead to incitement of an offence;

(b) information which has been expressly forbidden to be published by any court of law or tribunal or the disclosure of which may constitute contempt of court;

(c) information, the disclosure of which would cause a breach of privilege of Parliament or the State Legislature;

(d) information including commercial confidence, trade secrets or intellectual property, the disclosure of which would harm the competitive position of a third party, unless the competent authority is satisfied that larger public interest warrants the disclosure of such information;

(e) information available to a person in his fiduciary relationship, unless the competent authority is satisfied that the larger public interest warrants the disclosure of such information;

(f) information received in confidence from foreign Government;

(g) information, the disclosure of which would endanger the life or physical safety of any person or identify the source of information or assistance given in confidence for law enforcement or security purposes;

(h) information which would impede the process of investigation or apprehension or prosecution of offenders;

(i) cabinet papers including records of deliberations of the Council of Ministers, Secretaries and other officers:

Provided that the decisions of Council of Ministers, the reasons thereof, and the material on the basis of which the decisions were taken shall be made public after the decision has been taken, and the matter is complete, or over:

Provided further that those matters which come under the exemptions specified in this section shall not be disclosed;

(j) information which relates to personal information the disclosure of which has no relationship to any public activity or interest, or which would cause unwarranted invasion of the privacy of the individual unless the Central Public Information Officer or the State Public Information Officer or the appellate authority, as the case may be, is satisfied that the larger public interest justifies the disclosure of such information:

Provided that the information, which cannot be denied to the Parliament or a State Legislature shall not be denied to any person.

(2) Notwithstanding anything in the Official Secrets Act, 1923 (19 of 2023) nor any of the exemptions permissible in accordance with sub-section (1), a public authority may allow access to information, if public interest in disclosure outweighs the harm to the protected interests.

(3) Subject to the provisions of clauses (a), (c) and (i) of sub-section (1), any information relating to any occurrence, event or matter which has taken place, occurred or happened twenty years before the date on which any request is made under section 6 shall be provided to any person making a request under that section:

Provided that where any question arises as to the date from which the said period of twenty years has to be computed, the decision of the Central Government shall be final, subject to the usual appeals provided for in this Act.

**9. Grounds for rejection to access in certain cases.**—Without prejudice to the provisions of section 8, a Central Public Information Officer or a State Public Information Officer, as the case may be, may reject a request for information where such a request for providing access would involve an infringement of copyright subsisting in a person other than the State.

**10. Severability.**—(1) Where a request for access to information is rejected on the ground that it is in relation to information which is exempt from disclosure, then, notwithstanding anything contained in this Act, access may be provided to that part of the record which does not contain any information which is exempt from disclosure under this Act and which can reasonably be severed from any part that contains exempt information.

(2) Where access is granted to a part of the record under sub-section (1), the Central Public Information Officer or State Public Information Officer, as the case may be, shall give a notice to the applicant, informing—

(a) that only part of the record requested, after severance of the record containing information which is exempt from disclosure, is being provided;

(b) the reasons for the decision, including any findings on any material question of fact, referring to the material on which those findings were based;

(c) the name and designation of the person giving the decision;

(d) the details of the fees calculated by him or her and the amount of fee which the applicant is required to deposit; and

(e) his or her rights with respect to review of the decision regarding non-disclosure of part of the information, the amount of fee charged or the form of access provided, including the particulars of the senior officer specified under sub-section (1) of section 19 or the Central Information Commission or the State Information Commission, as the case may be, time limit, process and any other form of access.

**11. Third party information.**—(1) Where a Central Public Information Officer or a State Public Information Officer, as the case may be, intends to disclose any information or record, or part thereof on a request made under this Act, which relates to or has been supplied by a third party and has been treated as confidential by that third party, the Central Public Information Officer or State Public Information Officer, as the case may be, shall, within five days from the receipt of the request, give a written notice to such third party of the request and of the fact that the Central Public Information Officer or State Public Information Officer, as the case may be, intends to disclose the information or record, or part thereof, and invite the third party to make a submission in writing or orally, regarding whether the information should be disclosed, and such submission of the third party shall be kept in view while taking a decision about disclosure of information:

Provided that except in the case of trade or commercial secrets protected by law, disclosure may be allowed if the public interest in disclosure outweighs in importance any possible harm or injury to the interests of such third party.

(2) Where a notice is served by the Central Public Information Officer or State Public Information Officer, as the case may be, under sub-section (1) to a third party in respect of any information or record or part thereof, the third party shall, within ten days from the date of receipt of such notice, be given the opportunity to make representation against the proposed disclosure.

(3) Notwithstanding anything contained in section 7, the Central Public Information Officer or State Public Information Officer, as the case may be,

shall, within forty days after receipt of the request under section 6, if the third party has been given an opportunity to make representation under sub-section (2), make a decision as to whether or not to disclose the information or record or part thereof and give in writing the notice of his decision to the third party.

(4) A notice given under sub-section (3) shall include a statement that the third party to whom the notice is given is entitled to prefer an appeal under section 19 against the decision.

## CHAPTER III
## THE CENTRAL INFORMATION COMMISSION

**12. Constitution of Central Information Commission.**—(1) The Central Government shall, by notification in the Official Gazette, constitute a body to be known as the Central Information Commission to exercise the powers conferred on, and to perform the functions assigned to, it under this Act.

(2) The Central Information Commission shall consist of—

(a) the Chief Information Commissioner; and

(b) such number of Central Information Commissioners, not exceeding ten, as may be deemed necessary.

(3) The Chief Information Commissioner and Information Commissioners shall be appointed by the President on the recommendation of a committee consisting of—

(i) the Prime Minister, who shall be the Chairperson of the committee;

(ii) the Leader of Opposition in the Lok Sabha; and

(iii) a Union Cabinet Minister to be nominated by the Prime Minister.

*Explanation.*—For the purposes of removal of doubts, it is hereby declared that where the Leader of Opposition in the House of the People has not been recognised as such, the Leader of the single largest group in opposition of the Government in the House of the People shall be deemed to be the Leader of Opposition.

(4) The general superintendence, direction and management of the affairs of the Central Information Commission shall vest in the Chief Information Commissioner who shall be assisted by the Information Commissioners and may exercise all such powers and do all such acts and things which may be exercised or done by the Central Information Commission autonomously without being subjected to directions by any other authority under this Act.

(5) The Chief Information Commissioner and Information Commissioners shall be persons of eminence in public life with wide knowledge and experience in law, science and technology, social service, management, journalism, mass media or administration and governance.

(6) The Chief Information Commissioner or an Information Commissioner shall not be a Member of Parliament or Member of the Legislature of any State or Union territory, as the case may be, or hold any other office of

profit or connected with any political party or carrying on any business or pursuing any profession.

(7) The headquarters of the Central Information Commission shall be at Delhi and the Central Information Commission may, with the previous approval of the Central Government, establish offices at other places in India.

**13. Term of office and conditions of service.**—(1) The Chief Information Commissioner shall hold office [1][for such term as may be prescribed by the Central Government] and shall not be eligible for reappointment:

Provided that no Chief Information Commissioner shall hold office as such after he has attained the age of sixty-five years.

(2) Every Information Commissioner shall hold office [1][for such term as may be prescribed by the Central Government] or till he attains the age of sixty-five years, whichever is earlier, and shall not be eligible for reappointment as such Information Commissioner:

Provided that every Information Commissioner shall, on vacating his office under this sub-section be eligible for appointment as the Chief Information Commissioner in the manner specified in sub-section (3) of section 12:

Provided further that where the Information Commissioner is appointed as the Chief Information Commissioner, his term of office shall not be more than five years in aggregate as the Information Commissioner and the Chief Information Commissioner.

(3) The Chief Information Commissioner or an Information Commissioner shall before he enters upon his office make and subscribe before the President or some other person appointed by him in that behalf, an oath or affirmation according to the form set out for the purpose in the First Schedule.

(4) The Chief Information Commissioner or an Information Commissioner may, at any time, by writing under his hand addressed to the President, resign from his office:

Provided that the Chief Information Commissioner or an Information Commissioner may be removed in the manner specified under section 14.

[2][(5) The salaries and allowances payable to and other terms and conditions of service of the Chief Information Commissioner and the Information Commissioners shall be such as may be prescribed by the Central Government:

Provided that the salaries, allowances and other conditions of service of the Chief Information Commissioner or the Information Commissioners shall not be varied to their disadvantage after their appointment:

Provided further that the Chief Information Commissioner and the Information Commissioners appointed before the commencement of the Right to Information (Amendment) Act, 2019 shall continue to be governed by the provisions of this Act and the rules made thereunder as if the Right to Information (Amendment) Act, 2019 had not come into force.]

1. Subst. by Act 24 of 2019, Section 2, for "for a term of five years from the date on which he enters upon his office" (w.e.f. October 24, 2019).
2. Subst. by Act 24 of 2019, Section 2, for Sub-s. (5) (w.e.f. October 24, 2019).

(6) The Central Government shall provide the Chief Information Commissioner and the Information Commissioners with such officers and employees as may be necessary for the efficient performance of their functions under this Act, and the salaries and allowances payable to, and the terms and conditions of service of the officers and other employees appointed for the purpose of this Act shall be such as may be prescribed.

Provided also that the salaries, allowances and other conditions of service of the Chief Information Commissioner and the Information Commissioners shall not be varied to their disadvantage after their appointment.

**14. Removal of Chief Information Commissioner or Information Commissioner.**—(1) Subject to the provisions of sub-section (3), the Chief Information Commissioner or any Information Commissioner shall be removed from his office only by order of the President on the ground of proved misbehaviour or incapacity after the Supreme Court, on a reference made to it by the President, has, on inquiry, reported that the Chief Information Commissioner or any Information Commissioner, as the case may be, ought on such ground be removed.

(2) The President may suspend from office, and if deem necessary prohibit also from attending the office during inquiry, the Chief Information Commissioner or Information Commissioner in respect of whom a reference has been made to the Supreme Court under sub-section (1) until the President has passed orders on receipt of the report of the Supreme Court on such reference.

(3) Notwithstanding anything contained in sub-section (1), the President may by order remove from office the Chief Information Commissioner or any Information Commissioner if the Chief Information Commissioner or a Information Commissioner, as the case may be,—

(a) is adjudged an insolvent; or

(b) has been convicted of an offence which, in the opinion of the President, involves moral turpitude; or

(c) engages during his term of office in any paid employment outside the duties of his office; or

(d) is, in the opinion of the President, unfit to continue in office by reason of infirmity of mind or body; or

(e) has acquired such financial or other interest as is likely to affect prejudicially his functions as the Chief Information Commissioner or a Information Commissioner.

(4) If the Chief Information Commissioner or a Information Commissioner in any way, concerned or interested in any contract or agreement made by or on behalf of the Government of India or participates in any way in the profit thereof or in any benefit or emolument arising therefrom otherwise than as a member and in common with the other members of an incorporated company, he shall, for the purposes of sub-section (1), be deemed to be guilty of misbehaviour.

## CHAPTER IV

## THE STATE INFORMATION COMMISSION

**15. Constitution of State Information Commission.** (1) Every State Government shall, by notification in the Official Gazette, constitute a body to be known as the .............. (name of the State) Information Commission to exercise the powers conferred on, and to perform the functions assigned to, it under this Act.

(2) The State Information Commission shall consist of—

(a) the State Chief Information Commissioner, and

(b) such number of State Information Commissioners, not exceeding ten, as may be deemed necessary.

(3) The State Chief Information Commissioner and the State Information Commissioners shall be appointed by the Governor on the recommendation of a committee consisting of—

(i) the Chief Minister, who shall be the Chairperson of the committee;

(ii) the Leader of Opposition in the Legislative Assembly; and

(iii) a Cabinet Minister to be nominated by the Chief Minister.

*Explanation.*—For the purposes of removal of doubts, it is hereby declared that where the Leader of Opposition in the Legislative Assembly has not been recognised as such, the Leader of the single largest group in opposition of the Government in the Legislative Assembly shall be deemed to be the Leader of Opposition.

(4) The general superintendence, direction and management of the affairs of the State Information Commission shall vest in the State Chief Information Commissioner who shall be assisted by the State Information Commissioners and may exercise all such powers and do all such acts and things which may be exercised or done by the State Information Commission autonomously without being subjected to directions by any other authority under this Act.

(5) The State Chief Information Commissioner and the State Information Commissioners shall be persons of eminence in public life with wide knowledge and experience in law, science and technology, social service, management, journalism, mass media or administration and governance.

(6) The State Chief Information Commissioner or a State Information Commissioner shall not be a Member of Parliament or Member of the Legislature of any State or Union territory, as the case may be, or hold any other office of profit or connected with any political party or carrying on any business or pursuing any profession.

(7) The headquarters of the State Information Commission shall be at such place in the State as the State Government may, by notification in the Official Gazette, specify and the State Information Commission may, with the previous approval of the State Government, establish offices at other places in the State.

**16. Term of office and conditions of service.**—(1) The State Chief Information Commissioner shall hold office [1][for such term as may be prescribed by the Central Government] and shall not be eligible for reappointment:

Provided that no State Chief Information Commissioner shall hold office as such after he has attained the age of sixty-five years.

(2) Every State Information Commissioner shall hold office [1][for such term as may be prescribed by the Central Government] or till he attains the age of sixty-five years, whichever is earlier, and shall not be eligible for reappointment as such State Information Commissioner:

Provided that every State Information Commissioner shall, on vacating his office under this sub-section, be eligible for appointment as the State Chief Information Commissioner in the manner specified in sub-section (3) of section 15:

Provided further that where the State Information Commissioner is appointed as the State Chief Information Commissioner, his term of office shall not be more than five years in aggregate as the State Information Commissioner and the State Chief Information Commissioner.

(3) The State Chief Information Commissioner or a State Information Commissioner, shall before he enters upon his office make and subscribe before the Governor or some other person appointed by him in that behalf, an oath or affirmation according to the form set out for the purpose in the First Schedule.

(4) The State Chief Information Commissioner or a State Information Commissioner may, at any time, by writing under his hand addressed to the Governor, resign from his office:

Provided that the State Chief Information Commissioner or a State Information Commissioner may be removed in the manner specified under section 17.

[2][(5) The salaries and allowances payable to and other terms and conditions of service of the State Chief Information Commissioner and the State Information Commissioners shall be such as may be prescribed by the Central Government:

Provided that the salaries, allowances and other conditions of service of the State Chief Information Commissioner and the State Information Commissioners shall not be varied to their disadvantage after their appointment:

Provided further that the State Chief Information Commissioner and the State Information Commissioners appointed before the commencement of the Right to Information (Amendment) Act, 2019 shall continue to be governed by the provisions of this Act and the rules made there under as if the Right to Information (Amendment) Act, 2019 had not come into force.]

(6) The State Government shall provide the State Chief Information Commissioner and the State Information Commissioners with such officers

1. Subst. by Act 24 of 2019, Section 3, for, "for a term of five years from the date on which he enters upon his office"(w.e.f. October 24, 2019).
2. Subst. by Act 24 of 2019, Section 3, for Sub-s. (5), (w.e.f. October 24, 2019).

and employees as may be necessary for the efficient performance of their functions under this Act, and the salaries and allowances payable to and the terms and conditions of service of the officers and other employees appointed for the purpose of this Act shall be such as may be prescribed.

**17. Removal of State Chief Information Commissioner or State Information Commissioner.**—(1) Subject to the provisions of sub-section (3), the State Chief Information Commissioner or a State Information Commissioner shall be removed from his office only by order of the Governor on the ground of proved misbehaviour or incapacity after the Supreme Court, on a reference made to it by the Governor, has on inquiry, reported that the State Chief Information Commissioner or a State Information Commissioner, as the case may be, ought on such ground be removed.

(2) The Governor may suspend from office, and if deem necessary prohibit also from attending the office during inquiry, the State Chief Information Commissioner or a State Information Commissioner in respect of whom a reference has been made to the Supreme Court under sub-section (1) until the Governor has passed orders on receipt of the report of the Supreme Court on such reference.

(3) Notwithstanding anything contained in sub-section (1), the Governor may by order remove from office the State Chief Information Commissioner or a State Information Commissioner if a State Chief Information Commissioner or a State Information Commissioner, as the case may be,—

(a) is adjudged an insolvent; or

(b) has been convicted of an offence which, in the opinion of the Governor, involves moral turpitude; or

(c) engages during his term of office in any paid employment outside the duties of his office; or

(d) is, in the opinion of the Governor, unfit to continue in office by reason of infirmity of mind or body; or

(e) has acquired such financial or other interest as is likely to affect prejudicially his functions as the State Chief Information Commissioner or a State Information Commissioner.

(4) If the State Chief Information Commissioner or a State Information Commissioner in any way, concerned or interested in any contract or agreement made by or on behalf of the Government of the State or participates in any way in the profit thereof or in any benefit or emoluments arising therefrom otherwise than as a member and in common with the other members of an incorporated company, he shall, for the purposes of sub-section (1), be deemed to be guilty of mis behaviour.

## CHAPTER V

## POWERS AND FUNCTIONS OF THE INFORMATION COMMISSIONS, APPEAL AND PENALTIES

**18. Powers and functions of Information Commissions.**—(1) Subject to the provisions of this Act, it shall be the duty of the Central Information

Commission or State Information Commission, as the case may be, to receive and inquire into a complaint from any person,—

(a) who has been unable to submit a request to a Central Public Information Officer or State Public Information Officer, as the case may be, either by reason that no such officer has been appointed under this Act, or because the Central Assistant Public Information Officer or State Assistant Public Information Officer, as the case may be, has refused to accept his or her application for information or appeal under this Act for forwarding the same to the Central Public Information Officer or State Public Information Officer or senior officer specified in sub-section (1) of section 19 or the Central Information Commission or the State Information Commission, as the case may be;

(b) who has been refused access to any information requested under this Act;

(c) who has not been given a response to a request for information or access to information within the time limit specified under this Act;

(d) who has been required to pay an amount of fee which he or she considers unreasonable;

(e) who believes that he or she has been given incomplete, misleading or false information under this Act; and

(f) in respect of any other matter relating to requesting or obtaining access to records under this Act.

(2) Where the Central Information Commission or State Information Commission, as the case may be, is satisfied that there are reasonable grounds to inquire into the matter, it may initiate an inquiry in respect thereof.

(3) The Central Information Commission or State Information Commission, as the case may be, shall, while inquiring into any matter under this section, have the same powers as are vested in a civil court while trying a suit under the Code of Civil Procedure, 1908, in respect of the following matters, namely:—

(a) summoning and enforcing the attendance of persons and compel them to give oral or written evidence on oath and to produce the documents or things;

(b) requiring the discovery and inspection of documents;

(c) receiving evidence on affidavit;

(d) requisitioning any public record or copies thereof from any court or office;

(e) issuing summons for examination of witnesses or documents; and

(f) any other matter which may be prescribed.

(4) Notwithstanding anything inconsistent contained in any other Act of Parliament or State Legislature, as the case may be, the Central Information Commission or the State Information Commission, as the case may be, may, during the inquiry of any complaint under this Act, examine any record to which this Act applies which is under the control of the public authority, and no such record may be withheld from it on any grounds.

**19. Appeal.**—(1) Any person who, does not receive a decision within the time specified in sub-section (1) or clause (a) of sub-section (3) of section 7, or is aggrieved by a decision of the Central Public Information Officer or State Public Information Officer, as the case may be, may within thirty days from the expiry of such period or from the receipt of such a decision prefer an appeal to such officer who is senior in rank to the Central Public Information Officer or State Public Information Officer as the case may be, in each public authority:

Provided that such officer may admit the appeal after the expiry of the period of thirty days if he or she is satisfied that the appellant was prevented by sufficient cause from filing the appeal in time.

(2) Where an appeal is preferred against an order made by a Central Public Information Officer or a State Public Information Officer, as the case may be, under section 11 to disclose third party information, the appeal by the concerned third party shall be made within thirty days from the date of the order.

(3) A second appeal against the decision under sub-section (1) shall lie within ninety days from the date on which the decision should have been made or was actually received, with the Central Information Commission or the State Information Commission:

Provided that the Central Information Commission or the State Information Commission, as the case may be, may admit the appeal after the expiry of the period of ninety days if it is satisfied that the appellant was prevented by sufficient cause from filing the appeal in time.

(4) If the decision of the Central Public Information Officer or State Public Information Officer, as the case may be, against which an appeal is preferred relates to information of a third party, the Central Information Commission or State Information Commission, as the case may be shall give a reasonable opportunity of being heard to that third party.

(5) In any appeal proceedings, the onus to prove that a denial of a request was justified shall be on the Central Public Information Officer or State Public Information Officer, as the case may be, who denied the request.

(6) An appeal under sub-section (1) or sub-section (2) shall be disposed of within thirty days of the receipt of the appeal or within such extended period not exceeding a total of forty-five days from the date of filing thereof, as the case may be, for reasons to be recorded in writing.

(7) The decision of the Central Information Commission or State Information Commission, as the case may be, shall be binding.

(8) In its decision, the Central Information Commission or State Information Commission, as the case may be, has the power to—

(a) require the public authority to take any such steps as may be necessary to secure compliance with the provisions of this Act, including—

(i) by providing access to information, if so requested, in a particular form;

(ii) by appointing a Central Public Information Officer or State Public Information Officer, as the case may be;

(iii) by publishing certain information or categories of information;

(iv) by making necessary changes to its practices in relation to the maintenance, management and destruction of records;

(v) by enhancing the provision of training on the right to information for its officials;

(vi) by providing it with an annual report in compliance with clause (b) of sub-section (1) of section 4;

(b) require the public authority to compensate the complainant for any loss or other detriment suffered;

(c) impose any of the penalties provided under this Act;

(d) reject the application.

(9) The Central Information Commission or State Information Commission, as the case may be, shall give notice of its decision, including any right of appeal, to the complainant and the public authority.

(10) The Central Information Commission or State Information Commission, as the case may be, shall decide the appeal in accordance with such procedure as may be prescribed.

**20. Penalties.**—(1) Where the Central Information Commission or the State Information Commission, as the case may be, at the time of deciding any complaint or appeal is of the opinion that the Central Public Information Officer or the State Public Information Officer, as the case may be, has, without any reasonable cause, refused to receive an application for information or has not furnished information within the time specified under sub-section (1) of section 7 or malafidely denied the request for information or knowingly given incorrect, incomplete or misleading information or destroyed information which was the subject of the request or obstructed in any manner in furnishing the information, it shall impose a penalty of two hundred and fifty rupees each day till application is received or information is furnished, so however, the total amount of such penalty shall not exceed twenty-five thousand rupees:

Provided that the Central Public Information Officer or the State Public Information Officer, as the case may be, shall be given a reasonable opportunity of being heard before any penalty is imposed on him:

Provided further that the burden of proving that he acted reasonably and diligently shall be on the Central Public Information Officer or the State Public Information Officer, as the case may be.

(2) Where the Central Information Commission or the State Information Commission, as the case may be, at the time of deciding any complaint or appeal is of the opinion that the Central Public Information Officer or the State Public Information Officer, as the case may be, has, without any reasonable cause and persistently, failed to receive an application for information or has not furnished information within the time specified under sub-section (1) of section 7 or malafidely denied the request for information or knowingly given incorrect, incomplete or misleading information or destroyed information which was the subject of the request or obstructed in any manner in furnishing the information, it shall recommend for disciplinary action against the Central Public Information Officer or the State Public Information Officer, as the case may be, under the service rules applicable to him.

## CHAPTER VI
## MISCELLANEOUS

**21. Protection of action taken in good faith.**—No suit, prosecution or other legal proceeding shall lie against any person for anything which is in good faith done or intended to be done under this Act or any rule made there under.

**22. Act to have overriding effect.**—The provisions of this Act shall have effect notwithstanding anything inconsistent therewith contained in the Official Secrets Act, 1923 (19 of 1923), and any other law for the time being in force or in any instrument having effect by virtue of any law other than this Act.

**23. Bar of jurisdiction of courts.**—No court shall entertain any suit, application or other proceeding in respect of any order made under this Act and no such order shall be called in question otherwise than by way of an appeal under this Act.

**24. Act not to apply in certain organisations.**—(1) Nothing contained in this Act shall apply to the intelligence and security organisations specified in the Second Schedule, being organisations established by the Central Government or any information furnished by such organisations to that Government:

Provided that the information pertaining to the allegations of corruption and human rights violations shall not be excluded under this sub-section:

Provided further that in the case of information sought for is in respect of allegations of violation of human rights, the information shall only be provided after the approval of the Central Information Commission, and notwithstanding anything contained in section 7, such information shall be provided within forty-five days from the date of the receipt of request.

(2) The Central Government may, by notification in the Official Gazette, amend the Schedule by including therein any other intelligence or security organisation established by that Government or omitting therefrom any

organisation already specified therein and on the publication of such notification, such organisation shall be deemed to be included in or, as the case may be, omitted from the Schedule.

(3) Every notification issued under sub-section (2) shall be laid before each House of Parliament.

(4) Nothing contained in this Act shall apply to such intelligence and security organisation being organisations established by the State Government, as that Government may, from time to time, by notification in the Official Gazette, specify:

Provided that the information pertaining to the allegations of corruption and human rights violations shall not be excluded under this sub-section:

Provided further that in the case of information sought for is in respect of allegations of violation of human rights, the information shall only be provided after the approval of the State Information Commission and, notwithstanding anything contained in section 7, such information shall be provided within forty-five days from the date of the receipt of request.

(5) Every notification issued under sub-section (4) shall be laid before the State Legislature.

**25. Monitoring and reporting.**—(1) The Central Information Commission or State Information Commission, as the case may be, shall, as soon as practicable after the end of each year, prepare a report on the implementation of the provisions of this Act during that year and forward a copy thereof to the appropriate Government.

(2) Each Ministry or Department shall, in relation to the public authorities within their jurisdiction, collect and provide such information to the Central Information Commission or State Information Commission, as the case may be, as is required to prepare the report under this section and comply with the requirements concerning the furnishing of that information and keeping of records for the purposes of this section.

(3) Each report shall state in respect of the year to which the report relates,—

(a) the number of requests made to each public authority;

(b) the number of decisions where applicants were not entitled to access to the documents pursuant to the requests, the provisions of this Act under which these decisions were made and the number of times such provisions were invoked;

(c) the number of appeals referred to the Central Information Commission or State Information Commission, as the case may be, for review, the nature of the appeals and the outcome of the appeals;

(d) particulars of any disciplinary action taken against any officer in respect of the administration of this Act;

(e) the amount of charges collected by each public authority under this Act;

(f) any facts which indicate an effort by the public authorities to administer and implement the spirit and intention of this Act;

(g) recommendations for reform, including recommendations in respect of the particular public authorities, for the development, improvement, modernisation, reform or amendment to this Act or other legislation or common law or any other matter relevant for operationalising the right to access information.

(4) The Central Government or the State Government, as the case may be, may, as soon as practicable after the end of each year, cause a copy of the report of the Central Information Commission or the State Information Commission, as the case may be, referred to in sub-section (1) to be laid before each House of Parliament or, as the case may be, before each House of the State Legislature, where there are two Houses, and where there is one House of the State Legislature before that House.

(5) If it appears to the Central Information Commission or State Information Commission, as the case may be, that the practice of a public authority in relation to the exercise of its functions under this Act does not conform with the provisions or spirit of this Act, it may give to the authority a recommendation specifying the steps which ought in its opinion to be taken for promoting such conformity.

**26. Appropriate Government to prepare programmes.**—(1) The appropriate Government may, to the extent of availability of financial and other resources,—

(a) develop and organise educational programmes to advance the understanding of the public, in particular of disadvantaged communities as to how to exercise the rights contemplated under this Act;

(b) encourage public authorities to participate in the development and organisation of programmes referred to in clause (a) and to undertake such programmes themselves;

(c) promote timely and effective dissemination of accurate information by public authorities about their activities; and

(d) train Central Public Information Officers or State Public Information Officers, as the case may, be of public authorities and produce relevant training materials for use by the public authorities themselves.

(2) The appropriate Government shall, within eighteen months from the commencement of this Act, compile in its official language a guide containing such information, in an easily comprehensible form and manner, as may reasonably be required by a person who wishes to exercise any right specified in this Act.

(3) The appropriate Government shall, if necessary, update and publish the guidelines referred to in sub-section (2) at regular intervals which shall, in particular and without prejudice to the generality of sub-section (2), include—

(a) the objects of this Act;

(b) the postal and street address, the phone and fax number and, if available, electronic mail address of the Central Public Information Officer or State Public Information Officer, as the case may be, of every public authority appointed under sub-section (1) of section 5;

(c) the manner and the form in which request for access to an information shall be made to a Central Public Information Officer or State Public Information Officer, as the case may be;

(d) the assistance available from and the duties of the Central Public Information Officer or State Public Information Officer, as the case may be, of a public authority under this Act;

(e) the assistance available from the Central Information Commission or State Information Commission, as the case may be;

(f) all remedies in law available regarding an act or failure to act in respect of a right or duty conferred or imposed by this Act including the manner of filing an appeal to the Commission;

(g) the provisions providing for the voluntary disclosure of categories of records in accordance with section 4;

(h) the notices regarding fees to be paid in relation to requests for access to an information; and

(i) any additional regulations or circulars made or issued in relation to obtaining access to an information in accordance with this Act.

(4) The appropriate Government must, if necessary, update and publish the guidelines at regular intervals.

**27. Power to make rules by appropriate Government.**—(1) The appropriate Government may, by notification in the Official Gazette, make rules to carry out the provisions of this Act.

(2) In particular, and without prejudice to the generality of the foregoing power, such rules may provide for all or any of the following matters, namely:—

(a) the cost of the medium or print cost price of the materials to be disseminated under sub-section (4) of section 4;

(b) the fee payable under sub-section (1) of section 6;

(c) the fee payable under sub-sections (1) and (5) of section 7;

[1][(ca) the term of office of the Chief Information Commissioner and Information Commissioners under sub-sections (1) and (2) of section 13 and the State Chief Information Commissioner and State Information Commissioners under sub-sections (1) and (2) of section 16;

(cb) the salaries, allowances and other terms and conditions of service of the Chief Information Commissioner and the Information

1. Inst. by Act 24 of 2019, Section 4, (w.e.f. October 24, 2019).

Commissioners under sub-section (5) of section 13 and the State Chief Information Commissioner and the State Information Commissioners under sub-section (5) of section 16;]

(d) the salaries and allowances payable to and the terms and conditions of service of the officers and other employees under sub-section (6) of section 13 and sub-section (6) of section 16;

(e) the procedure to be adopted by the Central Information Commission or State Information Commission, as the case may be, in deciding the appeals under sub-section (10) of section 19; and

(f) any other matter which is required to be, or may be, prescribed.

**28. Power to make rules by competent authority.**—(1) The competent authority may, by notification in the Official Gazette, make rules to carry out the provisions of this Act.

(2) In particular, and without prejudice to the generality of the foregoing power, such rules may provide for all or any of the following matters, namely:—

(i) the cost of the medium or print cost price of the materials to be disseminated under sub-section (4) of section 4;

(ii) the fee payable under sub-section (1) of section 6;

(iii) the fee payable under sub-section (1) of section 7; and

(iv) any other matter which is required to be, or may be, prescribed.

**29. Laying of rules.**—(1) Every rule made by the Central Government under this Act shall be laid, as soon as may be after it is made, before each House of Parliament, while it is in session, for a total period of thirty days which may be comprised in one session or in two or more successive sessions, and if, before the expiry of the session immediately following the session or the successive sessions aforesaid, both Houses agree in making any modification in the rule or both Houses agree that the rule should not be made, the rule shall thereafter have effect only in such modified form or be of no effect, as the case may be; so, however, that any such modification or annulment shall be without prejudice to the validity of anything previously done under that rule.

(2) Every rule made under this Act by a State Government shall be laid, as soon as may be after it is notified, before the State Legislature.

**30. Power to remove difficulties.**—(1) If any difficulty arises in giving effect to the provisions of this Act, the Central Government may, by order published in the Official Gazette, make such provisions not inconsistent with the provisions of this Act as appear to it to be necessary or expedient for removal of the difficulty:

Provided that no such order shall be made after the expiry of a period of two years from the date of the commencement of this Act.

(2) Every order made under this section shall, as soon as may be after it is made, be laid before each House of Parliament.

**[31. Repeal.**—*The Freedom of Information Act, 2002 (5 of 2003) is hereby repealed.*]

## THE FIRST SCHEDULE

[*See* sections 13 (3) and 16(3)]

## FORM OF OATH OR AFFIRMATION TO BE MADE BY THE CHIEF INFORMATION COMMISSIONER/THE INFORMATION COMMISSIONER/THE STATE CHIEF INFORMATION COMMISSIONER/THE STATE INFORMATION COMMISSIONER

"I, ………, having been appointed Chief Information Commissioner/Information Commissioner/State Chief Information Commissioner/State Information Commissioner swear in the name of God / solemnly affirm that I will bear true faith and allegiance to the Constitution of India as by law established, that I will uphold the sovereignty and integrity of India, that I will duly and faithfully and to the best of my ability, knowledge and judgment perform the duties of my office without fear or favour, affection or ill-will and that I will uphold the Constitution and the laws.".

## THE SECOND SCHEDULE

(*See* section 24)

## INTELLIGENCE AND SECURITY ORGANISATION ESTABLISHED BY THE CENTRAL GOVERNMENT

1. Intelligence Bureau.

[1][2. Research and Analysis Wing including its technical wing namely, the Aviation Research Centre of the Cabinet Secretariat.]

3. Directorate of Revenue Intelligence.
4. Central Economic Intelligence Bureau.
5. Directorate of Enforcement.
6. Narcotics Control Bureau.
7. [2][***]
8. Special [1][Frontier] Force of the Cabinet Secretariat.
9. Border Security Force.
10. Central Reserve Police Force.
11. Indo-Tibetan Border Police.
12. Central Industrial Security Force.
13. National Security Guards.
14. Assam Rifles.

[3][15. Sashtra Seema Bal.]

1. Subst. by notification No. G.S.R. 319(E), dt. May 4, 2021.
2. Serial Number 7 stood omitted by notification No. G.S.R. 319(E), dt. May 4, 2021.
3. Subst. by notification No. G.S.R. 347, dt. September 28, 2005.

[1][16. Directorate General of Income-tax (Investigation).]

[1][17. National Technical Research Organisation.]

[1][18. Financial Intelligence Unit, India.]

[2][19. Special Protection Group.

20. Defence Research and Development Organisation.

21. Border Road Development Board.

[3][***]

[4][22. National Security Council Secretariat.]

[5][23. Central Bureau of Investigation.

24. National Investigation Agency.

25. National Intelligence Grid.]

[6][26. Strategic Forces Command.]

---

1. Subst. by notification No. G.S.R. 235(E) dt. March 27, 2008.
2. Inst. by notification No. G.S.R. 347, dt. September 28, 2005.
3. Omitted by G.S.R. 235(E) dt. March 27, 2008.
4. Add. by notification No. G.S.R. 726(E), dt. October 8, 2008.
5. Add. by notification No. G.S.R. 442(E), dt. June 9, 2011.
6. Inst. by notification No. G.S.R. 673(E) dt. July 8, 2016.

# THE SPECIAL COURT (TRIAL OF OFFENCES RELATING TO TRANSACTIONS IN SECURITIES) ACT, 1992

(27 of 1992)

[*18th August, 1992*]

*An Act to provide for the establishment of a Special Court for the trial of offences relating to transactions in securities and for matters connected therewith or incidental thereto.*

BE it enacted by Parliament in the Forty-third Year of the Republic of India as follows:—

**COMMENT**

**Scope of the Act**

The Act provides for stringent measure. It was enacted for dealing with an extra-ordinary situation in the sense that any person who was involved in any offence relating to transaction of any security may be notified whereupon, all his properties stand attached. The provision contained in the Act being stringent in nature, the purport and intent thereof must be ascertained having regard to the purpose and object it seeks to achieve. The right of a person notified to file an application or to raise a defence that he is not liable in terms of the provisions of the Act or in any event, the properties attached should not be sold in discharge of the liabilities can be taken at the initial stage by filing an application in terms of Sub-section (2) of Section 4 of the Act. But, at the stage when liabilities are required to be discharged, the notified person may *inter alia* raise a contention for the purpose of establishing that the properties held and possessed by them are sufficient to meet their liabilities. In terms of the provisions of the Act, the Special Court has been conferred a very wide power; *Ashwin S. Mehta v. Custodian*, (2006) 2 SCC 385.

**1. Short title and commencement.**—(1) This Act may be called the Special Court (Trial of Offences Relating to Transactions in Securities) Act, 1992.

(2) It shall be deemed to have come into force on the 6th day of June, 1992.

**2. Definitions.**—In this Act, unless the context otherwise requires,—

(a) "Code" means the Code of Criminal Procedure, 1973 (2 of 1974);

(b) "Custodian" means the Custodian appointed under sub-section (1) of section 3;

(c) "securities" includes—

(i) shares, scrips, stocks, bonds, debentures, debenture stock, units of the Unit Trust of India or any other mutual fund or other marketable securities of a like nature in or of any incorporated company or other body corporate;

(ii) Government securities; and

(iii) rights or interests in securities;

(d) "Special Court" means the Special Court established under sub-section (1) of section 5.

**3. Appointment and functions of Custodian.**—(1) The Central Government may appoint one or more Custodians as it may deem fit for the purposes of this Act.

(2) The Custodian may, on being satisfied on information received that any person has been involved in any offence relating to transactions in securities after the 1st day of April, 1991 and on and before the 6th June, 1992, notify the name of such person in the Official Gazette.

(3) Notwithstanding anything contained in the Code and any other law for the time being in force, on and from the date of notification under sub-section (2), any property, movable or immovable, or both, belonging to any person notified under that sub-section shall stand attached simultaneously with the issue of the notification.

(4) The property attached under sub-section (3) shall be dealt with by the Custodian in such manner as the Special Court may direct.

(5) The Custodian may take assistance of any person while exercising his powers or for discharging his duties under this section and section 4.

**4. Contracts entered into fraudulently may be cancelled.**—(1) If the Custodian is satisfied, after such inquiry as he may think fit, that any contract or agreement entered into at any time after the 1st day of April, 1991 and on and before the 6th June, 1992 in relation to any property of the person notified under sub-section (2) of section 3 has been entered into fraudulently or to defeat the provisions of this Act, he may cancel such contract or agreement and on such cancellation such property shall stand attached under this Act:

Provided that no contract or agreement shall be cancelled except after giving to the parties to the contract or agreement a reasonable opportunity of being heard.

(2) Any person aggrieved by a notification issued under sub-section (2) of section 3 or any cancellation made under sub-section (1) of section 4 or any other order made by the Custodian in exercise of the powers conferred on him under section 3 or 4 may file a petition objecting to the same within thirty days of the assent to the Special Court (Trial of Offences Relating to Transactions in Securities) Bill, 1992 by the President before the Special Court where such notification, cancellation or order has been issued before the date of assent to the Special Court (Trial of Offences Relating to Transactions in Securities) Bill, 1992 by the President and where such notification, cancellation or order has been issued on or after that date, within thirty days of the issuance of such notification, cancellation or order, as the case may be; and the Special Court after hearing the parties, may make such order as it deems fit.

## COMMENT

**Scope of Section 4**

Sub-section (2) of Section 4, however, provides for a hearing as regard correctness or otherwise of notification notifying a person in this behalf, in the event, an appropriate application thereof is filed within 30 days of the issuance of such notification, Section 5 provides for establishment of the Sepcial Court. Section 7 confers exclusive jurisdiction upon the Special Court. Any prosecution in respect of any offence referred to in sub-section (2) of Section 3 pending in any court is required to be transferred to the Special Court. Section 9 provides for the procedure and powers of the Special Court. Section 9A, which was inserted by Act 24 of 1994 with effect from 25th January, 1994, confers all such jurisdiction, powers and authority as where exercisable, immediately before such commencement by any Civil Court in relation to the matter specified therein; *Ashwin S. Mehta* v. *Custodian*, (2006) 2 SCC 385.

**5. Establishment of Special Court.**—(1) The Central Government shall, by notification in the Official Gazette, establish a Court to be called the Special Court.

(2) The Special Court shall consist of [1][one or more sitting Judges] of the High Court nominated by the Chief Justice of the High Court within the local limits of whose jurisdiction the Special Court is situated, with the concurrence of the Chief Justice of India.

[2][(3) When the office of [3][a Judge of the Special Court] is vacant by reason of absence or leave, the duties of the office shall be performed by such Judge of the High Court within the local limits of whose jurisdiction the Special Court is situated as the Chief Justice of that High Court may, with the concurrence of the Chief Justice of India, nominate for the purpose and the Judge so appointed shall have all the jurisdiction and powers of [3][a Judge of the Special Court] including the powers to pass final orders.]

## COMMENT

**Establishment of Special Court**

Under the Special Court (Trial of Offences Relating to Transactions in Securities) Act, 1992, Special Court was established for the speedy trial of cases relating to the Transactions in Securities Act, 1992; *S. Mohan v. Central Bureau of Investigation*, (2008) 7 SCC 1; (2008) 8 SCALE 66.

[4][**5A. Distribution of cases amongst Judges of Special Court.**—Where the Special Court consists of two or more Judges, the Chief Justice of the High Court within the local limits of whose jurisdiction the Special Court is situated may, from time to time, by general or special order, make provisions as to the distribution of cases amongst the Judges and specify the matters which may be dealt with by each of such Judge.]

**6. Cognizance of cases by Special Court.**—The Special Court shall take cognizance of or try such cases as are instituted before it or transferred to it as hereinafter provided.

**7. Jurisdiction of Special Court.**—Notwithstanding anything contained in any other law, any prosecution in respect of any offence referred to in sub-section (2) of section 3 shall be instituted only in the Special Court and any prosecution in respect of such offence pending in any court shall stand transferred to the Special Court.

**8. Jurisdiction of Special Court as to joint trials.**—The Special Court shall have jurisdiction to try any person concerned in the offence referred to in sub-section (2) of section 3 either as a principal, conspirator or abettor and all other offences and accused persons as can be jointly tried therewith at one trial in accordance with the Code.

---

1. Subst. by Act 6 of 1997, Section 2 for "a sitting Judge" (w.e.f. January 16, 1997).
2. Inst. by Act 24 of 1994, Section 2 (w.e.f. January 25, 1994).
3. Subst. by Act 6 of 1997, Section 2, for "the Judge of the Special Court" (w.e.f. January 16, 1997).
4. Inst. by Act 6 of 1997, Section 3 (w.e.f. January 16, 1997).

**9. Procedure and powers of Special Court.**—(1) The Special Court shall, in the trial of such cases, follow the procedure prescribed by the Code for the trial of warrant cases before a magistrate.

(2) Save as expressly provided in this Act, the provisions of the Code shall, in so far as they are not inconsistent with the provisions of this Act, apply to the proceedings before the Special Court and for the purposes of the said provisions of the Code, the Special Court shall be deemed to be a Court of Session and shall have all the powers of a Court of Session, and the person conducting a prosecution before the Special Court shall be deemed to be a Public Prosecutor.

(3) The Special Court may pass upon any person convicted by it any sentence authorised by law for the punishment of the offence of which such person is convicted.

(4) While dealing with any other matter brought before it, the Special Court may adopt such procedure as it may deem fit consistent with the principles of natural justice.

[1][**9A. Jurisdiction, powers, authority and procedure of Special Court in civil matters.**—(1) On and from the commencement of the Special Court (Trial of Offences Relating to Transactions in Securities) Amendment Act, 1994 (24 of 1994) the Special Court shall exercise all such jurisdiction, powers and authority as were exercisable, immediately before such commencement, by any civil court in relation to any matter or claim—

(a) relating to any property standing attached under sub-section (3) of section 3;

(b) arising out of transactions in securities entered into after the 1st day of April, 1991, and on or before the 6th day of June, 1992, in which a person notified under sub-section (2) of section 3 is involved as a party, broker, intermediary or in any other manner.

(2) Every suit, claim or other legal proceeding (other than an appeal) pending before any court immediately before the commencement of the Special Court (Trial of Offences Relating to Transactions in Securities) Amendment Act, 1994 (24 of 1994), being a suit, claim or proceeding, the cause of action whereon it is based is such that it would have been, if it had arisen after such commencement, within the jurisdiction of the Special Court under sub-section (1), shall stand transferred on such commencement to the Special Court and the Special Court may, on receipt of the records of such suit, claim or other legal proceeding, proceed to deal with it, so far as may be, in the same manner as a suit, claim or legal proceeding from the stage which was reached before such transfer or from any earlier stage or *de novo* as the Special Court may deem fit.

(3) On and from the commencement of the Special Court (Trial of Offences Relating to Transactions in Securities) Amendment Act, 1994 (24 of 1994), no court other than the Special Court shall have, or be entitled to exercise, any jurisdiction, power or authority in relation to any matter or claim referred to in sub-section (1).

1. Inst. by Act 24 of 1994, Section 3 (w.e.f. January 25, 1994).

(4) While dealing with cases relating to any matter or claim under this section, the Special Court shall not be bound by the procedure laid down by the Code of Civil Procedure, 1908 (5 of 1908), but shall be guided by the principles of natural justice, and subject to the other provisions of this Act and of any rules, the Special Court shall have power to regulate its own procedure.

(5) Without prejudice to the other powers conferred under this Act, the Special Court shall have, for the purposes of discharging its functions under this section, the same powers as are vested in a civil court under the Code of Civil Procedure, 1908 (5 of 1908), while trying a suit, in respect of the following matters, namely:—

(a) summoning and enforcing the attendance of any person and examining him on oath;

(b) requiring the discovery and production of documents;

(c) receiving evidence on affidavits;

(d) subject to the provisions of sections 123 and 124 of the Indian Evidence Act, 1872 (1 of 1872), requisitioning any public record or document or copy of such record or document from any office;

(e) issuing commissions for the examination of witnesses or documents;

(f) reviewing its decisions;

(g) dismissing a case for default or deciding it *ex parte*;

(h) setting aside any order of dismissal of any case for default or any order passed by it *ex parte*; and

(i) any other matter which may be prescribed by the Central Government under sub-section (1) of section 14.

[1][**9B. Powers of the Special Court in arbitration matters.**—(1) The Special Court shall have the jurisdiction and powers of a Court conferred under the Arbitration Act, 1940 (10 of 1940) to decide any question forming subject matter of a reference relating to any matter or claim mentioned in sub-section (1) of section 9A.

(2) Every suit or other proceeding (other than an appeal) in relation to any matter or claim referred to in sub-section (1) of section 9A pending before any Court and governed by the Arbitration Act, 1940 (10 of 1940), immediately before the date of commencement of the Special Court (Trial of Offences Relating to Transactions in Securities) Amendment Act, 1994 (24 of 1994) shall stand transferred on that date to the Special Court.

*Explanation.*—For the purposes of this section, the expressions "Court" and "reference" shall have respectively the same meanings as defined under clauses (c) and (e) of section 2 of the Arbitration Act, 1940 (10 of 1940).]

**10. Appeal.**—(1) Notwithstanding anything in the Code [1][or the Code of Civil Procedure, 1908 (5 of 1908) or the Arbitration Act, 1940 (19 of 1940)],

1. Inst. by Act 24 of 1994, Section 3 (w.e.f. January 25, 1994).

an appeal shall lie from any judgment [1][,decree] sentence or order, not being interlocutory order, of the Special Court to the Supreme Court both on facts and on law.

(2) Except as aforesaid, no appeal or revision shall lie to any Court from any judgment [1][,decree] sentence or order of the Special Court.

(3) Every appeal under this section shall be preferred within a period of thirty days from the date of any judgment, sentence or order of the Special Court:

Provided that the Supreme Court may entertain an appeal after the expiry of the said period of thirty days if it is satisfied that the appellant had sufficient cause for not preferring the appeal within the period of thirty days.

**11. Discharge of liabilities.**—(1) Notwithstanding anything contained in the Code and any other law for the time being in force, the Special Court may make such order as it may deem fit directing the Custodian for the disposal of the property under attachment.

(2) The following liabilities shall be paid or discharged in full, as far as may be, in the order as under:—

(a) all revenues, taxes, cesses and rates due from the persons notified by the Custodian under sub-section (2) of section 3 to the Central Government or any State Government or any local authority;

(b) all amounts due from the person so notified by the Custodian to any bank or financial institution or mutual fund;

(c) any other liability as may be specified by the Special Court from time to time.

[2][**11A. Power to punish for contempt.**—The Special Court shall have, and exercise, the same jurisdiction, powers and authority in respect of contempt of itself as a High Court has and may exercise and, for this purpose, the provisions of the Contempt of Courts Act, 1971 (70 of 1971), shall have effect subject to the modifications that—

(a) the references therein to a High Court shall be construed as including a reference to such Special Court;

(b) the references to the Advocate-General in section 15 of the said Act, shall be construed, in relation to the Special Court, as a reference to the Attorney-General or the Solicitor-General or the Additional Solicitor-General.]

**12. Protection of action taken in good faith.**—(1) No suit, prosecution or other legal proceeding shall lie against the Central Government or the Custodian for anything which is in good faith done or intended to be done under this Act.

(2) No suit or other legal proceeding shall lie against the Central Government or any of its officers or other employees for any damage caused

1. Inst. by Act 24 of 1994, Section 4 (w.e.f. January 25, 1994).
2. Inst. by Act 24 of 1994, Section 5, (w.e.f. January 25, 1994).

or likely to be caused by anything which is in good faith done or intended to be done under this Act.

**13. Act to have overriding effect.**—The provisions of this Act shall have effect notwithstanding anything inconsistent therewith contained in any other law for the time being in force or in any instrument having effect by virtue of any law, other than this Act, or in any decree or order of any court, tribunal or other authority.

**14. Power to make rules.**—(1) The Central Government may, by notification in the Official Gazette, make rules for carrying out the provisions of this Act.

(2) Every rule made by the Central Government under this Act shall be laid, as soon as may be after it is made, before each House of Parliament, while it is in session, for a total period of thirty days which may be comprised in one session or in two or more successive sessions, and if, before the expiry of the session immediately following the session or the successive sessions aforesaid, both Houses agree in making any modification in the rule or both Houses agree that the rule should not be made, the rule shall thereafter have effect only in such modified form or be of no effect, as the case may be; so, however, that any such modification or annulment shall be without prejudice to the validity of anything previously done under that rule.

**15. Repeal and savings.**—(1) The Special Court (Trial of Offences Relating to Transactions in Securities) Ordinance, 1992 (Ord. 10 of 1992) is hereby repealed.

(2) Notwithstanding such repeal, anything done or any action taken under the said Ordinance, shall be deemed to have been done or taken under the corresponding provisions of this Act.

# THE WHISTLE BLOWERS PROTECTION ACT, [1][2014]

(17 of 2014)

[*9th May, 2014*]

*An Act to establish a mechanism to receive complaints relating to disclosure on any allegation of corruption or wilful misuse of power or wilful misuse of discretion against any public servant and to inquire or cause an inquiry into such disclosure and to provide adequate safeguards against victimisation of the person making such complaint and for matters connected therewith and incidental thereto.*

BE it enacted by Parliament in the [2][Sixty-fifth Year] of the Republic of India as follows:—

## CHAPTER I

## PRELIMINARY

**1. Short title, extent and commencement.**—(1) This Act may be called the Whistle Blowers Protection Act, [1][2014].

(2) It extends to the whole of India except the State of Jammu and Kashmir.

(3) It shall come into force on such date as the Central Government may, by notification in the Official Gazette, appoint; and different dates may be appointed for different provisions of this Act and any reference in any provision to the commencement of this Act shall be construed as a reference to the coming into force of that provision.

**2. Provisions of this Act not to apply to Special Protection Group.**—The provisions of this Act shall not apply to the armed forces of the Union, being the Special Protection Group constituted under the Special Protection Group Act, 1988 (34 of 1988).

**3. Definitions.**—In this Act, unless the context otherwise requires,—

(a) "Central Vigilance Commission" means the Commission constituted under sub-section (1) of section 3 of the Central Vigilance Commission Act, 2003 (45 of 2003);

(b) "Competent Authority" means—

(i) in relation to a Member of the Union Council of Ministers, the Prime Minister;

(ii) in relation to a Member of Parliament, other than a Minister, the Chairman of the Council of States if such Member is a Member of the Council of States or the Speaker of the House of the People if such Member is a Member of the House of the People, as the case may be;

1. Subst. by Act 17 of 2015, Section 3 and the Second Schedule for "2011" (w.e.f. May 13, 2015).
2. Subst. by Act 17 of 2015, Section 3, and the Second Schedule, for "Sixty-second Year" (w.e.f. May 13, 2015).

(iii) in relation to a Member of the Council of Ministers in a State or Union territory, the Chief Minister of the State or Union territory, as the case may be;

(iv) in relation to a Member of Legislative Council or Legislative Assembly of a State or Union territory, other than a Minister, the Chairman of the Legislative Council if such Member is a Member of the Council or the Speaker of the Legislative Assembly if such Member is a Member of the Assembly, as the case may be;

(v) in relation to—

(A) any Judge (except a Judge of the Supreme Court or of a High Court) including any person empowered by law to discharge, whether by himself or as a member of any body of persons, any adjudicatory functions; or

(B) any person authorised by a court of justice to perform any duty, in connection with the administration of justice, including a liquidator, receiver or commissioner appointed by such court; or

(C) any arbitrator or other person to whom any cause or matter has been referred for decision or report by a court of justice or by a competent public authority,

the High Court;

(vi) in relation to—

(A) any person in the service or pay of the Central Government or remunerated by the Central Government by way of fees or commission for the performance of any public duty except Ministers, Members of Parliament and members or persons referred to in clause (a) or clause (b) or clause (c) or clause (d) of article 33 of the Constitution, or in the service or pay of a society or local authority or any corporation established by or under any Central Act, or an authority or a body owned or controlled or aided by the Central Government or a Government company as defined in section 617 of the Companies Act, 1956 (1 of 1956), owned or controlled by the Central Government; or

(B) any person who holds an office by virtue of which he is empowered to prepare, publish, maintain or revise an electoral roll or to conduct an election or part of an election in relation to elections to Parliament or a State Legislature; or

(C) any person who holds an office by virtue of which he is authorised or required to perform any public duty (except Ministers and Members of Parliament); or

(D) any person who is the president, secretary or other office-bearer of a registered co-operative society engaged in agriculture, industry, trade or banking, receiving or having received any financial aid from the Central Government or from any corporation established by or under a Central Act, or any authority or body or a Government company as defined in section 617 of the Companies Act, 1956 (1 of 1956) owned or controlled or aided by the Government; or

(E) any person who is a chairman, member or employee of any Central Service Commission or Board, by whatever name called, or a member of any selection committee appointed by such Commission or Board for the conduct of any examination or making any selection on behalf of such Commission or Board; or

(F) any person who is a Vice-Chancellor or member of any governing body, professor, associate professor, assistant professor, reader, lecturer or any other teacher or employee, by whatever designation called, of any University established by a Central Act or established or controlled or funded by the Central Government or any person whose services have been availed of by such University or any such other public authority in connection with holding or conducting examinations; or

(G) any person who is an office-bearer or an employee of an educational, scientific, social, cultural or other institution, in whatever manner established, receiving or having received any financial assistance from the Central Government or any local or other public authority,

the Central Vigilance Commission or any other authority, as the Central Government may, by notification in the Official Gazette, specify in this behalf under this Act.

(vii) in relation to—

(A) any person in the service or pay of the State Government or remunerated by the State Government by way of fees or commission, for the performance of any public duty except Ministers, Members of Legislative Council or Legislative Assembly of the State, or in the service or pay of a society or local authority or any corporation established by or under a Provincial or State Act, or an authority or a body owned or controlled or aided by the State Government or a Government company as defined in section 617 of the Companies Act, 1956 (1 of 1956), owned or controlled by the State Government; or

(B) any person who holds an office by virtue of which he is empowered to prepare, publish, maintain or revise an electoral roll or to conduct an election or part of an election in relation to municipality or Panchayats or other local body in the State; or

(C) any person who holds an office by virtue of which he is authorised or required to perform any public duty in relation to the affairs of the State Government (except Ministers and Members of Legislative Council or Legislative Assembly of the State); or

(D) any person who is the president, secretary or other office-bearer of a registered co-operative society engaged in agriculture, industry, trade or banking, receiving or having received any financial aid from the State Government or from any corporation established by or under a Provincial or State Act, or any authority or body or a Government company as defined in section 617 of the Companies Act, 1956 (1 of 1956) owned or controlled or aided by the State Government; or

(E) any person who is a chairman, member or employee of any State Service Commission or Board, by whatever name called, or a member of any selection committee appointed by such Commission or Board for the conduct of any examination or making any selection on behalf of such Commission or Board; or

(F) any person who is a Vice-Chancellor or member of any governing body, professor, associate professor, assistant professor, reader, lecturer or any other teacher or employee, by whatever designation called, of any University established by a Provincial or State Act or established or controlled or funded by the State Government and any person whose services have been availed of by such University or any such other public authority in connection with holding or conducting examinations; or

(G) any person who is an office-bearer or an employee of an educational, scientific, social, cultural or other institution, in whatever manner established, receiving or having received any financial assistance from the State Government or any local or other public authority,

the State Vigilance Commission, if any, or any officer of the State Government or any other authority, as the State Government may, by notification in the Official Gazette, specify in this behalf under this Act;

(viii) in relation to members or persons referred to in clause (a) or clause (b) or clause (c) or clause (d) of article 33 of the Constitution, any authority or authorities as the Central Government or the State Government, as the case may be, having jurisdiction in respect thereof, may, by notification in the Official Gazette, specify in this behalf under this Act;

(c) "complainant" means any person who makes a complaint relating to disclosure under this Act;

(d) "disclosure" means a complaint relating to,—

(i) an attempt to commit or commission of an offence under the Prevention of Corruption Act, 1988 (49 of 1988);

(ii) wilful misuse of power or wilful misuse of discretion by virtue of which demonstrable loss is caused to the Government or demonstrable wrongful gain accrues to the public servant or to any third party;

(iii) attempt to commit or commission of a criminal offence by a public servant,

made in writing or by electronic mail or electronic mail message, against the public servant and includes public interest disclosure referred to in sub-section (2) of section 4;

(e) "electronic mail" or "electronic mail message" means a message or information created or transmitted or received on any computer, computer system, computer resource or communication device including attachments in text, image, audio, video and any other electronic record, which may be transmitted with the message;

(f) "Government company" means a company referred to in section 617 of the Companies Act, 1956 (1 of 1956);

(g) "notification" means a notification published in the Gazette of India or, as the case may be, the Official Gazette of a State;

(h) "public authority" means any authority, body or institution falling within the jurisdiction of the Competent Authority;

(i) "public servant" shall have the same meaning as assigned to it in clause (c) of section 2 of the Prevention of Corruption Act, 1988 (49 of 1988) but shall not include a Judge of the Supreme Court or a Judge of a High Court;

(j) "prescribed" means prescribed by rules made by the Central Government and the State Government, as the case may be, under this Act;

(k) "regulations" means the regulations made by the Competent Authority under this Act.

## CHAPTER II

## PUBLIC INTEREST DISCLOSURE

**4. Requirement of public interest disclosure.**—(1) Notwithstanding anything contained in the provisions of the Official Secrets Act, 1923 (19 of 1923), any public servant or any other person including any non-governmental organisation, may make a public interest disclosure before the Competent Authority.

(2) Any disclosure made under this Act shall be treated as public interest disclosure for the purposes of this Act and shall be made before the Competent

Authority and the complaint making the disclosure shall, on behalf of the Competent Authority, be received by such authority as may be specified by regulations made by the Competent Authority.

(3) Every disclosure shall be made in good faith and the person making disclosure shall make a personal declaration stating that he reasonably believes that the information disclosed by him and allegation contained therein is substantially true.

(4) Every disclosure shall be made in writing or by electronic mail or electronic mail message in accordance with the procedure as may be prescribed and contain full particulars and be accompanied by supporting documents, or other materials, if any.

(5) The Competent Authority may, if it deems fit, call for further information or particulars from the person making the disclosure.

(6) No action shall be taken on public interest disclosure by the Competent Authority if the disclosure does not indicate the identity of the complainant or public servant making public interest disclosure or the identity of the complainant or public servant is found incorrect or false.

**Notes on Clause of the Bill**

This clause lays down the requirements of public interest disclosure. It provides that notwithstanding anything contained in the provisions of the Official Secrets Act, 1923, any public servant or any other person including any non-governmental organisation, may make a public interest disclosure before the Competent Authority.

It provides that any disclosure made under the Act shall be treated as public interest disclosure to be made before the Competent Authority which is made in good faith and the person making such disclosure shall make a personal declaration stating that he reasonably believes that the information disclosed by him and allegation contained therein is substantially true.

It further provides that every disclosure shall be made in writing or by electronic mail or electronic mail message in accordance with the procedure as may be prescribed which shall contain full particulars and be accompanied by supporting documents, or other material and the Competent Authority may, if it deems fit, call for further information or particulars from the person making such disclosure.

It also provides that no action will be taken on public interest disclosure by the Competent Authority if the disclosure does not indicate the identity of the complainant or public servant making public interest disclosure or the identity of the complainant or public servant is found incorrect or false. [Clause 4 of the Bill]

## CHAPTER III

## INQUIRY IN RELATION TO PUBLIC INTEREST DISCLOSURE

**5. Powers and functions of Competent Authority on receipt of public interest disclosure.**—(1) Subject to the provisions of this Act, the Competent Authority shall, on receipt of a public interest disclosure under section 4,—

(a) ascertain from the complainant or the public servant whether he was the person or the public servant who made the disclosure or not;

(b) conceal the [1][identity] of the complainant unless the complainant himself has revealed his identity to any other office or authority while making public interest disclosure or in his complaint or otherwise.

(2) The Competent Authority shall, upon receipt of the complaint and concealing the identity of the complainant, or the public servant in the first instance, make discreet inquiry, in such manner and within such time as may be prescribed, to ascertain whether there is any basis for proceeding further to investigate the disclosure.

(3) If the Competent Authority, either as a result of the discreet inquiry, or on the basis of the disclosure itself without any inquiry, is of the opinion that the disclosure requires to be investigated, it shall seek comments or explanation or report from the Head of the Department of the organisation or authority, board or corporation concerned or office concerned within such time as may be specified by it.

(4) While seeking comments or explanations or report referred to in sub-section (3), the Competent Authority shall not reveal the identity of the complainant or the public servant and direct the Head of the Department of the organisation concerned or office concerned not to reveal the identity of the complainant or public servant:

Provided that if the Competent Authority is of the opinion that it has, for the purpose of seeking comments or explanation or report from them under sub-section (3) on the public disclosure, become necessary to reveal the identity of the complainant or public servant to the Head of the Department of the organisation or authority, board or corporation concerned or office concerned, the Competent Authority may, with the prior written consent of the complainant or public servant, reveal the identity of the complainant or public servant to such Head of the Department of the organisation or authority, board or corporation concerned or office concerned for the said purpose:

Provided further that in case the complainant or public servant does not agree to his name being revealed to the Head of the Department, in that case, the complainant or public servant, as the case may be, shall provide all documentary evidence in support of his complaint to the Competent Authority.

(5) The Head of the organisation or office concerned shall not directly or indirectly reveal the identity of the complainant or public servant who made the disclosure.

(6) The Competent Authority, if after conducting an inquiry, is of the opinion that—

(a) the facts and allegations contained in the disclosure are frivolous or vexatious; or

(b) there are no sufficient grounds for proceeding with the inquiry,

it shall close the matter.

1. Corrected according corrigendum, for "indentity", published in the Gazette of India, Extra., Part II, Section 1, No. 22, dt. July 18, 2014.

(7) After receipt of the comments or explanations or report referred to in sub-section (3), if the Competent Authority is of the opinion that such comments or explanations or report reveals either wilful misuse of power or wilful misuse of discretion or substantiates allegations of corruption, it shall recommend to the public authority to take any one or more of the following measures, namely:—

(i) initiating proceedings against the concerned public servant;

(ii) taking appropriate administrative steps for redressing the loss caused to the Government as a result of the corrupt practice or misuse of office or misuse of discretion, as the case may be;

(iii) recommend to the appropriate authority or agency for initiation of criminal proceedings under the relevant laws for the time being in force, if so warranted by the facts and circumstances of the case;

(iv) recommend for taking of corrective measures;

(v) take any other measures not falling under clauses (i) to (iv) which may be necessary for the purpose of this Act.

(8) The public authority to whom a recommendation is made under sub-section (7) shall take a decision on such recommendation within three months of receipt of such recommendation, or within such extended period not exceeding three months, as the Competent Authority may allow on a request made by the public authority:

Provided that in case the public authority does not agree with the recommendation of the Competent Authority, it shall record the reasons for such disagreement.

(9) The Competent Authority shall, after making an inquiry, inform the complainant or public servant about the action taken on the complaint and the final outcome thereof:

Provided that in a case where, after making an inquiry, the Competent Authority decides to close the case, it shall, before passing the order for closure of the case, provide an opportunity of being heard to the complainant, if the complainant so desires.

**6. Matters not to be inquired by Competent Authority.**—(1) If any matter specified or an issue raised in a disclosure has been determined by a Court or Tribunal authorised to determine the issue, after consideration of the matters specified or issue raised in the disclosure, the Competent Authority shall not take notice of the disclosure to the extent that the disclosure seeks to reopen such issue.

(2) The Competent Authority shall not entertain or inquire into any disclosure—

(a) in respect of which a formal and public inquiry has been ordered under the Public Servants (Inquiries) Act, 1850 (37 of 1850); or

(b) in respect of a matter which has been referred for inquiry under the Commissions of Inquiry Act, 1952 (60 of 1952).

(3) The Competent Authority shall not investigate, any disclosure involving an allegation, if the complaint is made after the expiry of seven

years from the date on which the action complained against is alleged to have taken place.

(4) Nothing in this Act shall be construed as empowering the Competent Authority to question, in any inquiry under this Act, any *bona fide* action or *bona fide* discretion (including administrative or statutory discretion) exercised in discharge of duty by the employee.

## CHAPTER IV

## POWERS OF COMPETENT AUTHORITY

**7. Powers of Competent Authority.**—(1) Without prejudice to the powers conferred upon the Competent Authority under any other law for the time being in force, the Competent Authority, may require, for the purpose of any inquiry any public servant or any other person who in its opinion shall be able to furnish information or produce documents relevant to the inquiry or assist in the inquiry, to furnish any such information or produce any such document as may be necessary for the said purpose.

(2) For the purpose of any such inquiry (including the preliminary inquiry), the Competent Authority shall have all the powers of a Civil Court while trying a suit under the Code of Civil Procedure, 1908 (5 of 1908), in respect of the following matters, namely:—

(a) summoning and enforcing the attendance of any person and examining him on oath;

(b) requiring the discovery and production of any document;

(c) receiving evidence on affidavits;

(d) requisitioning any public record or copy thereof from any court or office;

(e) issuing commissions for the examination of witnesses or documents;

(f) such other matters as may be prescribed.

(3) The Competent Authority shall be deemed to be a Civil Court for the purpose of section 195 and Chapter XXVI of the Code of Criminal Procedure, 1973 (2 of 1974), and every proceeding before the Competent Authority shall be deemed to be a judicial proceeding within the meaning of sections 193 and 228 and for the purposes of section 196 of the Indian Penal Code (45 of 1860).

(4) Subject to the provisions of section 8, no obligation to maintain secrecy or other restriction upon the disclosure of information obtained by or furnished to the Government or any public servant, whether imposed by the Official Secrets Act, 1923 (19 of 1923) or any other law for the time being in force, shall be claimed by any public servant in the proceedings before the Competent Authority or any person or agency authorised by it in writing and the Government or any public servant shall not be entitled in relation to any such inquiry, to any such privilege in respect of the production of document or the giving of evidence as is allowed by any enactment or by any rules made thereunder:

Provided that the Competent Authority, while exercising such powers of the Civil Court, shall take steps as necessary to ensure that the identity of the person making complaint has not been revealed or compromised.

**8. Certain matters exempt from disclosure.**—(1) No person shall be required or be authorised by virtue of provisions contained in this Act to furnish any such information or answer any such question or produce any document or information or render any other assistance in the inquiry under this Act if such question or document or information is likely to prejudicially affect the interest of the sovereignty and integrity of India, the security of the State, friendly relations with foreign State, public order, decency or morality or in relation to contempt of court, defamation or incitement to an offence,—

(a) as might involve the disclosure of proceedings of the Cabinet of the Union Government or any Committee of the Cabinet;

(b) as might involve the disclosure of proceedings of the Cabinet of the State Government or any Committee of that Cabinet,

and for the purpose of this sub-section, a certificate issued by the Secretary to the Government of India or the Secretary to the State Government, as the case may be, or, any authority so authorised by the Central or State Government certifying that any information, answer or portion of a document is of the nature specified in clause (a) or clause (b), shall be binding and conclusive.

(2) Subject to the provisions of sub-section (1), no person shall be compelled for the purposes of inquiry under this Act to give any evidence or produce any document which he could not be compelled to give or produce in proceedings before a court.

**9. Superintendence of Competent Authority over appropriate machinery.**—(1) Every public authority shall, for the purposes of dealing or inquiry into the disclosures sent to it under sub-section (3) of section 5, create an appropriate machinery for the said purpose.

(2) The Competent Authority shall exercise superintendence over the working of machinery created under sub-section (1) for the purposes of dealing or inquiry into the disclosures and give such directions for its proper functioning, from time to time, as it may consider necessary.

**10. Competent Authority to take assistance of police authorities, etc., in certain cases.**—For the purpose of making discreet inquiry or obtaining information from the organisation concerned, the Competent Authority shall be authorised to take assistance of the Delhi Special Police Establishment or the police authorities, or any other authority as may be considered necessary, to render all assistance to complete the inquiry within the prescribed time pursuant to the disclosure received by the Competent Authority.

**Notes on Clause of the Bill**

This clause makes provisions for the Competent Authority to take assistance of public authorities. It provides that for the purpose of making discreet inquiry or obtaining information from the organisation concerned, the Competent Authority shall be authorised to take assistance of the Delhi Special Police Establishment or the police authorities, or any other authority as may be considered necessary, to render all assistance to complete the inquiry within the specified time pursuant to the disclosure received by the competent authority. [Clause 10 of the Bill]

## CHAPTER V

## PROTECTION TO THE PERSONS MAKING DISCLOSURE

**11. Safeguards against victimisation.**—(1) The Central Government shall ensure that no person or a public servant who has made a disclosure under this Act is victimised by initiation of any proceedings or otherwise merely on the ground that such person or a public servant had made a disclosure or rendered assistance in inquiry under this Act.

(2) If any person is being victimised or likely to be victimised on the ground that he had filed a complaint or made disclosure or rendered assistance in inquiry under this Act, he may file an application before the Competent Authority seeking redress in the matter, and such authority shall take such action, as deemed fit and may give suitable directions to the concerned public servant or the public authority, as the case may be, to protect such person from being victimised or avoid his victimisation:

Provided that the Competent Authority shall, before giving any such direction to the public authority or public servant, give an opportunity of hearing to the complainant and the public authority or public servant, as the case may be:

Provided further that in any such hearing, the burden of proof that the alleged action on the part of the public authority is not victimisation, shall lie on the public authority.

(3) Every direction given under sub-section (2) by the Competent Authority shall be binding upon the public servant or the public authority against whom the allegation of victimisation has been proved.

(4) Notwithstanding anything contained in any other law for the time being in force, the power to give directions under sub-section (2), in relation to a public servant, shall include the power to direct the restoration of the public servant making the disclosure, to the status *quo ante*.

(5) Any person who wilfully does not comply with the direction of the Competent Authority under sub-section (2), shall be liable to a penalty which may extend up to thirty thousand rupees.

**12. Protection of witnesses and other persons.**—If the Competent Authority either on the application of the complainant, or witnesses, or on the basis of information gathered, is of the opinion that either the complainant or public servant or the witnesses or any person rendering assistance for inquiry under this Act need protection, the Competent Authority shall issue appropriate directions to the concerned Government authorities (including police) which shall take necessary steps, through its agencies, to protect such complainant or public servant or persons concerned.

**13. Protection of identity of complainant.**—The Competent Authority shall, notwithstanding any law for the time being in force, conceal, as required under this Act, the identity of the complainant and the documents or information furnished by him, for the purposes of enquiry under this Act, unless so decided otherwise by the Competent Authority itself or it became necessary to reveal or produce the same by virtue of the order of the court.

**Notes on Clause of the Bill**

This clause provides for protection of identity of complainant. It provides that the Competent Authority shall, notwithstanding anything contained in any other law for the time being in force, conceal, the identity of the complainant and the documents or information furnished by him, for the purpose of enquiry, unless so decided otherwise by the Competent Authority itself or it became necessary to reveal or produce the same by virtue of the Order of the Court. [Clause 13 of the Bill]

**14. Power to pass interim orders.**—The Competent Authority, at any time after the making of disclosure by the complainant or public servant, if it is of the opinion that any corrupt practice required to be stopped during the continuation of any inquiry for the said purpose may pass such interim orders as it may deem fit, to prevent the immediate stoppage of such practice.

## CHAPTER VI

## OFFENCES AND PENALTIES

**15. Penalty for furnishing incomplete or incorrect or misleading comments or explanation or report.**—Where the Competent Authority, at the time of examining the report or explanations or report referred to in sub-section (3) of section 5 on the complaint submitted by organisation or official concerned, is of the opinion that the organisation or official concerned, without any reasonable cause, has not furnished the report within the specified time or *mala fidely* refused to submit the report or knowingly given incomplete, incorrect or misleading or false report or destroyed record or information which was the subject of the disclosure or obstructed in any manner in furnishing the report, it shall impose—

(a) where the organisation or official concerned, without any reasonable cause, has not furnished the report within the specified time or *mala fidely* refused to submit the report, a penalty which may extend to two hundred fifty rupees for each day till report is furnished, so, however, the total amount of such penalty shall not exceed fifty thousand rupees;

(b) where the organisation or official concerned, has knowingly given incomplete, incorrect or misleading or false report or destroyed record or information which was the subject of the disclosure or obstructed in any manner the furnishing of the report, a penalty which may extend to fifty thousand rupees:

Provided that no penalty shall be imposed against any person unless he has been given an opportunity of being heard.

**16. Penalty for revealing identity of complainant.**—Any person, who negligently or *mala fidely* reveals the identity of a complainant shall, without prejudice to the other provisions of this Act, be punishable with imprisonment for a term which may extend up to three years and also to fine which may extend up to fifty thousand rupees.

**Notes on Clause of the Bill**

This clause contains the provision for penalty for revealing identity of complainant. It provides that any person, who negligently or *mala fidely* reveals the identity of a complainant shall be punishable with imprisonment for a term which may extend upto three years and also the fine which may extend upto fifty thousand rupees. [Clause 16 of the Bill]

**17. Punishment for false or frivolous disclosure.**—Any person who makes any disclosure *mala fidely* and knowingly that it was incorrect or false or misleading shall be punishable with imprisonment for a term which may extend up to two years and also to fine which may extend up to thirty thousand rupees.

**18. Punishment to Head of Department in certain cases.**—(1) Where an offence under this Act has been committed by any Department of Government, the Head of the Department shall be deemed to be guilty of the offence and shall be liable to be proceeded against and punished accordingly unless he proves that the offence was committed without his knowledge or that he exercised all due diligence to prevent the commission of such offence.

(2) Notwithstanding anything contained in sub-section (1), where an offence under this Act has been committed by a Department of Government and it is proved that the offence has been committed with the consent or connivance of, or is attributable, such officer shall also be deemed to be guilty of that offence and shall be liable to be proceeded against and punished accordingly.

**19. Offences by companies.**—(1) Where an offence under this Act has been committed by a company, every person who at the time the offence was committed was in charge of, and was responsible to the company for the conduct of the business of the company as well as the company, shall be deemed to be guilty of the offence and shall be liable to be proceeded against and punished accordingly:

Provided that nothing contained in this sub-section shall render any such person liable to any punishment provided in this Act, if he proves that the offence was committed without his knowledge or that he has exercised all due diligence to prevent the commission of such offence.

(2) Notwithstanding anything contained in sub-section (1), where an offence under this Act has been committed by a company and it is proved that the offence has been committed with the consent or connivance of, or is attributable to, any neglect on the part of any director, manager, secretary or other officer of the company, such director, manager, secretary or other officer shall also be deemed to be guilty of the offence and shall be liable to be proceeded against and punished accordingly.

*Explanation.*—for the purposes of this section,—

(a) "Company" means anybody corporate and includes a firm or other association of individuals; and

(b) "director", in relation to a firm, means a partner in the firm.

**20. Appeal to High Court.**—Any person aggrieved by any order of the Competent Authority relating to imposition of penalty under section 14 or section 15 or section 16 may prefer an appeal to the High Court within a period of sixty days from the date of the order appealed against:

Provided that the High Court may entertain the appeal after the expiry of the said period of sixty days, if it is satisfied that the appellant was prevented by sufficient cause from preferring the appeal in time.

*Explanation.*—For the purposes of this section, the "High Court" means the High Court within whose jurisdiction the cause of action arose.

**21. Bar of jurisdiction.**—No Civil Court shall have jurisdiction in respect of any matter which the Competent Authority is empowered by or under this Act to determine and no injunction shall be granted by any court or other authority in respect of any action taken or to be taken in pursuance of any power conferred by or under this Act.

**22. Court to take cognizance.**—(1) No court shall take cognizance of any offence punishable under this Act or the rules or regulations made thereunder, save on a complaint made by the Competent Authority or any officer or person authorised by it.

(2) No court inferior to that of a Chief Metropolitan Magistrate or a Chief Judicial Magistrate shall try any offence punishable under this Act.

## CHAPTER VII
## MISCELLANEOUS

**23. Report on disclosures.**—(1) The Competent Authority shall prepare a consolidated annual report of the performance of its activities in such form as may be prescribed and forward it to the Central Government or State Government, as the case may be.

(2) On receipt of the annual report under sub-section (1), the Central Government or State Government, as the case may be, shall cause a copy thereof to be laid before each House of Parliament, or the State Legislature, as the case may be:

Provided that where any other law for the time being in force provides preparing of such annual report by the Competent Authority, then the said annual report shall contain a separate part on the performance of activities under this Act by the Competent Authority.

**Notes on Clause of the Bill**

This clause empowers the Competent Authority to prepare a report on disclosures. It provides that the Competent Authority shall prepare a consolidated annual report of the performance of its activities in such form as may be prescribed by the Central Government and forward it to the Central Government or State Government, as the case may be, which would be laid, before Parliament by the Central Government and, before State Legislature by the State Government.

It further provides that if any other law for the time being in force provides preparing of the annual report by the Competent Authority, then the said annual report shall contain a separate part on the performance of activities under the proposed legislation by the Competent Authority.

[Clause 23 of the Bill]

**24. Protection of action taken in good faith.**—No suit, prosecution or other legal proceedings shall lie against the Competent Authority or against any officer, employees, agency or person acting on its behalf, in respect of anything which is in good faith done or intended to be done under this Act.

**Notes on Clause of the Bill**

This clause provides for protection of action taken in good faith. It provides that no suit, prosecution or other legal proceedings shall lie against the Competent Authority or against any officer, employee, agency or person acting on its behalf, for anything which is in good faith done or intended to be done under the proposed legislation.

[Clause 24 of the Bill]

**25. Power of Central Government to make rules.**—(1) The Central Government may, by notification in the Official Gazette, make rules for the purpose of carrying out the provisions of this Act.

(2) In particular, and without prejudice to the generality of the foregoing power, such rules may provide for all or any of the following matters, namely:—

(a) the procedure for disclosure by writing or appropriate electronic means under sub-section (4) of section 4;

(b) the manner in which and the time within which the discreet inquiry shall be made by the Competent Authority under sub-section (2) of section 5;

(c) the additional matter in respect of which the Competent Authority may exercise the powers of a Civil Court under clause (f) of sub-section (2) of section 7;

(d) the form of annual report under sub-section (1) of section 23;

(e) any other matter which is required to be, or may be, prescribed.

**26. Power of State Government to make rules.**—The State Government may, by notification in the Official Gazette, make rules for the purpose of carrying out the provisions of this Act.

**27. Power to make regulations.**—The Competent Authority may, with the previous approval of the Central Government or the State Government, as the case may be, by notification in the Official Gazette, make regulations not inconsistent with the provisions of the Act and the rules made thereunder to provide for all matters for which provision is expedient for the purposes of giving effect to the provisions of this Act.

**28. Notification and rules to be laid before Parliament.**—Every notification issued and every rule made by the Central Government and every regulation made by the Competent Authority under this Act shall be laid, as soon as may be after it is issued or made, before each House of Parliament, while it is in session, for a total period of thirty days which may be comprised in one session or in two or more successive sessions, and if, before the expiry of the session immediately following the session or the successive sessions aforesaid, both Houses agree in making any modification in the notification or the rule or the regulation, or both Houses agree that the notification or the rule or the regulation should not be made, the notification or the rule or the regulation shall thereafter have effect only in such modified form or be of no effect, as the case may be; so, however, that any such modification or annulment shall be without prejudice to the validity of anything previously done under that notification or rule or regulation.

**29. Notification issued and rules made by State Government to be laid before State Legislature.**—Every notification issued by a State Government and every rule made by a State Government and every regulation made by the Competent Authority under this Act shall be laid, as soon as may be after it is issued, before the State Legislature.

**30. Power to remove difficulties.**—(1) If any difficulty arises in giving effect to the provisions of the Act, the Central Government may, by order, not inconsistent with the provisions of this Act, remove the difficulty:

Provided that no such order shall be made after the expiry of a period of three years from the date of the commencement of this Act.

(2) Every order made under this section shall, as soon as may be after it is made, be laid before each House of Parliament.

**31. Repeal and savings.**—(1) The Government of India, Ministry of Personnel, Public Grievances and Pensions (Department of Personnel and Training) Resolution No. 371/12/2002-AVD-III dated the 21st April, 2004 as amended *vide* Resolution of even number, dated the 29th April, 2004 is hereby repealed.

(2) Notwithstanding such repeal, anything done or any action taken under the said Resolution be deemed to have been done or taken under this Act.

# THE PREVENTION OF CORRUPTION ACT, 1947*

(2 of 1947)

[*12th March, 1947*]

*An Act for the more effective prevention of bribery and corruption.*

WHEREAS it is expedient to make more effective provision for the prevention of bribery and corruption; The Prevention of Corruption Act, 1947. It is hereby enacted as follows:—

**1. Short title and extent.**—(1) This Act may be called the Prevention of Corruption Act, 1947. (2) It extends to the whole of India except the State of Jammu and Kashmir, and it applies also to all citizens of India outside India.

**2. Definition.**—For the purposes of this Act, "public servant" means a public servant as defined in Section 21 of the Indian Penal Code.

**3. Offences under Section 165A of the Penal Code to be cognizable offences.**—An offence punishable under Section 165A of the Indian Penal Code shall be deemed to be a cognizable offence for the purposes of the Code of Criminal Procedure, 1898 notwithstanding anything to the contrary contained therein.

**4. Presumption where public servant accepts gratification other than legal remuneration.**—(1) Where in any trial of an offence punishable under section 161 or Section 165 of the Indian Penal Code (45 of 1860) [1][or of an offence referred to in clause (a) or clause (b) of sub-section (1) of Section 5 of this Act punishable under sub-section (2) thereof], it is proved that an accused person has accepted or obtained, or has agreed to accept or attempted to obtain, for himself or for any other person, any gratification (other than legal remuneration) or any valuable thing from any person, it shall be presumed unless the contrary is proved that he accepted or obtained, or agreed to accept or attempted to obtain that gratification or that valuable thing as the case may be, as a motive or reward such as is mentioned in the said Section 161, or as the case may be, without consideration or for a consideration which he knows to be inadequate.

(2) Where in any trial of an offence punishable under Section 165A of the Indian Penal Code or under clause (ii) of sub-section (3) of Section 5 of this Act, it is proved that any gratification (other than legal remuneration) or any valuable thing has been given or offered to be given or attempted to be given by an accused person, it shall be presumed unless the contrary is proved that he gave or offered to give or attempted to give that gratification or that valuable thing, as the case may be, as a motive or reward such as is mentioned in Section 161 of the Indian Penal Code, or, as the case may be, without consideration or for a consideration which he knows to be inadequate.

* Repealed by the Prevention of Corruption Act, 1988 (49 of 1988).

1. Inst. by Act 40 of 1964, Section 6.

(3) Notwithstanding anything contained in sub-sections (1) and (2) the Court may decline to draw the presumption referred to in either of the said sub-sections, if the gratification or thing aforesaid is, in its opinion, so trivial that no inference of corruption may fairly be drawn.

**5. Criminal misconduct in discharge of official duty.**—(1) A public servant is said to commit the offence of criminal misconduct [1][***]:—

(a) if he habitually accepts or obtains on agrees to accept or attempts to obtain from any person for himself or for any other person, any gratification (other than legal remuneration) as a motive or reward such as is mentioned in Section 161 of the Indian Penal Code; or

(b) if he habitually accepts or obtains or agrees to accept or attempts to obtain for himself or for any other person; any valuable thing without consideration or for a consideration which he knows to be inadequate, from any person whom he knows to have been; or to be, or to be likely to be "concerned in any proceeding or business transacted or about to be transacted by him, or having any connection with the official functions of himself or of any public servant to whom he is subordinate, or from any person whom he knows to be interested in or related to the person so concerned, or

(c) if he dishonestly or fraudulently misappropriates or otherwise converts for his own use any property entrusted to him or under his control as a public servant or allows any other person so to do, or

(d) if he, by corrupt or illegal means or by otherwise abusing his position as public servant, obtains for himself or for any other person any valuable thing or pecuniary advantage, [2][or]

(e) if he or any person on his behalf is in possession or has, at any time during the period of his office, been in possession, for which the public servant cannot satisfactorily account, of pecuniary resources or property disproportionate to his known sources of income.

[3][(2) Any public servant, who commits criminal misconduct [***] shall be punishable with imprisonment for a term which shall not be less than one year but which may extend to seven years and shall also be liable to fine:

Provided that the court may, for any special reasons recorded in writing impose a sentence of imprisonment of less than one year.

[4][(3) Whoever habitually commits :—

(i) an offence punishable under section 162 or section 163 of the Indian Penal Code, or 4

1. Omitted by Act 40 of 1964, Section 6.
2. Inst. by Act 40 of 1964, Section 6.
3. Inst. by Criminal Law (Amendment) Act, 1958.
4. Subst. by Act 40 of 1964, Section 6.

(ii) an offence punishable under section 165A of the Indian Penal Code, shall be punishable with imprisonment for a term which shall not be less than one year but which may extend to seven years and shall also be liable to fine:

Provided that the court may, for any special reasons recorded in writing, impose a sentence of imprisonment of less than one year.

(3A) Whoever attempts to commit an offence referred to in clause (c) or clause (d) of sub-section (1) shall be punishable with imprisonment for a term which may extend to three years, or with fine, or with both.

(3B) Where a sentence of fine is imposed under sub-section (2) or sub-section

(3) the Court in fixing the amount of line shall take into consideration. the amount or the value of the property if any, which the accused person has obtained by committing the offence or where the conviction is for an offence referred to in clause (e) of sub-section (1), the pecuniary resources or property referred to in that clause for which the accused person is unable to account satisfactorily.]

(4) The provisions of this section shall be in addition to, and not in derogation of, any other law for the time being in force and nothing contained herein shall exempt any public servant from any proceeding which might apart from this section, be instituted against him.

[1][**5A. Investigation into cases under this Act.**—(1) Notwithstanding anything contained in the Code of Criminal Procedure, 1898, no police officer below the rank:—

(a) in the case of the Delhi Special Police Establishment, of an Inspector of Police;

(b) in the presidency-towns of Calcutta and Madras, of as Assistant Commissioner of Police;

(c) in the presidency-town of Bombay, of a Superintendent of Police; and

(d) elsewhere, of a Deputy Superintendent of Police, shall investigate any offence punishable under Section 161, Section 165, or Section 165A. of the Indian Penal Code or under Section 5 of this Act, without the order of a Presidency Magistrate or a Magistrate of the first class, as the case may be, or make any arrest therefor without a warrant :

Provided that if a police officer not below the rank of an Inspector of Police is authorised by the State Government in this behalf by general or special order, he may also investigate any such offence without the order of a Presidency Magistrate or a Magistrate of the first class, as the case may be, or make arrest therefor without a warrant :

Provided further that an offence referred to in clause (e) of sub-section (1) of Section 5 shall not be investigated without the order of a police officer not below the rank of a Superintendent of Police.

1. Subst. by Act 40 of 1964, Section 6.

(2) If, from information received or otherwise, a police officer has reason to suspect the commission of an offence which he is empowered to investigate under sub-section (1) and considers that for the purpose of investigation or inquiry into such offence it is necessary to inspect any bankers' books, then, notwithstanding anything contained in any law for the time being in force, he may inspect any bankers, books in so far as they relate to the accounts of the person suspected to have committed that offence or of any other person suspected to be holding money on behalf of such person, and take or cause to be taken certified copies of the relevant entries there from, and the bank concerned shall be bound to assist the police officer in the exercise of his powers under this sub-section :

Provided that no power under this sub-section in relation to the accounts of any person shall be exercised by a police below the rank of a Superintendent of Police, unless he is specially authorised in this behalf by a police officer of or above the rank of a Superintendent of Police.

*Explanation.*—In this sub-section, the expressions "bank" and "bankers" "books" shall have the meanings assigned to them in the Bankers' Books Evidence Act, 1891.]

**6. Previous sanction necessary for prosecutions.**—(1) No Court shall take cognizance of an offence punishable under Section 161 or Section 164 or Section 165 of the Indian Penal Code or under sub-section (2) or sub-section (3A) of Section 5 of this Act, alleged to have been committed by a public servant, except with the previous sanction,—

(a) in the case of a person who is employed in connection with the affairs of the Union and is not removable from his office gave by or with the sanction of the Central Government, of the Central Government;

(b) in the case of a person who is employed in connection with the affairs of a State and is not removable from his office save by or with the sanction of the State Government, of the State Government;

(c) in the case of any other person, of the authority competent to remove him from his office.

(2) Where for any reason whatsoever any doubt arises whether the previous sanction as required under sub-section (1) should be given by the Central or State Government or any other authority, such sanction shall be given by that Government or authority, which would have been competent to remove the public servant from his office at the time when the offence was alleged to have been committed.

[1][**6A. Particulars in a charge in relation to an offence under Section 5(1)(c).**—Notwithstanding anything contained in the Code of Criminal Procedure, 1898 when an accused is charged with an offence under clause (c) of sub-section (1) of Section 5, it shall be sufficient to describe in the charge the property in respect of which the offence is alleged to have been committed, and the dates between which the offence is alleged to have been

1. Inst. by Act 40 of 1964, Section 6.

committed, without specifying particular items or exact dates, and the charge so framed shall be deemed to a charge of one offence within the meaning of Section 234 of the said Code:

Provided that the time included between the first and last of such dates shall not exceed one year.]

**7. Accused person to be competent witness.**—Any person charged with an offence punishable under Section 161 or Section 169 or Section 165A of the Indian Penal Code (45 of 1860), or under Section 5 of this Act shall be a competent witness for the defence and may give evidence on oath in disproof of the charges made against him or any person charged together with him at the same trial:

Provided that—

(a) he shall not he called as a witness except on his own request,

(b) his failure to give evidence shall not be made the subject of any comment by the prosecution or give rise to any presumption against himself or any person charged together with him at the same trial,

(c) he shall not be asked, and if asked shall not be required to answer, any question tending to show that he has committed or been convicted of any offence other than the offence with which he is charged, or is of bad character, unless—

(i) the proof that he has committed or been convicted of such offence is admissible evidence to show that he is guilty of the offence with which he is charged, or

(ii) he has personally or by his pleader asked questions of any witness for the prosecution with a view to establish his own good character, or has given evidence of his good. Character, or the nature or conduct of the defence is such as to involve imputations on the character of the prosecutor or of any witness for the prosecution, or

(iii) he has given evidence against any other person charged with the same offence.

[1][**7A. The Code of Criminal Procedure, 1898 to apply subject to certain modifications.**—The provisions of the Code of Criminal Procedure, 1898, shall, in their application to any proceeding in relation to an offence punishable under 7 Section 161, Section 165 or Section 165A of the Indian Penal Code, or under Section 5 of this Act, have effect as if,—

(a) in sub-section (8) of Section 251A, for the words "The accused shall then be called upon" the words "The accused shall then be required to give in writing at once or within such time as the Magistrate may allow, a list of the persons (if any) whom he proposes to examine as his witnesses and of the documents (if any) on which he proposes to rely, and he shall then be called upon" had been substituted;

1. Omitted by Act 40 of 1964, Section 6.

(b) in sub-section (1, 1) of Section 3, 4, after the second proviso, the following proviso had been inserted, namely :—

Provided also that the proceeding shall not be adjourned or postponed merely on the ground that an application under Section 435 has been made by a party to the proceeding;

(c) in sub-section (1) of Section 435, before the Explanation, the following proviso had been inserted, namely :—

"Provided that where the powers under this sub-section are exercised by a Court on an application made by a party to such proceedings, the Court shall not ordinarily call for the record of the proceeding :—

(a) without giving the other party an opportunity of showing cause why the record should not be called for; or

(b) if it is satisfied that an examination of the record of the proceeding may be made from the certified copies thereof; and in any case, the proceedings, before the inferior Court shall not be, stayed except for reasons to be recorded in writing";

(d) after sub-section (2) of Section 540A, the following sub-section had been inserted, namely :—

"(3) Notwithstanding anything contained in sub-section (1) or sub-section (2), the Judge or Magistrate may, if he thinks fit and for reasons to be recorded by him, proceed with inquiry or trial in the absence of the accused or his pleader and record the evidence of any witness, subject to the right of the accused to recall the witness for cross-examination".

**8. Statement by bribe giver not to subject him to prosecution.**—Notwithstanding anything contained in any law for the time being in force, a statement made by a person in any proceeding against a public servant for an offence under Section 161 or Section 165 of the Indian Penal Code or under sub-section (2) or [1][sub-section (3A)] of Section 5 of this Act, that he offered or agreed to offer any gratification (other than legal remuneration) or any valuable thing to the 8 public servant, shall not subject such person to a prosecution under Section 165A of the said Code.

---

1. Inst. by Act 40 of 1964, Section 6.

# THE PROHIBITION OF *BENAMI* PROPERTY TRANSACTIONS ACT, 1988

(45 of 1988)

[*5th September, 1988*]

*An Act to prohibit benami transactions and the right to recover property held benami and for matters connected therewith or incidental thereto.*

BE it enacted by Parliament in the Thirty-ninth Year of the Republic of India as follows:—

## [1][CHAPTER I
## PRELIMINARY]

**1. Short title, extent and commencement.**—[2][(1) This Act may be called the Prohibition of *Benami* Property Transactions Act, 1988.]

(2) It extends to the whole of India [3][***].

(3) The provisions of sections 3, 5 and 8 shall come into force at once, and the remaining provisions of this Act shall be deemed to have come into force on the 19th day of May, 1988.

[4][**2. Definitions.**—In this Act, unless the context otherwise requires,—

(1) "Adjudicating Authority" means the Adjudicating Authority [5][referred to in] section 7;

(2) "Administrator" means an Income-tax Officer as defined in clause (25) of section 2 of the Income-tax Act, 1961 (43 of 1961);

(3) "Appellate Tribunal" means the Appellate Tribunal established under section 30;

(4) "Approving Authority" means an Additional Commissioner or a Joint Commissioner as defined in clauses (1C) and (28C) respectively of section 2 of the Income-tax Act, 1961 (43 of 1961);

(5) "attachment" means the prohibition of transfer, conversion, disposition or movement of property, by an order issued under this Act;

---

1. Inst. by Act 43 of 2016, Section 2 (w.e.f. November 1, 2016, according to S.O. 3289(E), dt. October 25, 2016).
2. Subst. by Act 43 of 2016, Section 3, for Sub-s. (1) (w.e.f. November 1, 2016, according to S.O. 3289(E), dt. October 25, 2016). Sub-s. (1), prior to subst., ran as under:
   "(1) This Act may be called the *Benami* Transactions (Prohibition) Act, 1988.".
3. The words "except the State of Jammu and Kashmir" stood omitted by Act 34 of 2019, Section 95 and the Fifth Schedule (w.e.f. October 31, 2019).
4. Subst. by Act 43 of 2016, Section 4, for Section 2 (w.e.f. November 1, 2016, according to S.O. 3289(E), dt. October 25, 2016). Section 2, prior to subst., ran as under:
   "2. *Definitions.*—In this Act, unless the context otherwise requires,—
   (a) "*Benami* transaction" means any transaction in which property is transferred to one person for a consideration paid or provided by another person;
   (b) "prescribed" means prescribed by rules made under this Act;
   (c) "property" means property of any kind, whether movable or immovable, tangible or intangible, and includes any right or interest in such property."
5. Subst. by Act 13 of 2021, Section 154, for "appointed under" (w.e.f. July 1, 2021).

(6) "authority" means an authority referred to in sub-section (1) of section 18;

(7) "banking company" means a company to which the provisions of the Banking Regulation Act, 1949 (10 of 1949), applies and includes any bank or banking institution referred to in section 51 of that Act;

(8) "*benami* property" means any property which is the subject matter of a *benami* transaction and also includes the proceeds from such property;

(9) "*benami* transaction" means,—

(A) a transaction or an arrangement—

(a) where a property is transferred to, or is held by, a person, and the consideration for such property has been provided, or paid by, another person; and

(b) the property is held for the immediate or future benefit, direct or indirect, of the person who has provided the consideration,

except when the property is held by—

(i) a Karta, or a member of a Hindu undivided family, as the case may be, and the property is held for his benefit or benefit of other members in the family and the consideration for such property has been provided or paid out of the known sources of the Hindu undivided family;

(ii) a person standing in a fiduciary capacity for the benefit of another person towards whom he stands in such capacity and includes a trustee, executor, partner, director of a company, a depository or a participant as an agent of a depository under the Depositories Act, 1996 (22 of 1996) and any other person as may be notified by the Central Government for this purpose;

(iii) any person being an individual in the name of his spouse or in the name of any child of such individual and the consideration for such property has been provided or paid out of the known sources of the individual;

(iv) any person in the name of his brother or sister or lineal ascendant or descendant, where the names of brother or sister or lineal ascendant or descendant and the individual appear as joint-owners in any document, and the consideration for such property has been provided or paid out of the known sources of the individual; or

(B) a transaction or an arrangement in respect of a property carried out or made in a fictitious name; or

(C) a transaction or an arrangement in respect of a property where the owner of the property is not aware of, or, denies knowledge of, such ownership;

(D) a transaction or an arrangement in respect of a property where the person providing the consideration is not traceable or is fictitious;

*Explanation.*—For the removal of doubts, it is hereby declared that *benami* transaction shall not include any transaction involving the allowing of possession of any property to be taken or retained in part performance of a contract referred to in section 53A of the Transfer of Property Act, 1882 (4 of 1882), if, under any law for the time being in force,—

(i) consideration for such property has been provided by the person to whom possession of property has been allowed but the person who has granted possession thereof continues to hold ownership of such property;

(ii) stamp duty on such transaction or arrangement has been paid; and

(iii) the contract has been registered.

(10) "*benamidar*" means a person or a fictitious person, as the case may be, in whose name the *benami* property is transferred or held and includes a person who lends his name;

(11) "Bench" means a Bench of the Adjudicating Authority or the Appellate Tribunal, as the case may be;

(12) "beneficial owner" means a person, whether his identity is known or not, for whose benefit the *benami* property is held by a *benamidar*;

(13) "Board" means the Central Board of Direct Taxes constituted under the Central Boards of Revenue Act, 1963 (54 of 1963);

(14) "director" shall have the same meaning as assigned to it in clause (34) of section 2 of the Companies Act, 2013 (18 of 2013);

(15) "executor" shall have the same meaning as assigned to it in clause (c) of section 2 of the Indian Succession Act, 1925 (39 of 1925);

(16) "fair market value", in relation to a property, means—

(i) the price that the property would ordinarily fetch on sale in the open market on the date of the transaction; and

(ii) where the price referred to in sub-clause (i) is not ascertainable, such price as may be determined in accordance with such manner as may be prescribed;

(17) "firm" shall have the same meaning as assigned to it in section 4 of the Indian Partnership Act, 1932 (9 of 1932) and shall include a limited liability partnership as defined in the Limited Liability Partnership Act, 2008 (6 of 2009);

(18) "High Court" means—

(i) the High Court within the jurisdiction of which the aggrieved party ordinarily resides or carries on business or personally works for gain; and

(ii) where the Government is the aggrieved party, the High Court within the jurisdiction of which the respondent, or in a case where there are more than one respondent, any of the respondents, ordinarily resides or carries on business or personally works for gain;

(19) "Initiating Officer" means an Assistant Commissioner or a Deputy Commissioner as defined in clauses (9A) and (19A) respectively of section 2 of the Income-tax Act, 1961 (43 of 1961);

(20) "Member" means the Chairperson or the Member of the Adjudicating Authority or the Appellate Tribunal, as the case may be;

(21) "notification" means a notification published in the Official Gazette and the expression "notified" shall be construed accordingly;

(22) "partner" shall have the same meaning as assigned to it in section 4 of the Indian Partnership Act, 1932 (9 of 1932), and shall include,—

(a) any person who, being a minor, has been admitted to the benefits of partnership; and

(b) a partner of a limited liability partnership formed and registered under the Limited Liability Partnership Act, 2008 (6 of 2009);

(23) "partnership" shall have the same meaning as assigned to it in section 4 of the Indian Partnership Act, 1932 (9 of 1932), and shall include a limited liability partnership formed and registered under the Limited Liability Partnership Act, 2008 (6 of 2009);

(24) "person" shall include—

(i) an individual;

(ii) a Hindu undivided family;

(iii) a company;

(iv) a firm;

(v) an association of persons or a body of individuals, whether incorporated or not;

(vi) every artificial juridical person, not falling under sub-clauses (i) to (v);

(25) "prescribed" means prescribed by rules made under this Act;

(26) "property" means assets of any kind, whether movable or immovable, tangible or intangible, corporeal or incorporeal and includes any right or interest or legal documents or instruments evidencing title to or interest in the property and where the property is capable of conversion into some other form, then the property in the converted form and also includes the proceeds from the property;

(27) "public financial institution" shall have the same meaning as assigned to it in clause (72) of section 2 of the Companies Act, 2013 (18 of 2013);

(28) "Special Court" means a Court of Session designated as Special Court under sub-section (1) of section 50;

(29) "transfer" includes sale, purchase or any other form of transfer of right, title, possession or lien;

(30) "trustee" means the trustee as defined in the section 3 of the Indian Trusts Act, 1882 (2 of 1882);

(31) words and expressions used herein and not defined in this Act but defined in the Indian Trusts Act, 1882 (2 of 1882), the Indian Succession Act, 1925 (39 of 1925), the Indian Partnership Act, 1932 (9 of 1932), the Income-tax Act, 1961 (43 of 1961), the Depositories Act, 1996 (22 of 1996), the Prevention of Money-Laundering Act, 2002 (15 of 2003), the Limited Liability Partnership Act, 2008 (6 of 2009) and the Companies Act, 2013 (18 of 2013), shall have the same meanings respectively assigned to them in those Acts.]

## [1][CHAPTER II
## PROHIBITION OF *BENAMI* TRANSACTIONS]

**3. Prohibition of *benami* transactions.**—(1) No person shall enter into any *Benami* transaction.

[2][***]

[3][(2)] Whoever enters into any *benami* transaction shall be punishable with imprisonment for a term which may extend to three years or with fine or with both.

[4][(3) Whoever enters into any *benami* transaction on and after the date of commencement of the *Benami* Transactions (Prohibition) Amendment Act, 2016 (43 of 2016) shall, notwithstanding anything contained in sub-section (2), be punishable in accordance with the provisions contained in Chapter VII.]

[5][***]

---

1. Inst. by Act 43 of 2016, Section 5 (w.e.f. November 1, 2016), according to S.O. 3289(E), dt. October, 25 2016.
2. Sub-s. (2) stood omitted by Act 43 of 2016, Section 6(a) (w.e.f. November 1, 2016, according to S.O. 3289(E), dt. October 25, 2016). Previously Sub-s. (2) stood subst. by Act 22 of 1996, Section 30 and Schedule (w.r.e.f. September 30, 1995). Sub-s. (2), prior to omission, ran as under:
   "(2) Nothing in sub-section (1) shall apply to—
   (a) the purchase of property by any person in the name of his wife or unmarried daughter and it shall be presumed, unless the contrary is proved, that the said property had been purchased for the benefit of the wife or the unmarried daughter;
   (b) the securities held by a—
   (i) Depository as registered owner under sub-section (1) of section 10 of the Depositories Act, 1996;
   (ii) Participant as an agent of a depository.
   *Explanation.*—The expression "depository" and "Participant shall have the meanings respectively assigned to them in clause (e) and (g) of sub-section (1) of section 2 of the Depositories Act, 1996."
3. Sub-s. (3) stood renumbered as Sub-s. (2) thereof by Act 43 of 2016, Section 6(b) (w.e.f. November 1, 2016, according to S.O. 3289(E), dt. October 25, 2016).
4. Inst. by Act 43 of 2016, Section 6(c) (w.e.f. November 1, 2016, according to S.O. 3289(E), dt. October 25, 2016).
5. Sub-s. (4) stood omitted by Act 43 of 2016, Section 6(d) (w.e.f. November 1, 2016, according to S.O. 3289(E), dt. October 25, 2016). Sub-s. (4), prior to omission, ran as under:
   "(4) Notwithstanding anything contained in the Code of Criminal Procedure, 1973 (2 of 1974), an offence under this section shall be non cognizable and bailable".

**4. Prohibition of the right to recover property held *benami*.**—(1) No suit, claim or action to enforce any right in respect of any property held *Benami* against the person in whose name the property is held or against any other person shall lie by or on behalf of a person claiming to be the real owner of such property.

(2) No defence based on any right in respect of any property held *benami*, whether against the person in whose name the property is held or against any other person, shall be allowed in any suit, claim or action by or on behalf of a person claiming to be the real owner of such property.

[1][***]

### COMMENTS

**(i) Application of the Act to suit filed before the 1988 Act**

If the suit had been filed before the commencement of the Act of 1988, then such Act cannot be applicable to the suit.

*Vijay Kumar v. Dharam Pal*, (2009) 3 SCC 319

**(ii) Applicability and Scope of Section 4**

When a person in whose name a property is held as coparcener in Hindu Undivided Family and the property is held for the benefits of the coparcener in the property, the provisions of Section 4 would not be applicable.

*Vinod Kumar Dhall v. Dharampal Dhall*, AIR 2018 SC 3470: (2018) 7 SCALE 256.

[2][**5. Property held *benami* liable to confiscation.**—Any property, which is subject matter of *benami* transaction, shall be liable to be confiscated by the Central Government.]

[3][**6. Prohibition on re-transfer of property by *benamidar*.**—(1) No person, being a *benamidar* shall re-transfer the *Benami* property held by him to the beneficial owner or any other person acting on his behalf.

1. Sub-s. (3) stood omitted by Act 43 of 2016, Section 7 (w.e.f. November 1, 2016, according to S.O. 3289(E), dt. October 25, 2016. Sub-s. (3), prior to omission, ran as under:
"(3) Nothing in this section shall apply,-
(a) Where the person in whose name the property is held is a coparcener in a Hindu undivided family and the property is held for the benefit of the coparceners in the family; or
(b) Where the person in whose name the property is held is a trustee or other person standing in a fiduciary capacity, and the property is held for the benefit of another person for whom he is a trustee or towards whom he stands in such capacity.".
2. Subst. by Act 43 of 2016, Section 8, for Section 5 (w.e.f. November 1, 2016, according to S.O. 3289(E), dt. October 25, 2016). Section 5, prior to subst., ran as under:
"5. *Property held benami liable to acquisition.*—(1) All properties held *benami* shall be subject to acquisition by such authority, in such manner and after following such procedure, as may be prescribed.
(2) For the removal of doubts, it is hereby declared that no amount shall be payable for the acquisition of any property under sub-section(1)."
3. Subst. by Act 43 of 2016, Section 8, for Section 6 (w.e.f. November 1, 2016, according to S.O. 3289(E), dt. October 25, 2016). Section 6, prior to subst., ran as under:
"6. *Act not to apply in certain cases.*—Nothing I this Act shall effect the provisions of section 53 of the Transfer of Property Act, 1882 (4 of 1882), or any law relating to transfers for an illegal purpose."

(2) Where any property is re-transferred in contravention of the provisions of sub-section (1), the transaction of such property shall be deemed to be null and void.

(3) The provisions of sub-sections (1) and (2) shall not apply to a transfer made in accordance with the provisions of section 190 of the Finance Act, 2016 (28 of 2016).]

## [1][CHAPTER III
## AUTHORITIES

[2][**7. Adjudicating Authority.**—The competent authority authorised under sub-section (1) of section 5 of the Smugglers and Foreign Exchange Manipulators (Forfeiture of Property) Act, 1976 (13 of 1976) shall be the Adjudicating Authority to exercise jurisdiction, powers and authority conferred by or under this Act.]

**8. [Composition of Authority].**—*Omitted by Act 13 of 2021, Section 156 (w.e.f. July 01, 2021).*

**9. [Qualifications for appointment of Chairperson and Members].**—*Omitted by Act 13 of 2021, Section 156 (w.e.f. July 1, 2021).*

**10. [Constitution of Benches of Adjudicating Authority].**—*Omitted by Act 13 of 2021, Section 156 (w.e.f. July 1, 2021).*

**11. [Power of Adjudicating Authority to regulate its own procedure].**—*Omitted by Act 13 of 2021, Section 156 (w.e.f. July 1, 2021).*

**12. [Term of office of Chairperson and Members of Adjudicating Authority].**—*Omitted by Act 13 of 2021, Section 156 (w.e.f. July 1, 2021).*

**13. [Terms and conditions of services of Chairperson and Members of Adjudicating Authority].**—*Omitted by Act 13 of 2021, Section 156 (w.e.f. July 1, 2021).*

**14. [Removal of Chairperson and Members of Adjudicating Authority].**—*Omitted by Act 13 of 2021, Section 156 (w.e.f. July 1, 2021).*

**15. [Member to act as Chairperson in certain circumstances].**—*Omitted by Act 13 of 2021, Section 156 (w.e.f. July 1, 2021).*

**16. [Vacancies, etc., not to invalidate proceedings of Adjudicating Authority].**—*Omitted by Act 13 of 2021, Section 156 (w.e.f. July 1, 2021).*

**17. [Officers and employees of Adjudicating Authority].**—*Omitted by Act 13 of 2021, Section 156 (w.e.f. July 1, 2021).*

**18. Authorities and jurisdiction.**—(1) The following shall be the authorities for the purposes of this Act, namely:—

(a) the Initiating Officer;

(b) the Approving Authority;

(c) the Administrator; and

(d) the Adjudicating Authority.

---

1. Chapter III (containing Sections 24 to 23) inst. by Act 43 of 2016, Section 9 (w.e.f. November 1, 2016, according to S.O. 3289(E), dt. October 25, 2016).
2. Subst. by Act 13 of 2021, Section 155, for Section 7 (w.e.f. July 1, 2021).

(2) The authorities shall exercise all or any of the powers and perform all or any of the functions conferred on, or, assigned, as the case may be, to it under this Act or in accordance with such rules as may be prescribed.

**19. Powers of authorities.**—(1) The authorities shall, for the purposes of this Act, have the same powers as are vested in a civil court under the Code of Civil Procedure, 1908 (5 of 1908), while trying a suit in respect of the following matters, namely:—

(a) discovery and inspection;

(b) enforcing the attendance of any person, including any official of a banking company or a public financial institution or any other intermediary or reporting entity, and examining him on oath;

(c) compelling the production of books of account and other documents;

(d) issuing commissions;

(e) receiving evidence on affidavits; and

(f) any other matter which may be prescribed.

(2) All the persons summoned under sub-section (1) shall be bound to attend in person or through authorised agents, as any authority under this Act may direct, and shall be bound to state the truth upon any subject respecting which they are examined or make statements, and produce such documents as may be required.

(3) Every proceeding under sub-section (1) or sub-section (2) shall be deemed to be a judicial proceeding within the meaning of section 193 and section 228 of the Indian Penal Code (45 of 1860).

(4) For the purposes of this Act, any authority under this Act may requisition the service of any police officer or of any officer of the Central Government or State Government or of both to assist him for all or any of the purposes specified in sub-section (1), and it shall be the duty of every such officer to comply with the requisition or direction.

(5) For the purposes of this section, "reporting entity" means any intermediary or any authority or of the Central or the State Government or any other person as may be notified in this behalf.

*Explanation*.—For the purposes of sub-section (5), "intermediary" shall have the same meaning as assigned to it in clause (n) of sub-section (1) of section 2 of the Prevention of Money-Laundering Act, 2002 (15 of 2003).

**20. Certain officers to assist in inquiry, etc.**—The following officers shall assist the authorities in the enforcement of this Act, namely:—

(a) income-tax authorities appointed under sub-section (1) of section 117 of the Income-tax Act, 1961 (43 of 1961);

(b) officers of the Customs and Central Excise Departments;

(c) officers appointed under sub-section (1) of section 5 of the Narcotic Drugs and Psychotropic Substances Act, 1985 (61 of 1985);

(d) officers of the stock exchange recognised under section 4 of the Securities Contracts (Regulation) Act, 1956 (42 of 1956);

(e) officers of the Reserve Bank of India constituted under sub-section (1) of section 3 of the Reserve Bank of India Act, 1934 (2 of 1934);

(f) police;

(g) officers of enforcement appointed under sub-section (1) of section 36 of the Foreign Exchange Management Act, 1999 (40 of 1999);

(h) officers of the Securities and Exchange Board of India established under section 3 of the Securities and Exchange Board of India Act, 1992 (15 of 1992);

(i) officers of any other body corporate constituted or established under a Central or a State Act; And

(j) such other officers of the Central Government, State Government, local authorities or banking companies as the Central Government may, by notification, specify, in this behalf.

**21. Power to call for information.**—(1) The Initiating Officer or the Approving Authority or the Adjudicating Authority shall have power to require any officer of the Central Government or State Government or a local body or any person or officer who is responsible for registering and maintaining books of account or other documents containing a record of any transaction relating to any property or any other person to furnish any information in relation to any person, point or matter as in his opinion shall be useful for or relevant for the purposes of this Act.

(2) Without prejudice to sub-section (1), every officer or person referred to in sub-section (1) shall furnish such information to any authority under this Act in such form and manner as may be prescribed.

**22. Power of authority to impound documents.**—(1) Where any books of account or other documents are produced before the authority in any proceedings under this Act and the authority in this behalf has reason to believe that any of the books of account or other documents are required to be impounded and retained for any inquiry under this Act, it may impound and retain the books of account or other documents for a period not exceeding three months from the date of order of attachment made by the Adjudicating Authority under sub-section (3) of section 26:

Provided that the period for retention of the books of account or other documents may be extended beyond a period exceeding three months from the date of order of attachment made by the Adjudicating Authority under sub-section (3) of section 26 where the authority records in writing the reasons for extending the same.

(2) Where the authority impounding and retaining the books of account or other documents, under sub-section (1) is the Initiating Officer, he shall obtain approval of the Approving Authority within a period of fifteen days from the date of initial impounding and seek further approval of the Approving Authority for extending the period of initial retention, before the expiry of the period of initial retention, if so required.

(3) The period of retention of the books of account or other documents under sub-section (1) shall in no case exceed a period of thirty days from the date of conclusion of all the proceedings under this Act.

(4) The person, from whom the books of account or other documents were impounded under sub-section (1), shall be entitled to obtain copies thereof.

(5) On the expiry of the period specified under sub-section (1), the books of account or other documents shall be returned to the person from whom such books of account or other documents were impounded unless the Approving Authority or the Adjudicating Authority permits their release to any other person.

**23. Power of authority to conduct inquiry, etc.**—The Initiating Officer, after obtaining prior approval of the Approving Authority, shall have power to conduct or cause to be conducted any inquiry or investigation in respect of any person, place, property, assets, documents, books of account or other documents, in respect of any other relevant matters under this Act.]

[1][*Explanation*.—For the removal of doubts, it is hereby clarified that nothing contained in this section shall apply and shall be deemed to have ever applied where a notice under sub-section (1) of section 24 has been issued by the Initiating Officer.]

## [2][CHAPTER IV

## ATTACHMENT, ADJUDICATION AND CONFISCATION

**24. Notice and attachment of property involved in *benami* transaction.**—(1) Where the Initiating Officer, on the basis of material in his possession, has reason to believe that any person is a *benamidar* in respect of a property, he may, after recording reasons in writing, issue a notice to the person to show cause within such time as may be specified in the notice why the property should not be treated as *benami* property.

(2) Where a notice under sub-section (1) specifies any property as being held by a *benamidar* referred to in that sub-section, a copy of the notice shall also be issued to the beneficial owner if his identity is known.

(3) Where the Initiating Officer is of the opinion that the person in possession of the property held *benami* may alienate the property during the period specified in the notice, he may, with the previous approval of the Approving Authority, by order in writing, attach provisionally the property in the manner as may be prescribed, for a period not exceeding ninety days [3][from the last day of the month in which the notice under sub-section (1) is issued.]

(4) The Initiating Officer, after making such inquires and calling for such reports or evidence as he deems fit and taking into account all relevant materials, shall, within a period of ninety days [3][from the last day of the month in which the notice under sub-section (1) is issued],—

(a) where the provisional attachment has been made under sub-section (3),—

1. Inst. by Act 23 of 2019, Section 173 (w.e.f. November 1, 2016).
2. Chapter IV (containing Sections 24 to 29) inst. by Act 43 of 2016, Section 5 (w.e.f. November 1, 2016, according to S.O. 3289(E), dt. October 25, 2016).
3. Subst. by Act 23 of 2019, Section 174, for "from the date of issue of notice under sub-section. (1)" (w.e.f. September 1, 2019).

(i) pass an order continuing the provisional attachment of the property with the prior approval of the Approving Authority, till the passing of the order by the Adjudicating Authority under sub-section (3) of section 26; or

(ii) revoke the provisional attachment of the property with the prior approval of the Approving Authority.

(b) where provisional attachment has not been made under sub-section (3),—

(i) pass an order provisionally attaching the property with the prior approval of the Approving Authority, till the passing of the order by the Adjudicating Authority under sub-section (3) of section 26; or

(ii) decide not to attach the property as specified in the notice, with the prior approval of the Approving Authority.

[1][*Explanation*.— For the purposes of this section, in computing the period of limitation, the period during which the proceeding is stayed by an order or injunction of any court shall be excluded:

Provided that where immediately after the exclusion of the aforesaid period, the period of limitation referred to in sub-section (4) available to the Initiating Officer for passing order of attachment is less than thirty days, such remaining period shall be deemed to be extended to thirty days:

Provided further that where immediately after the exclusion of the aforesaid period, the period of limitation referred to in sub-section (5) available to the Initiating Officer to refer the order of attachment to Adjudicating Authority is less than seven days, such remaining period shall be deemed to be extended to seven days.]

(5) Where the Initiating Officer passes an order continuing the provisional attachment of the property under sub-clause (i) of clause (a) of sub-section (4) or passes an order provisionally attaching the property under sub-clause (i) of clause (b) of that sub-section, he shall, within fifteen days from the date of the attachment, draw up a statement of the case and refer it to the Adjudicating Authority.

**25. Manner of service of notice.**—(1) A notice under sub-section (1) of section 24 may be served on the person named therein either by post or as if it were a summons issued by a Court under the Code of Civil Procedure, 1908 (5 of 1908).

(2) Any notice referred to in sub-section (1) may be addressed—

(i) in case of an individual, to such individual;

(ii) in the case of a firm, to the managing partner or the manager of the firm;

(iii) in the case of a Hindu undivided family, to *Karta* or any member of such family;

(iv) in the case of a company, to the principal officer thereof;

1. Inst. by Act 23 of 2019, Section 174 (w.e.f. September 1, 2019).

(v) in the case of any other association or body of individuals, to the principal officer or any member thereof;

(vi) in the case of any other person (not being an individual), to the person who manages or controls his affairs.

**26. Adjudication of *benami* property.**—(1) On receipt of a reference under sub-section (5) of section 24, the Adjudicating Authority shall issue notice, to furnish such documents, particulars or evidence as is considered necessary on a date to be specified therein, on the following persons, namely:—

(a) the person specified as a *benamidar* therein;

(b) any person referred to as the beneficial owner therein or identified as such;

(c) any interested party, including a banking company;

(d) any person who has made a claim in respect of the property:

Provided that the Adjudicating Authority shall issue notice within a period of thirty days from the date on which a reference has been received:

Provided further that the notice shall provide a period of not less than thirty days to the person to whom the notice is issued to furnish the information sought.

(2) Where the property is held jointly by more than one person, the Adjudicating Authority shall make all endeavours to serve notice to all persons holding the property:

Provided that where the notice is served on anyone of the persons, the service of notice shall not be invalid on the ground that the said notice was not served to all the persons holding the property.

(3) The Adjudicating Authority shall, after —

(a) considering the reply, if any, to the notice issued under sub-section (1);

(b) making or causing to be made such inquiries and calling for such reports or evidence as it deems fit; and

(c) taking into account all relevant materials,

provide an opportunity of being heard to the person specified as a *benamidar* therein, the Initiating Officer, and any other person who claims to be the owner of the property, and, thereafter, pass an order—

(i) holding the property not to be a *benami* property and revoking the attachment order; or

(ii) holding the property to be a *benami* property and confirming the attachment order, in all other cases.

(4) Where the Adjudicating Authority is satisfied that some part of the properties in respect of which reference has been made to him is *benami* property, but is not able to specifically identify such part, he shall record a finding to the best of his judgment as to which part of the properties is held *benami*.

(5) Where in the course of proceedings before it, the Adjudicating Authority has reason to believe that a property, other than a property referred to it by the Initiating Officer is *benami* property, it shall provisionally attach the property and the property shall be deemed to be a property referred to it on the date of receipt of the reference under sub-section (5) of section 24.

(6) The Adjudicating Authority may, at any stage of the proceedings, either on the application of any party, or *suo motu*, strike out the name of any party improperly joined or add the name of any person whose presence before the Adjudicating Authority may be necessary to enable him to adjudicate upon and settle all the questions involved in the reference.

(7) No order under sub-section (3) shall be passed after the expiry of one year from the end of the month in which the reference under sub-section (5) of section 24 was received.

[1][*Explanation.*—For the purposes of this sub-section, in computing the period of limitation, the period during which the proceeding is stayed by an order or injunction of any court shall be excluded:

Provided that where immediately after the exclusion of the aforesaid period, the period of limitation available to the Adjudicating Authority for passing order is less than sixty days, such remaining period shall be deemed to be extended to sixty days.]

[2][Provided that where the time limit for passing order under this sub-section expires during the period beginning from the 1st day of July, 2021 and ending on the 29th day of September, 2021, the time limit for passing such order shall be extended to the 30th day of September, 2021.]

(8) The *benamidar* or any other person who claims to be the owner of the property may either appear in person or take the assistance of an authorised representative of his choice to present his case.

*Explanation.*—For the purposes of sub-section (8), authorised representative means a person authorised in writing, being—

(i) a person related to the *benamidar* or such other person in any manner, or a person regularly employed by the *benamidar* or such other person as the case may be; or

(ii) any officer of a scheduled bank with which the *benamidar* or such other person maintains an account or has other regular dealings; or

(iii) any legal practitioner who is entitled to practice in any civil court in India; or

(iv) any person who has passed any accountancy examination recognised in this behalf by the Board; or

(v) any person who has acquired such educational qualifications as the Board may prescribe for this purpose.

**27. Confiscation and vesting of *benami* property.**—(1) Where an order is passed in respect of any property under sub-section (3) of section 26

1. Inst. by Act 23 of 2019, Section 175 (w.e.f. September 1, 2019).
2. Inst. by Act 13 of 2021, Section 157 (w.e.f. July 1, 2021).

holding such property to be a *benami* property, the Adjudicating Authority shall, after giving an opportunity of being heard to the person concerned, make an order confiscating the property held to be a *benami* property:

Provided that where an appeal has been filed against the order of the Adjudicating Authority, the confiscation of property shall be made subject to the order passed by the Appellate Tribunal under section 46:

Provided further that the confiscation of the property shall be made in accordance with such procedure as may be prescribed.

(2) Nothing in sub-section (1) shall apply to a property held or acquired by a person from the *benamidar* for adequate consideration, prior to the issue of notice under sub-section (1) of section 24 without his having knowledge of the *benami* transaction.

(3) Where an order of confiscation has been made under sub-section (1), all the rights and title in such property shall vest absolutely in the Central Government free of all encumbrances and no compensation shall be payable in respect of such confiscation.

(4) Any right of any third person created in such property with a view to defeat the purposes of this Act shall be null and void.

(5) Where no order of confiscation is made upon the proceedings under this Act attaining finality, no claim shall lie against the Government.]

**28. Management of properties confiscated.**—(1) The Administrator shall have the power to receive and manage the property, in relation to which an order of confiscation under sub-section (1) of section 27 has been made, in such manner and subject to such conditions, as may be prescribed.

(2) The Central Government may, by order published in the Official Gazette, notify as many of its officers as it thinks fit, to perform the functions of Administrators.

(3) The Administrator shall also take such measures, as the Central Government may direct, to dispose of the property which is vested in the Central Government under sub-section (3) of section 27, in such manner and subject to such conditions as may be prescribed.

**29. Possession of the property.**—(1) Where an order of confiscation in respect of a property under sub-section (1) of section 27, has been made, the Administrator shall proceed to take the possession of the property.

(2) The Administrator shall,—

(a) by notice in writing, order within seven days of the date of the service of notice to any person, who may be in possession of the *benami* property, to surrender or deliver possession thereof to the Administrator or any other person duly authorised in writing by him in this behalf;

(b) in the event of non-compliance of the order referred to in clause (a), or if in his opinion, taking over of immediate possession is warranted, for the purpose of forcibly taking over possession, requisition the service of any police officer to assist him and it shall be the duty of the officer to comply with the requisition.]

## [1][CHAPTER V
## APPELLATE TRIBUNAL

**30. Establishment of Appellate Tribunal.**—The Central Government shall, by notification, establish an Appellate Tribunal to hear appeals against the orders of [2][any authority] under this Act.

**31. Composition, etc., of Appellate Tribunal.**—(1) The Appellate Tribunal shall consist of a Chairperson and at least two other Members of which one shall be a Judicial Member and other shall be an Administrative Member.

(2) Subject to the provisions of this Act,—

(a) the jurisdiction of the Appellate Tribunal may be exercised by Benches thereof;

(b) a Bench may be constituted by the Chairperson with two Members as the Chairperson may deem fit;

(c) the Benches of the Appellate Tribunal shall ordinarily sit in the National Capital Territory of Delhi and at such other places as the Central Government may, in consultation with the Chairperson, by notification, specify;

(d) the Central Government shall, by notification, specify the areas in relation to which each Bench of the Appellate Tribunal may exercise its jurisdiction.

(3) Notwithstanding anything contained in sub-section (2), the Chairperson may transfer a Member from one Bench to another Bench.]

**32. Qualifications for appointment of Chairperson and Members of Appellate Tribunal.**—(1) A person shall not be qualified for appointment as Chairperson of the Appellate Tribunal unless he is a sitting or retired Judge of a High Court, who has completed not less than five years' of service.

(2) A person shall not be qualified for appointment as a Member unless he—

(a) in the case of a Judicial Member, has been a Member of the Indian Legal Service and has held the post of Additional Secretary or equivalent post in that Service;

(b) in the case of an Administrative Member, has been a Member of the Indian Revenue Service and has held the post of Chief Commissioner of Income-tax or equivalent post in that Service.

(3) No sitting Judge of a High Court shall be appointed under this section except after consultation with the Chief Justice of the High Court.

(4) The Chairperson or a Member holding a post as such in any other Tribunal, established under any law for the time being in force, in addition to his being the Chairperson or a Member of that Tribunal, may be appointed as the Chairperson or a Member, as the case may be, of the Appellate Tribunal under this Act.

---

1. Chapter V (containing section 30 to 49) inst. by Acy 43 of 2016, Section 9 (w.e.f. November 1, 2016, according to S.O. 3289(E), dt. October 25, 2016).
2. Subst. by Act 23 of 2019, Section 176, for "the Adjudicating Authority" (w.e.f. September 1, 2019).

**33. Terms and conditions of services of Chairperson and Members of Appellate Tribunal.**—(1) The salary and allowances payable to, and the other terms and conditions of service of the Chairperson and other Members shall be such as may be prescribed and shall not be varied to their disadvantage during their tenure.

(2) Any vacancy caused to the office of the Chairperson or any other Member shall be filled up within a period of three months from the date on which such vacancy occurs.

**34. Term of office of Chairperson and Members.**—The Chairperson and Members of the Appellate Tribunal shall hold office for a term not exceeding five years from the date on which they enter upon their office, or until they attain the age of sixty-five years, whichever is earlier and shall not be eligible for reappointment.

**35. Removal of Chairperson and Member from office in certain circumstances.**—(1) The Central Government may, in consultation with the Chief Justice of High Court, remove from office of the Chairperson or any Member, who—

(a) has been adjudged as an insolvent; or

(b) has been convicted of an offence which, in the opinion of the Central Government involves moral turpitude; or

(c) has become physically or mentally incapable; or

(d) has acquired such financial or other interest as is likely to affect prejudicially his functions; or

(e) has so abused his position as to render his continuance in office prejudicial to the public interest.

(2) The Chairperson or Judicial Member shall not be removed from his office except by an order made by the Central Government after an inquiry made by Chief Justice of the High Court in which the Chairperson or Judicial Member has been informed of the charges against him and given a reasonable opportunity of being heard in respect of those charges.

(3) The Central Government may suspend from office the Chairperson or Judicial Member in respect of whom a reference of conducting an inquiry has been made to the Chief Justice of the High Court under sub-section (2), until the Central Government passes an order on receipt of the report of inquiry made by Chief Justice of the High Court on the reference.

(4) The Central Government may regulate the procedure for inquiry referred to in sub-section (2) in the manner as may be prescribed.

(5) The Administrative Member may be removed from his office by an order of the Central Government on the grounds specified in sub-section (1) and in accordance with the procedure notified by the Central Government:

Provided that the Administrative Member shall not be removed unless he has been given an opportunity of being heard in the matter.

**36. Vacancies, etc., not to invalidate proceedings of Appellate Tribunal.**—No act or proceeding of the Appellate Tribunal shall be invalid merely by reason of—

(a) any vacancy in, or any defect in the constitution of the Tribunal; or

(b) any defect in the appointment of a person acting as a Member of the Tribunal; or

(c) any irregularity in the procedure of the Tribunal not affecting the merits of the case.

**37. Resignation and removal.**—The Chairperson or any other Member may, by notice in writing under his hand addressed to the Central Government, resign his office:

Provided that the Chairperson or any other Member shall, unless he is permitted by the Central Government to relinquish his office sooner, continue to hold office until the expiry of three months from the date of receipt of the notice or until a person duly appointed as his successor enters upon his office or until the expiry of his term of office, whichever is earlier.

**38. Member to act as Chairperson in certain circumstances.**—(1) In the event of the occurrence of any vacancy in the office of the Chairperson of the Appellate Tribunal by reason of his death, resignation or otherwise, the senior-most Member shall act as the Chairperson until the date on which a new Chairperson, appointed in accordance with the provisions of this Act to fill such vacancy, enters upon his office.

(2) When the Chairperson is unable to discharge his functions owing to absence, illness or any other cause, the senior-most Member shall discharge the functions of the Chairperson until the date on which the Chairperson resumes his duties.

**39. Staff of Appellate Tribunal.**—(1) The Central Government shall provide the Appellate Tribunal with such officers and employees as it may thinks fit.

(2) The officers and employees of the Appellate Tribunal shall discharge their functions under the general superintendence of the Chairperson.

(3) The salaries and allowances and other conditions of service of the officers and employees of the Appellate Tribunal shall be such, as may be prescribed.

**40. Procedure and powers of Appellate Tribunal.**—(1) The Appellate Tribunal shall not be bound by the procedure laid down by the Code of Civil Procedure, 1908 (5 of 1908), but shall be guided by the principles of natural justice and, subject to the other provisions of this Act, the Appellate Tribunal shall have powers to regulate its own procedure.

(2) The Appellate Tribunal shall, for the purposes of discharging its functions under this Act, have the same powers as are vested in a civil court under the Code of Civil Procedure, 1908 (5 of 1908) while trying a suit, in respect of the following matters, namely:—

(a) summoning and enforcing the attendance of any person and examining him on oath;

(b) requiring the discovery and production of documents;

(c) receiving evidence on affidavits;

(d) subject to the provisions of sections 123 and 124 of the Indian Evidence Act, 1872 (1 of 1872), requisitioning any public record or document or copy of such record or document from any office;

(e) issuing commissions for the examination of witnesses or documents;

(f) reviewing its decisions;

(g) dismissing a representation for default or deciding it *ex parte*;

(h) setting aside any order of dismissal of any representation for default or any order passed by it *ex parte*; and

(i) any other matter, which may be, prescribed by the Central Government.

(3) An order made by the Appellate Tribunal under this Act shall be executable by it as a decree of civil court and, for this purpose, the Appellate Tribunal shall have all the powers of a civil court.

(4) Notwithstanding anything contained in sub-section (3), the Appellate Tribunal may transmit any order made by it to a civil court having jurisdiction and the civil court shall execute the order as if it were a decree made by that court.

(5) All proceedings before the Appellate Tribunal shall be deemed to be judicial proceedings within the meaning of sections 193 and 228 of the Indian Penal Code (45 of 1860) and the Appellate Tribunal shall be deemed to be a civil court for the purposes of sections 345 and 346 of the Code of Criminal Procedure, 1973 (2 of 1974).

**41. Distribution of business amongst Benches of Appellate Tribunal.**— Where any Benches are constituted, the Chairperson may, from time to time, by notification, make provision as to the distribution of the business of the Appellate Tribunal amongst the Benches and also provide for the matters which may be dealt with by each Bench.

**42. Power of Chairperson of Appellate Tribunal to transfer cases.**— On the application of any of the parties and notice to the parties, and after hearing them, or on his own motion without any notice, the Chairperson of the Appellate Tribunal may transfer any case pending before one Bench, for disposal, to any other Bench.

**43. Decision to be by majority.**—If the Members of a Bench consisting of two Members differ in opinion on any point, they shall state the point or points on which they differ, and make a reference to the Chairperson of the Appellate Tribunal who shall either hear the point or points himself or refer the case for hearing on the point or points by one or more of the other Members and the point or points shall be decided according to the opinion of the majority of the Members of the Appellate Tribunal who have heard the case, including those who first heard it.

**44. Members, etc., to be public servants.**—The Chairperson, Members and other officers and employees of the Appellate Tribunal, the Adjudicating Authority, Approving Authority, Initiating Officer, Administrator and the officers subordinate to all of them shall be deemed to be public servants within the meaning of section 21 of the Indian Penal Code (45 of 1860).

**45. Bar of jurisdiction of civil courts.**—No civil court shall have jurisdiction to entertain any suit or proceeding in respect of any matter which any of the authorities, an Adjudicating Authority or the Appellate Tribunal is empowered by or under this Act to determine, and no injunction shall be granted by any court or other forum in respect of any action taken or to be taken in pursuance of any power conferred by or under this Act.

**46. Appeals to Appellate Tribunal.**—(1) Any person, including the Initiating Officer, aggrieved by an order of the Adjudicating Authority may prefer an appeal in such form and along with such fees, as may be prescribed, to the Appellate Tribunal against the order passed by the Adjudicating Authority under sub-section (3) of section 26, within a period of forty-five days from the date of the order.

[1][(1A) Any person aggrieved by an order passed by the authority under section 54A may prefer an appeal in such form along with such fees, as may be prescribed, to the Appellate Tribunal against the said order within a period of forty-five days from the date of that order.]

(2) The Appellate Tribunal may entertain any appeal after the said period of forty-five days, if it is satisfied that the appellant was prevented, by sufficient cause, from filing the appeal in time.

(3) On receipt of an appeal under sub-section (1), [1][or sub-section (1A)] the Appellate Tribunal may, after giving the parties to the appeal an opportunity of being heard, pass such orders thereon as it thinks fit.

(4) An Appellate Tribunal while deciding the appeal shall have the power—

(a) to determine a case finally, where the evidence on record is sufficient;

(b) to take additional evidence or to require any evidence to be taken by the Adjudicating Authority, where the Adjudicating Authority has refused to admit evidence, which ought to have been admitted;

(c) to require any document to be produced or any witness to be examined for the purposes of proceeding before it;

(d) to frame issues which appear to the Appellate Tribunal essential for adjudication of the case and refer them to the Adjudicating Authority for determination;

(e) to pass final order and affirm, vary or reverse an order of adjudication passed by the Adjudicating Authority and pass such other order or orders as may be necessary to meet the ends of justice.

(5) The Appellate Tribunal, as far as possible, may hear and finally decide the appeal within a period of one year from the last date of the month in which the appeal is filed.

**47. Rectification of mistakes.**—[2][(1) The Appellate Tribunal or any authority may, in order to rectify any mistake apparent on the face of the record, amend any order passed by it under the provisions of this Act,

1. Inst. by Act 23 of 2019, Section 177 (w.e.f. September 1, 2019).
2. Subst. by Act 23 of 2019, Section 178, for Sub-s. (1) (w.e.f. September 1, 2019).

within a period of one year from the end of the month in which such order was passed.]

(2) No amendment shall be made under sub-section (1), if the amendment is likely to affect any person prejudicially, unless he has been given notice of intention to do so and has been given an opportunity of being heard.

**48. Right to representation.**—(1) [1][A person, including the Initiating Officer, who is a party to any proceedings before] the Appellate Tribunal under this Act may either appear in person or take the assistance of an authorised representative of his choice to present his case before the Appellate Tribunal.

(2) The Central Government may authorise one or more of its officers to act as presenting officers on its behalf, and every person so authorised may present the case with respect to any appeal before the Appellate Tribunal.

*Explanation*.—For the purposes of this section, "authorised representative" [2][in relation to—

(i) the Initiating Officer, means a person authorised by the Central Government;

(ii) any other party to the proceedings, means a person authorised by the party]

in writing to appear on his behalf, being —

(i) a person related to [3][the party] in any manner, or a person regularly employed by the [3][the party]; or

(ii) any officer of a scheduled bank with which [3][the party] maintains an account or has other regular dealings; or

(iii) any legal practitioner who is entitled to practice in any civil court in India; or

(iv) any person who has passed any accountancy examination recognised in this behalf by the Board; or

(v) any person who has acquired such educational qualifications as the Board may prescribe for this purpose.

**49. Appeal to High Court.**—(1) Any party aggrieved by any decision or order of the Appellate Tribunal may file an appeal to the High Court within a period of sixty days from the date of communication of the decision or order of the Appellate Tribunal to him on any question of law arising out of such order.

(2) The High Court may entertain any appeal after the said period of sixty days, if it is satisfied that the appellant was prevented by sufficient cause from filing the appeal within the period specified in sub-section (1).

(3) Where the High Court is satisfied that a substantial question of law is involved in any case, it shall formulate that question.

1. Subst. by S.O. 5194(E), dt. October 9, 2018, for "A person preferring an appeal to"(w.e.f. October 9, 2018).
2. Subst. by S.O. 5194(E), dt. October 9, 2018, for " means a person authorised by the appellant" (w.e.f. October 9, 2018).
3. Subst. by S.O. 5194(E), dt. October 9, 2018 for "the appellant" (w.e.f. October 9, 2018).

(4) The appeal shall be heard only on the question so formulated, and the respondents shall, at the hearing of the appeal, be allowed to argue that the case does not involve such question.

(5) Nothing in this sub-section shall be deemed to take away or abridge the power of the court to hear, for reasons to be recorded, the appeal on any other substantial question of law not formulated by it, if it is satisfied that the case involves such question.

(6) The High Court shall decide the question of law so formulated and deliver the judgment thereon containing the grounds on which any decision is founded and may award any cost as it deems fit.

(7) The High Court may determine any issue which—

(a) has not been determined by the Appellate Tribunal; or

(b) has been wrongly determined by the Appellate Tribunal, by reason of a decision on such question of law as is referred to in sub-section (1).

(8) Save as otherwise provided in this Act, the provisions of the Code of Civil Procedure, 1908 (5 of 1908), relating to appeals to the High Court shall, as far as may be, apply in the case of appeals under this section.]

## [1][CHAPTER VI
## SPECIAL COURTS

**50. Special Courts.**—(1) The Central Government, in consultation with the Chief Justice of the High Court, shall, for trial of an offence punishable under this Act, by notification, designate one or more Courts of Session as Special Court or Special Courts for such area or areas or for such case or class or group of cases as may be specified in the notification.

(2) While trying an offence under this Act, a Special Court shall also try an offence other than an offence referred to in sub-section (1), with which the accused may, under the Code of Criminal Procedure, 1973 (2 of 1974), be charged at the same trial.

(3) The Special Court shall not take cognizance of any offence punishable under this Act except upon a complaint in writing made by—

(i) the authority; or

(ii) any officer of the Central Government or State Government authorised in writing by that Government by a general or special order made in this behalf.

(4) Every trial under this section shall be conducted as expeditiously as possible and every endeavour shall be made by the Special Court to conclude the trial within six months from the date of filing of the complaint.

**51. Application of Code of Criminal Procedure, 1973 to proceedings before Special Court.**—(1) Save as otherwise provided in this Act, the provisions of the Code of Criminal Procedure, 1973 (2 of 1974), shall apply

1. Chapter VI (containing Section 50 to 52) inst. by Act 43 of 2016, Section 9 (w.e.f. November 1, 2016, according to S.O. 3289(E), dt. October 25, 2016).

to the proceedings before a Special Court and the persons conducting the prosecution before the Special Court, shall be deemed to be Public Prosecutors:

Provided that the Central Government may also appoint for any case or class or group of cases, a Special Public Prosecutor.

(2) A person shall not be qualified to be appointed as a Public Prosecutor or a Special Public Prosecutor under this section unless, the Public Prosecutor has been in practice as an advocate for not less than seven years, and the Special Public Prosecutor has been in practice as an advocate for not less than ten years in any court.

(3) Every person appointed as a Public Prosecutor or a Special Public Prosecutor under this section shall be deemed to be a Public Prosecutor within the meaning of clause (u) of section 2 of the Code of Criminal Procedure, 1973 (2 of 1974) and the provisions of that Code shall have effect accordingly.

**52. Appeal and revision.**—The High Court may exercise, so far as may be applicable, all the powers conferred by Chapter XXIX or Chapter XXX of the Code of Criminal Procedure, 1973 (2 of 1974), on a High Court, as if a Special Court within the local limits of the jurisdiction of the High Court were a Court of Session trying cases within the local limits of the jurisdiction of the High Court.

## [1][CHAPTER VII
## OFFENCES AND PROSECUTION

**53. Penalty for *benami* transaction.**—(1) Where any person enters into a *benami* transaction in order to defeat the provisions of any law or to avoid payment of statutory dues or to avoid payment to creditors, the beneficial owner, *benamidar* and any other person who abets or induces any person to enter into the *benami* transaction, shall be guilty of the offence of *benami* transaction.

(2) Whoever is found guilty of the offence of *benami* transaction referred to in sub-section (1) shall be punishable with rigorous imprisonment for a term which shall not be less than one year, but which may extend to seven years and shall also be liable to fine which may extend to twenty-five per cent. of the fair market value of the property.

**54. Penalty for false information.**—Any person who is required to furnish information under this Act knowingly gives false information to any authority or furnishes any false document in any proceeding under this Act, shall be punishable with rigorous imprisonment for a term which shall not be less than six months but which may extend to five years and shall also be liable to fine which may extend to ten per cent. of the fair market value of the property.

[2][**54A. Penalty for failure to comply with notices or furnish information.**— (1) Any person who fails to,—

(i) comply with summons issued under sub-section (1) of section 19; or

---

1. Chapter VII (containing Sections 53 to 55) inst. by Act 43 of 2016, Section 9 (w.e.f. November 1, 2016, according to S.O. 3289 (E), dt. October 25, 2016).
2. Inst. by Act 23 of 2019, Section 179 (w.e.f. September 1, 2019).

(ii) furnish information as required under section 21, shall be liable to pay penalty of twenty-five thousand rupees for each such failure.

(2) The penalty under sub-section (1) shall be imposed by the authority who had issued the summons or called for the information.

(3) No order under sub-section (2) shall be passed by the authority unless the person on whom the penalty is to be imposed has been given an opportunity of being heard:

Provided that no penalty shall be imposed if, such person proves that there were good and sufficient reasons which prevented him from complying with the summons or furnishing information.

**54B. Proof of entries in records or documents.**—The entries in the records or other documents in the custody of an authority shall be admitted in evidence in any proceedings for the prosecution of any person for an offence under section 3 or this Chapter, as the case may be, and all such entries may be proved either by—

(i) the production of the records or other documents in the custody of the authority containing such entries; or

(ii) the production of a copy of the entries certified by the authority having custody of the records or other documents under its signature stating that it is a true copy of the original entries and that such original entries are contained in the records or other documents in its custody.]

**55. Previous sanction.**—No prosecution shall be instituted against any person in respect of any offence under sections 3, 53 or section 54 without the previous sanction of the [1][competent authority].]

[2][*Explanation*.—For the purposes of this section, "competent authority" means a Commissioner, a Director, a Principal Commissioner of Income-tax or a Principal Director of Income-tax as defined in clause (16), clause (21), clause (34B) and clause (34C), respectively, of section 2 of the Income-tax Act, 1961 (43 of 1961).]

## [3][CHAPTER VIII
## MISCELLANEOUS

**56. Repeal of provisions of certain Acts.**—(1) Sections 81, 82 and 94 of the Indian Trusts Act, 1882 (2 of 1882), section 66 of the Code of Civil

1. Subst. by Act 23 of 2019, Section 180, for "Board" (w.e.f. September 1, 2019).
2. Inst. by Act 23 of 2019, Section 180 (w.e.f. September 1, 2019).
3. Chapter VIII (containing Sections 56 to 71) subst. by Act 43 of 2016, Section 10, for Sections 7 and 8 (w.e.f. November 1, 2016, according to S.O. 3289(E), dt. October 25, 2016). Sections 7 and 8, prior to subst., ran as under:

"*7. Repeal of provisions of certain Acts.*—(1) Sections 81, 82 and 94 of the Indian Trusts Act, 1882 (2 of 1882), Section 66 of the Code of Civil Procedure, 1908 (5 of 1908), and Section 281A of the Income-tax Act, 1961 (43 of 1961), are hereby repealed.

(2) For the removal of doubts, it is hereby declared that nothing in sub-section (1) shall affect the continued operation of Section 281A of the Income-tax Act, 1961 (43 of 1961), in the State of Jammu and Kashmir.

*Contd. on next page...*

Procedure, 1908 (5 of 1908) and section 281A of the Income-tax Act, 1961 (43 of 1961), are hereby repealed.

(2) For the removal of doubts, it is hereby declared that nothing in sub-section (1) shall affect the continued operation of section 281A of the Income-tax Act, 1961 (43 of 1961) in the State of Jammu and Kashmir.

**57. Certain transfers to be *null* and *void*.**—Notwithstanding anything contained in the Transfer of the Property Act, 1882 (4 of 1882) or any other law for the time being in force, where, after the issue of a notice under section 24, any property referred to in the said notice is transferred by any mode whatsoever, the transfer shall, for the purposes of the proceedings under this Act, be ignored and if the property is subsequently confiscated by the Central Government under section 27, then, the transfer of the property shall be deemed to be null and void.

**58. Exemption.**—(1) The Central Government may, by notification, exempt any property relating to charitable or religious trusts from the operation of this Act.

(2) Every notification issued under sub-section (1) shall be laid before each House of Parliament.

**59. Power of Central Government to issue directions, etc.**—(1) The Central Government may, from time to time, issue such orders, instructions or directions to the authorities or require any person to furnish information as it may deem fit for the proper administration of this Act and such authorities and all other persons employed in execution of this Act shall observe and follow the orders, instructions and directions of the Central Government.

(2) In issuing the directions or orders referred to in sub-section (1), the Central Government may have regard to any one or more of the following criteria, namely:—

(a) territorial area;

(b) classes of persons;

---

*...contd. from previous page*

8. *Power to make rules.*—(1) The Central Government may, by notification in the Official Gazette, make rules for carrying out the purposes of this Act.

(2) In particular, and without prejudice to the generality of the foregoing power, such rules may provide for all or any of the following matters, namely:—

(a) the authority competent to acquire properties under Section 5;

(b) the manner in which, and the procedure to be followed for, the acquisition of properties under Section 5;

(c) any other matter which is required to be, or may be, prescribed.

(3) Every rule made under this Act shall be laid, as soon as may be after it is made, before each House of Parliament, while it is in session for a total period of thirty days which may be comprised in one session or in two or more successive sessions, and if, before the expiry of the session immediately following the session or the successive sessions aforesaid, both Houses agree in making any modification in the rule or both Houses agree that the rule should not be made, the rule shall thereafter have effect only in such modified form or be of no effect, as the case may be; so, however, that any such modification form or be of no effect, as the case may be; so, however, that any such modification or annulment shall be without prejudice to the validity of anything previously done under that rule.".

(c) classes of cases; and

(d) any other criterion that may be specified by the Central Government in this behalf.

(3) No orders, instructions or directions under sub-section (1) shall be issued so as to —

(a) require any authority to decide a particular case in a particular manner; or

(b) interfere with the discretion of the Adjudicating Authority in the discharge of its functions.

**60. Application of other laws not barred.**—The provisions of this Act shall be in addition to, and not, save as hereinafter expressly provided, in derogation of any other law for the time being in force.

**61. Offences to be non-cognizable.**—Notwithstanding anything contained in the Code of Criminal Procedure, 1973 (2 of 1974), an offence under this Act shall be non-cognizable.

**62. Offences by companies.**—(1) Where a person committing contravention of any of the provisions of this Act or of any rule, direction or order made thereunder is a company, every person who, at the time the contravention was committed, was in charge of, and was responsible to, the company, for the conduct of the business of the company as well as the company, shall be deemed to be guilty of the contravention and shall be liable to be proceeded against and punished accordingly.

(2) Nothing contained in sub-section (1), shall render any person liable to punishment if he proves that the contravention took place without his knowledge.

(3) Notwithstanding anything contained in sub-section (1), where a contravention of any of the provisions of this Act or of any rule, direction or order made thereunder has been committed by a company and it is proved that the contravention has taken place with the consent or connivance of, or is attributable to any neglect on the part of any director, manager, secretary or other officer of the company, the director, manager, secretary or other officer shall also be deemed to be guilty of the contravention and shall be liable to be proceeded against and punished accordingly.

*Explanation*.—For the purposes of this section,—

(a) "company" means a body corporate, and includes—

(i) a firm; and

(ii) an association of persons or a body of individuals whether incorporated or not; and

(b) "director", in relation to—

(i) a firm, means a partner in the firm;

(ii) any association of persons or a body of individuals, means any member controlling the affairs thereof.

**63. Notice, etc., not to be invalid on certain grounds.**—No notice, summons, order, document or other proceeding, furnished or made or issued or taken or purported to have been furnished or made or issued or taken in pursuance of any of the provisions of this Act shall be invalid, or shall be deemed to be invalid merely by reason of any mistake, defect or omission in the notice, summons, order, document or other proceeding if the notice, summons, order, document or other proceeding is in substance and effect in conformity with or according to the intent and purpose of this Act.

**64. Protection of action taken in good faith.**—No prosecution, suit or other proceeding shall lie against the Government or any officer of the Government or the Appellate Tribunal or the Adjudicating Authority established under this Act, for anything done or intended to be done in good faith under this Act.

**65. Transfer of pending cases.**—(1) Every suit or proceeding in respect of a *benami* transaction pending in any Court (other than a High Court) or Tribunal or before any forum on the date of the commencement of this Act shall stand transferred to the Adjudicating Authority or the Appellate Tribunal, as the case may be, having jurisdiction in the matter.

(2) Where any suit, or other proceeding stands transferred to the Adjudicating Authority or the Appellate Tribunal under sub-section (1),—

(a) the court, Tribunal or other forum shall, as soon as may be, after the transfer, forward the records of the suit, or other proceeding to the Adjudicating Authority or the Appellate Tribunal, as the case may be;

(b) the Adjudicating Authority may, on receipt of the records, proceed to deal with the suit, or other proceeding, so far as may be, in the same manner as in the case of a reference made under sub-section (5) of section 24, from the stage which was reached before the transfer or from any earlier stage or *de novo* as the Adjudicating Authority may deem fit.

**66. Proceedings, etc., against legal representative.**—(1) Where a person dies during the course of any proceeding under this Act, any proceeding taken against the deceased before his death shall be deemed to have been taken against the legal representative and may be continued against the legal representative from the stage at which it stood on the date of the death of the deceased.

(2) Any proceeding which could have been taken against the deceased if he had survived may be taken against the legal representative and all the provisions of this Act, except sub-section (2) of section 3 and the provisions of Chapter VII, shall apply accordingly.

(3) Where any property of a person has been held *benami* under sub-section (3) of section 26, then, it shall be lawful for the legal representative of the person to prefer an appeal to the Appellate Tribunal, in place of the person and the provisions of section 46 shall, so far as may be, apply, or continue to apply, to the appeal.]

**67. Act to have overriding effect.**—The provisions of this Act shall have effect, notwithstanding anything inconsistent therewith contained in any other law for the time being in force.

**68. Power to make rules.**—(1) The Central Government may, by notification, make rules for carrying out the provisions of this Act.

(2) In particular, and without prejudice to the generality of the foregoing power, such rules may provide for all or any of the following matters, namely:—

(a) manner of ascertaining the fair market value under clause 16 of section 2;

1[***]

(d) the powers and functions of the authorities under sub-section (2) of section 18;

(e) other powers of the authorities under clause (f) of sub-section (1) of section 19;

(f) the form and manner of furnishing any information to the authority under sub-section (2) of section 21;

(g) the manner of provisional attachment of property under sub-section (3) of section 24;

(h) the procedure for confiscation of *benami* property under the second proviso to sub-section (1) of section 27;

(i) the manner and conditions to receive and manage the property under sub-section (1) of section 28;

(j) the manner and conditions of disposal of property vested in the Central Government under sub-section (3) of section 28;

(k) the salaries and allowances payable to and the other terms and conditions of service of the Chairperson and other Members of the Appellate Tribunal under sub-section (1) of section 33;

(l) the manner of prescribing procedure for removal of Chairperson or Member under sub-section (4) of section 35;

(m) the salaries and allowances payable to and the other terms and conditions of service of the officers and employees of the Appellate Tribunal under sub-section (3) of section 39;

(n) any power of the Appellate Tribunal under clause (i) of sub-section (2) of section 40;

(o) the form in which appeal shall be filed and the fee for filing the appeal under sub-section (1) of section 46;

(p) any other matter which is to be, or may be, prescribed, or in respect of which provision is to be made, by rules.

**69. Laying of rules and notifications before Parliament.**—Every rule made and notification issued under this Act shall be laid, as soon as may be after it is made or issued, before each House of Parliament, while it is in session, for a total period of thirty days which may be comprised in one

1. Clauses (b) and (c) stood omitted by Act 13 of 2021, Section 158 (w.e.f. July 1, 2021).

session or in two or more successive sessions, and if, before the expiry of the session immediately following the session or the successive sessions aforesaid, both Houses agree in making any modification in the rules or notifications, as the case may be, both Houses agree that the rules or notifications, as the case may be, should not be made or issued, the rule or notification, as the case may be, shall thereafter have effect only in such modified form or be of no effect, as the case may be; so, however, that any such modification or annulment shall be without prejudice to the validity of anything previously done under that rule or notification, as the case may be.

**70. Power to remove difficulties.**—(1) If any difficulty arises in giving effect to the provisions of this Act, the Central Government may, by order, published in the Official Gazette, make such provisions not inconsistent with the provisions of this Act as may appear to be necessary for removing the difficulty.

(2) No order shall be made under this section after the expiry of two years from the commencement of this Act.

(3) Every order made under this section shall be laid, as soon as may be after it is made, before each House of Parliament.

**71. Transitional provision.**—The Central Government may, by notification, provide that until the Adjudicating Authorities are appointed and the Appellate Tribunal is established under this Act, the Adjudicating Authority appointed under sub-section (1) of section 6 of the Money-Laundering Act, 2002 (15 of 2003) and the Appellate Tribunal established under section 25 of that Act may discharge the functions of the Adjudicating Authority and Appellate Tribunal, respectively, under this Act [1][for such period and in respect of such cases or class of cases as may be specified in the said notification.].]

[2][**72.] Repeal and saving.**—(1) The benami Transactions (Prohibition of the Right to Recover Property) Ordinance, 1988 (Ord. 2 of 1988) is hereby repealed.

(2) Notwithstanding such repeal, anything done or any action taken under the said Ordinance shall be deemed to have been done or taken under the corresponding provisions of this Act.

---

1. Inst. by S.O. 5602(E), dt. October 31, 2018 (w.e.f. October 31, 2018).
2. Section 9 stood renumbered as Section 72 by Act 43 of 2016, Section 11 (w.e.f. November 1, 2016, according to S.O. 3289 (E), dt. October 25, 2016).

# THE BLACK MONEY (UNDISCLOSED FOREIGN INCOME AND ASSETS) AND IMPOSITION OF TAX ACT, 2015[1]

(22 of 2015)

[*26th May, 2015*]

*An Act to make provisions to deal with the problem of the Black money that is undisclosed foreign income and assets, the procedure for dealing with such income and assets and to provide for imposition of tax on any undisclosed foreign income and asset held outside India and for matters connected therewith or incidental thereto.*

BE it enacted by Parliament in the Sixty-sixth Year of the Republic of India as follows:—

## CHAPTER I
## PRELIMINARY

**1. Short title, extent and commencement.**—(1) This Act may be called the Black Money (Undisclosed Foreign Income and Assets) and Imposition of Tax Act, 2015.

(2) It extends to the whole of India.

(3) Save as otherwise provided in this Act, it shall come into force on the 1st day of April, 2016.

**2. Definitions.**—In this Act, unless the context otherwise requires,—

(1) "Appellate Tribunal" means the Appellate Tribunal constituted under section 252 of the Income-tax Act;

[2][(2) "assessee" means a person,—

(a) being a resident in India within the meaning of section 6 of the Income-tax Act, 1961 (43 of 1961) in the previous year; or

(b) being a non-resident or not ordinarily resident in India within the meaning of clause (6) of section 6 of the Income-tax Act, 1961 (43 of 1961) in the previous year, who was resident in India either in the previous year to which the income referred to in section 4 relates; or in the previous year in which the undisclosed asset located outside India was acquired:

Provided that the previous year, in case of acquisition of undisclosed asset outside India, shall be determined without giving effect to the provisions of clause (c) of section 72;]

(3) "assessment" includes reassessment;

(4) "assessment year" means the period of twelve months commencing on the 1st day of April every year;

(5) "Board" means the Central Board of Direct Taxes constituted under the Central Boards of Revenue Act, 1963 (54 of 1963);

(6) "Income-tax Act" means the Income-tax Act, 1961 (43 of 1961);

1. Published in the Gazette of India , Extra., Part II, Section 1, No.26, dt. May 27, 2015.
2. Subst. by Act 23 of 2019, Section 205, for clause (2) (w.e.f. July 1, 2015).

(7) "participant" means—

(a) a partner in relation to a firm; or

(b) a member in relation to an association of persons or body of individuals;

(8) "prescribed" means prescribed by rules made under this Act;

(9) "previous year" means—

(a) the period beginning with the date of setting up of a business and ending with the date of the closure of the business or the 31st day of March following the date of setting up of such business, whichever is earlier;

(b) the period beginning with the date on which a new source of income comes into existence and ending with the date of closure of the business or the 31st day of March following the date on which such new source comes into existence, whichever is earlier;

(c) the period beginning with the 1st day of the financial year and ending with the date of discontinuance of the business other than business referred to in clause (b) or dissolution of an unincorporated body or liquidation of a company, as the case may be; or

(d) the period of twelve months commencing on the 1st day of April of the relevant year in any other case,

and which immediately precedes the assessment year.

(10) "resident" means a person who is resident in India within the meaning of section 6 of the Income-tax Act;

(11) "undisclosed asset located outside India" means an asset (including financial interest in any entity) located outside India, held by the assessee in his name or in respect of which he is a beneficial owner, and he has no explanation about the source of investment in such asset or the explanation given by him is in the opinion of the Assessing Officer unsatisfactory;

(12) "undisclosed foreign income and asset" means the total amount of undisclosed income of an assessee from a source located outside India and the value of an undisclosed asset located outside India, referred to in section 4, and computed in the manner laid down in section 5;

(13) "unincorporated body" means—

(a) a firm;

(b) an association of persons; or

(c) a body of individuals;

(14) "value of an undisclosed asset" shall have the meaning assigned to it in sub-section (2) of section 3;

(15) all other words and expressions used herein but not defined and defined in the Income-tax Act shall have the meanings respectively assigned to them in that Act.

## CHAPTER II

## BASIS OF CHARGE

**3. Charge of Tax.**—(1) There shall be charged on every assessee for every assessment year commencing on or after the 1st day of April, 2016, subject to the provisions of this Act, a tax in respect of his total undisclosed foreign income and asset of the previous year at the rate of thirty per cent. of such undisclosed income and asset:

Provided that an undisclosed asset located outside India shall be charged to tax on its value in the previous year in which such asset comes to the notice of the Assessing Officer.

(2) For the purposes of this section, "value of an undisclosed asset" means the fair market value of an asset (including financial interest in any entity) determined in such manner as may be prescribed.

**4. Scope of total undisclosed foreign income and asset.**—(1) Subject to the provisions of this Act, the total undisclosed foreign income and asset of any previous year of an assessee shall be,—

(a) the income from a source located outside India, which has not been disclosed in the return of income furnished within the time specified in *Explanation* 2 to sub-section (1) or under sub-section (4) or sub-section (5) of section 139 of the Income-tax Act;

(b) the income, from a source located outside India, in respect of which a return is required to be furnished under section 139 of the Income-tax Act but no return of income has been furnished within the time specified in *Explanation* 2 to sub-section (1) or under sub-section (4) or sub-section (5) of section 139 of the said Act; and

(c) the value of an undisclosed asset located outside India.

(2) Notwithstanding anything contained in sub-section (1), any variation made in the income from a source outside India in the assessment or reassessment of the total income of any previous year, of the assessee under the Income-tax Act in accordance with the provisions of section 29 to section 43C or section 57 to section 59 or section 92C of the said Act, shall not be included in the total undisclosed foreign income.

(3) The income included in the total undisclosed foreign income and asset under this Act shall not form part of the total income under the Income-tax Act.

### Notes on Clause of the Bill

Clause 4 deals with the scope of total undisclosed foreign income and asset. It provides that the total undisclosed foreign income and asset of any previous year of an assessee shall be, —

(a) the income from a source located outside India, which has not been disclosed in the return of income furnished under sub-clause (1) or sub-clause (4) or sub-clause (5) of Clause 139 of the Income-tax Act;

(b) the income, from a source located outside India, in respect of which a return is required to be furnished under Clause 139 of the Income-tax Act but no return of income has been furnished under sub-clause (1) or sub-clause (4) or sub-clause (5) of Clause 139 of the Income-tax Act;

(c) the value of any undisclosed asset located outside India.

It further provides that any variation made in the income from a source outside India in the assessment or reassessment of the total income of any previous year, of the assessee under the Income-tax Act in accordance with the provisions of Clause 29 to Clause 43C or Clause 57 to Clause 59 or Clause 92C of the said Act shall not be included in the total undisclosed foreign income.

It provides that the income included in the total undisclosed foreign income and asset under this Act not form part of the total income under the Income-tax Act. [Clause 4 of the Bill]

**5. Computation of total undisclosed foreign income and asset.**—(1) In computing the total undisclosed foreign income and asset of any previous year of an assessee,—

(i) no deduction in respect of any expenditure or allowance or set off of any loss shall be allowed to the assessee, whether or not it is allowable in accordance with the provisions of the Income-tax Act;

(ii) any income,—

(a) which has been assessed to tax for any assessment year under the Income-tax Act prior to the assessment year to which this Act applies; or

(b) which is assessable or has been assessed to tax for any assessment year under this Act,

shall be reduced from the value of the undisclosed asset located outside India, if, the assessee furnishes evidence to the satisfaction of the Assessing Officer that the asset has been acquired from the income which has been assessed or is assessable, as the case may be, to tax.

(2) The amount of deduction referred to in clause (ii) of sub-section (1) in case of an immovable property shall be the amount which bears to the value of the asset as on the first day of the financial year in which it comes to the notice of the Assessing Officer, the same proportion as the assessable or assessed foreign income bears to the total cost of the asset.

*Illustration*

A house property located outside India was acquired by an assessee in the previous year 2009-10 for fifty lakh rupees. Out of the investment of fifty lakh rupees, twenty lakh rupees was assessed to tax in the total income of the previous year 2009-10 and earlier years. Such undisclosed asset comes to the notice of the Assessing Officer in the year 2017-18. If the value of the asset in the year 2017-18 is one crore rupees, the amount chargeable to tax shall be A-B=C

where,

A=Rs.1 crore, B=Rs. (100 x 20/50) lakh=Rs. 40 lakh, C=Rs. (100-40) lakh=Rs.60 lakh.

## CHAPTER III
## TAX MANAGEMENT

**6. Tax authorities.**—(1) The income-tax authorities specified in section 116 of the Income-tax Act shall be the tax authorities for the purposes of this Act.

(2) Every such authority shall exercise the powers and perform the functions of a tax authority under this Act in respect of any person within his jurisdiction.

(3) Subject to the provisions of sub-section (4), the jurisdiction of a tax authority under this Act shall be the same as he has under the Income-tax Act by virtue of orders or directions issued under section 120 of that Act (including orders or directions assigning the concurrent jurisdiction) or under any other provision of that Act.

(4) The tax authority having jurisdiction in relation to an assessee who has no income assessable to income-tax under the Income-tax Act shall be the tax authority having jurisdiction in respect of the area in which the assessee resides or carries on its business or has its principal place of business.

(5) Section 118 of the Income-tax Act and any notification issued thereunder shall apply in relation to the control of tax authorities as they apply in relation to the control of the corresponding income-tax authorities, except to the extent to which the Board may, by notification in the Official Gazette, otherwise direct in respect of any tax authority.

**7. Change of incumbent.**—(1) The tax authority who succeeds another authority as a result of change in jurisdiction or for any other reason, shall continue the proceedings from the stage at which it was left by his predecessor.

(2) The assessee in such a case may be given an opportunity of being heard, if he so requests in writing, before passing any order in his case.

**8. Powers regarding discovery and production of evidence.**—(1) The prescribed tax authorities shall, for the purposes of this Act, have the same powers as are vested in a court under the Code of Civil Procedure, 1908 (5 of 1908), while trying a suit in respect of the following matters, namely:—

(a) discovery and inspection;

(b) enforcing the attendance of any person, including any officer of a banking company and examining him on oath;

(c) compelling the production of books of account and other documents; and

(d) issuing commissions.

(2) For the purposes of making any inquiry or investigation, the prescribed tax authority shall be vested with the powers referred to in sub-section (1), whether or not any proceedings are pending before it.

(3) Any tax authority prescribed for the purposes of sub-section (1) or sub-section (2) may, subject to the rules made in this behalf, impound any books of account or other documents produced before it and retain them in its custody for such period as it thinks fit.

(4) Any tax authority below the rank of Commissioner shall not—

(a) impound any books of account or other documents without recording his reasons for doing so; or

(b) retain in his custody any such books or documents for a period exceeding thirty days without obtaining the approval of the Principal Chief Commissioner or the Chief Commissioner or the Principal Commissioner or the Commissioner.

**9. Proceedings before tax authorities to be judicial proceedings.**—(1) Any proceeding under this Act before a tax authority shall be deemed to be a judicial proceeding within the meaning of section 193 and section 228 and for the purposes of section 196 of the Indian Penal Code (45 of 1860).

(2) Every tax authority shall be deemed to be a civil court for the purposes of section 195, but not for the purposes of Chapter XXVI of the Code of Criminal Procedure, 1973 (2 of 1974).

**Notes on Clause of the Bill**

Clause 9 provides that any proceeding under this Bill before a tax authority shall be deemed to be a judicial proceeding within the meaning of Clause 193 and Clause 228 and for the purposes of Section 196 of the Indian Penal Code, 1860.

It further provides that every tax authority shall be deemed to be a civil court for the purposes of Clause 195, but not for the purposes of Chapter XXVI of the Code of Criminal Procedure, 1973 (2 of 1974). [Clause 9 of the Bill]

**10. Assessment.**—(1) For the purposes of making an assessment or reassessment under this Act, the Assessing Officer may, on receipt of an information from an income-tax authority under the Income-tax Act or any other authority under any law for the time being in force or on coming of any information to his notice, serve on any person, a notice requiring him on a date to be specified to produce or cause to be produced such accounts or documents or evidence as the Assessing Officer may require for the purposes of this Act and may, from time to time, serve further notices requiring the production of such other accounts or documents or evidence as he may require.

(2) The Assessing Officer may make such inquiry, as he considers necessary, for the purpose of obtaining full information in respect of undisclosed foreign income and asset of any person for the relevant financial year or years.

(3) The Assessing Officer, after considering such accounts, documents or evidence, as he has obtained under sub-section (1), and after taking into account any relevant material which he has gathered under sub-section (2) and any other evidence produced by the assessee, shall by an order in writing, assess [1][or reassess] the undisclosed foreign income and asset and determine the sum payable by the assessee.

(4) If any person fails to comply with all the terms of the notice under sub-section (1), the Assessing Officer shall, after taking into account all the relevant material which he has gathered and after giving the assessee

1. Inst. by Act 23 of 2019, Section 206 (w.e.f. July 1, 2015).

an opportunity of being heard, make the assessment [1][or reassessment] of undisclosed foreign income and asset to the best of his judgment and determine the sum payable by the assessee.

**11. Time limit for completion of assessment and reassessment.**—(1) No order of assessment or reassessment shall be made under section 10 after the expiry of two years from the end of the financial year in which the notice under sub-section (1) of section 10 was issued by the Assessing Officer.

(2) Notwithstanding anything contained in sub-section (1), an order of fresh assessment in pursuance of an order passed under section 18 setting aside or cancelling an assessment, may be made at any time before the expiry of the period of two years from the end of the financial year in which the order under section 18 is received by the Principal Commissioner or the Commissioner.

(3) The provisions of sub-section (1) shall not apply to the assessment or reassessment made in consequence of, or to give effect to, any finding or direction contained in an order under section 15 or section 18 or section 19 or section 22 of this Act or in an order of any court in a proceeding otherwise than by way of appeal under this Act and such assessment or reassessment may, subject to the provisions of sub-section (2), be completed at any time, before the expiry of the period of two years from the end of the financial year in which such order is received by the Principal Commissioner or the Commissioner.

*Explanation 1.*—In computing the period of limitation for the purpose of this section—

(i) the time taken in reopening the whole or any part of the proceeding; or

(ii) the period during which the assessment proceeding is stayed by an order or injunction of any court; or

(iii) the period commencing from the date on which a reference or first of the references for exchange of information is made by an authority competent under an agreement referred to in section 90 or section 90A of the Income-tax Act or under section 73 of this Act and ending with the date on which the Principal Commissioner or the Commissioner last receives, the information so requested or a period of one year, whichever is less,

shall be excluded:

Provided that where immediately after the exclusion of the aforesaid time or period, the period of limitation referred to in sub-sections (1), (2) and (3) available to the Assessing Officer for making an order of assessment or reassessment, as the case may be, is less than sixty days, such remaining period shall be extended to sixty days and the aforesaid period of limitation shall be deemed to be extended accordingly.

*Explanation 2.*—Where, by an order referred to in sub-section (3), any undisclosed foreign income and asset is excluded from the total undisclosed

1. Inst. by Act 23 of 2019, Section 206 (w.e.f. July 1, 2015).

foreign income and asset for an assessment year in respect of an assessee, then, an assessment of such undisclosed foreign income and asset for another assessment year shall, for the purposes of section 10 and this section, be deemed to be one made in consequence of, or to give effect to, any finding or direction contained in the said order.

**12. Rectification of mistake.**—(1) A tax authority may amend any order passed by it under this Act so as to rectify any mistake apparent from the record.

(2) No amendment under this section shall be made after a period of four years from the end of the financial year in which the order sought to be amended was passed.

(3) The tax authority shall not make any amendment, which has the effect of enhancing the undisclosed foreign income and asset or reducing a refund or otherwise increasing the liability of the assessee, unless the authority concerned has given to the assessee an opportunity of being heard.

(4) The tax authority concerned may make an amendment under this section—

(a) on its own motion; or

(b) on an application made to it by the assessee or, as the case may be, by the Assessing Officer.

(5) Any application received by the tax authority for amendment of an order shall be decided within a period of six months from the end of the month in which such application is received by it.

(6) In a case where the order has been made in an appeal or revision, the power of the tax authority to amend the order shall be restricted to matters other than those decided in appeal or revision.

**13. Notice of demand.**—Any sum payable in consequence of any order made under this Act shall be demanded by a tax authority by serving upon the assessee a notice of demand in such form and manner as may be prescribed.

**14. Direct assessment or recovery not barred.**—Nothing in this Chapter shall prevent either the direct assessment of the person on whose behalf or for whose benefit the undisclosed income from a source located outside India is receivable or undisclosed asset located outside India is held, or the recovery from such person of the tax or any other sum of money payable in respect of such income and asset.

**15. Appeals to the Commissioner (Appeals).**—(1) Any person,—

(a) objecting to the amount of tax on undisclosed foreign income and asset for which he is assessed by the Assessing Officer; or

(b) denying his liability to be assessed under this Act; or

(c) objecting to any penalty imposed by the Assessing Officer; or

(d) objecting to an order of rectification having the effect of enhancing the assessment or reducing the refund; or

(e) objecting to an order refusing to allow the claim made by the assessee for a rectification under section 12, may appeal to the Commissioner (Appeals).

(2) Every appeal shall be filed in such form and verified in such manner and be accompanied by a fee as may be prescribed.

(3) An appeal shall be presented within a period of thirty days from—

(a) the date of service of the notice of demand relating to the assessment or penalty, or

(b) the date on which the intimation of the order sought to be appealed against is served in any other case.

(4) The Commissioner (Appeals) may admit an appeal after the expiration of the period referred to in sub-section (3)—

(a) if he is satisfied that the appellant had sufficient cause for not presenting it within that period; and

(b) the delay in preferring the appeal does not exceed a period of one year.

(5) The Commissioner (Appeals) shall hear and determine the appeal and, subject to the provisions of this Act, pass such orders as he thinks fit and such orders may include an order enhancing the assessment or penalty:

Provided that an order enhancing the assessment or penalty shall not be made unless the assessee has been given a reasonable opportunity of being heard.

**16. Procedure to be followed in appeal.**—(1) The Commissioner (Appeals) shall fix a date and place for the hearing of the appeal, and shall give notice of the same to the appellant and the Assessing Officer against whose order the appeal is preferred.

(2) The following shall have the right to be heard at the hearing of the appeal, namely:—

(a) the appellant, either in person or by an authorised representative;

(b) the Assessing Officer, either in person or by a representative.

(3) The Commissioner (Appeals) may adjourn the hearing of the appeal whenever he considers it necessary or expedient to do so.

(4) The Commissioner (Appeals) may, before disposing of any appeal, make such further inquiry as he thinks fit.

(5) The Commissioner (Appeals) may, during the proceedings before him, direct the Assessing Officer to make an inquiry and report to him on the points arising out of any question of law or fact.

(6) The Commissioner (Appeals) may, at the hearing of an appeal, allow the appellant to go into any ground of appeal not specified in the grounds of appeal, if the Commissioner (Appeals) is satisfied that the omission was not wilful or unreasonable.

(7) The order of the Commissioner (Appeals) disposing of the appeal shall be in writing and shall state the points for determination, the decision thereon and the reasons therefor.

(8) Every appeal preferred under section 15 shall be heard and disposed of by the Commissioner (Appeals) as expeditiously as possible and endeavour shall be made to dispose of such appeal within a period of one year from the end of the financial year in which the appeal is preferred.

(9) On the disposal of the appeal, the Commissioner (Appeals) shall communicate the order passed by him to the assessee and to the Principal Chief Commissioner or the Chief Commissioner or the Principal Commissioner or the Commissioner.

**17. Powers of Commissioner (Appeals).**—(1) In disposing of an appeal, the Commissioner (Appeals) shall have the following powers, namely:—

(a) in an appeal against an order of assessment, he may confirm, reduce, enhance or annul the assessment;

(b) in an appeal against an order imposing a penalty, he may confirm or cancel [1][or vary such order either to enhance or reduce the penalty];

(c) in any other case, he may determine the issues arising in the appeal and pass such orders thereon, as he thinks fit.

(2) The Commissioner (Appeals) may consider and decide any matter which was not considered by the Assessing Officer.

(3) The Commissioner (Appeals) shall not enhance an assessment or a penalty unless the appellant has been given an opportunity of being heard.

(4) In disposing of an appeal, the Commissioner (Appeals) may consider and decide any matter arising out of the proceedings in which the order appealed against was passed, notwithstanding that such matter was not raised before him by the appellant.

**Notes on Clause of the Bill**

Clause 17 relates to the powers of the Commissioner (Appeals) and, *inter alia*, provides that in case of an appeal before him, the Commissioner (Appeals) shall have the power to confirm, reduce, enhance or annul the assessment or to confirm or cancel a penalty.

[Clause 17 of the Bill]

**18. Appeals to Appellate Tribunal.**—(1) Any assessee aggrieved by an order passed by the Commissioner (Appeals) under section 15, or an order passed by the Principal Commissioner or the Commissioner under any provision of this Act, may appeal to the Appellate Tribunal against such order.

(2) The Principal Commissioner or the Commissioner may, if he objects to any order passed by the Commissioner (Appeals) under any provision of this Act, direct the Assessing Officer to appeal to the Appellate Tribunal against the order.

(3) Every appeal under sub-section (1) or sub-section (2) shall be filed within a period of sixty days from the date on which the order sought to be appealed against is communicated to the assessee or to the Principal Commissioner or the Commissioner, as the case may be.

1. Subst. by Act 23 of 2019, Section 207, for "such order" (w.e.f. September 1, 2019).

(4) The Assessing Officer or the assessee, as the case may be, on receipt of notice that an appeal against the order of the Commissioner (Appeals) has been preferred under sub-section (1) or sub-section (2) by the other party may, notwithstanding that he may not have appealed against such order or any part thereof, within thirty days of the receipt of the notice, file a memorandum of cross-objections, verified in the prescribed manner, against any part of the order of the Commissioner (Appeals), and such memorandum shall be disposed of by the Appellate Tribunal as if it were an appeal presented within the time specified in sub-section (3).

(5) The Appellate Tribunal may admit an appeal or permit the filing of a memorandum of cross-objections after the expiry of the period referred to in sub-section (3) or sub-section (4), if—

(a) it is satisfied that there was sufficient cause for not presenting it within that period; and

(b) the delay in filing the appeal does not exceed a period of one year.

(6) An appeal to the Appellate Tribunal shall be filed in such form, and verified in such manner, and shall, except in the case of an appeal referred to in sub-section (2) or a memorandum of cross-objections referred to in sub-section (4), be accompanied by a fee as may be prescribed.

(7) Subject to the provisions of this Act, in hearing and making an order on any appeal under this section, the Appellate Tribunal shall exercise the same powers and follow the procedure as it exercises and follows in hearing and making an order on any appeal under the Income-tax Act.

**19. Appeal to High Court.**—(1) An appeal shall lie to the High Court from every order passed in appeal by the Appellate Tribunal, if the High Court is satisfied that the case involves a substantial question of law.

(2) The Principal Chief Commissioner or the Chief Commissioner or the Principal Commissioner or the Commissioner or an assessee, may file an appeal to the High Court on being aggrieved by any order passed by the Appellate Tribunal and such appeal shall be—

(a) filed within a period of one hundred and twenty days from the date on which the order appealed against is received by the Principal Chief Commissioner or the Chief Commissioner or the Principal Commissioner or the Commissioner or the assessee;

(b) in the form of a memorandum of appeal precisely stating therein the substantial question of law involved.

(3) The High Court may admit an appeal after the expiry of the period of one hundred and twenty days referred to in sub-section (2), if it is satisfied that there was sufficient cause for not filing the appeal within that period.

(4) If the High Court is satisfied that a substantial question of law is involved in any case, it shall formulate that question.

(5) The appeal shall be heard only on the question so formulated, and the respondents shall, at the hearing of the appeal, be allowed to argue that the case does not involve such question.

(6) Notwithstanding anything in sub-sections (4) and (5), the High Court may exercise its power to hear the appeal on any other substantial question of law not formulated by it, if it is satisfied that the case involves such question of law.

(7) The High Court shall decide the question of law so formulated and deliver such judgment thereon containing the grounds on which such decision is founded and may award such cost as it deems fit.

(8) The High Court may determine any issue which—

(a) has not been determined by the Appellate Tribunal; or

(b) has been wrongly determined by the Appellate Tribunal, by reason of a decision on the question of law referred to in sub-section (1).

(9) The provisions of the Code of Civil Procedure, 1908 (5 of 1908), relating to appeals to the High Court shall, so far as may be, apply in the case of appeals under this section.

(10) When the High Court delivers a judgment in an appeal filed before it under sub-section (7), effect shall be given to the order passed on the appeal by the Assessing Officer on the basis of a certified copy of the judgment.

**20. Case before High Court to be heard by not less than two Judges.**—(1) An appeal filed before the High Court shall be heard by a Bench of not less than two Judges of the High Court and shall be decided in accordance with the opinion of such Judges or if the Bench is of more than two Judges, by the majority of such Judges.

(2) Where there is no such majority, the Judges shall state the point of law upon which they differ and the case shall then be heard upon that point only by one or more of the other Judges of the High Court and such point shall be decided according to the opinion of the majority of the Judges who have heard the case including those who first heard it.

**21. Appeal to Supreme Court.**—An appeal shall lie to the Supreme Court from any judgment of the High Court delivered under section 19 which the High Court certifies to be a fit case for appeal to the Supreme Court.

**22. Hearing before Supreme Court.**—(1) The provisions of the Code of Civil Procedure, 1908 (5 of 1908), relating to appeals to the Supreme Court shall, so far as may be, apply in the case of appeals under section 21 as they apply in the case of appeals from decrees of a High Court.

(2) The costs of the appeal shall be in the discretion of the Supreme Court.

(3) Where the judgment of the High Court is varied or reversed in the appeal, effect shall be given to the order of the Supreme Court in the manner provided in sub-section (10) of section 19.

**Notes on Clause of the Bill**

Clause 22 relates to hearing before the Supreme Court and provides that the provisions of the Code of Civil Procedure, 1908, relating to appeals to the Supreme Court shall, so far as may be, apply in the case of appeals under Section 21 as they apply in the case of appeals from decrees of a High Court. [Clause 22 of the Bill]

**23. Revision of orders prejudicial to revenue.**—(1) The Principal Commissioner or the Commissioner may, for the purposes of revising any order passed in any proceeding under this Act before any tax authority subordinate to him, call for and examine all available records relating thereto.

(2) The Principal Commissioner or the Commissioner may, after giving the assessee an opportunity of being heard, pass an order (hereinafter referred to as the revision order) as the circumstances of the case justify, if he is satisfied that the order sought to be revised is erroneous in so far as it is prejudicial to the interests of the revenue.

(3) The Principal Commissioner or the Commissioner may make, or cause to be made, such inquiry as he considers necessary for the purposes of passing an order under sub-section (2).

(4) The revision order passed by the Principal Commissioner or the Commissioner under sub-section (2) may have the effect of enhancing or modifying the assessment but shall not be an order cancelling the assessment and directing a fresh assessment.

(5) The power of the Principal Commissioner or the Commissioner under sub-section (2) for revising an order shall extend to such matters as have not been considered and decided in any appeal.

(6) No order under sub-section (2) shall be made after the expiry of a period of two years from the end of the financial year in which the order sought to be revised was passed.

(7) Notwithstanding anything in sub-section (6), an order in revision under this section may be passed at any time in respect of an order which has been passed in consequence of, or to give effect to, any finding or direction contained in an order of the Appellate Tribunal, the High Court or the Supreme Court.

(8) In computing the period of limitation under sub-section (6), the following shall not be included, namely:—

(a) the time taken in giving an opportunity to the assessee to be reheard under section 7; or

(b) any period during which any proceeding under this section is stayed by an order or injunction of any court.

(9) Without prejudice to the generality of the foregoing provisions, an order passed by a tax authority shall be deemed to be erroneous in so far as it is prejudicial to the interests of the revenue, if in the opinion of the Principal Commissioner or the Commissioner—

(a) the order is passed without making inquiries or verification which, should have been made; or

(b) the order has not been made in accordance with any order, direction or instruction issued by the Board; or

(c) the order has not been passed in accordance with any decision, prejudicial to the assessee, rendered by the jurisdictional High Court or the Supreme Court in the case of the assessee or any other person under this Act or the Income-tax Act.

(10) In this section, "record" shall include all records relating to any proceeding under this Act available at the time of examination by the Principal Commissioner or the Commissioner.

**24. Revision of other orders.**—(1) The Principal Commissioner or the Commissioner may, either *suo motu* or on an application made by the assessee, for the purposes of revising any order passed by an authority subordinate to him, other than an order to which section 23 applies, call for and examine all available records relating thereto.

(2) The Principal Commissioner or the Commissioner may pass an order, as he considers necessary, which is not prejudicial to the assessee.

(3) The power of the Principal Commissioner or the Commissioner under sub-section (2) to revise an order shall not extend to such order—

(a) against which an appeal has not been filed but the time for filing an appeal before the Commissioner (Appeals) has not expired;

(b) against which an appeal is pending before the Commissioner (Appeals); or

(c) which has been considered and decided in any appeal.

(4) The assessee shall make the application for revision of any order referred to in sub-section (1), within a period of one year from the date on which the order sought to be revised was communicated to him, or the date on which he otherwise came to know of it, whichever is earlier.

(5) The Principal Commissioner or the Commissioner may, if he is satisfied that the assessee was prevented by sufficient cause from making the application within the period of one year, admit an application made after the expiry of one year but before expiry of two years from the date referred to in sub-section (4).

(6) Every application by an assessee for revision under this section shall be accompanied by such fees as may be prescribed.

(7) No order under sub-section (2) shall be made after the expiry of—

(a) a period of one year from the end of the financial year in which an application is made by the assessee under sub-section (4); or

(b) a period of one year from the date of the order sought to be revised, if the order is revised *suo motu* by the Commissioner.

(8) In computing the period of limitation under sub-section (7), the following shall not be included, namely:—

(a) the time taken in giving an opportunity to the assessee to be reheard under section 7; or

(b) any period during which any proceeding under this section is stayed by an order or injunction of any court.

(9) An order by the Principal Commissioner or the Commissioner declining to interfere shall, for the purposes of this section, be deemed not to be an order prejudicial to the assessee.

**25. Tax to be paid pending appeal.**—Notwithstanding any appeal preferred to the High Court or the Supreme Court, the tax shall be paid in accordance with the assessment made under this Act.

**26. Execution of order for costs awarded by Supreme Court.**—The High Court may, on petition made for the execution of the order in respect of the costs awarded by the Supreme Court, transmit such order for execution to any court subordinate to it.

**27. Amendment of assessment on appeal.**—Where as a result of an appeal under section 15 or section 18, any change is made in the assessment of a body of individuals or an association of persons or an order for new assessment of a body of individuals or an association of persons is made, the Commissioner (Appeals) or the Appellate Tribunal, as the case may be, shall pass an order authorising the Assessing Officer either to amend the assessment made or make a fresh assessment on any member of the body or association.

**28. Exclusion of time taken for obtaining copy.**—In computing the period of limitation prescribed for an appeal under this Act, the day on which the notice of the order was served upon the assessee without serving a copy of the order, the time taken for obtaining a copy of such order, shall be excluded.

**29. Filing of appeal by tax authority.**—(1) The Board may, from time to time, issue orders, instructions or directions to other tax authorities, fixing such monetary limits as it may deem fit, for the purpose of regulating the filing of appeal by any tax authority under this Chapter.

(2) Where, in pursuance of the orders, instructions or directions issued under sub-section (1), a tax authority has not filed any appeal on any issue in the case of an assessee for any financial year, it shall not preclude such authority from filing an appeal on the same issue in the case of—

(a) the same assessee for any other financial year; or

(b) any other assessee for the same or any other financial year.

(3) Notwithstanding that no appeal has been filed by a tax authority pursuant to the orders or instructions or directions issued under sub-section (1), it shall not be lawful for an assessee, being a party in any appeal, to contend that the tax authority has acquiesced in the decision on the disputed issue by not filing an appeal in any case.

(4) The Appellate Tribunal, hearing such appeal, shall have regard to the orders, instructions or directions issued under sub-section (1) and the circumstances under which such appeal was filed or not filed in respect of any case.

(5) Every order, instruction or direction which has been issued by the Board fixing monetary limits for filing an appeal shall be deemed to have been issued under sub-section (1) and the provisions of sub-sections (2), (3) and (4) shall apply accordingly.

**30. Recovery of tax dues by Assessing Officer.**—(1) Any amount specified as payable in a notice of demand under section 13 shall be paid within a period of thirty days of the service of the notice, to the credit of the Central Government in such manner as may be prescribed.

(2) Where the Assessing Officer has any reason to believe that it will be detrimental to the interests of revenue, if the period of thirty days referred to in sub-section (1) is allowed, he may, with the previous approval of the Joint Commissioner, reduce such period as he deems fit.

(3) The Assessing Officer may, on an application made by the assessee, before the expiry of a period of thirty days or the period reduced under sub-section (2) or during the pendency of appeal with the Commissioner (Appeals), extend the time for payment, or allow payment by instalments, subject to such conditions as he may think fit to impose in the circumstances of the case.

(4) An assessee shall be deemed to be an assessee in default, if the tax arrear is not paid within the time allowed under sub-section (1) or the period reduced under sub-section (2) or extended under sub-section (3), as the case may be.

(5) Where an assessee defaults in paying any one of the instalments within the time fixed under sub-section (3), he shall be deemed to be an assessee in default in respect of the whole of the then outstanding amount.

(6) The Assessing Officer may, in a case where no certificate has been drawn up under section 31 by the Tax Recovery Officer, recover the amount in respect of which the assessee is in default, or is deemed to be in default, by any one or more of the modes provided in section 32.

(7) The Tax Recovery Officer shall be vested with the powers to recover the tax arrear on drawing up of a statement of tax arrear under section 31.

**31. Recovery of tax dues by Tax Recovery Officer.**—(1) The Tax Recovery Officer may draw up under his signature a statement of tax arrears of an assessee referred to in sub-section (4) or sub-section (5) of section 30, in such form, as may be prescribed (such statement hereafter in this Chapter referred to as "certificate").

(2) The certificate under sub-section (1) shall stand amended from time-to-time consequent to any proceeding under this Act and the Tax Recovery Officer shall recover the amount so modified.

(3) The Tax Recovery Officer may rectify any mistake apparent from the record.

(4) The Tax Recovery Officer shall have the power to extend the time for payment, or allow payment by instalments, subject to such conditions as he may think fit to impose in the circumstances of the case.

(5) The Tax Recovery Officer shall proceed to recover from the assessee the amount specified in the certificate by one or more of the modes referred to in section 32 or in the Second Schedule to the Income-tax Act.

(6) It shall not be open to the assessee to dispute the correctness of any certificate drawn up by the Tax Recovery Officer on any ground whatsoever,

but it shall be lawful for the Tax Recovery Officer to cancel the certificate if, for any reason, he thinks it necessary so to do.

**Notes on Clause of the Bill**

This Clause relates to recovery of tax dues by the Tax Recovery Officer and *inter alia*, provides that such officer may draw up under his signature a statement of tax arrears (certificate) and shall proceed to recover from the assessee the amount specified in the certificate by one or more of the modes referred to in Clause 32 of this Bill or in the Second Schedule to the Income-tax Act. [Clause 31 of the Bill]

**32. Modes of recovery of tax dues.**—(1) The Assessing Officer or the Tax Recovery Officer may require the employer of the assessee to deduct from any payment to the assessee such amount as is sufficient to meet the tax arrear from the assessee.

(2) Upon requisition under sub-section (1), the employer shall comply with the requisition and shall pay the sum so deducted to the credit of the Central Government in such manner as may be prescribed.

(3) Any part of the salary, exempt from attachment in execution of a decree of a civil court under section 60 of the Code of Civil Procedure, 1908 (5 of 1908), shall be exempt from any requisition made under sub-section (1).

(4) The Assessing Officer or the Tax Recovery Officer may, by notice in writing, require any debtor of the assessee to pay such amount, not exceeding the amount of debt, as is sufficient to meet the tax arrear of the assessee.

(5) Upon receipt of the notice under sub-section (4), the debtor shall comply with the requisition and shall pay the sum to the credit of the Central Government in such manner as may be prescribed within the time (not being before the debt becomes due to the assessee) specified in the notice.

(6) A copy of the notice issued under sub-section (4) shall be forwarded to the assessee at his last address known to the Assessing Officer or the Tax Recovery Officer and in the case of a joint account, to all the joint holders at their last addresses known to the Assessing Officer or the Tax Recovery Officer.

(7) It shall not be necessary for any pass book, deposit receipt, policy or any other document to be produced for the purpose of any entry, endorsement or the like being made before payment is made, notwithstanding any rule, practice or requirement to the contrary if the notice under sub-section (4) is issued to a post office, banking company, insurer or any other person.

(8) Any claim in respect of any property, in relation to which a notice under sub-section (4) has been issued, arising after the date of the notice, shall be void as against any demand contained in the notice.

(9) A person to whom a notice under sub-section (4) has been issued, shall not be required to pay the amount of tax arrear specified therein, or part thereof, if he objects to it by a statement on oath that the sum demanded, or any part thereof, is not due to the assessee or that he does not hold any money for, or on account of, the assessee.

(10) The person referred to in sub-section (9) shall be personally liable to the Assessing Officer or the Tax Recovery Officer, as the case may be, to

the extent of his own liability to the assessee on the date of the notice, or to the extent of the liability of the assessee for any sum due under this Act, whichever is less, if it is discovered that the statement made by him was false in any respect.

(11) The Assessing Officer or the Tax Recovery Officer may amend or revoke any notice issued under sub-section (4) or extend the time for making any payment in pursuance of such notice.

(12) The Assessing Officer or the Tax Recovery Officer shall grant a receipt for any amount paid in compliance with a notice issued under sub-section (4), and the person so paying shall be fully discharged from his liability to the assessee to the extent of the amount so paid.

(13) Any person discharging any liability to the assessee after receipt of a notice under sub-section (4) shall be personally liable to the Assessing Officer or the Tax Recovery Officer to the extent of his own liability to the assessee so discharged or to the extent of the liability of the assessee for any sum due under this Act, whichever is less.

(14) The debtor to whom a notice under sub-section (4) is sent shall be deemed to be an assessee in default, if he fails to make such payment and further proceedings may be initiated against him for the realisation of the amount in the manner provided in this section and the Second Schedule to the Income-tax Act.

(15) The Assessing Officer or the Tax Recovery Officer may apply to the court, in whose custody there is money belonging to the assessee, for payment to him of the entire amount of such money or if it is more than the tax arrear, an amount sufficient to meet the tax arrear.

(16) The Assessing Officer or the Tax Recovery Officer shall effect the recovery of any tax arrear in the same manner as attachment, distraint and sale of any movable property under the Second Schedule to the Income-tax Act, if he is so authorised by the Principal Chief Commissioner or the Chief Commissioner, or the Principal Commissioner or the Commissioner, by general or special order.

(17) In this section,—

(a) "debtor", in relation to an assessee, means,—

(i) any person from whom any money is due, or may become due, to the assessee; or

(ii) any person who holds, or may subsequently hold, any money for, or on account of, the assessee; or

(iii) any person who holds, or may subsequently hold, any money for, or on account of, the assessee jointly with any other person;

(b) shares of the joint holders in the account shall be presumed, until the contrary is proved, to be equal.

**33. Tax Recovery Officer by whom recovery of tax dues is to be effected.**—(1) The Tax Recovery Officer competent to take action under section 31 shall be the Tax Recovery Officer—

(a) within whose jurisdiction—

(i) the assessee carries on his business;

(ii) the principal place of business of the assessee is situate;

(iii) the assessee resides; or

(iv) any movable or immovable property of the assessee is situate; or

(b) who has been assigned jurisdiction under section 6.

(2) The Tax Recovery Officer, referred to in sub-section (1), may send a certificate, in such manner as may be prescribed, specifying the tax arrear to be recovered, to another Tax Recovery Officer within whose jurisdiction the assessee resides or has property, if the first mentioned Tax Recovery Officer—

(a) is not able to recover the entire amount by sale of the property, movable or immovable, within his jurisdiction; or

(b) is of the opinion that, for the purpose of expediting, or securing, the recovery of the whole, or any part, of the amount under this Chapter, it is necessary to send such certificate.

(3) The second-mentioned Tax Recovery Officer shall, on receipt of the certificate, assume jurisdiction for recovery of the amount of tax arrear specified therein and proceed to recover the amount in accordance with the provisions of this Chapter.

**34. Recovery of tax dues in case of a company in liquidation.**—(1) The liquidator shall inform the Assessing Officer, who has jurisdiction to assess the undisclosed foreign income and asset of the company, of his appointment within a period of thirty days of his becoming the liquidator.

(2) The Assessing Officer shall, within a period of three months from the date on which he receives the information, intimate to the liquidator the amount which, in his opinion, would be sufficient to provide for any tax arrears or any amount which is likely to become payable thereafter, by the company under this Act.

(3) The liquidator—

(a) shall not part with any of the assets of the company, or the properties, in his custody until he has been intimated by the Assessing Officer under sub-section (2); and

(b) on being so intimated, shall set aside an amount equal to the amount intimated.

(4) Upon receipt of the intimation from the Assessing Officer under sub-section (2), the amount so intimated shall, notwithstanding anything in any other law for the time being in force, be the first charge on the assets of the company remaining after payment of the following dues, namely:—

(a) workmen's dues; and

(b) debts due to secured creditors to the extent such debts under clause (iii) of the proviso to sub-section (1) of section 325 of the Companies Act, 2013 (18 of 2013) are *pari passu* with such dues.

(5) The liquidator shall be personally liable for the payment of the amount payable by the company, if he—

(a) fails to inform in accordance with sub-section (1); or

(b) fails to set aside the amount as required by sub-section (3).

(6) The obligations and liabilities attached to the liquidator under this section shall attach to all the liquidators jointly and severally in a case where there is more than one liquidator.

(7) The provisions of this section shall prevail over anything to the contrary contained in any other law for the time being in force.

(8) In this section,—

(a) "liquidator" in relation to a company which is being wound up, whether under the orders of a court or otherwise, shall include a receiver of the assets of the company;

(b) "workmen's dues" shall have the meaning assigned to it in section 325 of the Companies Act, 2013 (18 of 2013).

**35. Liability of manager of a company.**—(1) Every person being a manager at any time during the financial year shall be jointly and severally liable for the payment of any amount due under this Act in respect of the company for the financial year, if the amount cannot be recovered from the company.

(2) The provisions of sub-section (1) shall not apply, if the manager proves that non-recovery cannot be attributed to any neglect, misfeasance or breach of duty on his part in relation to the affairs of the company.

(3) The provisions of this section shall prevail over anything to the contrary contained in the Companies Act, 2013 (18 of 2013).

(4) In this section, "manager" shall include a managing director and both shall have the meaning respectively assigned to them in clause (53) and clause (54) of section 2 of the Companies Act, 2013 (18 of 2013).

**36. Joint and several liability of participants.**—(1) Every person, being a participant in an unincorporated body at any time during the financial year, or the representative assessee of the deceased participant, shall be jointly and severally liable, along with the unincorporated body, for payment of any amount payable by the unincorporated body under this Act and all the provisions of this Act shall apply accordingly.

(2) In case of a limited liability partnership, the provisions of sub-section (1) shall not apply, if the partner proves that non-recovery cannot be attributed to any neglect, misfeasance or breach of duty on his part in relation to the affairs of the partnership.

(3) The provisions of this section shall prevail over anything to the contrary contained in the Limited Liability Partnership Act, 2008 (6 of 2009).

**37. Recovery through State Government.**—If the recovery of tax in any area has been entrusted to a State Government under clause (1) of article 258 of the Constitution, the State Government may direct, with respect to that area or any part thereof, that tax shall be recovered therein with, and as an addition to, any municipal tax or local rate, by the same person and in the manner as the municipal tax or local rate is recovered.

**38. Recovery of tax dues in pursuance of agreements with foreign countries or specified territory.**—(1) The Tax Recovery Officer may, in a case where an assessee has property in a country or a specified territory outside India, forward a certificate to the Board for recovery of the tax arrears from the assessee, where the Central Government or any specified association in India has entered into an agreement with that country or territory under section 90 or section 90A of the Income-tax Act or under sub-sections (1), (2) or sub-section (4) of section 73 of this Act, as the case may be, for the purposes of recovery of tax.

(2) On receipt of the certificate under sub-section (3) from the Tax Recovery Officer, the Board may take such action thereon as it may deem appropriate having regard to the terms of the agreement with such country or a specified territory.

**39. Recovery by suit or under other law not affected.**—(1) The several modes of recovery specified in this Chapter shall not affect in any way—

(a) any other law for the time being in force relating to the recovery of debts due to the Government; or

(b) the right of the Government to institute a suit for the recovery of the tax arrears from the assessee.

(2) It shall be lawful for the Assessing Officer, or the Government, to have recourse to any such law or suit, notwithstanding that the tax arrears are being recovered from the assessee by any mode specified in this Chapter.

**Notes on Clause of the Bill**

Clause 39 relates to recovery by suit or under other law not affected. It *inter alia*, provides that the several modes of recovery specified in this Chapter shall not affect in any way any other law for the time being in force relating to the recovery of debts due to the Government, or the right of the Government to institute a suit for the recovery of the tax arrears from the assessee. [Clause 39 of the Bill]

**40. Interest for default in furnishing return and payment or deferment of advance tax.**—(1) Where the assessee has any income from a source outside India which has not been disclosed in the return of income furnished under sub-section (1) of section 139 of the Income-tax Act or the return of income has not been furnished under the said sub-section, interest shall be chargeable in accordance with the provisions of section 234A of the Income-tax Act.

(2) Where the assessee has any undisclosed income from a source outside India and the advance tax on such income has not been paid in accordance with Part C of Chapter XVII of the Income-tax Act, interest shall be chargeable in accordance with the provisions of sections 234B and 234C of the Income-tax Act.

## CHAPTER IV
## PENALTIES

**41. Penalty in relation to undisclosed foreign income and asset.**—The Assessing Officer may direct that in a case where tax has been computed under section 10 in respect of undisclosed foreign income and asset, the assessee shall pay by way of penalty, in addition to tax, if any, payable by him, a sum equal to three times the tax computed under that section.

**42. Penalty for failure to furnish return in relation to foreign income and asset.**—If a person, being a resident other than not ordinarily resident in India within the meaning of clause (6) of section 6 of the Income-tax Act, who is required to furnish a return of his income for any previous year, as required under sub-section (1) of section 139 of the Income-tax Act or by the provisos to that sub-section, and who at any time during such previous year,—

(i) held any asset (including financial interest in any entity) located outside India as a beneficial owner or otherwise; or

(ii) was a beneficiary of any asset (including financial interest in any entity) located outside India; or

(iii) had any income from a source located outside India,

and fails to furnish such return before the end of the relevant assessment year, the Assessing Officer may direct that such person shall pay, by way of penalty, a sum of ten lakh rupees:

Provided that this section shall not apply in respect of an asset, being one or more bank accounts having an aggregate balance which does not exceed a value equivalent to five hundred thousand rupees at any time during the previous year.

*Explanation*.—For determining the value equivalent in rupees of the balance in an account maintained in foreign currency, the rate of exchange for calculation of the value in rupees shall be the telegraphic transfer buying rate of such currency as on the date for which the value is to be determined as adopted by the State Bank of India constituted under the State Bank of India Act, 1955 (23 of 1955).

**43. Penalty for failure to furnish in return of income, an information or furnish inaccurate particulars about an asset (including financial interest in any entity) located outside India.**—If any person, being a resident other than not ordinarily resident in India within the meaning of clause (6) of section 6 of the Income-tax Act, who has furnished the return of income for any previous year under sub-section (1) or sub-section (4) or sub-section (5) of section 139 of the said Act, fails to furnish any information or furnishes inaccurate particulars in such return relating to any asset (including financial interest in any entity) located outside India, held by him as a beneficial owner or otherwise, or in respect of which he was a beneficiary, or relating to any income from a source located outside India, at any time during such previous year, the Assessing Officer may direct that such person shall pay, by way of penalty, a sum of ten lakh rupees:

Provided that this section shall not apply in respect of an asset, being one or more bank accounts having an aggregate balance which does not exceed a value equivalent to five hundred thousand rupees at any time during the previous year.

*Explanation*.—The value equivalent in rupees shall be determined in the manner provided in the *Explanation* to section 42.

**44. Penalty for default in payment of tax arrear.**—(1) Every person who is an assessee in default, or an assessee deemed to be in default, as the case may be, in making payment of tax, and in case of continuing default by such assessee, he shall be liable to a penalty of an amount, equal to the amount of tax arrear.

(2) An assessee shall not cease to be liable to any penalty under sub-section (1) merely by reason of the fact that before the levy of such penalty he has paid the tax.

**45. Penalty for other defaults.**—(1) A person shall be liable to a penalty if he has, without reasonable cause, failed to—

(a) answer any question put to him by a tax authority in the exercise of its powers under this Act;

(b) sign any statement made by him in the course of any proceedings under this Act which a tax authority may legally require him to sign;

(c) attend or produce books of account or documents at the place or time, if he is required to attend or to give evidence or produce books of account or other documents, at certain place and time in response to summons issued under section 8.

(2) The penalty referred to in sub-section (1) shall be a sum which shall not be less than fifty thousand rupees but which may extend to two lakh rupees.

**46. Procedure.**—(1) The tax authority shall, for the purposes of imposing any penalty under this Chapter, issue a notice to an assessee requiring him to show cause why the penalty should not be imposed on him.

(2) The notice referred to in sub-section (1) shall be issued—

(a) during the pendency of any proceedings under this Act for the relevant previous year, in respect of penalty referred to in section 41;

(b) within a period of three years from the end of the financial year in which the default is committed, in respect of penalties referred to in section 45.

(3) No order imposing a penalty under this Chapter shall be made unless the assessee has been given an opportunity of being heard.

(4) An order imposing a penalty under this Chapter shall be made with the approval of the Joint Commissioner, [1][or the Joint Director] if—

(a) the penalty exceeds one lakh rupees and the tax authority levying the penalty is in the rank of Income-tax Officer; or

(b) the penalty exceeds five lakh rupees and the tax authority levying the penalty is in the rank of Assistant Commissioner or Deputy Commissioner [2][or Assistant Director or Deputy Director].

1. Inst. by Act 13 of 2018, Section 219(a)(i) (w.e.f. April 1, 2018).
2. Inst. by Act 13 of 2018, Section 219(a)(ii) (w.e.f. April 1, 2018).

(5) Every order of penalty issued under this Chapter shall be accompanied by a notice of demand in respect of the amount of penalty imposed and such notice of demand shall be deemed to be a notice under section 13.

**47. Bar of limitation for imposing penalty.**—(1) No order imposing a penalty under this Chapter shall be passed after the expiry of a period of one year from the end of the financial year in which the notice for imposition of penalty is issued under section 46.

(2) An order imposing, or dropping the proceedings for imposition of, penalty under this Chapter may be revised, or revived, as the case may be, on the basis of assessment of the undisclosed foreign income and asset as revised after giving effect to the order of the Commissioner (Appeals), the Appellate Tribunal, the High Court or the Supreme Court or order of revision under section 23 or section 24.

(3) An order revising or reviving the penalty under sub-section (2) shall not be passed after the expiry of a period of six months from the end of the month in which order of the Commissioner (Appeals), the Appellate Tribunal, the High Court or the Supreme Court is received by the Principal Chief Commissioner or the Chief Commissioner or the Principal Commissioner or the Commissioner or the order of revision under section 23 or section 24 is passed.

(4) In computing the period of limitation for the purposes of this section, the following time or period shall not be included—

(a) the time taken in giving an opportunity to the assessee to be reheard under section 7; and

(b) any period during which a proceeding under this Chapter for the levy of penalty is stayed by an order, or injunction, of any court.

**Notes on Clause of the Bill**

Clause 47 relates to bar of limitation for imposing penalty. It, *inter alia*, provides for the time limit for passing the penalty orders. It further provides that in computing that period of limitation, certain specified time periods shall be excluded. It also provides that an order imposing or dropping the proceedings for imposition of penalty may be revised or revived on the basis of assessment of the undisclosed foreign income and asset as revised after giving effect to the Appellate Order or the order of revision under Clause 23 or Clause 24.

[Clause 47 of the Bill]

## CHAPTER V

## OFFENCES AND PROSECUTIONS

**48. Chapter not in derogation of any other law or any other provision of this Act.**—(1) The provisions of this Chapter shall be in addition to, and not in derogation of, the provisions of any other law providing for prosecution for offences thereunder.

(2) The provisions of this Chapter shall be independent of any order under this Act that may be made, or has not been made, on any person and it shall be no defence that the order has not been made on account of time limitation or for any other reason.

**49. Punishment for failure to furnish return in relation to foreign income and asset.**—If a person, being a resident other than not ordinarily resident in India within the meaning of clause (6) of section 6 of the Income-tax Act, who at any time during the previous year, held any asset (including financial interest in any entity) located outside India as a beneficial owner or otherwise, or was a beneficiary of such asset or had income from a source outside India and wilfully fails to furnish in due time the return of income which he is required to furnish under sub-section (1) of section 139 of that Act, he shall be punishable with rigorous imprisonment for a term which shall not be less than six months but which may extend to seven years and with fine:

Provided that a person shall not be proceeded against under this section for failure to furnish in due time the return of income under sub-section (1) of section 139 of the Income-tax Act if the return is furnished by him before the expiry of the assessment year.

**50. Punishment for failure to furnish in return of income, any information about an asset (including financial interest in any entity) located outside India.**—If any person, being a resident other than not ordinarily resident in India within the meaning of clause (6) of section 6 of the Income-tax Act, who has furnished the return of income for any previous year under sub-section (1) or sub-section (4) or sub-section (5) of section 139 of that Act, wilfully fails to furnish in such return any information relating to an asset (including financial interest in any entity) located outside India, held by him, as a beneficial owner or otherwise or in which he was a beneficiary, at any time during such previous year, or disclose any income from a source outside India, he shall be punishable with rigorous imprisonment for a term which shall not be less than six months but which may extend to seven years and with fine.

**51. Punishment for wilful attempt to evade tax.**—(1) If a person, being a resident other than not ordinarily resident in India within the meaning of clause (6) of section 6 of the Income-tax Act, wilfully attempts in any manner whatsoever to evade any tax, penalty or interest chargeable or imposable under this Act, he shall be punishable with rigorous imprisonment for a term which shall not be less than three years but which may extend to ten years and with fine.

(2) If a person wilfully attempts in any manner whatsoever to evade the payment of any tax, penalty or interest under this Act, he shall, without prejudice to any penalty that may be imposable on him under any other provision of this Act, be punishable with rigorous imprisonment for a term which shall not be less than three months but which may extend to three years and shall, in the discretion of the court, also be liable to fine.

(3) For the purposes of this section, a wilful attempt to evade any tax, penalty or interest chargeable or imposable under this Act or the payment thereof shall include a case where any person—

(i) has in his possession or control any books of account or other documents (being books of account or other documents relevant to any proceeding under this Act) containing a false entry or statement; or

(ii) makes or causes to be made any false entry or statement in such books of account or other documents; or

(iii) wilfully omits or causes to be omitted any relevant entry or statement in such books of account or other documents; or

(iv) causes any other circumstance to exist which will have the effect of enabling such person to evade any tax, penalty or interest chargeable or imposable under this Act or the payment thereof.

**52. Punishment for false statement in verification.**—If a person, makes a statement in any verification under this Act or under any rule made thereunder, or delivers an account or statement which is false, and which he either knows or believes to be false, or does not believe to be true, he shall be punishable with rigorous imprisonment for a term which shall not be less than six months but which may extend to seven years and with fine.

**53. Punishment for abetment.**—If a person abets or induces in any manner another person to make and deliver an account or a statement or declaration relating to tax payable under this Act which is false and which he either knows to be false or does not believe to be true or to commit an offence under sub-section (1) of section 51, he shall be punishable with rigorous imprisonment for a term which shall not be less than six months but which may extend to seven years and with fine.

**54. Presumption as to culpable mental state.**—(1) In any prosecution for any offence under this Act which requires a culpable mental state on the part of the accused, the court shall presume the existence of such mental state but it shall be a defence for the accused to prove the fact that he had no such mental state with respect to the act charged as an offence in that prosecution.

*Explanation.*—In this sub-section, "culpable mental state" includes intention, motive or knowledge of a fact or belief in, or reason to believe, a fact.

(2) For the purposes of this section, a fact is said to be proved only when the court believes it to exist beyond reasonable doubt and not merely when its existence is established by a preponderance of probability.

**55. [1][Prosecution to be at instance of Principal Chief Commissioner or Principal Director General or Chief Commissioner or Director General or Principal Commissioner or Commissioner].**—(1) A person shall not be proceeded against for an offence under section 49 to section 53 (both inclusive) except with the sanction of the Principal Commissioner or Commissioner or the Commissioner (Appeals), as the case may be.

(2) The Principal Chief Commissioner or the Chief Commissioner [2][or the Principal Director General or the Director General] may issue such instructions, or directions, to the tax authorities referred to in sub-section (1) as he may think fit for the institution of proceedings under this section.

1. Subst. by Act 13 of 2018, Section 219, for marginal heading (w.e.f. April 1, 2018).
2. Inst. by Act 13 of 2018, Section 219 (w.e.f. April 1, 2018).

(3) The power of the Board to issue orders, instructions or directions under this Act shall include the power to issue orders, instructions or directions (including instructions or directions to obtain its previous approval) to other tax authorities for the proper initiation of proceedings of offences (including an authorisation to file and pursue complaints by one or more Inspectors of tax) under this section.

**56. Offences by companies.**—(1) Where an offence under this Act has been committed by a company, every person who, at the time the offence was committed, was in charge of, and was responsible to, the company for the conduct of the business of the company as well as the company shall be deemed to be guilty of the offence and shall be liable to be proceeded against and punished accordingly.

(2) Nothing in sub-section (1) shall render any such person liable to any punishment if he proves that the offence was committed without his knowledge or that he had exercised all due diligence to prevent the commission of such offence.

(3) Notwithstanding anything in sub-section (1), where an offence under this Act has been committed by a company and it is proved that the offence has been committed with the consent or connivance of, or is attributable to any neglect on the part of, any director, manager, secretary or other officer of the company, such director, manager, secretary or other officer shall also be deemed to be guilty of that offence and shall be liable to be proceeded against and punished accordingly.

(4) Where an offence under this Act has been committed by a person, being a company, and the punishment for such offence is imprisonment and fine, then, without prejudice to sub-section (1) or sub-section (3), such company shall be punished with fine and every person, referred to in sub-section (1), or the director, manager, secretary or other officer of the company referred to in sub-section (3), shall be liable to be proceeded against and punished in accordance with the provisions of this Act.

(5) In this section—

(a) "company" means a body corporate, and includes—

(i) an unincorporated body;

(ii) a Hindu undivided family;

(b) "director", in relation to—

(i) an unincorporated body, means a participant in the body;

(ii) a Hindu undivided family, means an adult member of the family; and

(iii) a company, means a whole-time director, or where there is no such director, any other director or manager or officer, who is in charge of the affairs of the company.

**Notes on Clause of the Bill**

Clause 56 relates to offences by companies. In respect of any such offence, this clause provides that the company as well as every person who, at the time the offence was committed, was in charge of, and was responsible to, the company for the conduct of the business of the company as well as the company shall be deemed to be guilty of the offence and shall be liable to be proceeded against and punished accordingly. However, it further provides that any such person shall not be so liable if he proves that the offence was committed without his knowledge or that he had exercised all due diligence to prevent the commission of such offence.

[Clause 56 of the Bill]

**57. Proof of entries in records or documents.**—(1) The entries in the records, or other documents, in the custody of a tax authority shall be admitted in evidence in any proceeding for the prosecution of any person for an offence under this Chapter.

(2) The entries referred to in sub-section (1) may be proved by the production of—

(a) the records or other documents (containing such entries) in the custody of the tax authority; or

(b) a copy of the entries certified by that authority under its signature, as true copy of the original entries contained in the records or other documents in its custody.

**58. Punishment for second and subsequent offences.**—If any person convicted of an offence under section 49 to section 53 (both inclusive) is again convicted of an offence under any of the aforesaid provisions, he shall be punishable for the second and every subsequent offence with rigorous imprisonment for a term which shall not be less than three years, but which may extend to ten years and with fine which shall not be less than five lakh rupees, but which may extend to one crore rupees.

## CHAPTER VI

## TAX COMPLIANCE FOR UNDISCLOSED FOREIGN INCOME AND ASSETS

**59. Declaration of undisclosed foreign asset.**—Subject to the provisions of this Chapter, any person may make, on or after the date of commencement of this Act but on or before a date to be notified by the Central Government in the Official Gazette, a declaration in respect of any undisclosed asset located outside India and acquired from income chargeable to tax under the Income-tax Act for any assessment year prior to the assessment year beginning on 1st day of April, 2016—

(a) for which he has failed to furnish a return under section 139 of the Income-tax Act;

(b) which he has failed to disclose in a return of income furnished by him under the Income-tax Act before the date of commencement of this Act;

(c) which has escaped assessment by reason of the omission or failure on the part of such person to make a return under the Income-tax Act or to disclose fully and truly all material facts necessary for the assessment or otherwise.

**NOTIFICATION**

*In exercise of the powers conferred by section 59 and sub-section (1) of section 63 of the Black Money (Undisclosed Foreign Income and Assets) and Imposition of Tax Act, 2015 (22 of 2015), the Central Government hereby appoints:—*

(i) the 30th day of September, 2015 as the date on or before which a person may make a declaration in respect of an undisclosed asset located outside India;

(ii) the 31st day of December, 2015 as the date on or before which a person shall pay the tax and penalty in respect of the undisclosed asset located outside India so declared, under the provisions of section 59 of the said Act.

[According to Notification S.O. 1791(E), dt. July 1, 2005, published in the Gazette of India, Extraordinary, Part. II, Section 3(ii).]

**60. Charge of tax.**—Notwithstanding anything contained in the Income-tax Act or in any Finance Act, the undisclosed asset located outside India and declared under section 59 within the time specified therein shall be chargeable to tax at the rate of thirty per cent. of value of such undisclosed asset on the date of commencement of this Act.

**61. Penalty.**—Notwithstanding anything contained in the Income-tax Act or in any Finance Act, the person making a declaration of undisclosed asset located outside India shall, in addition to tax charged under section 60, be liable to penalty at the rate of one hundred per cent. of such tax.

**62. Manner of declaration.**—(1) A declaration under section 59 shall be made to the Principal Commissioner or the Commissioner and shall be in such form and shall be verified in such manner as may be prescribed.

(2) The declaration shall be signed,—

(i) where the declarant is an individual, by the individual himself; where such individual is absent from India, by the individual concerned or by some person duly authorised by him in this behalf; and where the individual is mentally incapacitated from attending to his affairs, by his guardian or by any other person competent to act on his behalf;

(ii) where the declarant is a Hindu undivided family, by the *karta*, and where the *karta* is absent from India or is mentally incapacitated from attending to his affairs, by any other adult member of such family;

(iii) where the declarant is a company, by the managing director thereof, or where for any unavoidable reason such managing director is not able to sign the declaration or where there is no managing director, by any director thereof;

(iv) where the declarant is a firm, by the managing partner thereof, or where for any unavoidable reason such managing partner is not able to sign the declaration, or where there is no managing partner as such, by any partner thereof, not being a minor;

(v) where the declarant is any other association, by any member of the association or the principal officer thereof; and

(vi) where the declarant is any other person, by that person or by some other person competent to act on his behalf.

(3) Any person, who has made a declaration under sub-section (1) in respect of his asset or as a representative assessee in respect of the asset of any other person, shall not be entitled to make any other declaration, under that sub-section in respect of his asset or the asset of such other person, and any such other declaration, if made, shall be deemed to be void.

**63. Time for payment of tax.**—(1) The tax payable under section 60 and penalty payable under section 61 in respect of the undisclosed asset located outside India, shall be paid on or before a date to be notified by the Central Government in the Official Gazette.

(2) The declarant shall file the proof of payment of tax and penalty on or before the date notified under sub-section (1), with the Principal Commissioner or the Commissioner before whom the declaration under section 59 was made.

(3) If the declarant fails to pay the tax in respect of the declaration made under section 59 on or before the date notified under sub-section (1), the declaration filed by him shall be deemed never to have been made under this Chapter.

**64. Undisclosed foreign asset declared not to be included in total income.**—The amount of undisclosed investment in an asset located outside India declared in accordance with section 59 shall not be included in the total income of the declarant for any assessment year under the Income-tax Act, if the declarant makes the payment of tax referred to in section 60 and the penalty referred to in section 61 by the date notified under sub-section (1) of section 63.

**Notes on Clause of the Bill**

Clause 64 provides that the amount of undisclosed investment in an asset located outside India declared in accordance with clause 59 shall not be included in the total income of the declarant for any assessment year under the Income-tax Act, if the declarant makes the payment of tax referred to in Clause 60 and the penalty referred to in Clause 61 by the notified date. [Clause 64 of the Bill]

**65. Undisclosed foreign asset declared not to affect finality of completed assessments.**—The declarant shall not be entitled, in respect of undisclosed asset located outside India declared or any amount of tax paid thereon, to reopen any assessment or reassessment made under the Income-tax Act or the Wealth-tax Act, 1957 (27 of 1957) or claim any set off or relief in any appeal, reference or other proceeding in relation to any such assessment or reassessment.

**66. Tax in respect of voluntarily disclosed asset not refundable.**—Any amount of tax paid under section 60 or penalty paid under section 61 in pursuance of a declaration made under section 59 shall not be refundable.

**67. Declaration not admissible in evidence against declarant.**—Notwithstanding anything contained in any other law for the time being in force, nothing contained in any declaration made under section 59 shall be admissible in evidence against the declarant for the purpose of any proceeding relating to imposition of penalty, other than the penalty leviable under section 61, or for the purposes of prosecution under the Income-tax Act or the Wealth-tax Act, 1957 (27 of 1957) or the Foreign Exchange Management Act, 1999 (42 of 1999) or the Companies Act, 2013 (18 of 2013) or the Customs Act, 1962 (52 of 1962).

**68. Declaration by misrepresentation of facts to be void.**—Notwithstanding anything contained in this Chapter, where a declaration has been made by misrepresentation or suppression of facts, such declaration shall be void and shall be deemed never to have been made under this Chapter.

**69. Exemption from wealth-tax in respect of assets specified in declaration.**—(1) Where the undisclosed asset located outside India is represented by cash (including bank deposits), bullion or any other assets specified in the declaration made under section 59—

(a) in respect of which the declarant has failed to furnish a return under section 14 of the Wealth-tax Act, 1957 (27 of 1957) for the assessment year commencing on or before the 1st day of April, 2015; or

(b) which have not been shown in the return of net wealth furnished by him for the said assessment year or years; or

(c) which have been understated in value in the return of net wealth furnished by him for the said assessment year or years,

then, notwithstanding anything contained in the Wealth-tax Act, 1957 (27 of 1957) or any rules made thereunder,—

(I) wealth-tax shall not be payable by the declarant in respect of the assets referred to in clause (a) or clause (b) and such assets shall not be included in his net wealth for the said assessment year or years;

(II) the amount by which the value of the assets referred to in clause (c) has been understated in the return of net wealth for the said assessment year or years, to the extent such amount does not exceed the voluntarily disclosed income utilised for acquiring such assets, shall not be taken into account in computing the net wealth of the declarant for the said assessment year or years.

*Explanation.*—Where a declaration under section 59 is made by a firm, the assets referred to in clause (I) or, as the case may be, the amount referred to in clause (II) shall not be taken into account in computing the net wealth of any partner of the firm or, as the case may be, in determining the value of the interest of any partner in the firm.

(2) The provisions of sub-section (1) shall not apply unless the conditions specified in sub-sections (1) and (2) of section 63 are fulfilled by the declarant.

**70. Applicability of certain provisions of Income-tax Act and of Chapter V of Wealth-tax Act.**—The provisions of Chapter XV of the Income-tax Act relating to liability in special cases and of section 189 of that Act or of Chapter V of the Wealth-tax Act, 1957 (27 of 1957) relating to liability to assessment in special cases shall, so far as may be, apply in relation to proceedings under this Chapter as they apply in relation to proceedings under the Income-tax Act or, as the case may be, the Wealth-tax Act.

**71. Chapter not to apply to certain persons.**—The provisions of this Chapter shall not apply—

(a) to any person in respect of whom an order of detention has been made under the Conservation of Foreign Exchange and Prevention of Smuggling Activities Act, 1974 (52 of 1974):

Provided that—

(i) such order of detention, being an order to which the provisions of section 9 or section 12A of the said Act do not apply, has not been revoked on the report of the Advisory Board under section 8 of the said Act or before the receipt of the report of the Advisory Board; or

(ii) such order of detention, being an order to which the provisions of section 9 of the said Act apply, has not been revoked before the expiry of the time for, or on the basis of, the review under sub-section (3) of section 9, or on the report of the Advisory Board under section 8, read with sub-section (2) of section 9, of the said Act; or

(iii) such order of detention, being an order to which the provisions of section 12A of the said Act apply, has not been revoked before the expiry of the time for, or on the basis of, the first review under sub-section (3) of that section, or on the basis of the report of the Advisory Board under section 8, read with sub-section (6) of section 12A, of the said Act; or

(iv) such order of detention has not been set aside by a court of competent jurisdiction;

(b) in relation to prosecution for any offence punishable under Chapter IX or Chapter XVII of the Indian Penal Code (45 of 1860), the Narcotic Drugs and Psychotropic Substances Act, 1985 (61 of 1985), the Unlawful Activities (Prevention) Act, 1967 (37 of 1967), the Prevention of Corruption Act, 1988 (49 of 1988);

(c) to any person notified under section 3 of the Special Court (Trial of Offences Relating to Transactions in Securities) Act, 1992 (27 of 1992).

(d) in relation to any undisclosed asset located outside India which has been acquired from income chargeable to tax under the Income-tax Act for any previous year relevant to an assessment year prior to the assessment year beginning on the 1st day of April, 2016—

(i) where a notice under section 142 or sub-section (2) of section 143 or section 148 or section 153A or section 153C of the Income-tax Act has been issued in respect of such assessment year and the proceeding is pending before the Assessing Officer; or

(ii) where a search has been conducted under section 132 or requisition has been made under section 132A or a survey has been carried out under section 133A of the Income-tax Act in a previous year and a notice under sub-section (2) of section 143 for the assessment year relevant to such previous year or a notice under section 153A or under section 153C of the said Act for an assessment year relevant to any previous year prior to such previous year has not been issued and the time for issuance of such notice has not expired; or

(iii) where any information has been received by the competent authority under an agreement entered into by the Central Government under section 90 or section 90A of the Income-tax Act in respect of such undisclosed asset.

*Explanation.*—For the purpose of this sub-clause asset shall include a bank account whether having any balance or not.

**Notes on Clause of the Bill**

Clause 71 *inter alia,* provides that the Chapter VI relating to tax compliance for undisclosed foreign income and assets shall not apply to the persons and under the circumstances specified therein. [Clause 71 of the Bill]

**72. Removal of doubts.**—For the removal of doubts, it is hereby declared that—

(a) save as otherwise expressly provided in the *Explanation* to sub-section (1) of section 69, nothing contained in this Chapter shall be construed as conferring any benefit, concession or immunity on any person other than the person making the declaration under this Chapter;

(b) where any declaration has been made under section 59 but no tax and penalty has been paid within the time specified under section 60 and section 61, the value of such asset shall be chargeable to tax under this Act in the previous year in which such declaration is made;

(c) where any asset has been acquired or made prior to commencement of this Act, and no declaration in respect of such asset is made under this Chapter, such asset shall be deemed to have been acquired or made in the year in which a notice under section 10 is issued by the Assessing Officer and the provisions of this Act shall apply accordingly.

## CHAPTER VII
## GENERAL PROVISIONS

**73. Agreement with foreign countries or specified territories.**—(1) The Central Government may enter into an agreement with the Government of any other country—

(a) for exchange of information for the prevention of evasion or avoidance of tax on undisclosed foreign income chargeable under this Act or under the corresponding law in force in that country, or investigation of cases of such evasion or avoidance;

(b) for recovery of tax under this Act and under the corresponding law in force in that country.

(2) The Central Government may enter into an agreement with the Government of any specified territory outside India for the purposes specified in sub-section (1).

(3) The Central Government may, by notification, make such provisions as may be necessary for implementing the agreements referred to in sub-sections (1) and (2).

(4) Any specified association in India may enter into an agreement with any specified association in the specified territory outside India for the purposes of sub-section (1) and the Central Government may by notification make such provisions as may be necessary for adopting and implementing such agreement.

(5) Any term used but not defined in this Act or in the agreement referred to in sub-sections (1), (2) or sub-section (4) shall, unless the context otherwise requires, and is not inconsistent with the provisions of this Act or the agreement, have the meaning assigned to it in the notification issued by the Central Government and such meaning shall be deemed to have effect from the date on which the said agreement came into force.

**74. Service of notice generally.**—(1) The service of any notice, summons, requisition, order or any other communication under this Act (herein referred to in this section as "communication") may be made by delivering or transmitting a copy thereof, to the person named therein,—

(a) by post or by such courier service as may be approved by the Board;

(b) in such manner as provided under the Code of Civil Procedure, 1908 (5 of 1908) for the purposes of service of summons;

(c) in the form of any electronic record as provided in Chapter IV of the Information Technology Act, 2000 (21 of 2000); or

(d) by any other means of transmission of documents, including fax message or electronic mail message, as may be prescribed.

(2) The Board may make rules providing for the addresses including the address for electronic mail or electronic mail message to which the communication referred to in sub-section (1) may be delivered or transmitted to the person named therein.

(3) In this section, the expressions "electronic mail" and "electronic mail message" shall have the same meanings as assigned to them in the Explanation to section 66A of the Information Technology Act, 2000 (21 of 2000).

**Notes on Clause of the Bill**

Clause 74 relates to service of notice generally. This clause provides for the manner of service of any notice, summons, requisition, order etc. under this Act.

[Clause 74 of the Bill]

**75. Authentication of notices and other documents.**—(1) A notice or any other document required to be issued, served or given for the purposes of this Act by any tax authority shall be authenticated by that authority.

(2) Every notice or other document to be issued, served or given for the purposes of this Act by any tax authority shall be deemed to be authenticated, if the name and office of a designated tax authority is printed, stamped or otherwise written thereon.

(3) In this section, a designated tax authority shall mean any tax authority authorised by the Board to issue, serve or give such notice or other document after authentication in the manner as provided in sub-section (2).

**76. Notice deemed to be valid in certain circumstances.**—(1) A notice which is required to be served upon a person for the purposes of assessment under this Act shall be deemed to have been duly served upon him in accordance with the provisions of this Act, if the person has appeared in any proceeding or co-operated in any inquiry relating to an assessment.

(2) The person, referred to in sub-section (1), shall be precluded from taking any objection in any proceeding or inquiry under this Act that the notice was—

(a) not served upon him;

(b) not served upon him in time; or

(c) served upon him in an improper manner.

(3) The provisions of this section shall not apply, if the person has raised the objection before the completion of the assessment.

**77. Appearance by approved valuer in certain matters.**—(1) Any assessee who is entitled or required to attend before any tax authority or the Appellate Tribunal, in connection with any matter relating to the valuation of any asset, may attend through a valuer approved by the Principal Commissioner or the Commissioner in accordance with such rules as may be prescribed.

(2) The provisions of sub-section (1) shall not apply in a case where the assessee is required to attend personally for examination on oath or affirmation under section 8.

**78. Appearance by authorised representative.**—(1) Any assessee who is entitled or required to attend before any tax authority or the Appellate Tribunal, in connection with any proceeding under this Act, may attend through an authorised representative.

(2) The provisions of sub-section (1) shall not apply in a case where the assessee is required to attend personally for examination on oath or affirmation under section 8.

(3) In this section, "authorised representative" means a person authorised by the assessee in writing to appear on his behalf, being—

(a) a person related to the assessee in any manner, or a person regularly employed by the assessee;

(b) any officer of a scheduled bank with which the assessee maintains a current account or has other regular dealings;

(c) any legal practitioner who is entitled to practice in any civil court in India;

(d) an accountant;

(e) any person who has passed any accountancy examination recognised in this behalf by the Board; or

(f) any person who has acquired such educational qualifications as may be prescribed.

(4) The following persons shall not be qualified to represent an assessee under sub-section (1), namely:—

(a) a person who has been dismissed or removed from Government service;

(b) a legal practitioner, or an accountant, who is found guilty of misconduct in his professional capacity by any authority entitled to institute disciplinary proceedings against him;

(c) a person, not being a legal practitioner or an accountant, who is found guilty of misconduct in any tax proceedings by such authority as may be prescribed.

(5) The Principal Chief Commissioner or the Chief Commissioner may, by an order in writing, specify the period up to which the disqualification under sub-section (4) shall continue, having regard to the nature of misconduct and such disqualification shall not exceed—

(i) in case of clauses (a) and (c) of sub-section (4), a period of ten years;

(ii) in case of clause (b) of sub-section (4), the period for which the legal practitioner or an accountant is not entitled to practice.

(6) A person shall not be allowed to appear as an authorised representative, if he has committed any fraud or misrepresented the facts which resulted in loss to the revenue and that person has been declared as such by an order of the Principal Chief Commissioner or the Chief Commissioner.

*Explanation.*—In this section, "accountant" means a chartered accountant as defined in clause (b) of sub-section (1) of section 2 of the Chartered Accountants Act, 1949 (38 of 1949) who holds a valid certificate of practice under sub-section (1) of section 6 of that Act.

**Notes on Clause of the Bill**

Clause 78 relates to appearance by authorised representative. This clause, *inter alia*, provides that any assessee entitled or required to attend before any tax authority or the Appellate Tribunal, in connection with any proceeding under this Act, may attend through an authorised representative except where he is required to attend personally.

It further seeks to provide the meaning of "authorised representative" and persons not qualified to represent an assessee. [Clause 78 of the Bill]

**79. Rounding off of income, value of asset and tax.**—(1) The amount of undisclosed foreign income and asset computed in accordance with this Act shall be rounded off to the nearest multiple of one hundred rupees.

(2) Any amount payable or receivable by the assessee under this Act shall be rounded off to the nearest multiple of ten rupees.

(3) The method of rounding off under sub-section (1) or sub-section (2), shall be such as may be prescribed.

**80. Cognizance of offences.**—No court inferior to that of a metropolitan magistrate or a magistrate of the First Class shall try any offence under this Act.

**81. Assessment not to be invalid on certain grounds.**—No assessment, notice, summons or other proceedings, made or issued or taken or purported to have been made or issued or taken in pursuance of any of the provisions of this Act shall be invalid or shall be deemed to be invalid merely by reason of any mistake, defect or omission in such assessment, notice, summons or other proceeding if such assessment, notice, summons or other proceeding is in substance and effect in conformity with or according to the intent and purpose of this Act.

**82. Bar of suits in civil courts.**—(1) No suit shall be brought in any civil court to set aside or modify any proceeding taken or order made under this Act.

(2) No prosecution, suit or other proceeding shall lie against the Government or any officer of the Government, for anything in good faith done or intended to be done, under this Act.

**83. Income-tax papers to be available for purposes of this Act.**—Notwithstanding anything contained in the Income-tax Act, all information contained in any statement or return made or furnished under the provisions of that Act or obtained or collected for the purposes of the said Act may be used for the purposes of this Act.

**84. Application of provisions of Income-tax Act.**—The provisions of clauses (c) and (d) of sub-section (1) of section 90, clauses (c) and (d) of sub-section (1) of section 90A, sections 119, 133, 134, 135, [1][138, 144A] Chapter XV and sections 237, 240, 245, 280, 280A, 280B, 280D, 281, 281B and 284 of the Income-tax Act shall apply with necessary modifications as if the said provisions refer to undisclosed foreign income and asset instead of to income-tax.

**85. Power to make rules.**—(1) The Board may, subject to the approval of the Central Government, by notification in the Official Gazette, make rules for carrying out the provisions of this Act.

(2) In particular, and without prejudice to the generality of the foregoing power, such rules may provide for all or any of the following matters, namely:—

(a) the manner of determination of the value of an undisclosed foreign asset referred to in sub-section (2) of section 3;

(b) the tax authority to be prescribed for any of the purposes of this Act;

(c) the form and manner of service of a notice of demand under section 13;

1. Subst. by Act 23 of 2019, Section 208, for the figures "138" (w.e.f. September 1, 2019).

(d) the form in which any appeal, revision or cross-objection may be filed under this Act, the manner in which they may be verified and the fee payable in respect thereof;

(e) the form in which the Tax Recovery Officer may draw up the statement of tax arrears under sub-section (1) of section 31;

(f) the manner in which the sum is to be paid to the credit of Central Government under sub-section (2) or sub-section (5) of section 32;

(g) the manner in which the Tax Recovery Officer shall send a certificate referred to in sub-section (2) of section 33;

(h) the form in which a declaration referred to in sub-section (1) of section 62 is to be made and the manner in which it is to be verified;

(i) the means of transmission of documents under clause (d) of sub-section (1) of section 74;

(j) the procedure for approval of a valuer by the Principal Commissioner or the Commissioner under section 77;

(k) the educational qualifications required, to be an authorised representative under clause (f) of sub-section (3) of section 78;

(l) the tax authority under clause (c) of sub-section (4) of section 78;

(m) the method of rounding off of the amount referred to in sub-section (1) or sub-section (2) of section 79;

(n) any other matter which by this Act is to be, or may be, prescribed.

(3) The power to make rules conferred by this section shall include the power to give retrospective effect to the rules or any of them from a date not earlier than the date of commencement of this Act and no retrospective effect shall be given to any rule so as to prejudicially affect the interest of assessees.

(4) The Central Government shall cause every rule made under this Act to be laid as soon as may be after it is made before each House of Parliament while it is in session for a total period of thirty days which may be comprised in one session or in two or more successive sessions and if, before the expiry of the session immediately following the session or the successive sessions aforesaid, both Houses agree in making any modification in the rule or both Houses agree that the rule should not be made, the rule shall thereafter have effect only in such modified form or be of no effect, as the case may be; so, however, that any such modification or annulment shall be without prejudice to the validity of anything previously done under that rule.

**86. Power to remove difficulties.**—(1) If any difficulty arises in giving effect to the provisions of this Act, the Central Government may, by order, not inconsistent with the provisions of this Act, remove the difficulty :

Provided that no such order shall be made after the expiry of a period of two years from the date on which the provisions of this Act come into force.

(2) Every order made under this section shall be laid before each House of Parliament.

**87. Amendment of section 2 of Act 54 of 1963.**—In section 2 of the Central Boards of Revenue Act, 1963, in sub-clause (1) of clause (c),—

(a) in item (vii), the word "and" occurring at the end shall be omitted; and

(b) after item (ix) as so amended, the following item shall be inserted, namely:—

"(*x*) the Black Money (Undisclosed Foreign Income and Assets) and Imposition of Tax Act, 2015; and"

**88. Amendment of Act 15 of 2003.**—In the Prevention of Money-laundering Act, 2002, in the Schedule, in Part C, after entry (3), relating to the offences against property under Chapter XVII of the Indian Penal Code (45 of 1860), the following entry shall be inserted, namely:—

"(4) The offence of wilful attempt to evade any tax, penalty or interest referred to in section 51 of the Black Money (Undisclosed Foreign Income and Assets) and Imposition of Tax Act, 2015.".

# THE LOKPAL AND LOKAYUKTAS ACT, 2013[1]

(1 of 2014)

[*1st January, 2014*]

*An Act to provide for the establishment of a body of Lokpal for the Union and Lokayukta for States to inquire into allegations of corruption against certain public functionaries and for matters connected therewith or incidental thereto.*

WHEREAS the Constitution of India established a Democratic Republic to ensure justice for all;

AND WHEREAS India has ratified the United Nations Convention Against Corruption;

AND WHEREAS the Government's commitment to clean and responsive governance has to be reflected in effective bodies to contain and punish acts of corruption;

NOW, THEREFORE, it is expedient to enact a law, for more effective implementation of the said Convention and to provide for prompt and fair investigation and prosecution in cases of Corruption.

BE it enacted by Parliament in the Sixty-fourth Year of the Republic of India as follows:—

## PART I
## PRELIMINARY

**1. Short title, extent, application and commencement.**—(1) This Act may be called the Lokpal and Lokayuktas Act, 2013.

(2) It extends to the whole of India.

(3) It shall apply to public servants in and outside India.

(4) It shall come into force on such date[2] as the Central Government may, by notification in the Official Gazette, appoint.

## PART II
## LOKPAL FOR THE UNION

### CHAPTER I
### DEFINITIONS

**2. Definitions.**—(1) In this Act, unless the context otherwise requires,—

(a) "bench" means a bench of the Lokpal;

(b) "Chairperson" means the Chairperson of the Lokpal;

(c) "competent authority", in relation to—

(i) the Prime Minister, means the House of the People;

(ii) a member of the Council of Ministers, means the Prime Minister;

---

1. Published in the Gazette of India, Extraordinary, Part II, Section 1, No. 1, dt. January 1, 2014.
2. Came into force on 16th January, 2014, according to S.O.No. 119(E), dt. January 16, 2014, published in the Gazette of India, Extraordinary, Part II, Section 3(ii).

(iii) a member of Parliament other than a Minister, means—

(A) in the case of a member of the Council of States, the Chairman of the Council; and

(B) in the case of a member of the House of the People, the Speaker of the House;

(iv) an officer in the Ministry or Department of the Central Government, means the Minister in charge of the Ministry or Department under which the officer is serving;

(v) a chairperson or members of any body or Board or corporation or authority or company or society or autonomous body (by whatever name called) established or constituted under any Act of Parliament or wholly or partly financed by the Central Government or controlled by it, means the Minister in charge of the administrative Ministry of such body or Board or corporation or authority or company or society or autonomous body;

(vi) an officer of any body or Board or corporation or authority or company or society or autonomous body (by whatever name called) established or constituted under any Act of Parliament or wholly or partly financed by the Central Government or controlled by it, means the head of such body or Board or corporation or authority or company or society or autonomous body;

(vii) in any other case not falling under sub-clauses (i) to (vi) above, means such Department or authority as the Central Government may, by notification, specify:

Provided that if any person referred to in sub-clause (v) or sub-clause (vi) is also a member of Parliament, then, the competent authority shall be—

(A) in case such member is a member of the Council of States, the Chairman of the Council; and

(B) in case such member is a member of the House of the People, the Speaker of the House;

(d) "Central Vigilance Commission" means the Central Vigilance Commission constituted under sub-section (1) of section 3 of the Central Vigilance Commission Act, 2003 (45 of 2003);

(e) "complaint" means a complaint, made in such form as may be prescribed, alleging that a public servant has committed an offence punishable under the Prevention of Corruption Act, 1988 (49 of 1988);

(f) "Delhi Special Police Establishment" means the Delhi Special Police Establishment constituted under sub-section (1) of section 2 of the Delhi Special Police Establishment Act, 1946 (25 of 1946);

(g) "investigation" means an investigation as defined under clause (h) of section 2 of the Code of Criminal Procedure, 1973 (2 of 1974);

(h) "Judicial Member" means a Judicial Member of the Lokpal;

(i) "Lokpal" means the body established under section 3;

(j) "Member" means a Member of the Lokpal;

(k) "Minister" means a Union Minister but does not include the Prime Minister;

(l) "notification" means notification published in the Official Gazette and the expression "notify" shall be construed accordingly;

(m) "preliminary inquiry" means an inquiry conducted under this Act;

(n) "prescribed" means prescribed by rules made under this Act;

(o) "public servant" means a person referred to in clauses (a) to (h) of sub-section (1) of section 14 but does not include a public servant in respect of whom the jurisdiction is exercisable by any court or other authority under the Army Act, 1950 (45 of 1950), the Air Force Act, 1950 (46 of 1950), the Navy Act, 1957 (62 of 1957) and the Coast Guard Act, 1978 (30 of 1978) or the procedure is applicable to such public servant under those Acts;

(p) "regulations" means regulations made under this Act;

(q) "rules" means rules made under this Act;

(r) "Schedule" means a Schedule appended to this Act;

(s) "Special Court" means the court of a Special Judge appointed under sub-section (1) of section 3 of the Prevention of Corruption Act, 1988 (49 of 1988).

(2) The words and expressions used herein and not defined in this Act but defined in the Prevention of Corruption Act, 1988 (49 of 1988), shall have the meanings respectively assigned to them in that Act.

(3) Any reference in this Act to any other Act or provision thereof which is not in force in any area to which this Act applies shall be construed to have a reference to the corresponding Act or provision thereof in force in such area.

## CHAPTER II

## ESTABLISHMENT OF LOKPAL

**3. Establishment of Lokpal.**—(1) On and from the commencement of this Act, there shall be established, for the purpose of this Act, a body to be called the "Lokpal".

(2) The Lokpal shall consist of—

(a) a Chairperson, who is or has been a Chief Justice of India or is or has been a Judge of the Supreme Court or an eminent person who fulfills the eligibility specified in clause (b) of sub-section (3); and

(b) such number of Members, not exceeding eight out of whom fifty per cent. shall be Judicial Members:

Provided that not less than fifty per cent. of the Members of the Lokpal shall be from amongst the persons belonging to the Scheduled Castes, the Scheduled Tribes, Other Backward Classes, Minorities and women.

(3) A person shall be eligible to be appointed,—

(a) as a Judicial Member if he is or has been a Judge of the Supreme Court or is or has been a Chief Justice of a High Court;

(b) as a Member other than a Judicial Member, if he is a person of impeccable integrity and outstanding ability having special knowledge and expertise of not less than twenty-five years in the matters relating to anti-corruption policy, public administration, vigilance, finance including insurance and banking, law and management.

(4) The Chairperson or a Member shall not be—

(i) a member of Parliament or a member of the Legislature of any State or Union territory;

(ii) a person convicted of any offence involving moral turptitude;

(iii) a person of less than forty-five years of age, on the date of assuming office as the Chairperson or Member, as the case may be;

(iv) a member of any Panchayat or Municipality;

(v) a person who has been removed or dismissed from the service of the Union or a State,

and shall not hold any office of trust or profit (other than his office as the Chairperson or a Member) or be affiliated with any political party or carry on any business or practise any profession and, accordingly, before he enters upon his office, a person appointed as the Chairperson or a Member, as the case may be, shall, if—

(a) he holds any office of trust or profit, resign from such office; or

(b) he is carrying on any business, sever his connection with the conduct and management of such business; or

(c) he is practising any profession, cease to practise such profession.

**COMMENT**

**Opinion of Chief Justice of India**

The provision for conferring the primacy of opinion of CJI or his nominee does not itself render as unconstitutional.

*Just Society v. Union of India*, AIR 2017 SC 2428.

**4. Appointment of Chairperson and Members on recommendations of Selection Committee.**—(1) The Chairperson and Members shall be appointed by the President after obtaining the recommendations of a Selection Committee consisting of—

(a) the Prime Minister—Chairperson;

(b) the Speaker of the House of the People—Member;

(c) the Leader of Opposition in the House of the People—Member;

(d) the Chief Justice of India or a Judge of the Supreme Court nominated by him—Member;

(e) one eminent jurist, as recommended by the Chairperson and Members referred to in clauses (a) to (d) above, to be nominated by the President—Member.

(2) No appointment of a Chairperson or a Member shall be invalid merely by reason of any vacancy in the Selection Committee.

(3) The Selection Committee shall for the purposes of selecting the Chairperson and Members of the Lokpal and for preparing a panel of persons to be considered for appointment as such, constitute a Search Committee consisting of at least seven persons of standing and having special knowledge and expertise in the matters relating to anti-corruption policy, public administration, vigilance, policy making, finance including insurance and banking, law and management or in any other matter which, in the opinion of the Selection Committee, may be useful in making the selection of the Chairperson and Members of the Lokpal:

Provided that not less than fifty per cent. of the members of the Search Committee shall be from amongst the persons belonging to the Scheduled Castes, the Scheduled Tribes, Other Backward Classes, Minorities and women:

Provided further that the Selection Committee may also consider any person other than the persons recommended by the Search Committee.

(4) The Selection Committee shall regulate its own procedure in a transparent manner for selecting the Chairperson and Members of the Lokpal.

(5) The term of the Search Committee referred to in sub-section (3), the fees and allowances payable to its members and the manner of selection of panel of names shall be such as may be prescribed.

**COMMENT**

**Appointment of Chairperson and Member of Lokpal**

The selection and recommendation for appointment can be made by the Selection Committee even if the Leader of Opposition is not the member of Committee.

*Common cause: A Registered Society v. Union of India,* AIR 2017 SC 3084: (2017) 5 SCALE 333.

**5. Filling of vacancies of Chairperson or Members.**—The President shall take or cause to be taken all necessary steps for the appointment of a new Chairperson and Members at least three months before the expiry of the term of the Chairperson or Member, as the case may be, in accordance with the procedure laid down in this Act.

**6. Term of office of Chairperson and Members.**—The Chairperson and every Member shall, on the recommendations of the Selection Committee, be appointed by the President by warrant under his hand and seal and hold office as such for a term of five years from the date on which he enters upon his office or until he attains the age of seventy years, whichever is earlier:

Provided that he may—

(a) by writing under his hand addressed to the President, resign his office; or

(b) be removed from his office in the manner provided in section 37.

**7. Salary, allowances and other conditions of service of Chairperson and Members.**—The salary, allowances and other conditions of service of—

(i) the Chairperson shall be the same as those of the Chief Justice of India;

(ii) other Members shall be the same as those of a Judge of the Supreme Court:

Provided that if the Chairperson or a Member is, at the time of his appointment, in receipt of pension (other than disability pension) in respect of any previous service under the Government of India or under the Government of a State, his salary in respect of service as the Chairperson or, as the case may be, as a Member, be reduced—

(a) by the amount of that pension; and

(b) if he has, before such appointment, received, in lieu of a portion of the pension due to him in respect of such previous service, the commuted value thereof, by the amount of that portion of the pension:

Provided further that the salary, allowances and pension payable to, and other conditions of service of, the Chairperson or a Member shall not be varied to his disadvantage after his appointment.

**8. Restriction on employment by Chairperson and Members after ceasing to hold office.**—(1) On ceasing to hold office, the Chairperson and every Member shall be ineligible for—

(i) reappointment as the Chairperson or a Member of the Lokpal;

(ii) any diplomatic assignment, appointment as administrator of a Union territory and such other assignment or appointment which is required by law to be made by the President by warrant under his hand and seal;

(iii) further employment to any other office of profit under the Government of India or the Government of a State;

(iv) contesting any election of President or Vice-President or Member of either House of Parliament or Member of either House of a State Legislature or Municipality or Panchayat within a period of five years from the date of relinquishing the post.

(2) Notwithstanding anything contained in sub-section (1), a Member shall be eligible to be appointed as a Chairperson, if his total tenure as Member and Chairperson does not exceed five years.

*Explanation.*—For the purposes of this section, it is hereby clarified that where the Member is appointed as the Chairperson, his term of office shall not be more than five years in aggregate as the Member and the Chairperson.

**9. Member to act as Chairperson or to discharge his functions in certain circumstances.**—(1) In the event of occurrence of any vacancy in the office of the Chairperson by reason of his death, resignation or otherwise, the President may, by notification, authorise the senior-most Member to act as the Chairperson until the appointment of a new Chairperson to fill such vacancy.

(2) When the Chairperson is unable to discharge his functions owing to absence on leave or otherwise, the senior-most Member available, as the President may, by notification, authorise in this behalf, shall discharge the functions of the Chairperson until the date on which the Chairperson resumes his duties.

**10. Secretary, other officers and staff of Lokpal.**—(1) There shall be a Secretary to the Lokpal in the rank of Secretary to Government of India, who shall be appointed by the Chairperson from a panel of names sent by the Central Government.

(2) There shall be a Director of Inquiry and a Director of Prosecution not below the rank of Additional Secretary to the Government of India or equivalent, who shall be appointed by the Chairperson from a panel of names sent by the Central Government.

(3) The appointment of officers and other staff of the Lokpal shall be made by the Chairperson or such Member or officer of Lokpal as the Chairperson may direct:

Provided that the President may by rule require that the appointment in respect of any post or posts as may be specified in the rule, shall be made after consultation with the Union Public Service Commission.

(4) Subject to the provisions of any law made by Parliament, the conditions of service of Secretary and other officers and staff of the Lokpal shall be such as may be specified by regulations made by the Lokpal for the purpose:

Provided that the regulations made under this sub-section shall, so far as they relate to salaries, allowances, leave or pensions, require the approval of the President.

## CHAPTER III
## INQUIRY WING

**11. Inquiry Wing.**—(1) Notwithstanding anything contained in any law for the time being in force, the Lokpal shall constitute an Inquiry Wing headed by the Director of Inquiry for the purpose of conducting preliminary inquiry into any offence alleged to have been committed by a public servant punishable under the Prevention of Corruption Act, 1988 (49 of 1988):

Provided that till such time the Inquiry Wing is constituted by the Lokpal, the Central Government shall make available such number of officers and other staff from its Ministries or Departments, as may be required by the Lokpal, for conducting preliminary inquiries under this Act.

(2) For the purposes of assisting the Lokpal in conducting a preliminary inquiry under this Act, the officers of the Inquiry Wing not below the rank of the Under Secretary to the Government of India, shall have the same powers as are conferred upon the Inquiry Wing of the Lokpal under section 27.

## CHAPTER IV
## PROSECUTION WING

**12. Prosecution Wing.**—(1) The Lokpal shall, by notification, constitute a Prosecution Wing headed by the Director of Prosecution for the purpose of prosecution of public servants in relation to any complaint by the Lokpal under this Act:

Provided that till such time the Prosecution Wing is constituted by the Lokpal, the Central Government shall make available such number of officers and other staff from its Ministries or Departments, as may be required by the Lokpal, for conducting prosecution under this Act.

(2) The Director of Prosecution shall, after having been so directed by the Lokpal, file a case in accordance with the findings of investigation report, before the Special Court and take all necessary steps in respect of the prosecution of public servants in relation to any offence punishable under the Prevention of Corruption Act, 1988 (49 of 1988).

(3) The case under sub-section (2), shall be deemed to be a report, filed on completion of investigation, referred to in section 173 of the Code of Criminal Procedure, 1973 (2 of 1974).

## CHAPTER V
## EXPENSES OF LOKPAL TO BE CHARGED ON CONSOLIDATED FUND OF INDIA

**13. Expenses of Lokpal to be charged on Consolidated Fund of India.**—The administrative expenses of the Lokpal, including all salaries, allowances and pensions payable to or in respect of the Chairperson, Members or Secretary or other officers or staff of the Lokpal, shall be charged upon the Consolidated Fund of India and any fees or other moneys taken by the Lokpal shall form part of that Fund.

## CHAPTER VI
## JURISDICTION IN RESPECT OF INQUIRY

**14. Jurisdiction of Lokpal to include Prime Minister, Ministers, Members of Parliament, Groups A, B, C and D officers and officials of Central Government.**—(1) Subject to the other provisions of this Act, the Lokpal shall inquire or cause an inquiry to be conducted into any matter involved in, or arising from, or connected with, any allegation of corruption made in a complaint in respect of the following, namely:—

(a) any person who is or has been a Prime Minister:

Provided that the Lokpal shall not inquire into any matter involved in, or arising from, or connected with, any such allegation of corruption against the Prime Minister,—

(i) in so far as it relates to international relations, external and internal security, public order, atomic energy and space;

(ii) unless a full bench of the Lokpal consisting of its Chairperson and all Members considers the initiation of inquiry and at least two-thirds of its Members approves of such inquiry:

Provided further that any such inquiry shall be held *in camera* and if the Lokpal comes to the conclusion that the complaint deserves to be dismissed, the records of the inquiry shall not be published or made available to anyone;

(b) any person who is or has been a Minister of the Union;

(c) any person who is or has been a member of either House of Parliament;

(d) any Group 'A' or Group 'B' officer or equivalent or above, from amongst the public servants defined in sub-clauses (i) and (ii) of clause (c) of section 2 of the Prevention of Corruption Act, 1988 (49 of 1988) when serving or who has served, in connection with the affairs of the Union;

(e) any Group 'C' or Group 'D' official or equivalent, from amongst the public servants defined in sub-clauses (i) and (ii) of clause (c) of section 2 of the Prevention of Corruption Act, 1988 (49 of 1988) when serving or who has served in connection with the affairs of the Union subject to the provision of sub-section (1) of section 20;

(f) any person who is or has been a chairperson or member or officer or employee in any body or Board or corporation or authority or company or society or trust or autonomous body (by whatever name called) established by an Act of Parliament or wholly or partly financed by the Central Government or controlled by it:

Provided that in respect of such officers referred to in clause (d) who have served in connection with the affairs of the Union or in any body or Board or corporation or authority or company or society or trust or autonomous body referred to in clause (e) but are working in connection with the affairs of the State or in any body or Board or corporation or authority or company or society or trust or autonomous body (by whatever name called) established by an Act of the State Legislature or wholly or partly financed by the State Government or controlled by it, the Lokpal and the officers of its Inquiry Wing or Prosecution Wing shall have jurisdiction under this Act in respect of such officers only after obtaining the consent of the concerned State Government;

(g) any person who is or has been a director, manager, secretary or other officer of every other society or association of persons or trust (whether registered under any law for the time being in force or not), by whatever name called, wholly or partly financed by the Government and the annual income of which exceeds such amount as the Central Government may, by notification, specify;

(h) any person who is or has been a director, manager, secretary or other officer of every other society or association of persons or trust (whether registered under any law for the time being in force or not) in receipt of any donation from any foreign source under the Foreign Contribution (Regulation) Act, 2010 (42 of 2010) in excess of ten lakh rupees in a year or such higher amount as the Central Government may, by notification, specify.

*Explanation.*—For the purpose of clauses (f) and (g), it is hereby clarified that any entity or institution, by whatever name called, corporate, society, trust, association of persons, partnership, sole proprietorship, limited liability partnership (whether registered under any law for the time being in force or not), shall be the entities covered in those clauses:

Provided that any person referred to in this clause shall be deemed to be a public servant under clause (c) of section 2 of the Prevention of Corruption Act, 1988 (49 of 1988) and the provisions of that Act shall apply accordingly.

(2) Notwithstanding anything contained in sub-section (1), the Lokpal shall not inquire into any matter involved in, or arising from, or connected with, any such allegation of corruption against any member of either House of Parliament in respect of anything said or a vote given by him in Parliament or any committee thereof covered under the provisions contained in clause (2) of article 105 of the Constitution.

(3) The Lokpal may inquire into any act or conduct of any person other than those referred to in sub-section (1), if such person is involved in the act of abetting, bribe giving or bribe taking or conspiracy relating to any allegation of corruption under the Prevention of Corruption Act, 1988 (49 of 1988) against a person referred to in sub-section (1):

Provided that no action under this section shall be taken in case of a person serving in connection with the affairs of a State, without the consent of the State Government.

(4) No matter in respect of which a complaint has been made to the Lokpal under this Act, shall be referred for inquiry under the Commissions of Inquiry Act, 1952 (60 of 1952).

*Explanation.*—For the removal of doubts, it is hereby declared that a complaint under this Act shall only relate to a period during which the public servant was holding or serving in that capacity.

**15. Matters pending before any court or committee or authority for inquiry not to be affected.**—In case any matter or proceeding related to allegation of corruption under the Prevention of Corruption Act, 1988

(49 of 1988) has been pending before any court or committee of either House of Parliament or before any other authority prior to commencement of this Act or prior to commencement of any inquiry after the commencement of this Act, such matter or proceeding shall be continued before such court, committee or authority.

**16. Constitution of benches of Lokpal.**—(1) Subject to the provisions of this Act,—

(a) the jurisdiction of the Lokpal may be exercised by benches thereof;

(b) a bench may be constituted by the Chairperson with two or more Members as the Chairperson may deem fit;

(c) every bench shall ordinarily consist of at least one Judicial Member;

(d) where a bench consists of the Chairperson, such bench shall be presided over by the Chairperson;

(e) where a bench consists of a Judicial Member, and a non-Judicial Member, not being the Chairperson, such bench shall be presided over by the Judicial Member;

(f) the benches of the Lokpal shall ordinarily sit at New Delhi and at such other places as the Lokpal may, by regulations, specify.

(2) The Lokpal shall notify the areas in relation to which each bench of the Lokpal may exercise jurisdiction.

(3) Notwithstanding anything contained in sub-section (2), the Chairperson shall have the power to constitute or reconstitute benches from time to time.

(4) If at any stage of the hearing of any case or matter it appears to the Chairperson or a Member that the case or matter is of such nature that it ought to be heard by a bench consisting of three or more Members, the case or matter may be transferred by the Chairperson or, as the case may be, referred to him for transfer, to such bench as the Chairperson may deem fit.

**17. Distribution of business amongst benches.**—Where benches are constituted, the Chairperson may, from time to time, by notification, make provisions as to the distribution of the business of the Lokpal amongst the benches and also provide for the matters which may be dealt with by each bench.

**18. Power of Chairperson to transfer cases.**—On an application for transfer made by the complainant or the public servant, the Chairperson, after giving an opportunity of being heard to the complainant or the public servant, as the case may be, may transfer any case pending before one bench for disposal to any other bench.

**19. Decision to be by majority.**—If the Members of a bench consisting of an even number of Members differ in opinion on any point, they shall state the point or points on which they differ, and make a reference to the Chairperson who shall either hear the point or points himself or refer the case for hearing on such point or points by one or more of the other Members of the Lokpal and such point or points shall be decided according to the opinion of the majority of the Members of the Lokpal who have heard the case, including those who first heard it.

## CHAPTER VII

## PROCEDURE IN RESPECT OF PRELIMINARY INQUIRY AND INVESTIGATION

**20. Provisions relating to complaints and preliminary inquiry and investigation.**—(1) The Lokpal on receipt of a complaint, if it decides to proceed further, may order—

(a) preliminary inquiry against any public servant by its Inquiry Wing or any agency (including the Delhi Special Police Establishment) to ascertain whether there exists a *prima facie* case for proceeding in the matter; or

(b) investigation by any agency (including the Delhi Special Police Establishment) when there exists a *prima facie* case:

Provided that the Lokpal shall if it has decided to proceed with the preliminary inquiry, by a general or special order, refer the complaints or a category of complaints or a complaint received by it in respect of public servants belonging to Group A or Group B or Group C or Group D to the Central Vigilance Commission constituted under sub-section (1) of section 3 of the Central Vigilance Commission Act, 2003 (45 of 2003):

Provided further that the Central Vigilance Commission in respect of complaints referred to it under the first proviso, after making preliminary inquiry in respect of public servants belonging to Group A and Group B, shall submit its report to the Lokpal in accordance with the provisions contained in sub-sections (2) and (4) and in case of public servants belonging to Group C and Group D, the Commission shall proceed in accordance with the provisions of the Central Vigilance Commission Act, 2003 (45 of 2003):

Provided also that before ordering an investigation under clause (b), the Lokpal shall call for the explanation of the public servant so as to determine whether there exists a *prima facie* case for investigation:

Provided also that the seeking of explanation from the public servant before an investigation shall not interfere with the search and seizure, if any, required to be undertaken by any agency (including the Delhi Special Police Establishment) under this Act.

(2) During the preliminary inquiry referred to in sub-section (1), the Inquiry Wing or any agency (including the Delhi Special Police Establishment) shall conduct a preliminary inquiry and on the basis of material, information and documents collected seek the comments on the allegations made in the complaint from the public servant and the competent authority and after obtaining the comments of the concerned public servant and the competent authority, submit, within sixty days from the date of receipt of the reference, a report to the Lokpal.

(3) A bench consisting of not less than three Members of the Lokpal shall consider every report received under sub-section (2) from the Inquiry

Wing or any agency (including the Delhi Special Police Establishment), and after giving an opportunity of being heard to the public servant, decide whether there exists a *prima facie* case, and proceed with one or more of the following actions, namely:—

(a) investigation by any agency or the Delhi Special Police Establishment, as the case may be;

(b) initiation of the departmental proceedings or any other appropriate action against the concerned public servants by the competent authority;

(c) closure of the proceedings against the public servant and to proceed against the complainant under section 46.

(4) Every preliminary inquiry referred to in sub-section (1) shall ordinarily be completed within a period of ninety days and for reasons to be recorded in writing, within a further period of ninety days from the date of receipt of the complaint.

(5) In case the Lokpal decides to proceed to investigate into the complaint, it shall direct any agency (including the Delhi Special Police Establishment) to carry out the investigation as expeditiously as possible and complete the investigation within a period of six months from the date of its order:

Provided that the Lokpal may extend the said period by a further period not exceeding of six months at a time for the reasons to be recorded in writing.

(6) Notwithstanding anything contained in section 173 of the Code of Criminal Procedure, 1973 (2 of 1974), any agency (including the Delhi Special Police Establishment) shall, in respect of cases referred to it by the Lokpal, submit the investigation report under that section to the court having jurisdiction and forward a copy thereof to the Lokpal.

(7) A bench consisting of not less than three Members of the Lokpal shall consider every report received by it under sub-section (6) from any agency (including the Delhi Special Police Establishment) and after obtaining the comments of the competent authority and the public servant may—

(a) grant sanction to its Prosecution Wing or investigating agency to file charge-sheet or direct the closure of report before the Special Court against the public servant;

(b) direct the competent authority to initiate the departmental proceedings or any other appropriate action against the concerned public servant.

(8) The Lokpal may, after taking a decision under sub-section (7) on the filing of the charge-sheet, direct its Prosecution Wing or any investigating agency (including the Delhi Special Police Establishment) to initiate prosecution in the Special Court in respect of the cases investigated by the agency.

(9) The Lokpal may, during the preliminary inquiry or the investigation, as the case may be, pass appropriate orders for the safe custody of the documents relevant to the preliminary inquiry or, as the case may be, investigation as it deems fit.

(10) The website of the Lokpal shall, from time to time and in such manner as may be specified by regulations, display to the public, the status of number of complaints pending before it or disposed of by it.

(11) The Lokpal may retain the original records and evidences which are likely to be required in the process of preliminary inquiry or investigation or conduct of a case by it or by the Special Court.

(12) Save as otherwise provided, the manner and procedure of conducting a preliminary inquiry or investigation (including such material and documents to be made available to the public servant) under this Act, shall be such as may be specified by regulations.

**21. Persons likely to be prejudicially affected to be heard.**—If, at any stage of the proceeding, the Lokpal—

(a) considers it necessary to inquire into the conduct of any person other than the accused; or

(b) is of opinion that the reputation of any person other than an accused is likely to be prejudicially affected by the preliminary inquiry,

the Lokpal shall give to that person a reasonable opportunity of being heard in the preliminary inquiry and to produce evidence in his defence, consistent with the principles of natural justice.

**22. Lokpal may require any public servant or any other person to furnish information, etc.**—Subject to the provisions of this Act, for the purpose of any preliminary inquiry or investigation, the Lokpal or the investigating agency, as the case may be, may require any public servant or any other person who, in its opinion, is able to furnish information or produce documents relevant to such preliminary inquiry or investigation, to furnish any such information or produce any such document.

**23. Power of Lokpal to grant sanction for initiating prosecution.**—(1) Notwithstanding anything contained in section 197 of the Code of Criminal Procedure, 1973 (2 of 1974) or section 6A of the Delhi Special Police Establishment Act, 1946 (25 of 1946) or section 19 of the Prevention of Corruption Act, 1988 (49 of 1988), the Lokpal shall have the power to grant sanction for prosecution under clause (a) of sub-section (7) of section 20.

(2) No prosecution under sub-section (1) shall be initiated against any public servant accused of any offence alleged to have been committed by him while acting or purporting to act in the discharge of his official duty, and no court shall take cognizance of such offence except with the previous sanction of the Lokpal.

(3) Nothing contained in sub-sections (1) and (2) shall apply in respect of the persons holding office in pursuance of the provisions of the Constitution and in respect of which a procedure for removal of such person has been specified therein.

(4) The provisions contained in sub-sections (1), (2) and (3) shall be without prejudice to the generality of the provisions contained in article 311 and sub-clause (c) of clause (3) of article 320 of the Constitution.

**24. Action on investigation against public servant being Prime Minister, Ministers or Members of Parliament.**—Where, after the conclusion of the investigation, the findings of the Lokpal disclose the commission of an offence under the Prevention of Corruption Act, 1988 (49 of 1988) by a public servant referred to in clause (a) or clause (b) or clause (c) of sub-section (1) of section 14, the Lokpal may file a case in the Special Court and shall send a copy of the report together with its findings to the competent authority.

## CHAPTER VIII
## POWERS OF LOKPAL

**25. Supervisory powers of Lokpal.**—(1) The Lokpal shall, notwithstanding anything contained in section 4 of the Delhi Special Police Establishment Act, 1946 (25 of 1946) and section 8 of the Central Vigilance Commission Act, 2003 (45 of 2003), have the powers of superintendence over, and to give direction, to the Delhi Special Police Establishment in respect of the matters referred by the Lokpal for preliminary inquiry or investigation to the Delhi Special Police Establishment under this Act:

Provided that while exercising powers of superintendence or giving direction under this sub-section, the Lokpal shall not exercise powers in such a manner so as to require any agency (including the Delhi Special Police Establishment) to whom the investigation has been given, to investigate and dispose of any case in a particular manner.

(2) The Central Vigilance Commission shall send a statement, at such interval as the Lokpal may direct, to the Lokpal in respect of action taken on complaints referred to it under the second proviso to sub-section (1) of section 20 and on receipt of such statement, the Lokpal may issue guidelines for effective and expeditious disposal of such cases.

(3) Any officer of the Delhi Special Police Establishment investigating a case referred to it by the Lokpal, shall not be transferred without the approval of the Lokpal.

(4) The Delhi Special Police Establishment may, with the consent of the Lokpal, appoint a panel of Advocates, other than the Government Advocates, for conducting the cases referred to it by the Lokpal.

(5) The Central Government may from time to time make available such funds as may be required by the Director of the Delhi Special Police Establishment for conducting effective investigation into the matters referred to it by the Lokpal and the Director shall be responsible for the expenditure incurred in conducting such investigation.

**26. Search and seizure.**—(1) If the Lokpal has reason to believe that any document which, in its opinion, shall be useful for, or relevant to, any investigation under this Act, are secreted in any place, it may authorise any agency (including the Delhi Special Police Establishment) to whom the investigation has been given to search for and to seize such documents.

(2) If the Lokpal is satisfied that any document seized under sub-section (1) may be used as evidence for the purpose of any investigation under this

Act and that it shall be necessary to retain the document in its custody or in the custody of such officer as may be authorised, it may so retain or direct such authorised officer to retain such document till the completion of such investigation:

Provided that where any document is required to be returned, the Lokpal or the authorised officer may return the same after retaining copies of such document duly authenticated.

**27. Lokpal to have powers of civil court in certain cases.**—(1) Subject to the provisions of this section, for the purpose of any preliminary inquiry, the Inquiry Wing of the Lokpal shall have all the powers of a civil court, under the Code of Civil Procedure, 1908 (5 of 1908), while trying a suit in respect of the following matters, namely:—

(i) summoning and enforcing the attendance of any person and examining him on oath;

(ii) requiring the discovery and production of any document;

(iii) receiving evidence on affidavits;

(iv) requisitioning any public record or copy thereof from any court or office;

(v) issuing commissions for the examination of witnesses or documents:

Provided that such commission, in case of a witness, shall be issued only where the witness, in the opinion of the Lokpal, is not in a position to attend the proceeding before the Lokpal; and

(vi) such other matters as may be prescribed.

(2) Any proceeding before the Lokpal shall be deemed to be a judicial proceeding within the meaning of section 193 of the Indian Penal Code (45 of 1860).

**28. Power of Lokpal to utilise services of officers of Central or State Government.**—(1) The Lokpal may, for the purpose of conducting any preliminary inquiry or investigation, utilise the services of any officer or organisation or investigating agency of the Central Government or any State Government, as the case may be.

(2) For the purpose of preliminary inquiry or investigating into any matter pertaining to such inquiry or investigation, any officer or organisation or agency whose services are utilised under sub-section (1) may, subject to the superintendence and direction of the Lokpal,—

(a) summon and enforce the attendance of any person and examine him;

(b) require the discovery and production of any document; and

(c) requisition any public record or copy thereof from any office.

(3) The officer or organisation or agency whose services are utilised under sub-section (2) shall inquire or, as the case may be, investigate into any matter pertaining to the preliminary inquiry or investigation and submit

a report thereon to the Lokpal within such period as may be specified by it in this behalf.

**29. Provisional attachment of assets.**—(1) Where the Lokpal or any officer authorised by it in this behalf, has reason to believe, the reason for such belief to be recorded in writing, on the basis of material in his possession, that—

(a) any person is in possession of any proceeds of corruption;

(b) such person is accused of having committed an offence relating to corruption; and

(c) such proceeds of offence are likely to be concealed, transferred or dealt with in any manner which may result in frustrating any proceedings relating to confiscation of such proceeds of offence,

the Lokpal or the authorised officer may, by order in writing, provisionally attach such property for a period not exceeding ninety days from the date of the order, in the manner provided in the Second Schedule to the Income-tax Act, 1961 (43 of 1961) and the Lokpal and the officer shall be deemed to be an officer under sub-rule (e) of rule 1 of that Schedule.

(2) The Lokpal or the officer authorised in this behalf shall, immediately after attachment under sub-section (1), forward a copy of the order, along with the material in his possession, referred to in that sub-section, to the Special Court, in a sealed envelope, in the manner as may be prescribed and such Court may extend the order of attachment and keep such material for such period as the Court may deem fit.

(3) Every order of attachment made under sub-section (1) shall cease to have effect after the expiry of the period specified in that sub-section or after the expiry of the period as directed by the Special Court under sub-section (2).

(4) Nothing in this section shall prevent the person interested in the enjoyment of the immovable property attached under sub-section (1) or sub-section (2), from such enjoyment.

*Explanation.*—For the purposes of this sub-section, "person interested", in relation to any immovable property, includes all persons claiming or entitled to claim any interest in the property.

**30. Confirmation of attachment of assets.**—(1) The Lokpal, when it provisionally attaches any property under sub-section (1) of section 29 shall, within a period of thirty days of such attachment, direct its Prosecution Wing to file an application stating the facts of such attachment before the Special Court and make a prayer for confirmation of attachment of the property till completion of the proceedings against the public servant in the Special Court.

(2) The Special Court may, if it is of the opinion that the property provisionally attached had been acquired through corrupt means, make an order for confirmation of attachment of such property till the completion of the proceedings against the public servant in the Special Court.

(3) If the public servant is subsequently acquitted of the charges framed against him, the property, subject to the orders of the Special Court, shall be restored to the concerned public servant along with benefits from such property as might have accrued during the period of attachment.

(4) If the public servant is subsequently convicted of the charges of corruption, the proceeds relatable to the offence under the Prevention of Corruption Act, 1988 (49 of 1988) shall be confiscated and vest in the Central Government free from any encumbrance or leasehold interest excluding any debt due to any bank or financial institution.

*Explanation*.—For the purposes of this sub-section, the expressions "bank", "debt" and "financial institution" shall have the meanings respectively assigned to them in clauses (d), (g) and (h) of section 2 of the Recovery of Debts Due to Banks and Financial Institutions Act, 1993 (51 of 1993).

**31. Confiscation of assets, proceeds, receipts and benefits arisen or procured by means of corruption in special circumstances.**—(1) Without prejudice to the provisions of sections 29 and 30, where the Special Court, on the basis of *prima facie* evidence, has reason to believe or is satisfied that the assets, proceeds, receipts and benefits, by whatever name called, have arisen or procured by means of corruption by the public servant, it may authorise the confiscation of such assets, proceeds, receipts and benefits till his acquittal.

(2) Where an order of confiscation made under sub-section (1) is modified or annulled by the High Court or where the public servant is acquitted by the Special Court, the assets, proceeds, receipts and benefits, confiscated under sub-section (1) shall be returned to such public servant, and in case it is not possible for any reason to return the assets, proceeds, receipts and benefits, such public servant shall be paid the price thereof including the money so confiscated with interest at the rate of five per cent. per annum thereon calculated from the date of confiscation.

**32. Power of Lokpal to recommend transfer or suspension of public servant connected with allegation of corruption.**—(1) Where the Lokpal, while making a preliminary inquiry into allegations of corruption, is *prima facie* satisfied, on the basis of evidence available,—

(i) that the continuance of the public servant referred to in clause (d) or clause (e) or clause (f) of sub-section (1) of section 14 in his post while conducting the preliminary inquiry is likely to affect such preliminary inquiry adversely; or

(ii) such public servant is likely to destroy or in any way tamper with the evidence or influence witnesses,

then, the Lokpal may recommend to the Central Government for transfer or suspension of such public servant from the post held by him till such period as may be specified in the order.

(2) The Central Government shall ordinarily accept the recommendation of the Lokpal made under sub-section (1), except for the reasons to be recorded in writing in a case where it is not feasible to do so for administrative reasons.

**33. Power of Lokpal to give directions to prevent destruction of records during preliminary inquiry.**—The Lokpal may, in the discharge of its functions under this Act, issue appropriate directions to a public servant entrusted with the preparation or custody of any document or record—

(a) to protect such document or record from destruction or damage; or

(b) to prevent the public servant from altering or secreting such document or record; or

(c) to prevent the public servant from transferring or alienating any assets allegedly acquired by him through corrupt means.

**34. Power to delegate.**—The Lokpal may, by general or special order in writing, and subject to such conditions and limitations as may be specified therein, direct that any administrative or financial power conferred on it may also be exercised or discharged by such of its Members or officers or employees as may be specified in the order.

## CHAPTER IX
## SPECIAL COURTS

**35. Special Courts to be constituted by Central Government.**—(1) The Central Government shall constitute such number of Special Courts, as recommended by the Lokpal, to hear and decide the cases arising out of the Prevention of Corruption Act, 1988 (49 of 1988) or under this Act.

(2) The Special Courts constituted under sub-section (1) shall ensure completion of each trial within a period of one year from the date of filing of the case in the Court:

Provided that in case the trial cannot be completed within a period of one year, the Special Court shall record reasons therefore and complete the trial within a further period of not more than three months or such further periods not exceeding three months each, for reasons to be recorded in writing before the end of each such three months period, but not exceeding a total period of two years.

**36. Letter of request to a contracting State in certain cases.**—(1) Notwithstanding anything contained in this Act or the Code of Criminal Procedure, 1973 (2 of 1974) if, in the course of an preliminary inquiry or investigation into an offence or other proceeding under this Act, an application is made to a Special Court by an officer of the Lokpal authorised in this behalf that any evidence is required in connection with the preliminary inquiry or investigation into an offence or proceeding under this Act and he is of the opinion that such evidence may be available in any place in a contracting State, and the Special Court, on being satisfied that such evidence is required in connection with the preliminary inquiry or investigation into an offence or proceeding under this Act, may issue a letter of request to a court or an authority in the contracting State competent to deal with such request to—

(i) examine the facts and circumstances of the case;

(ii) take such steps as the Special Court may specify in such letter of request; and

(iii) forward all the evidence so taken or collected to the Special Court issuing such letter of request.

(2) The letter of request shall be transmitted in such manner as the Central Government may prescribe in this behalf.

(3) Every statement recorded or document or thing received under sub-section (1) shall be deemed to be evidence collected during the course of the preliminary inquiry or investigation.

## CHAPTER X

## COMPLAINTS AGAINST CHAIRPERSON, MEMBERS AND OFFICIALS OF LOKPAL

**37. Removal and suspension of Chairperson and Members of Lokpal.**—(1) The Lokpal shall not inquire into any complaint made against the Chairperson or any Member.

(2) Subject to the provisions of sub-section (4), the Chairperson or any Member shall be removed from his office by order of the President on grounds of misbehaviour after the Supreme Court, on a reference being made to it by the President on a petition signed by at least one hundred Members of Parliament has, on an inquiry held in accordance with the procedure prescribed in that behalf, reported that the Chairperson or such Member, as the case may be, ought to be removed on such ground.

(3) The President may suspend from office the Chairperson or any Member in respect of whom a reference has been made to the Supreme Court under sub-section (2), on receipt of the recommendation or interim order made by the Supreme Court in this regard until the President has passed orders on receipt of the final report of the Supreme Court on such reference.

(4) Notwithstanding anything contained in sub-section (2), the President may, by order, remove from the office, the Chairperson or any Member if the Chairperson or such Member, as the case may be,—

(a) is adjudged an insolvent; or

(b) engages, during his term of office, in any paid employment outside the duties of his office; or

(c) is, in the opinion of the President, unfit to continue in office by reason of infirmity of mind or body.

(5) If the Chairperson or any Member is, or becomes, in any way concerned or interested in any contract or agreement made by or on behalf of the Government of India or the Government of a State or participates in any way in the profit thereof or in any benefit or emolument arising therefrom otherwise than as a member and in common with the other members of an incorporated company, he shall, for the purposes of sub-section (2), be deemed to be guilty of misbehaviour.

**38. Complaints against officials of Lokpal.**—(1) Every complaint of allegation or wrongdoing made against any officer or employee or agency (including the Delhi Special Police Establishment), under or associated with the Lokpal for an offence punishable under the Prevention of Corruption Act, 1988 (49 of 1988) shall be dealt with in accordance with the provisions of this section.

(2) The Lokpal shall complete the inquiry into the complaint or allegation made within a period of thirty days from the date of its receipt.

(3) While making an inquiry into the complaint against any officer or employee of the Lokpal or agency engaged or associated with the Lokpal, if it is *prima facie* satisfied on the basis of evidence available, that—

(a) continuance of such officer or employee of the Lokpal or agency engaged or associated in his post while conducting the inquiry is likely to affect such inquiry adversely; or

(b) an officer or employee of the Lokpal or agency engaged or associated is likely to destroy or in any way tamper with the evidence or influence witnesses,

then, the Lokpal may, by order, suspend such officer or employee of the Lokpal or divest such agency engaged or associated with the Lokpal of all powers and responsibilities hereto before exercised by it.

(4) On the completion of the inquiry, if the Lokpal is satisfied that there is *prima facie* evidence of the commission of an offence under the Prevention of Corruption Act, 1988 (49 of 1988) or of any wrongdoing, it shall, within a period of fifteen days of the completion of such inquiry, order to prosecute such officer or employee of the Lokpal or such officer, employee, agency engaged or associated with the Lokpal and initiate disciplinary proceedings against the official concerned:

Provided that no such order shall be passed without giving such officer or employee of the Lokpal, such officer, employee, agency engaged or associated, a reasonable opportunity of being heard.

## CHAPTER XI

## ASSESSMENT OF LOSS AND RECOVERY THEREOF BY SPECIAL COURT

**39. Assessment of loss and recovery thereof by Special Court.**—If any public servant is convicted of an offence under the Prevention of Corruption Act, 1988 (49 of 1988) by the special Court, notwithstanding and without prejudice to any law for the time being in force, it may make an assessment of loss, if any, caused to the public exchequer on account of the actions or decisions of such public servant not taken in good faith and for which he stands convicted, and may order recovery of such loss, if possible or quantifiable, from such public servant so convicted:

Provided that if the Special Court, for reasons to be recorded in writing, comes to the conclusion that the loss caused was pursuant to a conspiracy with the beneficiary or beneficiaries of actions or decisions of the public servant so convicted, then such loss may, if assessed and quantifiable under this section, also be recovered from such beneficiary or beneficiaries proportionately.

## CHAPTER XII
## FINANCE, ACCOUNTS AND AUDIT

**40. Budget.**—The Lokpal shall prepare, in such form and at such time in each financial year as may be prescribed, its budget for the next financial year, showing the estimated receipts and expenditure of the Lokpal and forward the same to the Central Government for information.

**41. Grants by Central Government.**—The Central Government may, after due appropriation made by Parliament by law in this behalf, make to the Lokpal grants of such sums of money as are required to be paid for the salaries and allowances payable to the Chairperson and Members and the administrative expenses, including the salaries and allowances and pension payable to or in respect of officers and other employees of the Lokpal.

**42. Annual statement of accounts.**—(1) The Lokpal shall maintain proper accounts and other relevant records and prepare an annual statement of accounts in such form as may be prescribed by the Central Government in consultation with the Comptroller and Auditor-General of India.

(2) The accounts of the Lokpal shall be audited by the Comptroller and Auditor-General of India at such intervals as may be specified by him.

(3) The Comptroller and Auditor-General of India or any person appointed by him in connection with the audit of the accounts of the Lokpal under this Act shall have the same rights, privileges and authority in connection with such audit, as the Comptroller and Auditor-General of India generally has, in connection with the audit of the Government accounts and, in particular, shall have the right to demand the production of books, accounts, connected vouchers and other documents and papers and to inspect any of the offices of the Lokpal.

(4) The accounts of the Lokpal, as certified by the Comptroller and Auditor-General of India or any other person appointed by him in this behalf, together with the audit report thereon, shall be forwarded annually to the Central Government and the Central Government shall cause the same to be laid before each House of Parliament.

**43. Furnishing of returns, etc., to Central Government.**—The Lokpal shall furnish to the Central Government, at such time and in such form and manner as may be prescribed or as the Central Government may request, such returns and statements and such particulars in regard to any matter under the jurisdiction of the Lokpal, as the Central Government may, from time to time, require.

## CHAPTER XIII
## DECLARATION OF ASSETS

[1][**44. Declaration of assets.**—On and from the date of commencement of this Act, every public servant shall make a declaration of his assets and liabilities in such form and manner as may be prescribed.]

1. Subst. by Act 37 of 2016, Section 2, for Section 44 (w.e.f. January 16, 2014). Section 44, prior to subst., ran as under:

*Contd. on next page...*

**45. Presumption as to acquisition of assets by corrupt means in certain cases.**—If any public servant wilfully or for reasons which are not justifiable, fails to—

(a) to declare his assets; or

(b) gives misleading information in respect of such assets and is found to be in possession of assets not disclosed or in respect of which misleading information was furnished,

then, such assets shall, unless otherwise proved, be presumed to belong to the public servant and shall be presumed to be assets acquired by corrupt means:

Provided that the competent authority may condone or exempt the public servant from furnishing information in respect of assets not exceeding such minimum value as may be prescribed.

## CHAPTER XIV
## OFFENCES AND PENALTIES

**46. Prosecution for false complaint and payment of compensation, etc., to public servant.**—(1) Notwithstanding anything contained in this Act, whoever makes any false and frivolous or vexatious complaint under this Act shall, on conviction, be punished with imprisonment for a term which may extend to one year and with fine which may extend to one lakh rupees.

(2) No Court, except a Special Court, shall take cognizance of an offence under sub-section (1).

(3) No Special Court shall take cognizance of an offence under sub-section (1) except on a complaint made by a person against whom the false,

---

*Contd. from previous page...*

"*44. Declaration of Assets.*—(1) Every public servant shall make a declaration of his assets and liabilities in the manner as provided by or under this Act.

(2) A public servant shall, within a period of thirty days from the date on which he makes and subscribes an oath or affirmation to enter upon his office, furnish to the competent authority the information relating to—

(a) the assets of which he, his spouse and his dependent children are, jointly or severally, owners or beneficiaries;

(b) his liabilities and that of his spouse and his dependent children.

(3) A public servant holding his office as such, at the time of the commencement of this Act, shall furnish information relating to such assets and liabilities, as referred to in sub-section (2), to the competent authority within thirty days of the coming into force of this Act.

(4) Every public servant shall file with the competent authority, on or before the 31st July of every year, an annual return of such assets and liabilities, as referred to in sub-section (2), as on the 31st March of that year.

(5) The information under sub-section (2) or sub-section (3) and annual return under sub-section (4) shall be furnished to the competent authority in such form and in such manner as may be prescribed.

(6) The competent authority in respect of each Ministry or Department shall ensure that all such statements are published on the website of such Ministry or Department by 31st August of that year.

*Explanation.*—For the purposes of this section, "dependent children" means sons and daughters who have no separate means of earning and are wholly dependent on the public servant for their livelihood."

frivolous or vexatious complaint was made or by an officer authorised by the Lokpal.

(4) The prosecution in relation to an offence under sub-section (1) shall be conducted by the public prosecutor and all expenses connected with such prosecution shall be borne by the Central Government.

(5) In case of conviction of a person [being an individual or society or association of persons or trust (whether registered or not)], for having made a false complaint under this Act, such person shall be liable to pay compensation to the public servant against whom he made the false complaint in addition to the legal expenses for contesting the case by such public servant, as the Special Court may determine.

(6) Nothing contained in this section shall apply in case of complaints made in good faith.

*Explanation.*—For the purpose of this sub-section, the expression "good faith" means any act believed or done by a person in good faith with due care, caution and sense of responsibility or by mistake of fact believing himself justified by law under section 79 of the Indian Penal Code (45 of 1860).

**47. False complaint made by society or association of persons or trust.**—(1) Where any offence under sub-section (1) of section 46 has been committed by any society or association of persons or trust (whether registered or not), every person who, at the time the offence was committed, was directly in charge of, and was responsible to, the society or association of persons or trust, for the conduct of the business or affairs or activities of the society or association of persons or trust as well as such society or association of persons or trust shall be deemed to be guilty of the offence and shall be liable to be proceeded against and punished accordingly:

Provided that nothing contained in this sub-section shall render any such person liable to any punishment provided in this Act, if he proves that the offence was committed without his knowledge or that he had exercised all due diligence to prevent the commission of such offence.

(2) Notwithstanding anything contained in sub-section (1), where an offence under this Act has been committed by a society or association of persons or trust (whether registered or not) and it is proved that the offence has been committed with the consent or connivance of, or is attributable to any neglect on the part of, any director, manager, secretary or other officer of such society or association of persons or trust, such director, manager, secretary or other officer shall also be deemed to be guilty of that offence and shall be liable to be proceeded against and punished accordingly.

## CHAPTER XV

## MISCELLANEOUS

**48. Reports of Lokpal.**—It shall be the duty of the Lokpal to present annually to the President a report on the work done by the Lokpal and on receipt of such report the President shall cause a copy thereof together with a memorandum explaining, in respect of the cases, if any, where the advice of the Lokpal was not accepted, the reason for such non-acceptance to be laid before each House of Parliament.

**49. Lokpal to function as appellate authority for appeals arising out of any other law for the time being in force.**—The Lokpal shall function as the final appellate authority in respect of appeals arising out of any other law for the time being in force providing for delivery of public services and redressal of public grievances by any public authority in cases where the decision contains findings of corruption under the Prevention of Corruption Act, 1988 (49 of 1988).

**50. Protection of action taken in good faith by any public servant.**—No suit, prosecution or other legal proceedings under this Act shall lie against any public servant, in respect of anything which is done in good faith or intended to be done in the discharge of his official functions or in exercise of his powers.

**51. Protection of action taken in good faith by others.**—No suit, prosecution or other legal proceedings shall lie against the Lokpal or against any officer, employee, agency or any person, in respect of anything which is done in good faith or intended to be done under this Act or the rules or the regulations made thereunder.

**52. Members, officers and employees of Lokpal to be public servants.**—The Chairperson, Members, officers and other employees of the Lokpal shall be deemed, when acting or purporting to act in pursuance of any of the provisions of this Act, to be public servants within the meaning of section 21 of the Indian Penal Code (45 of 1860).

**53. Limitation to apply in certain cases.**—The Lokpal shall not inquire or investigate into any complaint, if the complaint is made after the expiry of a period of seven years from the date on which the offence mentioned in such complaint is alleged to have been committed.

**54. Bar of jurisdiction.**—No civil court shall have jurisdiction in respect of any matter which the Lokpal is empowered by or under this Act to determine.

**55. Legal assistance.**—The Lokpal shall provide to every person against whom a complaint has been made, before it, under this Act, legal assistance to defend his case before the Lokpal, if such assistance is requested for.

**56. Act to have overriding effect.**—The provisions of this Act shall have effect notwithstanding anything inconsistent therewith contained in any enactment other than this Act or in any instrument having effect by virtue of any enactment other than this Act.

**57. Provisions of this Act to be in addition of other laws.**—The provisions of this Act shall be in addition to, and not in derogation of, any other law for the time being in force.

**58. Amendment of certain enactments.**—The enactments specified in the Schedule shall be amended in the manner specified therein.

**59. Power to make rules.**—(1) The Central Government may, by notification in the Official Gazette, make rules to carry out the provisions of this Act.

(2) In particular, and without prejudice to the generality of the foregoing power, such rules may provide for all or any of the following matters, namely:—

(a) the form of complaint referred to in clause (e) of sub-section (1) of section 2;

(b) the term of the Search Committee, the fee and allowances payable to its members and the manner of selection of panel of names under sub-section (5) of section 4;

(c) the post or posts in respect of which the appointment shall be made after consultation with the Union Public Service Commission under the proviso to sub-section (3) of section 10;

(d) other matters for which the Lokpal shall have the powers of a civil court under clause (vi) of sub-section (1) of section 27;

(e) the manner of sending the order of attachment along with the material to the Special Court under sub-section (2) of section 29;

(f) the manner of transmitting the letter of request under sub-section (2) of section 36;

(g) the form and the time for preparing in each financial year the budget for the next financial year, showing the estimated receipts and expenditure of the Lokpal under section 40;

(h) the form for maintaining the accounts and other relevant records and the form of annual statement of accounts under sub-section (1) of section 42;

(i) the form and manner and the time for preparing the returns and statements along with particulars under section 43;

(j) the form and the time for preparing an annual return giving a summary of its activities during the previous year under sub-section (5) of section 44;

[1][(k) the form and manner of declaration of assets and liabilities by public servants under section 44:

Provided that the rules may be made under this clause retrospectively from the date on which that provisions of this Act came into force;]

(l) the minimum value for which the competent authority may condone or exempt a public servant from furnishing information in respect of assets under the proviso to section 45;

(m) any other matter which is to be or may be prescribed.

**60. Power of Lokpal to make regulations.**—(1) Subject to the provisions of this Act and the rules made thereunder, the Lokpal may, by notification in the Official Gazette, make regulations to carry out the provisions of this Act.

1. Subst. by Act 37 of 2016, Section 3, for clause (k) (w.e.f. January 16, 2014). Clause (k), prior to subst., ran as under:
"(k) the form of annual return to be filed by a public servant under sub-section (5) of section 44;".

(2) In particular, and without prejudice to the generality of the foregoing power, such regulations may provide for all or any of the following matters, namely:—

(a) the conditions of service of the secretary and other officers and staff of the Lokpal and the matters which in so far as they relate to salaries, allowances, leave or pensions, require the approval of the President under sub-section (4) of section 10;

(b) the place of sittings of benches of the Lokpal under clause (f) of sub-section (1) of section 16;

(c) the manner for displaying on the website of the Lokpal, the status of all complaints pending or disposed of along with records and evidence with reference thereto under sub-section (10) of section 20;

(d) the manner and procedure of conducting preliminary inquiry or investigation under sub-section (11) of section 20;

(e) any other matter which is required to be, or may be, specified under this Act.

**61. Laying of rules and regulations.**—Every rule and regulation made under this Act shall be laid, as soon as may be after it is made, before each House of Parliament, while it is in session, for a total period of thirty days which may be comprised in one session or in two or more successive sessions, and if, before the expiry of the session immediately following the session or the successive sessions aforesaid, both Houses agree in making any modification in the rule or regulation, or both Houses agree that the rule or regulation should not be made, the rule or regulation shall thereafter have effect only in such modified form or be of no effect, as the case may be; so, however, that any such modification or annulment shall be without prejudice to the validity of anything previously done under that rule or regulation.

**62. Power to remove difficulties.**—(1) If any difficulty arises in giving effect to the provisions of this Act, the Central Government may, by order, published in the Official Gazette, make such provisions not inconsistent with the provisions of this Act, as appear to be necessary for removing the difficulty:

Provided that no such order shall be made under this section after the expiry of a period of two years from the commencement of this Act.

(2) Every order made under this section shall be laid, as soon as may be after it is made, before each House of Parliament.

## PART III

## ESTABLISHMENT OF THE LOKAYUKTA

**63. Establishment of Lokayukta.**—Every State shall establish a body to be known as the Lokayukta for the State, if not so established, constituted or appointed, by a law made by the State Legislature, to deal with complaints relating to corruption against certain public functionaries, within a period of one year from the date of commencement of this Act.

## THE SCHEDULE

[*See* section 58]

## AMENDMENT TO CERTAIN ENACTMENTS

### PART I

### AMENDMENT TO THE COMMISSIONS OF INQUIRY ACT, 1952

(60 OF 1952)

**Amendment of section 3.**—In section 3, in sub-section (1), for the words "The appropriate Government may", the words and figures "Save as otherwise provided in the Lokpal and Lokayuktas Act, 2013, the appropriate Government may" shall be substituted.

### PART II

### AMENDMENTS TO THE DELHI SPECIAL POLICE ESTABLISHMENT ACT, 1946

(25 OF 1946)

**1. Amendment of section 4A.**—In section 4A,—

(i) for sub-section (1), the following sub-section shall be substituted, namely:—

"(1) The Central Government shall appoint the Director on the recommendation of the Committee consisting of—

(a) the Prime Minister—Chairperson;

(b) the Leader of Opposition in the House of the People—Member;

(c) the Chief Justice of India or Judge of the Supreme Court nominated by him—Member.";

(ii) sub-section (2) shall be omitted.

**2. Insertion of new section 4BA.**—After section 4B, the following section shall be inserted, namely:—

"*4BA. Director of Prosecution.*—(1) There shall be a Directorate of Prosecution headed by a Director who shall be an officer not below the rank of Joint Secretary to the Government of India, for conducting prosecution of cases under this Act.

(2) The Director of Prosecution shall function under the overall supervision and control of the Director.

(3) The Central Government shall appoint the Director of Prosecution on the recommendation of the Central Vigilance Commission.

(4) The Director of Prosecution shall notwithstanding anything to the contrary contained in the rules relating to his conditions of service, continue to hold office for a period of not less than two years from the date on which he assumes office.".

**3. Amendment of section 4C.**—In section 4C, for sub-section (1), the following sub-section shall be substituted, namely:—

"(1) The Central Government shall appoint officers to the posts of the level of Superintendent of Police and above except Director, and also recommend the extension or curtailment of the tenure of such officers in the Delhi Special Police Establishment, on the recommendation of a committee consisting of:—

(a) the Central Vigilance Commissioner—Chairperson;

(b) Vigilance Commissioners—Members;

(c) Secretary to the Government of India in-charge of the Ministry of Home—Member;

(d) Secretary to the Government of India in-charge of the Department of Personnel—Member:

Provided that the Committee shall consult the Director before submitting its recommendation to the Central Government.".

## PART III

## AMENDMENTS TO THE PREVENTION OF CORRUPTION ACT, 1988

(49 OF 1988)

**1. Amendment of sections 7, 8, 9 and 12.**—In sections 7, 8, 9 and section 12,—

(a) for the words "six months", the words "three years" shall respectively be substituted;

(b) for the words "five years", the words "seven years" shall respectively be substituted.

**2. Amendment of section 13.**—In section 13, in sub-section (2),—

(a) for the words "one year", the words "four years" shall be substituted;

(b) for the words "seven years", the words "ten years" shall be substituted.

**3. Amendment of section 14.**—In section 14,—

(a) for the words "two years", the words "five years" shall be substituted;

(b) for the words "seven years", the words "ten years" shall be substituted.

**4. Amendment of section 15.**—In section 15, for the words "which may extend to three years", the words "which shall not be less than two years but which may extend to five years" shall be substituted.

**5. Amendment of section 19.**—In section 19, after the words "except with the previous sanction", the words "save as otherwise provided in the Lokpal and Lokayuktas Act, 2013" shall be inserted.

## PART IV
## AMENDMENT TO THE CODE OF CRIMINAL PROCEDURE, 1973
(2 OF 1974)

**Amendment of section 197.**—In section 197, after the words "except with the previous sanction", the words "save as otherwise provided in the Lokpal and Lokayuktas Act, 2013" shall be inserted.

## PART V
## AMENDMENTS TO THE CENTRAL VIGILANCE COMMISSION ACT, 2003
(45 OF 2003)

**1. Amendment of section 2.**—In section 2, after clause (d), the following clause shall be inserted, namely:—

'(da) "Lokpal" means the Lokpal established under sub-section (1) of section 3 of the Lokpal and Lokayuktas Act, 2013;'.

**2. Amendment of section 8.**—In section 8, in sub-section (2), after clause (b), the following clause shall be inserted, namely:—

"(c) on a reference made by the Lokpal under proviso to sub-section (1) of section 20 of the Lokpal and Lokayuktas Act, 2013, the persons referred to in clause (d) of sub-section (1) shall also include—

(i) members of Group B, Group C and Group D services of the Central Government;

(ii) such level of officials or staff of the corporations established by or under any Central Act, Government companies, societies and other local authorities, owned or controlled by the Central Government, as that Government may, by notification in the Official Gazette, specify in this behalf:

Provided that till such time a notification is issued under this clause, all officials or staff of the said corporations, companies, societies and local authorities shall be deemed to be the persons referred in clause (d) of sub-section (1).".

**3. Insertion of new sections 8A and 8B.**—After section 8, the following sections shall be inserted, namely:—

"8A. *Action on preliminary inquiry in relation to public servants.*—(1) Where, after the conclusion of the preliminary inquiry relating to corruption of public servants belonging to Group C and Group D officials of the Central Government, the findings of the Commission disclose, after giving an opportunity of being heard to the public servant, a *prima facie* violation of conduct rules relating to corruption under the Prevention of Corruption Act, 1988 (49 of 1988) by such public servant, the Commission shall proceed with one or more of the following actions, namely:—

(a) cause an investigation by any agency or the Delhi Special Police Establishment, as the case may be;

(b) initiation of the disciplinary proceedings or any other appropriate action against the concerned public servant by the competent authority;

(c) closure of the proceedings against the public servant and to proceed against the complainant under section 46 of the Lokpal and Lokayuktas Act, 2013.

(2) Every preliminary inquiry referred to in sub-section (1) shall ordinarily be completed within a period of ninety days and for reasons to be recorded in writing, within a further period of ninety days from the date of receipt of the complaint.

*8B. Action on investigation in relation to public servants.*—(1) In case the Commission decides to proceed to investigate into the complaint under clause (a) of sub-section (1) of section 8A, it shall direct any agency (including the Delhi Special Police Establishment) to carry out the investigation as expeditiously as possible and complete the investigation within a period of six months from the date of its order and submit the investigation report containing its findings to the Commission:

Provided that the Commission may extend the said period by a further period of six months for the reasons to be recorded in writing.

(2) Notwithstanding anything contained in section 173 of the Code of Criminal Procedure, 1973 (2 of 1974), any agency (including the Delhi Special Police Establishment) shall, in respect of cases referred to it by the Commission, submit the investigation report to the Commission.

(3) The Commission shall consider every report received by it under sub-section (2) from any agency (including the Delhi Special Police Establishment) and may decide as to—

(a) file charge-sheet or closure report before the Special Court against the public servant;

(b) initiate the departmental proceedings or any other appropriate action against the concerned public servant by the competent authority.".

**4. Insertion of new section 11A.**—After section 11, the following section shall be inserted, namely:—

"*11A. Director of inquiry for making preliminary inquiry.*—(1) There shall be a Director of Inquiry, not below the rank of Joint Secretary to the Government of India, who shall be appointed by the Central Government for conducting preliminary inquiries referred to the Commission by the Lokpal.

(2) The Central Government shall provide the Director of Inquiry such officers and employees as may be required for the discharge of his functions under this Act.".

# RELEVANT PROVISIONS OF THE CENTRAL CIVIL SERVICES (CONDUCT) RULES, 1964

(Relevant Provisions Under the Rules)

**1. Short title, commencement and application.**—(1) These rules may be called the Central Civil Services (Conduct) Rules, 1964.

(2) They shall come into force at once.

(3) Save as otherwise provided in these rules and subject to the provisions of the Indian Foreign Service (Conduct and Discipline) Rules, 1961, these rules shall apply to every person appointed to a civil service or post (including a civilian in Defence Service) in connection with the affairs of the Union:

Provided that nothing in these rules shall apply to any Government servant who is—

(a) (i) a railway servant as defined in Section 3 of the Indian Railways Act, 1890 (9 of 1890);

(ii) a person holding a post in the Railway Board and is subject to the Railway Services (Conduct) Rules;

(iii) holding any post under the administrative control of the Railway Board or of the Financial Commissioner of Railways;

(b) a member of an All India Service;

(c) a holder of any post in respect of which the President has, by a general or special order, directed that these rules shall not apply:

Provided further that Rules 4,6,7,12,14, sub-rule (3) of Rule 15, Rule 16, sub-rules (1), (2) and (3) of Rule 18, Rules 19, 20 and 21 shall not apply to any Government servant who draws a pay which does not exceed Rs.500 per mensem and holds a non-gazetted post in any of the following establishments, owned or managed by the Government, namely:—

(i) ports, docks, wharves or jetties;

(ii) defence installations except training establishments;

(iii) public works establishments, in so far as they relate to work-charged staff;

(iv) irrigation and electric power establishments;

(v) mines as defined in clause (j) of Section 2 of the Mines Act, 1952 (35 of 1952);

(vi) factories as defined in clause (m) of Section 2 of the Factories Act, 1948 (63 of 1948); and

(vii) field units of the Central Tractor Organisation employing workmen governed by labour laws:

Provided further that these rules shall apply to any person temporarily transferred to a service or post specified in clause (a) of the first proviso to whom but for such transfer these rules would have otherwise applied.

*Explanation.*—For the purposes of the second proviso, the expression 'establishment' shall not include any railway establishment or any office mainly concerned with administrative, managerial, supervisory, security or welfare functions.

**2. Definitions.**—In these rules, unless the context otherwise requires,—

(a) "The Government" means the Central Government;

(b) "Government servant" means any person appointed by Government to any civil service or post in connection with the affairs of the Union and includes a civilian in a Defence Service;

*Explanation.*—A Government servant whose services are placed at the disposal of a company, corporation, organisation or a local authority by the Government shall, for the purpose of these rules, be deemed to be a Government servant serving under the Government notwithstanding that his salary is drawn from sources other than the Consolidated Fund of India;

(c) "Members of family" in relation to a Government servant includes:—

(i) the wife or husband as the case may be, of the Government servant, whether residing with the Government servant or not but does not include a wife or husband, as the case may be, separated from the Government servant by a decree or order of a competent Court;

(ii) son or daughter or step-son or step-daughter of the Government servant and wholly dependent on him, but does not include a child or step-child who is no longer in any way dependent on the Government servant or of whose custody the Government servant has been deprived by or under any law;

(iii) any other person related, whether by blood or marriage to the Government servant or to the Government servant's wife or husband, and wholly dependent on the Government servant.

**3. General.**—(1) Every Government servant shall at all times—

(i) maintain absolute integrity;

(ii) maintain devotion to duty; and

(iii) do nothing which is unbecoming of a Government servant.

[1](iv) commit himself to and uphold the supremacy of the Constitution and democratic values;

(v) defend and uphold the sovereignty and integrity of India, the security of the State, public order, decency and morality;

(vi) maintain high ethical standards and honesty;

(vii) maintain political neutrality;

(viii) promote the principles of merit, fairness and impartiality in the discharge of duties;

(ix) maintain accountability and transparency;

(x) maintain responsiveness to the public, particularly to the weaker section;

(xi) maintain courtesy and good behaviour with the public;

1. According to GSR 845(E), dt. November 27, 2014.

(xii) take decisions solely in public interest and use or cause to use public resources efficiently, effectively and economically;

(xiii) declare any private interests relating to his public duties and take steps to resolve any conflicts in a way that protects the public interest;

(xiv) not place himself under any financial or other obligations to any individual or organisation which may influence him in the performance of his official duties;

(xv) not misuse his position as civil servant and not take decisions in order to derive financial or material benefits for himself, his family or his friends;

(xvi) make choices, take decisions and make recommendations on merit alone;

(xvii) act with fairness and impartiality and not discriminate against anyone, particularly the poor and the under-privileged sections of society;

(xviii) refrain from doing anything which is or may be contrary to any law, rules, regulations and established practices;

(xix) maintain discipline in the discharge of his duties and be liable to implement the lawful orders duly communicated to him;

(xx) maintain confidentiality in the performance of his official duties as required by any laws for the time being in force, particularly with regard to information, disclosure of which may prejudicially affect the sovereignty and integrity of India, the security of the State, strategic, scientific or economic interests of the State, friendly relation with foreign countries or lead to incitement of an offence or illegal or unlawful gain to any person;

(xxi) perform and discharge his duties with the highest degree of professionalism and dedication to the best of his abilities.

(2) (i) Every Government servant holding a supervisory post shall take all possible steps to ensure the integrity and devotion to duty of all Government servants for the time being under his control and authority;

[1](ii) No Government servant shall, in the performance of his official duties, or in the exercise of powers conferred on him, act otherwise than in his best judgement except when he is acting under the direction of his official superior;

(iii) The direction of the official superior shall ordinarily be in writing. Oral direction to subordinates shall be avoided, as far as possible. Where the issue of oral direction becomes unavoidable, the official superior shall confirm it in writing immediately thereafter;

(iv) A Government servant who has received oral direction from his official superior shall seek confirmation of the same in writing as early as possible, whereupon it shall be the duty of the official superior to confirm the direction in writing.

1. According to S.O. 3, dt. January 6, 1979.

[1]*Explanation I.*—A Government servant who habitually fails to perform the task assigned to him within the time set for the purpose and with the quality of performance expected to him shall be deemed to be lacking in devotion to duty within the meaning the cause (ii) of sub-rule (1).

*Explanation II.*—Nothing in clause (ii) of sub-rule (2) shall be construed as empowering a Government servant to evade his responsibilities by seeking instructions from, or approval of, a superior officer or authority when such instructions are not necessary under the scheme of distribution of powers and responsibilities.

****

[2]**11. Communication of Official Information.**—Every Government servant shall, in performance of his duties in good faith, communicate information to a person in accordance with the Right to Information Act, 2005 (22 of 2005) and the rules made there under :

Provided that no Government servant shall, except in accordance with any general or special order of the Government or in performance in good faith of the duties assigned to him, communicate, directly or indirectly, any official document or any part thereof or classified information to any Government servant or any other person to whom he is no authorized to communicate such document or classified information.

**12. Subscriptions.**—No Government servant shall, except with the previous sanction of the Government or of the prescribed authority, ask for or accept contributions to, or otherwise associate himself with the raising of, any funds or other collections in cash or in kind in pursuance of any object whatsoever.

[3]**13. Gifts.**—(1) Save as provided in these rules, no Government servant shall accept, or permit any member of his family or any other person acting on his behalf to accept, any gift.

*Explanation.*—The expression "gift" shall include free transport, boarding, lodging or other service or any other pecuniary advantage when provided by any person other than a near relative or personal friend having no official dealings with the Government servant.

**Note (1).**—A casual meal, lift or other social hospitality shall not be deemed to be a gift.

**Note (2).**—A Government servant shall avoid accepting lavish hospitality or frequent hospitality from any individual, industrial or commercial firms, organisations, etc., having official dealings with him.

[4][(2) On occasions such as weddings, anniversaries, funerals or religious functions, when the making of gift is in conformity with the prevailing religious and social practice, a Government servant may accept gifts from his near relatives or from his personal friends having no official dealings

1. According to S.O. 935, dt. March 8, 1986.
2. According to GSR 376, dt. October 22, 2005.
3. According to S.O. 2582, dt. October 6, 1990.
4. According to GSR 367, dt. August 31, 1996.

with him, but shall make a report to the Government, if the value of such gift exceeds;

(i) [1]rupees twenty five thousand in the case of a Government servant holding any Group 'A' post;

(ii) rupees fifteen thousand in the case of a Government servant holding any Group 'B' post;

(iii) rupees seven thousand five hundred in the case of a Government servant holding any Group 'C' post; and

(3) In any other case of a Government servant shall not accept any gift without sanction of the Government if the value thereof exceeds.

(i) rupees one thousand five hundred in the case of a Government servant holding any Group 'A' or Group 'B' post; and

(ii) rupees five hundred in the case of a Government servant holding any Group 'C' or Group 'D' post.

(4) Notwithstanding anything contained in sub-rules (2), and (3) a Government servant, being a member of the Indian delegation or otherwise, may receive and retain gifts from foreign dignitaries if the market value of gifts received on one occasion does not exceed rupees one thousand. In all other cases, the acceptance and retention of such gifts shall be regulated by the instructions issued by the Government in this regard from time to time.

(5) A Government servant shall not accept any gifts from any foreign firm which is either contracting with the Government of India or is one with which the Government servant had, has or is likely to have official dealings. Acceptance of gifts by a Government servant from any other firm shall be subject to the provisions of sub-rule (3).]

****

**18. Movable, immovable and valuable property.**—(1) (i) Every Government servant shall on his first appointment to any service or post submit a return of his assets and liabilities, in such form as may be prescribed by the Government, giving the full particulars regarding—

(a) the immovable property inherited by him, or owned or acquired by him or held by him on lease or mortgage, either in his own name or in the name of any member of his family or in the name of any other person;

(b) shares, debentures and cash including bank deposits inherited by him or similarly owned, acquired, or held by him;

(c) other movable property inherited by him or similarly owned, acquired or held by him; and

(d) debts and other liabilities incurred by him directly or indirectly.

**Note I.**—Sub-rule (1) shall not ordinarily apply to Group 'D' servants but the Government may direct that it shall apply to any such Government servant or class of such Government servants.

1. According to GSR 149(E), dt. March 4, 2014.

**Note II.**—In all returns, the values of items of movable property worth less than Rs. [1]10,000/- may be added and shown as a lump sum. The value of articles of daily use such as clothes, utensils, crockery, books, etc. need not be included in such return.

**Note III.**—[2]Where a Government servant already belonging to a service or holding a post in appointed to any other civil service or post, he shall not be required to submit a fresh return under this clause.

[3](ii) Every Government servant belonging to any service or holding any post included in Group 'A' and Group 'B' shall submit an annual return in such form as may be prescribed by the Government in this regard giving full particulars regarding the immovable property inherited by him or owned or acquired by him or held by him on lease or mortgage either in his own name or in the name of any member of his family or in the name of any other person.

(2) No Government servant shall, except with the previous knowledge of the prescribed authority, acquire or dispose of any immovable property by lease, mortgage, purchase, sale, gift or otherwise either in his own name or in the name of any member of his family:

[4]Provided that the previous sanction of the prescribed authority shall be obtained by the Government servant if any such transaction is with a person having official dealing with him.

[5](3) Where a Government servant enters into a transaction in respect of movable property either in his own name or in the name of the member of his family, he shall, within one month from the date of such transaction, report the same to the prescribed authority, if the value of such property exceeds two months' basic pay of the Government servant:

Provided that the previous sanction of the prescribed authority shall be obtained by the Government servant if any such transaction is with a person having official dealings with him.

(4) The Government or the prescribed authority may, at any time, by general or special order, require a Government servant to furnish, within a period specified in the order, a full and complete statement of such movable or immovable property held or acquired by him or on his behalf or by any member of his family as may be specified in the order. Such statement shall, if so required by the Government or by the prescribed authority, include the details of the means by which, or the source from which, such property was acquired.

(5) The Government may exempt any category of Government servants belonging to Group 'C' or Group 'D' from any of the provisions of this rule except sub-rule (4). No such exemption shall, however, be made without the concurrence of the [6]Cabinet Secretariat (Department of Personnel).

1. According to S.O. 3132, dt. December 26, 1992.
2. According to S.O. 4663, dt. December 11, 1976.
3. According to S.O. 2691, dt. July 24, 1976.
4. According to S.O. 1124, dt. March 22, 1986.
5. According to GSR 370(E), dt. May 9, 2011.
6. According to S.O. 3129, dt. September 26, 1970.

*Explanation.*—For the purposes of this rule—

(1) the expression "movable property" includes—

(a) jewellery, insurance policies, the annual premia of which exceeds Rs. [1]'two months' basic pay of the Government servant, shares, securities and debentures;

[2](b) all loans, whether secured or not, advanced or taken by the Government servant;

(c) motor cars, motor cycles, horses or any other means of conveyance; and

(d) refrigerators, radios radiograms and television sets.

[3]**18-A. Restrictions in relation to acquisition and disposal of immovable property outside India and transactions with foreigners, etc.**—Notwithstanding anything contained in sub-rule (2) of Rule 18, no Government servant shall, except with the previous sanction of the prescribed authority,—

(a) acquire, by purchase, mortgage, lease, gift or otherwise, either in his own name or in the name of any member of his family, any immovable property situated outside India;

(b) dispose of, by sale, mortgage, gift or otherwise or grant any lease in respect of any immovable property situated outside India which was acquired or is held by him either in his own name or in the name of any member of his family;

(c) enter into any transaction with any foreigner, foreign Government, foreign organisation or concern,—

(i) for the acquisition, by purchase, mortgage, lease, gift or otherwise, either in his own name or in the name of any member of his family, any immovable property;

(ii) for the disposal of, by sale, mortgage, gift or otherwise, or the grant of any lease in respect of any immovable property which was acquired or is held by him either in his own name or in the name of any member of his family.

*Explanation.*—In this rule "prescribed authority" has the same meaning as in Rule 18.

---

1. According to GSR 149(E), dt. March 4, 2014.
2. According to S.O. 1965, dt. August 8, 1987.
3. According to S.O. 83, dt. January 13, 1973.

# RELEVANT PROVISIONS OF [1]THE ALL INDIA SERVICES (CONDUCT) RULES, 1968

In exercise of the powers conferred by sub-section (1) of section 3 of the All India Services Act, 1951 (61 of 1951), the Central Government after consultation with the Governments of the State concerned, hereby makes the following rules, namely:—

**1. Short title and commencement.**—(1) These rules may be called the All India Services (Conduct) Rules, 1968.

(2) They shall come into force on the date[2] of their publication in the Official Gazette.

**2. Definitions.**—In these rules, unless the context otherwise requires-

(a) "Government" means—

(i) in the case of a member of the Service serving in connection with the affairs of the Union, the Central Government; or

(ii) in the case of a member of the Service serving under a Foreign Government or outside India (whether on duty or on leave), the Central Government; or

(iii) in the case of a member of the Service serving in connection with the affairs of a State, the Government of that State;

*Explanation.*—A member of the Service whose services are placed at the disposal of a company, corporation or other organisation or a local authority by the Central Government or the Government or the Government of a State shall for the purpose of these rules, be deemed to be a member of the Service serving in connection with the affairs of the Union or in connection with the affairs of that State, as the case may be, notwithstanding that his salary is drawn from the sources other than the Consolidated Fund of India or the Consolidated Fund of that State;

**3. General.**—(1) Every member of the Service shall at all times maintain absolute integrity and devotion to duty and shall do nothing which is unbecoming of a member of the Service.

[3](1A) Every member of the Service shall maintain:—

(i) high ethical standards, integrity and honesty;

(ii) political neutrality;

(iii) promoting of the principles of merit, fairness and impartiality in the discharge of duties;

(iv) accountability and transparency;

---

1. Published according to Notification No.8/91/62—AIS(III) dt. December 18, 1968 (GSR No. 3 dt. January 4, 1969)
2. According to Notification No. 8/91/62—AIS (III) dt. December 18, 1968 (GSR No. 3 dt. January 4, 1969).
3. Inst. according to DP & T Notification No. 11017/01/2014—AIS (III) dt. August 6, 2014 (GSR No. 573(E) dt. August 8, 2014.

(v) responsiveness to the public, particularly to the weaker section;

(vi) courtesy and good behavior with the public.

(2) Every member of the Service shall take all possible steps to ensure integrity of, and devotion to duty by, all Government servants for the time being under his control and authority.

[1](2A) Every member of the service shall in the discharge of his duties act in a courteous manner and shall not adopt dilatory tactics in his dealings with the public or otherwise

[2](2B) Every member of the Service shall:—

(i) commit himself to and uphold the supremacy of the Constitution and democratic values;

(ii) defend and uphold the sovereignty and integrity of India, the security of State, public order, decency and morality;

(iii) maintain integrity in public service;

(iv) take decisions solely in public interest and use or cause to use public resources efficiently, effectively and economically;

(v) declare any private interests relating to his public duties and take steps to resolve any conflicts in a way that protects the public interest;

(vi) not place himself under any financial or other obligations to any individual or organisation which may influence him in the performance of his official duties;

(vii) not misuse his position as civil servant and not take decisions in order to derive financial or material benefits for himself, his family or his friends;

(viii) make choices, take decisions and make recommendations on merit alone;

(ix) act with fairness and impartiality and not discriminate against anyone, particularly the poor and the under-privileged sections of society;

(x) refrain from doing anything which is or may be contrary to any law, rules, regulations and established practices

(xi) maintain discipline in the discharge of his duties and be liable to implement the lawful orders duly communicated to him;

(xii) be liable to maintain confidentiality in the performance of his official duties as required by any laws for the time being in force, particularly with regard to information, disclosure of which may prejudicially affect the sovereignty and integrity of India, the security of State, strategic, scientific or economic

1. Subst. according to DP & AR Notification No. 11017/27/93—AIS (III) dt. January 13, 1995 (GSR No. 52 dt. February 4, 1995).
2. Inst. according to DP & T Notification No. 11017/01/2014—AIS (III) dt. August 6, 2014 (GSR No. 573 (E) dt. August 8, 2014).

interests of the State, friendly relation with foreign countries or lead to incitement of an offence or illegal or unlawful gains to any person;

(xiii) perform and discharge his duties with the highest degree of professionalism and dedication to the best of his abilities.

(3) [1](i) No member of the Service shall, in the performance of his official duties, or in the exercise of powers conferred on him, act otherwise than in his own best judgment to be true and correct except when he is acting under the direction of his official superior.

(ii) The direction of the official superior shall ordinarily be in writing. Where the issue of oral direction becomes unavoidable, the official superior shall confirm it in writing immediately thereafter.

(iii) A member of the Service who has received oral direction from his official superior shall seek confirmation of the same in writing, as early as possible and in such case, it shall be the duty of the official superior to confirm the direction in writing.

[2]*Explanation I.*—A member of the Service who habitually fails to perform a task assigned to him within the time set for the purpose and with the quality of performance expected of him shall be deemed to be lacking in devotion to duty within the meaning of the sub-rule (1);

*Explanation II.*—Nothing in clause (i) of sub-rule (3) shall be construed as empowering a Government servant to evade his responsibilities by seeking instructions from or approval of, a superior officer or authority when such instructions are not necessary under the scheme of distribution of powers and responsibilities.

[3](iv) Prohibition regarding employment of children below 14 years of age:—No member of the Service shall employ to work any child below the age of 14 years.

****

[4]**11. Gifts.**—(1) A member of the service may accept gifts from his near relatives or from his personal friends having no official dealings with them, on occasions such as wedding, anniversaries, funerals and religious functions when the making of gifts is in conformity with the prevailing religious and social practice, but he shall make a report to the Government if the value of such gift exceeds [5]Rs.25,000/-.

---

1. Inst. according to DP&AR Notification No. 11017/2/79—AIS(III) dt. August 24, 1979 (GSR No. 1122 dt. September 8, 1979).
2. Subst. according to DP&AR Notification No. 11017/39/86—AIS(III) dt. January 1, 1987 (GSR No. 34 dt. January 17, 1987).
3. Inst. according to DOP&T Notification No. 11017/25/99—AIS(III) dt. February 1, 2000 (GSR No. 51 dt. February 12, 2000).
4. Inst. according to Notification No. 11017/27/93—AIS(III) dt. January 13, 1995 (GSR No. 52 dt. February 4, 1995).
5. Subst. according to DP&T Notification No.11017/31/1999—AIS(III), dt. April 10, 2015 (GSR No. 280 (E) dt. April 10, 2015.

(2) Save as otherwise provided in sub-rule (1), no member of the service shall accept any gift without the sanction of the Government if the value of gift exceeds [1]Rs.5,000/-.

(3) Member of the Service shall avoid accepting lavish hospitality or frequent hospitality from persons having official dealings with them or from industrial or commercial firms or other organisations.

**11-A. Giving or taking of dowry.**—No member of the Service shall—

(i) give or take or abet the giving or taking of dowry; or

(ii) demand, directly or indirectly, from the parents or guardian of a bride or bridegroom, as the case may be, any dowry.

*Explanation.*—For the purpose of the rule, "dowry" has the same meaning as in the Dowry Prohibition Act, 1961 (28 of 1961).

**12. Public demonstrations in honour of Government Servants.**—(1) No member of the Service shall except with the previous sanction of the Government, receive any complimentary or valedictory address or accept any testimonial or attend any meeting or entertainment held in his honour or in the honour of any other Government Servant.:

Provided that nothing in this rule shall apply to—

(i) a farewell entertainment of a substantially private and informal character held in honour of a member of the Service or any other Government servant on the occasion of his retirement or transfer or of any person who has recently quit service of Government; or

(ii) the acceptance of simple and inexpensive entertainments arranged by public bodies or institutions.

(2) No member of the Service shall exercise pressure of any sort on any Government servant to induce him to subscribe towards any farewell entertainment even if it is of a substantially private and informal character.

****

**16. Movable, immovable and valuable property.**—(1) Every person shall, where such person is a member of the Service at the commencement of these rules, before such date after such commencement as may be specified by the Government in this behalf, or where such person becomes a member of the Service after such commencement, on his first appointment to the Service, submit a return of his assets and liabilities in such form as may be prescribed by the Government giving the full particulars regarding :—

(a) the immovable property owned by him, or inherited or acquired by him or held by him on lease or mortgage, either in his own name or in the name of any member of his family or in the name of any other person;

(b) shares, debentures, postal Cumulative Time Deposits and cash including bank deposits inherited by him or similarly owned, acquired or held by him;

1. Subst. according to DP&T Notification No.11017/31/1999—AIS(III), dt. April 10, 2015 (GSR No. 280 (E) dt. April 10, 2015.

(c) other movable property inherited by him or similarly owned, acquired or held by him; and

(d) debts and other liabilities incurred by him directly or indirectly

**Note I.**—In all returns, the values of items of movable property worth less than an amount equal to two months basic pay of the member of Service*, in value may be added and shown as a lump sum. The value of articles of daily use such as clothes, utensils, crockery and books need not be included in such return

**Note II.**—Where a member of an All India Service is appointed as a member of another All India Service, he shall not be required to submit a fresh return under this sub-rule.

[1](2) Every member of the Service shall submit an annual return in such form as may be prescribed by the Government in this regard, giving full particulars regarding the immovable property inherited by him or owned or acquired by him or held by him on lease or mortgage, either in his own name or in the name of any member of his family or in the name of any other person.

(3) No member of the Service shall, except with the previous knowledge of the Government,—

(a) acquire any immovable property by lease, mortgage, purchase, gift or otherwise, either in his own name or in the name of any member of his family;or

(b) dispose of by lease, mortgage, sale gift or otherwise any immovable property owned by him or held by him either in his own name or in the name of any member of his family:

[2]Provided that the previous sanction of the Government shall be obtained if any such transaction is with a person having official dealings with the member of the Service.

(4) Every member of the Service shall intimate the Government in respect of each transaction, whose value exceeds [3]two months basic pay of the member of Service within a month of the completion of such transaction.

[4]Provided that the previous sanction of the Government shall be obtained if any such transaction is with a person having official dealings with the member of the Service.

(5) The Government or any authority empowered by it in this behalf may, at any time, by general or special order, require a member of the Service to furnish within a period specified in the order, a full and complete statement of such movable or immovable property held or acquired by him or on his

* Subst. according to Notification No.11017/5-A/2011—AIS(III) dt. May 5, 2011 (GSR No. 363(E) dt. May 5, 2011).

1. Subst. according to Notification No.11017/45/76—AIS(III) dt. January 11, 1978 (GSR No. 151 dt. January 28, 1978).
2. Subst. according to DP&T Notification No. 11017/85/84—AIS(III) dt. October 15, 1985 (GSR No. 1009 dt. November 2, 1985).
3. Subst. according to Notification No.11017/5-A/2011—AIS(III) dt. May 5, 2011 (GSR No. 363(E) dt. May 5, 2011).
4. Subst. according to DP&T Notification No. 11017/85/84—AIS(III) dt. October 15, 1985 (GSR No. 1009 dt. November 2, 1985).

behalf or by any member of his family as may be specified in the order and such statement shall if so required by the Government or by the authority so empowered, include details of the means by which, or the source from which such property was acquired.

[1]*Explanation I.*—For the purpose of this rule, the expression movable property includes inter alia the following property, namely:—

(a) jewellery, insurance policies the annual premia of which exceeds *two months basic pay of the member of Service, shares, securities and debentures;

(b) loans advanced by or to such member of the Service, whether secured or not;

(c) motor cars, motor cycles, horses, or any other means of conveyance; and

(d) refrigerators, radiograms and television sets.

*Explanation II.*—For the purpose of this rule, 'lease' means, except where it is obtained from, or granted to, a foreign national or foreign mission or a foreign organisation controlled by, or associated with, foreign missions, or a person having official dealings with the member of the Service, a lease of immovable property from year to year or for any term exceeding one year or receiving a yearly rent.

**16A. Transaction in immovable property outside India.**—Not with standing anything contained in sub-rule (3) of rule 16, no member of the Services shall except with the previous sanction of the Government,—

16A (a) acquire by lease, mortgage, purchase, gift or otherwise, either in his own name or in the name of any member of his family, any immovable property situated outside India; or

16A (b) dispose of by mortgage, sale, gift or otherwise, or grant any lease in respect of, any immovable property situated outside India which was acquired or is held by him either in his own name or in the name of any member of his family; or

16A (c) enter into any transaction with any foreigner, foreign Government, foreign organisation or concern,—

(i) for the acquisition, by lease, mortgage, purchase, gift or otherwise, either in his own name or in the name of any member of his family, or any immovable property.

(ii) for the disposal of, by mortgage, sale, gift or otherwise, or the grant of any lease in respect of any, immovable property which was acquired or is held by him either in his own name or in the name of any member of his family.

---

1. *Explanation* stood renumbered as *Explanation*, words "and radiograms" Subst. by words "radiograms and televisions sets" and *Explanation* II inst. according to DP&T Not. No.5/23/72 AIS(III) dt. July 27, 1774 (GSR No. 834 dt. August 10, 1974).

* Subst. according to Notification No.11017/5-A/2011—AIS(III) dt. May 5, 2011 (GSR No. 363(E) dt. May 5, 2011).

# RELEVANT PROVISIONS OF THE CENTRAL CIVIL SERVICES (CLASSIFICATION, CONTROL AND APPEAL) RULES, 1965[1]

In exercise of powers conferred by proviso to Article 309 and Clause (5) of Article 148 of the Constitution and after consultation with the Comptroller and Auditor General in relation to persons serving in Indian Audit and Accounts Department, the President hereby makes the following rules, namely:—

## PART I

## GENERAL

**1. Short title and commencement.**—(1) These Rules may be called the Central Civil Services Classification, Control and Appeal) Rules, 1965.

(2) They shall come into force on the 1st December, 1965.

****

## PART IV

## SUSPENSION

**10. Suspension.**—(1) The appointing authority or any authority to which it is subordinate or the disciplinary authority or any other authority empowered in that behalf by the President, by general or special order, may place a Government servant under suspension—

(a) where a disciplinary proceeding against him is contemplated or is pending; or

(aa) where, in the opinion of the authority aforesaid, he has engaged himself in activities prejudicial to the interest of the security of the State; or

(b) where a case against him in respect of any criminal offence is under investigation, inquiry or trial:

Provided that, except in case of an order of suspension made by the Comptroller and Auditor - General in regard to a member of the Indian Audit and Accounts Service and in regard to an Assistant Accountant General or equivalent (other than a regular member of the Indian Audit and Accounts Service), where the order of suspension is made by an authority lower than the appointing authority, such authority shall forthwith report to the appointing authority the circumstances in which the order was made.

(2) A Government servant shall be deemed to have been placed under suspension by an order of appointing authority—

(a) with effect from the date of his detention, if he is detained in custody, whether on a criminal charge or otherwise, for a period exceeding forty-eight hours;

1. Enforce from December 1, 1965.

(b) with effect from the date of his conviction, if, in the event of a conviction for an offence, he is sentenced to a term of imprisonment exceeding forty-eight hours and is not forthwith dismissed or removed or compulsorily retired consequent to such conviction.

*Explanation.*—The period of forty-eight hours referred to in clause (b) of this sub-rule shall be computed from the commencement of the imprisonment after the conviction and for this purpose, intermittent periods of imprisonment, if any, shall be taken into account.

(3) Where a penalty of dismissal, removal or compulsory retirement from service imposed upon a Government servant under suspension is set aside in appeal or on review under these rules and the case is remitted for further inquiry or action or with any other directions, the order of his suspension shall be deemed to have continued in force on and from the date of the original order of dismissal, removal or compulsory retirement and shall remain in force until further orders.

(4) Where a penalty of dismissal, removal or compulsory retirement from service imposed upon a Government servant is Central Civil Services (Classification, Control and Appeal) Rules, 1965 7 consequence of or by a decision of a Court of Law and the disciplinary authority, on a consideration of the circumstances of the case, decides to hold a further inquiry against him on the allegations on which the penalty of dismissal, removal or compulsory retirement was originally imposed, the Government servant shall be deemed to have been placed under suspension by the Appointing Authority from the date of the original order of dismissal, removal or compulsory retirement and shall continue to remain under suspension until further orders:

Provided that no such further inquiry shall be ordered unless it is intended to meet a situation where the Court has passed an order purely on technical grounds without going into the merits of the case.

(5) (a) Subject to the provisions contained in sub-rule (7), and order of suspension made or deemed to have been made under this rule shall continue to remain in force until it is modified or revoked by the authority competent to do so.

(b) Where a Government servant is suspended or is deemed to have been suspended (whether in connection with any disciplinary proceeding or otherwise), and any other disciplinary proceeding is commenced against him during the continuance of that suspension, the authority competent to place him under suspension may, for reasons to be recorded by him in writing, direct that the Government servant shall continue to be under suspension until the termination of all or any of such proceedings.

(c) An order of suspension made or deemed to have been made under this rule may at any time be modified or revoked by the authority which made or is deemed to have made the order or by any authority to which that authority is subordinate.

(6) An order of suspension made or deemed to have been made under this rule shall be reviewed by the authority which is competent to modify or revoke the suspension, before expiry of ninety days from the effective date of suspension, on the recommendation of the Review Committee constituted for the purpose and pass orders either extending or revoking the suspension. Subsequent reviews shall be made before expiry of the extended period of suspension. Extension of suspension shall not be for a period exceeding one hundred and eighty days at a time.

(7) An order of suspension made or deemed to have been made under sub-rule (1) or (2) of this rule shall not be valid after a period of ninety days unless it is extended after review, for a further period before the expiry of ninety days.

Provided that no such review of suspension shall be necessary in the case of deemed suspension under sub-rule (2), if the Government servant continues to be under suspension at the time of completion of ninety days of suspension and the ninety days period in such case will count from the date the Government servant detained in custody is released from detention or the date on which the fact of his release from detention is intimated to his appointing authority, whichever is later.

## PART V

## PENALTIES AND DISCIPLINARY AUHTORITIES

**11. Penalties.**—The following penalties may, for good and sufficient reasons and as hereinafter provided, be imposed on a Government servant, namely :—

*Minor Penalties*—

(i) censure;

(ii) withholding of his promotion;

(iii) recovery from his pay of the whole or part of any pecuniary loss caused by him to the Government by negligence or breach of orders;

(iii-a) reduction to lower stage in the time-scale of pay by one stage for a period not exceeding three years, without cumulative effect and not adversely affecting his pension.

(iv) withholding of increments of pay;

*Major Penalties*—

(v) save as provided for in clause (iii) (a), reduction to a lower stage in the timescale of pay for a specified period, with further directions as to whether or not the Government servant will earn increments of pay during the period of such reduction and whether on the expiry of such period, the reduction will or will not have the effect of postponing the future increments of his pay;

(vi) reduction to lower time-scale of pay, grade, post or Service for a period to be specified in the order of penalty, which shall be a bar to the promotion of the Government servant during such specified period to the time-scale of pay, grade, post or Service from which he was reduced, with direction as to whether or not, on promotion on the expiry of the said specified period—

(a) the period of reduction to time-scale of pay, grade, post or service shall operate to postpone future increments of his pay, and if so, to what extent; and

(b) the Government servant shall regain his original seniority in the higher time scale of pay, grade, post or service;

(vii) compulsory retirement;

(viii) removal from service which shall not be a disqualification for future employment under the Government;

(ix) dismissal from service which shall ordinarily be a disqualification for future employment under the Government.

Provided that, in every case in which the charge of possession of assets disproportionate to known-sources of income or the charge of acceptance from any person of any gratification, other than legal remuneration, as a motive or reward for doing or forbearing to do any official act is established, the penalty mentioned in clause (viii) or clause (ix) shall be imposed :

Provided further that in any exceptional case and for special reasons recorded in writing, any other penalty may be imposed.

*Explanation.*—The following shall not amounted to a penalty within the meaning of this rule, namely:—

(i) withholding of increments of pay of a Government servant for his failure to pass any departmental examination in accordance with the rules or orders governing the Service to which he belongs or post which he holds or the terms of his appointment;

(ii) stoppage of a Government servant at the efficiency bar in the timescale of pay on the ground of his unfitness to cross the bar;

(iii) non-promotion of a Government servant, whether in a substantive or officiating capacity, after consideration of his case, to a Service, grade or post for promotion to which he is eligible;

(iv) reversion of a Government servant officiating in a higher Service, grade, or post to a lower Service, grade or post, on the ground that he is considered to be unsuitable for such higher Service, grade or post or on any administrative ground unconnected with his conduct;

(v) reversion of a Government servant, appointed on probation to any other Service, grade or post, to his permanent Service, grade or post during or at the end of the period of probation in accordance with the terms of his appointment or the rules and orders governing such probation;

(vi) replacement of the services of a Government servant whose services had been borrowed from a State Government or an authority under the control of a State Government, at the disposal of the State Government or the authority from which the services of such Government servant had been borrowed;

(vii) compulsory retirement of a Government servant in accordance with the provisions relating to his superannuation or retirement;

(viii) termination of the services—

(a) of a Government servant appointed on probation, during or at the end of the period of his probation, in accordance with the terms of his appointment or the rules and orders governing such probation; or

(b) of a temporary Government servant in accordance with the provisions of sub-rule (1) of rule 5 of the Central Civil Services (Temporary Service) Rules, 1965; or

(c) of a Government servant, employed under an agreement, in accordance with the terms of such agreement.

(ix) Any compensation awarded on the recommendation of the Complaints Committee referred to in the proviso to sub-rule (2) of rule 14 and established in the Department of the Government of India for inquiring into any complaint of sexual harassment within the meaning of rule 3 C of the Central Civil Services (Conduct) Rules, 1964.

**12. Disciplinary Authorities.**—(1) The President may impose any of the penalties specified in Rule 11 on any Government servant.

(2) Without prejudice to the provisions of sub-rule (1), but subject to the provisions of sub-rule (4), any of the penalties specified in Rule 11 may be imposed on—

(a) a member of a Central Civil Service other than the General Central Service, by the appointing authority or the authority specified in the schedule in this behalf or by any other authority empowered in this behalf by a general or special order of the President;

(b) a person appointed to a Central Civil Post included in the General Central Service, by the authority specified in this behalf by a general or special order of the President or, where no such order has been made, by the appointing authority or the authority specified in the Schedule in this behalf.

(3) Subject to the provisions of sub-rule (4), the power to impose any of the penalties specified in Rule 11 may also be exercised, in the case of a member of a Central Civil Services, Group 'C' (other than the Central Secretariat Clerical Service), or a Central Civil Service, Group 'D',—

(a) if he is serving in a Ministry or Department of the Government of India, by the Secretary to the Government of India in that Ministry or Department, or

(b) if he is serving in any office, by the head of that office, except where the head of that office is lower in rank than the authority competent to impose the penalty under sub-rule (2).

(4) Notwithstanding anything contained in this rule—

(a) except where the penalty specified in clause (v) or clause (vi) of Rule 11 is imposed by the Comptroller and Auditor-General on a member of the Indian Audit and Accounts Service, no penalty specified in clause (v) to (ix) of that rule shall be imposed by any authority subordinate to the appointing authority;

(b) where a Government servant who is a member of a Service other than then General Central Service or who has been substantively appointed to any civil post in the General Central Service, is temporarily appointed to any other Service or post, the authority competent to impose on such Government servant any of the penalties specified in clauses (v) to (ix) of Rule 11 shall not impose any such penalties unless it has consulted such authority, not being an authority subordinate to it, as would have been competent under sub-rule (2) to impose on the Government servant any of the said penalties had he not been appointed to such other Service or post;

(c) in respect of a probationer undergoing training at the Lal Bahadur Shastri National Academy of Administration, the Director of the said Academy shall be the authority competent to impose on such probationer any of the penalties specified in clauses (i) and (iii) of rule 11 after observing the procedure laid down in rule 16.

*Explanation I.*—For the purposes of clause (c), 'probationer' means a person appointed to a Central Civil Service on probation.

*Explanation II.*—Where a Government servant belonging to a Service or holding a Central Civil post of any Group, is promoted, whether on probation or temporarily to the Service or Central Civil post of the next higher Group, he shall be deemed for the purposes of this rule to belong to the Service of, or hold the Central Civil post of, such higher Group.

**13. Authority to institute proceedings.**—(1) The President or any other authority empowered by him by general or special order may—

(a) institute disciplinary proceedings against any Government servant;

(b) direct a disciplinary authority to institute disciplinary proceedings against any Government servant on whom that disciplinary authority is competent to impose under these rules any of the penalties specified in rule 11.

(2) disciplinary authority competent under these rules to impose any of the penalties specified in clauses (i) to (iv) of rule 11 may institute disciplinary proceedings against any Government servant for the imposition of any of the penalties specified in clauses (v) to (ix) of rule 11 notwithstanding that such disciplinary authority is not competent under these rules to impose any of the latter penalties.

## PART VI

## PROCEDURE FOR IMPOSING PENALTIES

**14. Procedure for imposing major penalties.**—(1) No order imposing any of the penalties specified in clauses (v) to (ix) of Rule 11 shall be made except after an inquiry held, as far as may be, in the manner provided in this rule and rule 15, or in the manner provided by the Public Servants (Inquiries) Act, 1850 (37 of 1850), where such inquiry is held under that Act.

(2) Whenever the disciplinary authority is of the opinion that there are grounds for inquiring into the truth of any imputation of misconduct or misbehaviour against a Government servant, it may itself inquire into, or appoint under this rule or under the provisions of the Public Servants (Inquiries) Act, 1850, as the case may be, an authority to inquire into the truth thereof.

Provided that where there is a complaint of sexual harassment within the meaning of rule 3 C of the Central Civil Services (Conduct) Rules, 1964, the Complaints Committee established in each Ministry or Department or Office for inquiring into such complaints, shall be deemed to be the inquiring authority appointed by the disciplinary authority for the purpose of these rules and the Complaints Committee shall hold, if separate procedure has not been prescribed for the Complaints Committee for holding the inquiry into the complaints of sexual harassment, the inquiry as far as practicable in accordance with the procedure laid down in these rules.

*Explanation.*— (i) Where the disciplinary authority itself holds the inquiry, any reference in sub-rule (7) to sub-rule (20) and in sub-rule (22) to the inquiring authority shall be construed as a reference to the disciplinary authority.

(ii) Where the disciplinary authority appoints a retired Government servant as inquiring authority, any reference in sub-rule (7) to sub-rule (20) and in sub-rule (22) shall include such authority.

(3) Where it is proposed to hold an inquiry against a Government servant under this rule and rule 15, the disciplinary authority shall draw up or cause to be drawn up—

(i) the substance of the imputations of misconduct or misbehaviour into definite and distinct articles of charge;

(ii) a statement of the imputations of misconduct or misbehaviour in support of each article of charge, which shall contain—

(a) a statement of all relevant facts including any admission or confession made by the Government servant;

(b) a list of documents by which, and a list of witnesses by whom, the articles of charge are proposed to be sustained.

(4) (a) The Disciplinary Authority shall deliver or cause to be delivered to the Government servant a copy of the articles of charge, the statement of the imputations of misconduct or misbehaviour and a list of documents and witnesses by which each article or charges is proposed to be sustained.

(b) On receipt of the articles of charge, the Government servant shall be required to submit his written statement of defence, if he so desires, and also state whether he desires to be heard in person, within a period of fifteen days, which may be further extended for a period not exceeding fifteen days at a time for reasons to be recorded in writing by the Disciplinary Authority or any other Authority authorised by the Disciplinary Authority on his behalf:

Provided that under no circumstances, the extension of time for filing written statement of defence shall exceed forty-five days from the date of receipt of articles of charge.

(5) (a) On receipt of the written statement of defence, the disciplinary authority may itself inquire into such of the articles of charge as are not admitted, or, if it considers it necessary so to do, appoint, under sub-rule (2), an inquiring authority for the purpose, and where all the articles of charge have been admitted by the Government servant in his written statement of defence, the disciplinary authority shall record its findings on each charge after taking such evidence as it may think fit and shall act in the manner laid down in rule 15.

(b) If no written statement of defence is submitted by the Government servant, the disciplinary authority may itself inquire into the articles of charge, or may, if it considers it necessary to do so, appoint, under sub-rule (2), an inquiring authority for the purpose.

(c) Where the disciplinary authority itself inquires into any article of charge or appoints an inquiring authority for holding an inquiry into such charge, it may, by an order, appoint a Government servant or a legal practitioner, to be known as the "Presenting Officer" to present on its behalf the case in support of the articles of charge.

*Explanation.*—For the purposes of this rule, the expression 'Government servant' includes a person who has ceased to be in Government service.

(6) The disciplinary authority shall, where it is not the inquiring authority, forward to the inquiring authority—

(i) a copy of the articles of charge and the statement of the imputations of misconduct or misbehaviour;

(ii) a copy of the written statement of the defence, if any, submitted by the Government servant;

(iii) a copy of the statements of witnesses, if any, referred to in sub-rule (3);

(iv) evidence proving the delivery of the documents referred to in sub-rule (3) to the Government servant; and

(v) a copy of the order appointing the "Presenting Officer".

(7) The Government servant shall appear in person before the inquiring authority on such day and at such time within ten working days from the date of receipt by the inquiring authority of the articles of charge and the statement of the imputations of misconduct or misbehaviour, as the inquiring authority may, by notice in writing, specify, in this behalf, or within such further time, not exceeding ten days, as the inquiring authority may allow.

(8) (a) The Government servant may take the assistance of any other Government servant posted in any office either at his headquarters or at the place where the inquiry is held, to present the case on his behalf, but Central Civil Services (Classification, Control and Appeal) Rules, 1965 15 may not engage a legal practitioner for the purpose, unless the Presenting Officer appointed by the disciplinary authority is a legal practitioner, or, the disciplinary authority, having regard to the circumstances of the case, so permits;

Provided that the Government servant may take the assistance of any other Government servant posted at any other station, if the inquiring authority having regard to the circumstances of the case, and for reasons to be recorded in writing, so permits.

***Note.***—The Government servant shall not take the assistance of any other Government servant who has three pending disciplinary cases on hand in which he has to give assistance.

(b) The Government servant may also take the assistance of a retired Government servant to present the case on his behalf, subject to such conditions as may be specified by the President from time to time by general or special order in this behalf.

(9) If the Government servant who has not admitted any of the articles of charge in his written statement of defence or has not submitted any written statement of defence, appears before the inquiring authority, such authority shall ask him whether he is guilty or has any defence to make and if he pleads guilty to any of the articles of charge, the inquiring authority shall record the plea, sign the record and obtain the signature of the Government servant thereon.

(10) The inquiring authority shall return a finding of guilt in respect of those articles of charge to which the government servant pleads guilty.

(11) The inquiring authority shall, if the Government servant fails to appear within the specified time or refuses or omits to plead, require the Presenting Officer to produce the evidence by which he proposes to prove the articles of charge, and shall adjourn the case to a later date not exceeding thirty days, after recording an order that the Government servant may, for the purpose of preparing his defence:

(i) inspect within five days of the order or within such further time not exceeding five days as the inquiring authority may allow, the documents specified in the list referred to in sub-rule (3);

(ii) submit a list of witnesses to be examined on his behalf;

***Note.***—If the Government servant applies orally or in writing for the supply of copies of the statements of witnesses mentioned in the list referred to in sub- Central Civil Services (Classification, Control and Appeal) Rules, 1965 16 rule (3), the inquiring authority shall furnish him with such copies as early as possible and in any case not later than three days before the commencement of the examination of the witnesses on behalf of the disciplinary authority.

(iii) give a notice within ten days of the order or within such further time not exceeding ten days as the inquiring authority may allow, for the discovery or production of any documents which are in the possession of Government but not mentioned in the list referred to in sub-rule (3).

***Note.***—The Government servant shall indicate the relevance of the documents required by him to be discovered or produced by the Government.

(12) The inquiring authority shall, on receipt of the notice for the discovery or production of documents, forward the same or copies thereof to the authority in whose custody or possession the documents are kept, with a requisition for the production of the documents by such date as may be specified in such requisition:

Provided that the inquiring authority may, for reasons to be recorded by it in writing, refuse to requisition such of the documents as are, in its opinion, not relevant to the case.

(13) On receipt of the requisition referred to in sub-rule (12), every authority having the custody or possession of the requisitioned documents shall produce the same or issue a non-availability certificate before the Inquiring Authority within one month of the receipt of such requisition:

Provided that if the authority having the custody or possession of the requisitioned documents is satisfied for reasons to be recorded by it in writing that the production of all or any of such documents would be against the public interest or security of the State, it shall inform the Inquiring Authority accordingly and the Inquiring Authority shall, on being so informed, communicate the information to the Government servant and withdraw the requisition made by it for the production or discovery of such documents.

(14) On the date fixed for the inquiry, the oral and documentary evidence by which the articles of charge are proposed to be proved shall be produced by or on behalf of the disciplinary authority. The witnesses shall be examined by or on behalf of the Presenting Officer and may be cross-examined by or on behalf of the Government servant. The Presenting Officer shall be entitled to re-examine the witnesses on any points on which they have been cross-examined, but not on any new matter, without the leave of the inquiring authority. The inquiring authority may also put such questions to the witnesses as it thinks fit.

(15) If it shall appear necessary before the close of the case on behalf of the disciplinary authority, the inquiring authority may, in its discretion, allow

the Presenting Officer to produce evidence not included in the list given to the Government servant or may itself call for new evidence or recall and re-examine any witness and in such case the Government servant shall be entitled to have, if he demands it, a copy of the list of further evidence proposed to be produced and an adjournment of the inquiry for three clear days before the production of such new evidence, exclusive of the day of adjournment and the day to which the inquiry is adjourned. The inquiring authority shall give the Government servant an opportunity of inspecting such documents before they are taken on the record. The inquiring authority may also allow the Government servant to produce new evidence, if it is of the opinion that the production of such evidence is necessary, in the interests of justice.

***Note.***—New evidence shall not be permitted or called for or any witness shall not be recalled to fill up any gap in the evidence. Such evidence may be called for only when there is an inherent lacuna or defect in the evidence which has been produced originally.

(16) When the case for the disciplinary authority is closed, the Government servant shall be required to state his defence, orally or in writing, as he may prefer. If the defence is made orally, it shall be recorded and the Government servant shall be required to sign the record. In either case, a copy of the statement of defence shall be given to the Presenting Officer, if any, appointed.

(17) The evidence on behalf of the Government servant shall then be produced. The Government servant may examine himself in his own behalf if he so prefers. The witnesses produced by the Government servant shall then be examined and shall be liable to cross-examination, re-examination and examination by the inquiring authority according to the provisions applicable to the witnesses for the disciplinary authority.

(18) The inquiring authority may, after the Government servant closes his case, and shall, if the Government servant has not examined himself, generally question him on the circumstances appearing against him in the evidence for the purpose of enabling the Government servant to explain any circumstances appearing in the evidence against him.

(19) The inquiring authority may, after the completion of the production of evidence, hear the Presenting Officer, if any, appointed, and the Government servant, or permit them to file written briefs of their respective case, if they so desire.

(20) If the Government servant to whom a copy of the articles of charge has been delivered, does not submit the written statement of defence on or before Central Civil Services (Classification, Control and Appeal) Rules, 1965 18 the date specified for the purpose or does not appear in person before the inquiring authority or otherwise fails or refuses to comply with the provisions of this rule, the inquiring authority may hold the inquiry *ex parte*.

(21) (a) Where a disciplinary authority competent to impose any of the penalties specified in clause (i) to (iv) of rule 11 (but not competent to impose any of the penalties specified in clauses (v) to (ix) of rule 11), has itself inquired into or caused to be inquired into the articles of any charge and that authority, having regard to its own findings or having regard to its

decision on any of the findings of any inquiring authority appointed by it, is of the opinion that the penalties specified in clauses (v) to (ix) of rule 11 should be imposed on the Government servant, that authority shall forward the records of the inquiry to such disciplinary authority as is competent to impose the last mentioned penalties.

(b) The disciplinary authority to which the records are so forwarded may act on the evidence on the record or may, if it is of the opinion that further examination of any of the witnesses is necessary in the interests of justice, recall the witness and examine, cross-examine and re-examine the witness and may impose on the Government servant such penalty as it may deem fit in accordance with these rules.

(22) Whenever any inquiring authority, after having heard and recorded the whole or any part of the evidence in an inquiry ceases to exercise jurisdiction therein, and is succeeded by another inquiring authority which has, and which exercises, such jurisdiction, the inquiring authority so succeeding may act on the evidence so recorded by its predecessor, or partly recorded by its predecessor and partly recorded by itself:

Provided that if the succeeding inquiring authority is of the opinion that further examination of any of the witnesses whose evidence has already been recorded is necessary in the interests of justice, it may recall, examine, cross-examine and re-examine any such witnesses as hereinbefore provided.

(23) (i) After the conclusion of the inquiry, a report shall be prepared and it shall contain—

(a) the articles of charge and the statement of the imputations of misconduct or misbehaviour;

(b) the defence of the Government servant in respect of each article of charge;

(c) an assessment of the evidence in respect of each article of charge;

(d) the findings on each article of charge and the reasons therefor.

*Explanation.*—If in the opinion of the inquiring authority the proceedings of the inquiry establish any article of charge different from the original articles of the charge, it may record its findings on such article of charge:

Provided that the findings on such article of charge shall not be recorded unless the Government servant has either admitted the facts on which such article of charge is based or has had a reasonable opportunity of defending himself against such article of charge.

(ii) The inquiring authority, where it is not itself the disciplinary authority, shall forward to the disciplinary authority the records of inquiry which shall include :—

(a) the report prepared by it under clause (i);

(b) the written statement of defence, if any, submitted by the Government servant;

(c) the oral and documentary evidence produced in the course of the inquiry;

(d) written briefs, if any, filed by the Presenting Officer or the Government servant or both during the course of the inquiry; and

(e) the orders, if any, made by the disciplinary authority and the inquiring authority in regard to the inquiry.

(24) (a) The Inquiring Authority should conclude the inquiry and submit his report within a period of six months from the date of receipt of order of his appointment as Inquiring Authority.

(b) Where it is not possible to adhere to the time limit specified in clause (a), the Inquiring Authority may record the reasons and seek extension of time from the disciplinary authority in writing, who may allow an additional time not exceeding six months for completion of the Inquiry, at a time.

(c) The extension for a period not exceeding six months at a time may be allowed for any good and sufficient reasons to be recorded in writing by the Disciplinary Authority or any other Authority authorised by the Disciplinary Authority on his behalf.

**15. Action on inquiry report.**—(1) The disciplinary authority, if it is not itself the inquiring authority may, for reasons to be recorded by it in writing, remit the case to the inquiring authority for further inquiry and report and the inquiring authority shall thereupon proceed to hold the further inquiry according to the provisions of Rule 14, as far as may be.

(2) The disciplinary authority shall forward or cause to be forwarded a copy of the report of the inquiry, if any, held by the disciplinary authority or where the disciplinary authority is not the inquiring authority, a copy of the report of the inquiring authority together with its own tentative reasons for disagreement, if any, with the findings of inquiring authority on any article of charge to the Government servant who shall be required to submit, if he so desires, his written representation or submission to the disciplinary authority within fifteen days, irrespective of whether the report is favourable or not to the Government servant.

(3) (a) In every case where it is necessary to consult the Commission, the Disciplinary Authority shall forward or cause to be forwarded to the Commission for its advice:

(i) a copy of the report of the Inquiring Authority together with its own tentative reasons for disagreement, if any, with the findings of Inquiring Authority on any article of charge; and

(ii) comments of Disciplinary Authority on the representation of the Government servant on the Inquiry report and disagreement note, if any and all the case records of the inquiry proceedings.

(b) The Disciplinary Authority shall forward or cause to be forwarded a copy of the advice of the Commission received under clause (a) to the Government servant, who shall be required to submit, if he so desires, his written representation or submission to the Disciplinary Authority within fifteen days, on the advice of the Commission.

(4) The Disciplinary Authority shall consider the representation under sub-rule (2) and/or clause (b) of sub-rule (3), if any, submitted by the

Government servant and record its findings before proceedings further in the matter as specified in sub rules (5) and (6).

(5) If the Disciplinary Authority having regard to its findings on all or any of the articles of charge is of the opinion that any of the penalties specified in clauses (i) to (iv) of rule 11 should be imposed on the Government servant, it shall, notwithstanding anything contained in rule 16, make an order imposing such penalty.

(6) If the Disciplinary Authority having regard to its findings on all or any of the articles of charge and on the basis of the evidence adduced during the inquiry is of the opinion that any of the penalties specified in clauses (v) to (ix) of rule 11 should be imposed on the Government servant, it shall make an order imposing such penalty and it shall not be necessary to give the Government servant any opportunity of making representation on the penalty proposed to be imposed.

**16. Procedure for imposing minor penalties.**—(1) Subject to the provisions of sub-rule (5) of rule 15, no order imposing on a Government servant any of the penalties specified in clause (i) to (iv) of rule 11 shall be made except after—

(a) informing the Government servant in writing of the proposal to take action against him and of the imputations of misconduct or misbehaviour on which it is proposed to be taken, and giving him reasonable opportunity of making such representation as he may wish to make against the proposal;

(b) holding an inquiry in the manner laid down in sub-rules (3) to (24) of rule 14, in every case in which the disciplinary authority is of the opinion that such inquiry is necessary;

(c) taking the representation, if any, submitted by the Government servant under clause (a) and the record of inquiry, if any, held under clause (b) into consideration;

(d) consulting the Commission where such consultation is necessary. The Disciplinary Authority shall forward or cause to be forwarded a copy of the advice of the Commission to the Government servant, who shall be required to submit, if he so desires, his written representation or submission on the advice of the Commission, to the Disciplinary Authority within fifteen days; and

(e) recording a finding on each imputation or misconduct or misbehavior.

(1-A) Notwithstanding anything contained in clause (b) of sub-rule (1), if in a case it is proposed after considering the representation, if any, made by the Government servant under clause (a) of that sub-rule, to withhold increments of pay and such withholding of increments is likely to affect adversely the amount of pension payable to the Government servant or to withhold increments of pay for a period exceeding three years or to withhold increments of pay with cumulative effect for any period, an inquiry shall be held in the manner laid down in sub-rules (3) to (24) of

Rule 14, before making any order imposing on the Government servant any such penalty.

(2) The record of the proceedings in such cases shall include—

(i) a copy of the intimation to the Government servant of the proposal to take action against him;

(ii) a copy of the statement of imputations of misconduct or misbehaviour delivered to him;

(iii) his representation, if any;

(iv) the evidence produced during the inquiry;

(v) the advice of the Commission, if any;

(vi) representation, if any, of the Government servant on the advice of the Commission;

(vii) the findings on each imputation of misconduct or misbehavior; and

(viii) the orders on the case together with the reasons therefor.

**17. Communication of Orders.**—Orders made by the disciplinary authority shall be communicated to the Government servant who shall also be supplied with a copy of its finding on each article of charge, or where the disciplinary authority is not the inquiring authority, a statement of the findings of the disciplinary authority together with brief reasons for its disagreement, if any, with the findings of the inquiring authority and also a copy of the advice, if any, given by the Commission, and where the disciplinary authority has not accepted the advice of the Commission, a brief statement of the reasons for such non-acceptance.

**18. Common Proceedings.**—(1) Where two or more Government servants are concerned in any case, the President or any other authority competent to impose the penalty of dismissal from service on all such Government servants may make an order directing that disciplinary action against all of them may be taken in a common proceeding.

*Note.*—If the authorities competent to impose the penalty of dismissal on such Government servants are different, an order for taking disciplinary action in a common proceeding may be made by the highest of such authorities with the consent of the others.

(2) Subject to the provisions of sub-rule (4) of rule 12, any such order shall specify—

(i) the authority which may function as the disciplinary authority for the purpose of such common proceeding;

(ii) the penalties specified in rule 11 which such disciplinary authority shall be competent to impose;

(iii) whether the procedure laid down in rule 14 and rule 15 or rule 16 shall be followed in the proceeding.

**19. Special procedure in certain cases.**—Notwithstanding anything contained in rule 14 to rule 18—

(i) where any penalty is imposed on a Government servant on the ground of conduct which has led to his conviction on a criminal charge, or

(ii) where the disciplinary authority is satisfied for reasons to be recorded by it in writing that it is not reasonably practicable to hold an inquiry in the manner provided in these rules, or

(iii) where the President is satisfied that in the interest of the security of the State, it is not expedient to hold any inquiry in the manner provided in these rules, the disciplinary authority may consider the circumstances of the case and make such orders thereon as it deems fit:

Provided that the Government servant may be given an opportunity of making representation on the penalty proposed to be imposed before any order is made in a case under clause (i):

Provided that the Commission shall be consulted, where such consultation is necessary, and the Government servant has been given an opportunity of representing against the advice of the Commission, within the time limit specified in clause (b) of sub-rule (3) of rule 15, before any orders are made In any case under this rule.

**20. Provisions regarding officers lent to State Governments, etc.**—(1) Where the services of a Government servant are lent by one department to another department or to a State Government or an authority subordinate thereto or to a local or other authority (hereinafter in this rule referred to as "the borrowing authority"), the borrowing authority shall have the powers of the appointing authority for the purpose of placing such Government servant under suspension and of the disciplinary authority for the purpose of conducting a disciplinary proceeding against him:

Provided that the borrowing authority shall forthwith inform the authority which lent the services of the Government servant (hereinafter in this rule referred to as "the lending authority") of the circumstances leading to the order of suspension of such Government servant or the commencement of the disciplinary proceeding, as the case may be.

(2) In the light of the findings in the disciplinary proceeding conducted against the Government servant—

(i) if the borrowing authority is of the opinion that any of the penalties specified in clauses (i) to (iv) of rule 11 should be imposed on the Government servant, it may, after consultation with the lending authority, make such orders on the case as it deems necessary:

Provided that in the event of a difference of opinion between the borrowing authority and the lending authority, the services of the Government servant shall be replaced at the disposal of the lending authority;

(ii) if the borrowing authority is of the opinion that any of the penalties specified in clauses (v) to (ix) of rule 11 should be imposed on the Government servant, it shall replace his services at the disposal of the lending authority and transmit to it the proceedings of the inquiry and thereupon the lending authority may, if it is the disciplinary authority, pass such order thereon as it may deem necessary, or, if it is not the disciplinary authority, submit the case to the disciplinary authority which shall pass such orders on the case as it may deem necessary:

Provided that before passing any such order the disciplinary authority shall comply with the provisions of sub-rules (3) and (4) of rule 15.

*Explanation.*—The disciplinary authority may make an order under this clause on the record of the inquiry transmitted to it by the borrowing authority or after holding such further inquiry as it may deem necessary, as far as may be, in accordance with rule 14.

**21. Provisions regarding officers borrowed from State Governments, etc..**—(1) Where an order of suspension is made or a disciplinary proceeding is conducted against a Government servant whose services have been borrowed by one department from another department or from a State Government or an authority subordinate thereto or a local or other authority, the authority lending his services (hereinafter in this rule referred to as "the lending authority") shall forthwith be informed of the circumstances leading to the order of the suspension of the Government servant or of the commencement of the disciplinary proceeding, as the case may be.

(2) In the light of the findings in the disciplinary proceeding conducted against the Government servant, if the disciplinary authority is of the opinion that any of the penalties specified in clauses (i) to (iv) of rule 11 should be imposed on him, it may, subject to the provisions of sub-rule (3) of rule 15 and except in regard to a Government servant serving in the Intelligence Bureau up to the rank of Assistant Central Intelligence Officer, after consultation with the lending authority, pass such orders on the case as it may deem necessary—

(i) provided that in the event of a difference of opinion between the borrowing authority and the lending authority, the services of the Government servant shall be replaced at the disposal of the lending authority;

(ii) if the disciplinary authority is of the opinion that any of the penalties specified in clauses (v) to (ix) of Rule 11 should be imposed on the Government servant, it shall replace the services of such Government servant at the disposal of the lending authority and transmit to it the proceedings of the inquiry for such action, as it may deem necessary.

## PART VII
## APPEALS

**22. Orders against which no appeal lies.**—Notwithstanding anything contained in this Part, no appeal shall lie against—

(i) any order made by the President;

(ii) any order of an interlocutory nature or of the nature of a step-in-aid of the final disposal of a disciplinary proceeding, other than an order of suspension;

(iii) any order passed by an inquiring authority in the course of an inquiry under Rule 14.

**23. Orders against which appeal lies.**—Subject to the provisions of rule 22, a Government servant may prefer an appeal against all or any of the following orders, namely:—

(i) an order of suspension made or deemed to have been made under rule 10;

(ii) an order imposing any of the penalties specified in rule 11, whether made by the disciplinary authority or by any appellate or revising authority;

(iii) an order enhancing any penalty, imposed under rule 11;

(iv) an order which—

(a) denies or varies to his disadvantage his pay, allowances, pension or other conditions of service as regulated by rules or by agreement; or

(b) interprets to his disadvantage the provisions of any such rule or agreement;

(v) an order—

(a) stopping him at the efficiency bar in the time-scale of pay on the ground of his unfitness to cross the bar;

(b) reverting him while officiating in a higher service, grade or post, to a lower service, grade or post, otherwise than as a penalty;

(c) reducing or withholding the pension or denying the maximum pension admissible to him under the rules;

(d) determining the subsistence and other allowances to be paid to him for the period of suspension or for the period during which he is deemed to be under suspension or for any portion thereof;

(e) determining his pay and allowances—

(i) for the period of suspension, or

(ii) for the period from the date of his dismissal, removal or compulsory retirement from service, or from the date of his reduction to a lower service, grade, post, time-scale or stage in a time-scale of pay, to the date of his reinstatement or restoration to his service, grade or post; or

(f) determining whether or not the period from the date of his suspension or from the date of his dismissal, removal, compulsory retirement or reduction to a lower service, grade, post, time-scale of pay or stage in a time-scale of pay to the date of his reinstatement or restoration to his service, grade or post shall be treated as a period spent on duty for any purpose.

*Explanation.*—In this rule—

(i) the expression 'Government servant' includes a person who has ceased to be in Government service;

(ii) the expression 'pension' includes additional pension, gratuity and any other retirement benefits.

**24. Appellate Authority.**—(1) A Government servant, including a person who has ceased to be in Government service, may prefer an appeal against all or any of the orders specified in Rule 23 to the authority specified in this behalf either in the Schedule or by a general or special order of the President or, where no such authority is specified—

(i) where such Government servant is or was a member of a Central Service, Group 'A' or Group 'B' or holder of a Central Civil Post, Group 'A' or Group 'B'—

(a) to the appointing authority, where the order appealed against is made by an authority subordinate to it; or

(b) to the President where such order is made by any other authority;

(ii) where such Government servant is or was a member of a Central Civil Service, Group 'C' or Group 'D', or holder of a Central Civil Post, Group 'C' or Group 'D', to the authority to which the authority making the order appealed against his immediately subordinate.

(2) Notwithstanding anything contained in sub-rule (1)—

(i) an appeal against an order in a common proceeding held under Rule 18 shall lie to the authority to which the authority functioning as the disciplinary authority for the purpose of that proceeding is immediately subordinate :

Provided that where such authority is subordinate to the President in respect of a Government servant for whom President is the appellate authority in terms of sub-clause (b) of clause (i) of sub-rule (1), the appeal shall lie to the President.

(ii) where the person who made the order appealed against becomes, by virtue of his subsequent appointment or otherwise, the appellate authority in respect of such order, an appeal against such order shall lie to the authority to which such person is immediately subordinate.

(3) A Government servant may prefer an appeal against an order imposing any of the penalties specified in rule 11 to the President, where no such appeal lies to him under sub-rule (1) or sub-rule (2), if such penalty is imposed by any authority other than the President, on such Government servant in respect of his activities connected with his work as an office-bearer

of an association, federation or union, participating in the Joint Consultation and Compulsory Arbitration Scheme.

**25. Period of Limitation of appeals.**—No appeal preferred under this part shall be entertained unless such appeal is preferred within a period of forty-five days from the date on which a copy of the order appealed against is delivered to the appellant :

Provided that the appellate authority may entertain the appeal after the expiry of the said period, if it is satisfied that the appellant had sufficient cause for not preferring the appeal in time.

**26. Form and contents of appeal.**—(1) Every person preferring an appeal shall do so separately and in his own name.

(2) The appeal shall be presented to the authority to whom the appeal lies, a copy being forwarded by the appellant to the authority which made the order appealed against. It shall contain all material statements and arguments on which the appellant relies, shall not contain any disrespectful or improper language, and shall be complete in itself.

(3) The authority which made the order appealed against shall, on receipt of a copy of the appeal, forward the same with its comments thereon together with the relevant records to the appellate authority without any avoidable delay, and without waiting for any direction from the appellate authority.

**27. Consideration of appeal.**—(1) In the case of an appeal against an order of suspension, the appellate authority shall consider whether in the light of the provisions of rule 10 and having regard to the circumstances of the case, the order of suspension is justified or not and confirm or revoke the order accordingly.

(2) In the case of an appeal against an order imposing any of the penalties specified in rule 11 or enhancing any penalty imposed under the said rules, the appellate authority shall consider—

(a) whether the procedure laid down in these rules have been complied with and if not, whether such non-compliance has resulted in the violation of any provisions of the Constitution of India or in the failure of justice;

(b) whether the findings of the disciplinary authority are warranted by the evidence on the record; and

(c) whether the penalty or the enhanced penalty imposed is adequate, inadequate or severe;

and pass orders—

(i) confirming, enhancing, reducing, or setting aside the penalty; or

(ii) remitting the case to the authority which imposed or enhanced the penalty or to any other authority with such direction as it may deem fit in the circumstances of the case :

provided that—

(i) The Commission shall be consulted in all cases where such consultation is necessary, and the government servant has been given an opportunity of representing against the advice of the Commission within the time limit specified in clause (b) of sub-rule (3) of rule 15.

(ii) If such enhanced penalty which the appellate authority proposes to impose is one of the penalties specified in clauses (v) to (ix) of rule 11 and in inquiry under rule 14 has not already been held in the case, the appellate authority shall, subject to the provisions of rule 19, itself hold such inquiry or direct that such inquiry be held in accordance with the provisions of rule 14 and thereafter, on a consideration of the proceedings of such inquiry and make such orders as it may deem fit;

(iii) if the enhanced penalty which the appellate authority proposes to impose is one of the penalties specified in clauses (v) to (ix) of rule 11 and an enquiry under rule 14 has been held in the case, the appellate authority shall make such Central Civil Services (Classification, Control and Appeal) Rules, 1965 29 orders as it may deem fit after the appellant has been given a reasonable opportunity of making a representation against the proposed penalty; and

(iv) no order imposing an enhanced penalty shall be made in any other case unless the appellant has been given a reasonable opportunity, as far as may be, in accordance with the provisions of rule 16, of making a representation against such enhanced penalty.

(3) In an appeal against any other order specified in rule 23, the appellate authority shall consider all the circumstances of the case and make such orders as it may deem just and equitable.

**28. Implementation of orders in appeal.**—The authority which made the order appealed against shall give effect to the orders passed by the appellate authority.

# PART - 2

# ACQUITTAL OF PUBLIC SERVANTS FROM CORRUPTION CHARGES BY SUPREME COURT

## Neither the demand nor the seizure of money was proved beyond reasonable doubt

***State of Gujarat v. Babubha Ravjibhai Vaghela***
**(From Gujarat High Court)**

2023/GUJHC/17996 : MANU/GJ/0417/2023

**Judge:—** Justice Alpesh Y. Kogje

**Advocates:**

1. For Appellant :— Krina Calla, APP
2. For Respondents :— Rutviz Oza, Advocate and Poonam M. Maheta

R/Criminal Appeal No. 2358 of 2005

Date of Decision – 06.04.2023

Appeal preferred by the State-Section 378(1)(3) of the Code of Criminal Procedure - acquittal of respondent —Offense under Sections 7, 12, 13(1)(D) read with Section 13(2) of the Prevention of Corruption Act-neither the demand nor the seizure of money was proved beyond reasonable - probability of the defense taken sounded more probable based on the same set of evidence- presumption of innocence - fundamental principle of criminal jurisprudence- securing of acquittal- presumption is further reinforced, reaffirmed and strengthened.

---

## Illegal gratification by the Appellant was not proved by the prosecution

***K. Shanthamma v. The State of Telangana***
**(From Supreme Court of India)**

MANU/SC/0218/2022 : Neutral Citation: 2022/INSC/213

**Judges:—** Justice Ajay Rastogi and Justice Abhay Shreeniwas Oka

Criminal Appeal No. 261 of 2022

(Arising out of SLP (Criminal) No. 7182 of 2019)

Date of Decision – 21.02.2022

Special Court under the Prevention of Corruption Act, 1988 (for short 'the PC Act') convicted the Appellant— offences punishable under Sections 7 and 13(1)(d) read with Section 13(2) of the PC Act-order of conviction confirmed in appeal by the High Court - Appellant submitted demand for a bribe by him not proved-case where the demand of illegal gratification by the Appellant was not proved by the prosecution-demand which is sine quo non for establishing the offence under Section 7 was not established-conviction of the Appellant for the offences punishable under Sections 7 and 13(1)(d) read with Section 13(2) of the PC Act set aside - Appellant acquitted.

---

## Legality of Acquittal

***The State of Gujarat v. Unni Ikal Kunjiraman***
**(From Gujarat High Court)**

MANU/GJ/0415/2023 : Neutral Citation: 2023/GUJHC/17994

**Judge:**— Justice Alpesh Y. Kogje

**Advocates:**

1. For Appellant :— Krina Calla, APP
2. For Respondents :— Amit M. Nair and Vinit A. Nair

R/Criminal Appeal No. 205 of 2007

Date of Decision – 06.04.2023

Appeal preferred by the State under Section 378(1)(3) of the Code of Criminal Procedure, 1973-witness to demand is complainant, who is hostile and not supported case of demand at first instance -Double presumption in favour of accused - presumption of innocence is available to him under fundamental principle of criminal jurisprudence- securing of acquittal, presumption is further reinforced, reaffirmed and strengthened.

---

## Illegal gratification and Acquittal

***Neeraj Dutta v. State (Govt. of N.C.T. of Delhi)***
**(From Supreme Court of India)**

MANU/SC/0250/2023

**Judges:**— Justice Abhay Shreeniwas Oka and Justice Rajesh Bindal

Criminal Appeal No. 1669 of 2009

Datc of Decision – 17.03.2023

Appellant convicted by Special Judge for offence of illegal gratification- punishable under Section 7 and Clauses (i) and (ii) of Section 13(1)(d) read with Section 13(2) of PC Act - Co-Accused was convicted for offence punishable under Section 12 of PCAct -Special Court held — sufficient circumstantial evidence on record to prove guilt of Appellant - In appeal conviction of Appellant had been upheld by High Court- co-Accused was acquitted by High Court- court consider the issue of proof of demand within the meaning of Section 7- it could not be a simpliciter demand for money –it has be a demand of gratification other than legal remuneration- Every demand made for payment of money was not a demand for gratification.

---

## If gratification etc. is trivial then no interference of corruption may be drawn

***The State of Maharashtra v. Anil Kacharu Shinde***

**(From Bombay High Court)**

MANU/MH/3982/2023

**Judge:—** Justice Jitendra Jain

**Advocates:**

1. For Appellant :— S.H. Yadav, APP
2. For Respondents :— Sandeep S. Salunkhe

Criminal Appeal No. 1301 of 2012

Date of Decision – 03.10.2023

Appeal filed by the appellant/original complainant against judgment- delivered by the Special Judge (under the Prevention of Corruption Act, 1988)- acquitting the respondent-original accused from charges under Sections 7, 13(1) (d) and 13(2) PC Act- amount appears to be too small in the year 2007 and moreso, in the year 2023 when the appeal is being heard against the acquittal- in case of trivial matter, the provisions of the P. C. Act should not be invoked.

---

## Under PC Act obtaining valuable thing/ pecuniary advantage is material ingredient

***The State of Maharashtra v. Raghunath Dnyandev Katkar***

**(From Bombay High Court)**

MANU/MH/0531/2023

**Judge:**— Justice S.M. Modak

**Advocates:**

1. For Appellant :— H.J. Dedhia, APP
2. For Respondents :— Anand Patil, Advocate

Criminal Appeal No. 437 of 2018

Date of Decision – 17.02.2023

Sections 7, 13(1)(d) and 13(2) of Prevention of Corruption Act, 1988 (PC Act) - appeal filed against impugned judgment of acquittal thereby acquitting respondent from charges of commission of offenses punishable under Sections 7, 13(1)(d) and 13(2) of PC Act - Material ingredient not proved in present case - Demand for illegal gratification attempted by Respondent - Offense under Section 7 of PC Act proved - undergo sentence of simple imprisonment for six months .

---

## Sanction is required not only for acts done in the discharge of official duty but also required for any act purported to be done under colour of or in excess of such duty or authority

***A. Srinivasulu v. The State Rep. by the Inspector of Police***

**(From Supreme Court of India)**

MANU/SC/0723/2023

**Judges:**— Justice V. Ramasubramanian and Justice Pankaj Mithal

**Advocates:**

1. For Appellant :— Ranjeeta Rohatgi, AOR, Kaushik Mishra, Nishant Sharma, Adviteeya, Advs., Rakesh K. Sharma, Vijay Kumar, AORs, S. Nagamuthu,

V. Mohana, Sr. Advs., B. Ragunath, N.C. Kavitha, Sneha Batwe, B. Pande and S.R. Raghunathan, Advs.

2. For Respondents :— Sanjay Jain, A.S.G., A.K. Kaul, Shraddha Deshmukh, Madhav Sinhal, Srishti Mishra, Padmesh Mishra, Rajan Kumar Chourasia, Sweksha, Advs. and Arvind Kumar Sharma, AOR

Criminal Appeal Nos. 2417 of 2010,
16 of 2011 and 2444 of 2010

Date of Decision – 15.06.2023

Appeals arise out of a common judgment passed by the High Court confirming the conviction of the Appellants for various offences under the Indian Penal Code, 1860 and the Prevention of Corruption Act, 1988 - Whether Appellants are to be acquitted of all the charges-evidence of approver- approver is a reliable witness -His statement should be corroborated with sufficient evidence. -approver is a most unworthy friend -must prove his worthiness for credibility in court- Appellants are acquitted of all the charges.

---

## If some evidence which has relevance to the charges levelled, the order of Departmental Enquiry cannot be invalidated.

***Ram Niwas v. Union of India and Ors.***
**(From Delhi High Court)**

MANU/DE/4933/2023

**Judges:**— Justice Suresh Kait and Justice Neena Bansal Krishna

**Advocates:**

1. For Appellant :— Saahila Lamba, Advocate
2. For Respondents :— Rishabh Sahu, CGSC, Sameer Sharma, Chiranjiv Kumar and Mukesh Sachdeva, Advocates

W.P.(C) 8139/2010 and W.P.(C) 8141/2010

Date of Decision – 01.08.2023

Two petitioners —challenged the validity of Order of Suspension - dismissal was solely on the ground of corruption which has been disproved in the criminal case- So long as there is some evidence which has relevance to the charges levelled, the order of Departmental Enquiry cannot be invalidated- acquittal of an accused in a criminal case does not debar an employer from proceeding in the exercise of disciplinary jurisdiction.

## No circumstantial evidence of demand for gratification

***Soundarajan v. State Rep. by The Inspector of Police Vigilance Anticorruption Dindigul***

**(From Supreme Court of India)**

MANU/SC/0387/2023 : Neutral Citation: 2023/INSC/377

**Judges:**— Justice Abhay Shreeniwas Oka and Justice Rajesh Bindal

**Advocates:**

1. For Appellant :— B. Balaji, AOR
2. For Respondents :— Joseph Aristotle S., AOR and Vaidehi Rastogi, Adv.

Criminal Appeal No. 1592 of 2022

Date of Decision – 17.04.2023

Appellant convicted for the offences punishable Under Section 7 and Section 13(2) read with Section 13(1)(d) of the Prevention of Corruption Act, 1988 - sentenced to undergo imprisonment for one year and to pay a fine of Rs. 2,000/-. no circumstantial evidence of demand for gratification- . Unless both demand and acceptance are established, offence of obtaining pecuniary advantage by corrupt means covered by Clauses (i) and (ii) of Section 13(1)(d) cannot be proved.

## Proof of acceptance of illegal gratification can follow only if there is proof of demand

***State of Chhattisgarh v. Arun Kumar Mishra***

**(From High Court of Chattisgarh)**

MANU/CG/0511/2023 : Neutral Citation: 2023CGH 10391

**Judge:**— Justice Rajani Dubey

**Advocates:**

1. For Appellant :— Samir Uraon, G.A.
2. For Respondents :— Sudeep Agrawal and Sandhya Tiwari, Advocates

ACQA No. 101 of 2009

Date of Decision – 21.04.2023

Acquittal appeal preferred by the appellant/State against the impugned judgment dated 29.09.2007 —charges under Sections 7 & 13 (1)(d) r/w Section 13(2) of the Prevention of Corruption Act, 1988- it is necessary for the prosecution to prove that there was demand of money and the same was voluntarily accepted by the accused- Proof of acceptance of illegal gratification can follow only if there is proof of demand- prosecution failed in proving its case beyond all reasonable doubt.

---

## Failure to prove demand and acceptance of bribe amount

***The State of Andhra Pradesh v. S. Bulli Babu and Ors.***
**(From High Court of Andhra Pradesh)**

MANU/AP/0283/2023 : Neutral Citation: 2023/APHC/4207 : 2023/APHC/4209

**Judge:**— Justice A.V. Ravindra Babu

**Advocates:**

1. For Appellant :— S.M. Subhani, SC and Spl. PP
2. For Respondents :— Rayaprolu Srikanth and D. Kodandarami Reddy, Advocates

Criminal Appeal No. 1336 of 2007

Date of Decision – 20.02.2023

Criminal Appeal filed by the State, being represented by the Inspector of Police, Anti-Corruption Bureau, — Accused Officers not guilty of the charges under Sections 7 and 13(1)(d) r/w 13(2) of Prevention of Corruption Act, 1988 ("P.C. Act" for short) and accordingly— solitary circumstance is that amount was recovered from table drawer of AO2 - Same is not at all sufficient to prove allegations of demand - Prosecution before Court below miserably failed to prove demand and acceptance of bribe amount.

---

## In acquittal appeal the appellate Court is not required to re-write the judgment

***The State of Gujarat v. Ashokbhai Shankerbhai Patil***

**(From High Court of Gujarat)**

**Judge:—** Justice Mauna M. Bhatt

**Advocates:**

1. For Appellant :— Ms Jirga Jhaveri, Ld.Addl. Public Prosecutor
2. For Respondents :— Mr MP Shah(2418), Ms Dhruti Pandya, Ld.Advocate for Ms. Kruti M Shah(2428), Ld.Advocate for the Opponent(s)

R/CRIMINAL APPEAL NO. 123 of 2007

Date of Decision – 07.02.2023

Appeal preferred by the State of Gujarat under Section 378(3) of Code of Criminal Procedure, 1973 ("The Code" for short) against the judgment and order of acquittal - acquitted the respondent - accused from the charges for the offences punishable under Sections 7, 13(1)(d) read with 13(2) of the Prevention of Corruption Act, 1988 ('the Act' for short)- findings recorded by the trial Court are absolutely just and proper - no illegality or infirmity has been committed by it- settled legal position that in acquittal appeal, the appellate Court is not required to re-write the judgment or to give fresh reasonings when the reasons assigned by the Court below are found to be just and proper.

---

## Appellate court has full power to review, re-appreciate and reconsider the evidence upon which the order of acquittal is founded

***State of Gujarat v. Babubha Ravjibhai Vaghela***

**(From High Court of Gujarat)**

MANU/GJ/0417/2023 : Neutral Citation: 2023/GUJHC/17996

**Judge:—** Justice Alpesh Y. Kogje

**Advocates:**

1. For Appellant :— Krina Calla, APP
2. For Respondents :— Rutviz Oza, Advocate and Poonam M. Maheta

R/Criminal Appeal No. 2358 of 2005

Date of Decision – 06.04.2023

Appeals preferred by the State under Section 378(1)(3) of the Code of Criminal Procedure against the —acquittal of respondent for the offense under Sections 7, 12, 13(1)(D) read with Section 13(2) of the Prevention of Corruption Act.- appellate court has full power to review, re-appreciate and reconsider the evidence upon which the order of acquittal is founded- whenever there are two reasonable conclusions are possible on the basis of the evidence on record, ordinarily, the Apex Court would not disturb the findings of acquittal recorded by the Trial court.

---

## Acquittal in absence of any cogent evidence regarding demand of bribe

***Vijay Kumar Shankar v. The State of Jharkhand and Ors.***
**(From High Court of Jharkhand)**

MANU/JH/0124/2023

**Judge:**— Justice Anil Kumar Choudhary

**Advocates:**

1. For Appellant :— Ranjan Kr. Singh and Prabhas Chandra Jha, Advocates
2. For Respondents :— Nehala Sharmin, Spl P.P.

Cr. Appeal (SJ) No. 504 of 2003

Date of Decision – 10.02.2023

Corruption - Section 161 of Indian Penal Code,1860(IPC) and Sections 5(1)(d) and 5(2) of Prevention of Corruption Act, 1947 - Appeal filed against conviction under Section 161 of IPC and Sections 5(1)(d) and 5(2) of Act - Whether charges against accused was proved beyond all reasonable doubt - Held, there was no evidence to suggested that Appellantdemanded bribe - Testimony of witness failed short of establishing victim of demand and acceptance of bribe money by Appellant beyond reasonable doubt - Appellantbe acquitted by giving him benefit of doubtin absence of any cogent evidence regarding demand of bribe

## Illegal gratification

***Jagtar Singh v. State of Punjab***
**(From Supreme Court of India)**

MANU/SC/0288/2023 : Neutral Citation: 2023/INSC/279

**Judges:**— Justice Abhay Shreeniwas Oka and Justice Rajesh Bindal

**Advocates:**

1. For Appellant :— Gagan Gupta, AOR
2. For Respondents :— Abhinav Bajaj, Adv., Ajay Pal, AOR, Mayank Dahiya, Sugandh Rathor, Priyanka C. and Bhupinder, Advs.

Criminal Appeal No. 2136 of 2010

Date of Decision – 23.03.2023

Illegal gratification - Appellant was convicted by Trial Court for offence of illegal gratification in respect of getting of death certificate - - no evidence produced on record to prove the demand of illegal gratification- Appellant acquitted of the charges.

## No circumstantial evidence of demand for gratification

***Soundarajan Vs. State Rep. by The Inspector of Police Vigilance Anticorruption Dindigul***
**(From Supreme Court of India)**

MANU/SC/0387/2023 : Neutral Citation: 2023/INSC/377

**Judges:**— Justice Abhay Shreeniwas Oka and Justice Rajesh Bindal

**Advocates:**

1. For Appellant :— B. Balaji, AOR
2. For Respondents :— Joseph Aristotle S., AOR and Vaidehi Rastogi, Adv.

Criminal Appeal No. 1592 of 2022

Date of Decision – 17.04.2023

Appellant was convicted for the offences punishable Under Section 7 and Section 13(2) read with Section 13(1)(d) of the Prevention of Corruption Act, 1988 (for short, 'the PC Act')- no circumstantial evidence of demand for gratification- Unless both demand and acceptance are established, offence of obtaining pecuniary advantage by corrupt means covered by Clauses (i) and (ii) of Section 13(1)(d) cannot be proved.

---

## No evidence to substantiate the demand of illegal gratification

***Parveen Kumar v. State of Haryana***
**(From High Court of Punjab and Haryana)**

MANU/PH/2260/2022

**Judges:—** Justice Avneesh Jhingan

**Advocates:**

1. For Appellant :— Nikhil Ghai, Advocate
2. For Respondents :— Gurmeet Singh, Assistant Advocate General

CRA-S-2469-SB of 2004

Date of Decision – 17.10.2022

Appeal directed against conviction and sentence -Sections 7, 13(1)(d) read with 13(2) of the Prevention of Corruption Act, 1988- conviction under Section 7 of the Act, demand and acceptance has to be proved- no evidence to substantiate the demand of illegal gratification by the appellant-On failure to prove acceptance of bribe, presumption under Section 20 of the Act cannot be drawn against the appellant.

---

## Conviction of the Commercial Tax Officer for the offences punishable under PC Act set aside and acquitted of the charges

***K. Shanthamma v. The State of Telangana***
**(From Supreme Court of India)**

MANU/SC/0218/2022 : Neutral Citation: 2022/INSC/213

**Judges:**— Justice Ajay Rastogi and Justice Abhay Shreeniwas Oka

Criminal Appeal No. 261 of 2022
(Arising out of SLP (Criminal) No. 7182 of 2019)
Date of Decision – 21.02.2022

Appeal against impugned judgment of conviction under Sections 7 and 13(1)(d) read with Section 13(2) of the PC Act-Special Court under the Prevention of Corruption Act, 1988 convicted the Appellant for the offences - order of conviction confirmed in appeal -demand for bribe by the Appellant was not proved-conviction of the Appellant under PC Act is set aside

---

## Clerk accused of taking bribe acquitted

***Hari Narayan v. State of Rajasthan***
**(From High Court of Rajasthan)**

MANU/RH/0308/2023

**Judge:**— Justice Narendra Singh Dhaddha

**Advocates:**

1. For Appellant :— Mahesh Gupta, S.S. Sharma and Priyanshi Katta, Advs.
2. For Respondents :— Chandragupt Chopra, PP

S.B. Criminal Appeal No. 78/1985
Date of Decision – 13.02.2023

Appellant filed appeal challenging the judgment - appellant was convicted and sentenced for the offence(s) punishable under Section 161 IPC and Sections 5(1)(d) read with Section 5(2) of the Prevention of Corruption Act, 1947 -Only recovery of money could not be a ground to consider it as a bribe-Appellant acquitted of the charges framed against him.

---

## Court sets aside conviction of major generalfor alleged corruption

***A.K. Gupta v. State***
**(From High Court of Madras)**

MANU/TN/5531/2023

**Judge:—** Justice Dr. G. Jayachandran

**Advocates:**

1. For Appellant :— S. Ashok Kumar, Senior Counsel and A. Sasidharan
2. For Respondents :— K. Srinivasan, Senior Counsel Special Public Prosecutor

Criminal Appeal No. 443 of 2013

Date of Decision – 22.09.2023

Col.Mandanna M.M. violated prescribed procedures, rules and regulations in the transportation of procurement of supply/ration items - heavy loss to the State-Unlike Section 7 and 13(1) of P.C.Act 1988, proviso to Section 5(2) of P.C.Act, 1947 - discretion to the Court to record reason and impose sentence less than the minimum sentence prescribed-enormous delay in completing the investigation and the trial -prosecution has failed to prove the charges beyond doubt-acquittal

---

## Acquittal of doctor for taking bribe

***Pradeepta Kumar Praharaj v. State of Odisha***

**(From High Court of Orissa)**

MANU/OR/0974/2023

**Judge:—** Justice S.K. Sahoo

**Advocates:**

1. For Appellant :— Satya Smruti Mohanty
2. For Respondents :— M.S. Rizvi, Addl. Standing Counsel

Criminal Appeal No. 172 of 2007

Date of Decision – 21.08.2023

Appellant Pradeepta Kumar Praharaj faced trial - offences punishable under section 7 and section 13(2) read with section 13(1)(d) of the Prevention of Corruption Act, 1988 - illegal gratification-mere recovery of the bribe amount from the accused is not sufficient to fasten guilt-burden rests on the accused to displace the statutory presumption raised under section 20 of the 1988 Act by bringing on record evidence, either direct or circumstantial-failure of the prosecution to prove the demand for illegal gratification would be fatal and mere recovery of the amount from the person accused of the offence under sections 7 or 13 of the Act would not entail his conviction thereunder

---

## Acquittal of nurse accused of taking bribe

***State of Odisha v. Respondent: Sanjubala Rout***
**(From High Court of Orissa)**

MANU/OR/1198/2023

**Judge:**— Justice S.K. Sahoo

**Advocates:**

1. For Appellant :— Sangram Das, Standing Counsel
2. For Respondents :— S.C. Mekap, Advocate

GCRLA No. 29 of 2018

Date of Decision – 17.08.2023

Respondent Sanjubala Rout faced trial - accusation that she being a public servant functioning as Auxiliary Nurse Midwife -corrupt and illegal means or otherwise abusing her position as a public servant demanded a pecuniary advantage to the extent of Rs. 400-In a criminal trial it is not at all obligatory on the accused to produce evidence in support of his defence - defence is not supposed to prove its case beyond all reasonable doubts rather the prosecution has the solemn duty to discharge that burden.

---

## Proof of demand & acceptance of bribe mandatory

***Sayaji Dashrath Kawade v. The State of Maharashtra***
**(From High Court of Bombay (Aurangabad Bench)**

MANU/MH/3068/2022

**Judge:**— Justice Shrikant D. Kulkarni

**Advocates:**

1. For Appellant :— R.N. Dhorde, Senior Counsel i/b V.R. Dhorde, Advocate
2. For Respondents :— S.P. Deshmukh, APP

Criminal Appeal No. 491 of 2005

Date of Decision – 30.08.2022

Conviction recorded - Appeal against - Sections 7, 13(1)(d),13(2) and 20 of Prevention of Corruption Act, 1988 (PC Act) - Present appeal take exception to judgment of conviction and sentence passed by trial court against appellant herein under Sections 7, 13(1)(d) and 13(2) of PC Act - Whether judgment of conviction under appeal call for interference - Held, sanctioning authority has not applied his independent mind before according sanction for prosecution - He has not even considered whether material collected by Investigating Officer would prima facie establish offence by public servant concerned - Basic legal requirement of demand and acceptance of bribe and sanction order are not proved by prosecution - Impugned judgment on conviction passed by Trial Court quashed - Appeal allowed.

---

## Conviction cannot be upheld in the absence of the records of the trial court

***Jitendra Kumar Rode v. Union of India (UOI)***
**(From Supreme Court of India)**

MANU/SC/0450/2023 : Neutral Citation: 2023/INSC/605

**Judges:**— Justice Krishna Murari and Justice Sanjay Karol

**Advocates:**

1. For Appellant :— Sandeep Sudhakar Deshmukh, AOR, Nishant Sharma and Tushar D. Bhelkar, Advs.
2. For Respondents :— K.M. Nataraj, ASG, Sharath Nambiar, Indira Bhakar, Vatsal Joshi, Vinayak Sharma, Chitransh Sharma, Nahul Chengappa and Anuj Srinivas Udupa, Advs.

Criminal Appeal No. 1269 of 2023
(Arising out of Special Leave Petition
(Crl.) No. 2063 of 2023)

Decided On: 24.04.2023

Absence of record - Validity of conviction - Sections 7, 13(1) and 13(2) of Prevention of Corruption Act, 1988, Sections 313 and 385 of Code of Criminal Procedure, 1973 and Article 21 of Constitution of India - Trial Court convicted Appellant under Sections 7, 13(1) and 13(2) of Act, 1988 - Assailing judgment of conviction and sentence, High Court admitted Petitioner's appeal and despite repeated summoning of records of trial, no reply was received from Court concerned - Record further reveal that entire record had been lost and was not traceable and documents sent as reconstructed documents did not constituterelevant trial court record - High Court, upheld conviction despite having noted on earlier occasion that reconstruction of records was not in accordance with Rules - Hence, present appeal - Whether in absence of records of Court of Trial, appellate Court could have upheld conviction and enhanced quantum of fine and given language employed under Section 385 of Code, present situation constitutes violation of Accused's fundamental rights under Article 21 of Constitution of India-The Court below, by taking a mutually contradictory view, proceeded to decide the appeal on merits sentencing the Accused, forgetting that the challenge was also for conviction. And yet did not deal with the merits of the appeal, laying specific challenge to the judgment of conviction.

---

## Acquittal for taking bribe

***Eastern Coalfields Limited and Ors. v.***
***Rabindra Kumar Bharti***
**(From Supreme Court of India)**

MANU/SC/0466/2022, Neutral Citation: 2022/INSC/405

**Judges:**— Justice K.M. Joseph and Justice Hrishikesh Roy

**Advocates:**

1. For Appellant :— Parijat Kishore, AOR and Saurabh Tanwar, Adv.
2. For Respondents :— Mahesh Prasad, Mansha Ram Singh, Shambu Prasad, Naresh Kumar, Vaishali, Advs. and Rajesh Singh Chauhan, AOR

Civil Appeal No. 2794 of 2022
(Arising out of SLP (C) No. 12061/2021)
Date of Decision – 07.04.2022

Case where there is a criminal case against the Respondent- The Appellant(s) as employer also launched disciplinary proceedings- Court has taken the view that when the charges are identical and gives rise to complicated issues of the fact and law and evidence is the same- it may not be appropriate to proceed simultaneously in disciplinary proceedings, along with the criminal case-The rationale behind the principle largely is that the employee who is facing the disciplinary proceeding would necessarily have to take a stand- This in turn would amount to revealing his defense and therefore prejudice the employee in the criminal proceedings

---

## Acquittal and illegal gratification

***Jagtar Singh v. State of Punjab***

MANU/SC/0288/2023, Neutral Citation: 2023/INSC/279

**Judges:**— Justice Abhay Shreeniwas Oka and Justice Rajesh Bindal

**Advocates:**

1. For Appellant :— Gagan Gupta, AOR
2. For Respondents :— Abhinav Bajaj, Adv., Ajay Pal, AOR, Mayank Dahiya, Sugandh Rathor, Priyanka C. and Bhupinder, Advs.

Criminal Appeal No. 2136 of 2010

Date of Decision – 23.03.2023

Appellant convicted by Trial Court for offence of illegal gratification in respect of getting of death certificate - In appeal, conviction of appellant was upheld by High Court - Proof of demand and acceptance of illegal gratification by a public servant as a fact in issue by the prosecution is a sine qua non in order to establish the guilt of the Accused public servant-no evidence produced on record to prove the demand of illegal gratification-not a case where there was circumstantial evidence to prove the demand.

---

## Appellate court must not interfere with an order of acquittal merely because a contrary view is permissible

***Central Bureau of Investigation v. Shyam Bihari and Ors.***

**(From Supreme Court of India)**

MANU/SC/0774/2023, Neutral Citation: 2023/INSC/623

**Judges:**— Justice B.V. Nagarathna and Justice Manoj Misra

**Advocates:**

1. For Appellant :— B. Balaji, AOR
2. For Respondents :— Joseph Aristotle S., AOR and Vaidehi Rastogi, Adv.

Criminal Appeal No. 413 of 2013

Date of Decision – 17.07.2023

Aappeal assails the judgment and order of the High Court of Uttarakhand at Nainital -trite law that in an appeal against acquittal, the power of the appellate court to reappreciate evidence and come to its own conclusion is not circumscribed by any limitation- But it is equally settled that the appellate court must not interfere with an order of acquittal merely because a contrary view is permissible, particularly, where the view taken by the trial court is a plausible view based on proper appreciation of evidence and is not vitiated by ignorance/ misreading of relevant evidence on record

---

## Acquittal of a Junior Engineer from the bribe case though tainted money was recovered from him

### *V. Sejappa v. State By Police Inspector, Lokayukta*

***(From Karnataka High Court)***

2016 (2) Law Herald (SC) 1383: 2016 AIR (SC) 2045: 2016(2) R.C.R. (Criminal) 860: 2016(3) Recent Apex Judgements (R.A.J.) 89: 2016(4) JT 431: 2016(4) Scale 308: 2016 AIR (SCW) 2045: 2016(2) Crimes 116: 2016 All SCR (Crl.) 902: 2016(2) JLJR 460: 2016 CrilJ 2589: 2016(94) ACrC 984: 2016(1) Andh LD (Criminal) 922: 2016(162) AIC88: 2016(2) Apex Court Judgements (SC) 288: 2016 Cri. L.R. 561: 2016(2) Cri. CC 719: 2016(3) ECrC 157: 2016 RajCric 704: 2016(3) KCCR 1889: 2016(3) PLJR 106: 2016 (3) JCC 1488: 2016(3) ECrC 157: 2016 RajCriC 704: 2016(3) AICLR 96:2016 (3) GCD 1986: 2017(1) PCCR 74:2016 (sup2) CutLT (Criminal) 239: 2016(12) SCC 150:2017(3) SCC (Cri) 699:2016(64) Orrisa Cri. R. 364:2016(2) Ori. Law Rev. 155.

**Judges :–** Justice Dipak Misra and Justice R. Banumathi.

**Advocates:–**

1. For the Appellant :— Mr.T.V. Ratnam,
2. For the Respondent :— Mr.V.N. Raghupathy.

Criminal Appeal No. 747 of 2008.

Date of Decision - 12.4.2016.

A. **Prevention of Corruption Act, 1988, Sections 7, 13(1) (d), 13(2) and 20— Criminal Procedure Code, 1973, Section 378— Acquittal of accused— Tainted money recovered— Acquittal by Trial Court— Conviction by High Court— No proof of demand of bribe— Mere recovery of money does not attract punishment— Acquittal by Supreme Court.**

[Paras 17, 23 and 24]

B. **Prevention of Corruption Act, 1988, Section 19— Sanction for prosecution by Minister concerned— Proof of Validity of Sanction.**

[Para 7]

C. **Prevention of Corruption Act, 1988, Sections 13(1)(d), 13(2) and 20— Prosecution of public servant— Burden of proof on prosecution— If prosecution proves guilty of accused, presumption under Section 20 arises— Shifting of burden of proof to accused— Condition of— Held, mere recovery of bribe money does not amount to prosecution.**

[Para 18]

D. **Criminal Procedure Code, 1973, Section 378— Acquittal of accused— Appeal against— Reasonable Order of acquittal by Trial Court— Held, High Court should not interfere with its Order.**

[Para 21]

E. **Prevention of Corruption Act, 1988, Section 7— Question as to what constitute the elements of offence under the Section— Proof of demand is sine qua non of provision for prosecution— Acquittal.**

[Para 10]

## Cases Referred :

Aher Raja Khima, AIR 1956 SC 217.

Atley v. State of Uttar Pradesh, AIR 1955 SC 807.

B. Jayaraj v. State of Andhra Pradesh, 2014(2) R.C.R.(Criminal) 410 : 2014(2) Recent Apex Judgements (R.A.J.) 570 : (2014) 13 SCC 55.

Balbir Singh v. State of Punjab, AIR 1957 SC 216.

Bhagwan Singh, 2002(2) R.C.R.(Criminal) 593 : (2002) 4 SCC 85.

Bishan Singh, (1974) 3 SCC 288.

C. Antony, 2002(4) R.C.R.(Criminal) 750 : (2003) 1 SCC 1.

C.M. Girish Babu v. CBI, 2009(2) R.C.R.(Criminal) 134 : 2009(2) Recent Apex Judgements (R.A.J.) 101 : (2009) 3 SCC 779.

C.M. Sharma v. State of Andhra Pradesh, 2011(1) R.C.R.(Criminal) 183 : 2010(6) Recent Apex Judgments (R.A.J.) 636 : (2010) 15 SCC 1.

Chandrappa, 2007(2) R.C.R.(Criminal) 92 : 2007(1) Recent Apex Judgements (R.A.J.) 841 : (2007) 4 SCC 415

Harijana Thirupala, 2002(3) R.C.R.(Criminal) 861 : (2002) 6 SCC 470.

K. Gopal Reddy, (1979) 1 SCC 355.

K. Gopalakrishna, 2005(2) R.C.R.(Criminal) 20 : (2005) 9 SCC 291.

Khedu Mohton, (1970) 2 SCC 450.

Khem Karan, (1974) 4 SCC 603.

Lekha Yadav, (1973) 2 SCC 424.

M.G. Agarwal, AIR 1963 SC 200.

Madan Lal, 1997(4) R.C.R.(Criminal) 89 : (1997) 7 SCC 677.

Madan Mohan Singh, AIR 1954 SC 637.

Mukut Bihari v. State of Rajasthan, 2012(3) R.C.R.(Criminal) 980:(2012) 11 SCC 642.

Muralidhar alias Gidda v. State of Karnataka, 2014(2) R.C.R.(Criminal) 507 : 2014(2) Recent Apex Judgements (R.A.J.) 655 : (2014) 5 SCC 730.

Noor Khan, AIR 1964 SC 286.

P. Satyanarayana Murthy v. District Inspector of Police, State of Andhra Pradesh, 2015(4) R.C.R.(Criminal) 350:2015(4) Recent Apex Judgements (R.A.J.) 625:(2015) 10 SCC 152.

Ram Kumar, 1994(3) R.C.R.(Criminal) 631 : (1995) Supp 1 SCC 248.

Sambasivan, 1998(2) R.C.R.(Criminal) 693 : (1998) 5 SCC 412.

Sanjay Thakran, 2007(2) R.C.R.(Criminal) 458 : 2007(2) Recent Apex Judgements (R.A.J.) 101 : (2007) 3 SCC 755.

Shivaji Sahabrao Bobade, (1973) 2 SCC 793.

State of Kerala v. C.P. Rao, 2011(3) R.C.R.(Criminal) 688 : 2011(4) Recent Apex Judgements (R.A.J.) 183 : (2011) 6 SCC 450.

State through Inspector of Police, A.P. v. K. Narasimhachary, 2005(3) Apex Criminal 415 : (2005) 8 SCC 364.

Suraj Mal v. State (Delhi Admn.), (1979) 4 SCC 725.

T. Subramanian v. State of Tamil Nadu, 2006(1) Apex Criminal 159:(2006) 1 SCC 401.

Tota Singh, 1987(2) R.C.R.(Criminal) 35 : (1987) 2 SCC 529.

Tulsiram Kanu, AIR 1954 SC 1.

Umedbhai Jadavbhai, (1978) 1 SCC 228.

## Acquittal of Custom Officers though tainted money was recovered from their possession and as the demand and acceptance not proved

***Satvir Singh v. State of Delhi through CBI***

**(From Delhi High Court)**

2014(4) ECrC 189: 2014(10) JT 67: 2014 AIR (SCW) 4924: 2014(9) Scale 528: 2015(1) RLW 453: 2014(13) SCC 143: 2014(3) CCR 644:2014(5) SCC(Cri) 619:2014 AIR (SC) 3798: 2014(4) JLJR 412:2014(5) Recent Apex Judgements (R.A.J.) 20:2014(4) R.C.R. (Criminal) 40:2014(3) Law Herald (SC) 2386: 2014 All SCR 3184: 2014(3) Crimes 420: 2014(4) Cri. CC 1:2014(4) Law Herald 3286:2014 CriLJ 4399:2014 (4) JCC 2586:2014(144) AIC 249:2014(4) AICLR 559:2014 (sup) Cri. L.R. 447:2015(1) Andh LD (Criminal) 48:2014(3) Apex Court Judgements (SC) 199:2014(59) Orrisa Cri. R. 449.

**Judges :—** Justice Dipak Misra and Justice V. Gopala Gowda.

**Advocates:**

1. For the Appellant :— Mr. Sibo Sankar Mishra.
2. For the Respondent: — Mr. B. V. Balaram Das.

Criminal Appeal No. 920 of 2011.

Date of Decision - 20.08.2014.

**A. Prevention of Corruption Act, 1988, Sections 7,13(1) (d) and 13(2)— Criminal Procedure Code, 1973, Section 173— Acquittal of accused in corruption case— Recovery of cash from house of accused— No proof of— Demand and acceptance of bribe money— Held, though tainted money recovered and demand and acceptance not proved, accused must be acquitted from charges.**

[ Paras 11,34,40 and 41]

**B. Prevention of Corruption Act, 1988, Section 20— Absence of presumption under Section— Appreciation of evidence by Trial Court— Both oral and documentary evidence— No proof of demand, acceptance and gratification— Presumption of innocence— Grant of in favour of accused— Held acquittal.**

[Para 34]

The Law on the issue is well settled that demand of illegal gratification is sine qua non for constituting an offence ***under*** the ***1988 Act***. Mere recovery of tainted money is not sufficient to convict the accused, when the substantive evidence in the case is not reliable, unless there is evidence to prove payment of bribe or to show that the money was taken voluntarily as bribe. Mere receipt of amount by the accused is not sufficient to fasten the guilt, in the absence of any evidence with regard to demand and acceptance of the amount as illegal gratification, but the burden rests on the accused to displace the statutory presumption raised ***under*** Section 20 of the ***1988 Act***, by bringing on record evidence, either direct or circumstantial, to establish with reasonable probability, that the money was accepted by him, other than as a motive or reward as referred to in Section 7 of the ***1988 Act***. While invoking the provisions of Section 20 of the *Act*, the court is required to consider the explanation offered by the accused, if any, only on the touchstone of preponderance of probability and not on the touchstone of proof beyond all reasonable doubt. However, before the accused is called upon to explain as to how the amount in question was found in his possession, the foundational facts must be established by the prosecution. The complainant is an interested and partisan witness concerned with the success of the trap and his evidence must be tested in the same way as that of any other interested witness and in a proper case the court may look for independent corroboration before convicting the accused person.

**2013 (2) R.C.R. (Cri.)219, 2002 (3) RCR (Cri.) 188 and 2012(4) RAJ 206 revied.**

[Paras 11,34,40 and 41]

## Cases Referred :

Babu v. State of Kerala, 2011(5) R.C.R.(Criminal) 113 : (2010)9 SCC 189.

C.K. Damodaran Nair v. Government of India, 1997(2) R.C.R.(Criminal) 70 : (1997)9 SCC 477.

C.M. Girish Babu v. CBI, Cochin, High Court of Kerala, 2009(2) R.C.R.(Criminal) 134 : 2009(2) Recent Apex Judgments (R.A.J.) 101 : (2009)3 SCC 779.

K.S. Panduranga v. State of Karnataka, 2013(2) R.C.R.(Criminal) 219 : 2013(2) Recent Apex Judgments (R.A.J.) 113 : (2013)3 SCC 721.

M. Narsinga Rao v. State of Andhra Pradesh, 2001(1) R.C.R.(Criminal) 95 : 2001(1) SCC 691.

Mukut Bihari v. State of Rajasthan, 2012(3) R.C.R.(Criminal) 980 : 2012(4) Recent Apex Judgments (R.A.J.) 206 : (2012)11 SCC 642.

Murugesan v. State through Inspector of Police, 2013(1) R.C.R.(Criminal) 791 : 2013(1) Recent Apex Judgments (R.A.J.) 98 : (2012)10 SCC 383.

State of Kerala v. C.P. Rao, 2011(3) R.C.R.(Criminal) 688 : 2011(4) Recent Apex Judgments (R.A.J.) 183 : (2011)6 SCC 450.

State of Madras v. A Vaidhyanatha Iyer, AIR 1958 SC 61.

Subash Parbat Sonvane v. State of Gujarat, 2002(3) R.C.R.(Criminal) 188 : (2002)5 SCC 86.

# Acquittal of Tourism Development Officer from Bribe case though there was recovery of bribe money at his instance

***Rakesh Kapoor v. State of Himachal Pradesh***

**(From Himachal Pradesh High Court)**

2013(121) AIC 83:2013(1) R.C.R. (Criminal) 211:2012(6) Recent Apex Judgements (R.A.J.) 291:2012(6) Law Herald (SC) 4950:2013(2) CalCrilR 73:2013(1) Cri.CC 1:2013(1) AICLR 85:2013(1) Bom.C.R. (Cri.) 797:2013(1) Crimes 92:2012(13) SCR 148:2012(11) Scale 255:2012 Cri. L.R. 1131:2013 ALL MR (Cri) 324:2012(13) SCC 552:2013(1) ECrc 237:2013(1) JBCJ 78:2013(1) Apex Court Judgements (SC) 165:2012(9) SLT 33:2013(1) BBCJ 155:2013(54) Orrisa Cri. R. 108.

**Judges :—** Justice P. Sathasivam and Justicce Ranjan Gogoi.

**Advocates:**

1. For the Appellant :— Parag P. Tripathi, Senior Advocate, Kunal Bahri, Mukesh Anand and Suresh Chandra Tripathy.
2. For the Respondent: — Ms. Kiran Bala Sahay and Mohit Kumar Shah.

Criminal Appeal No. 1839 of 2012

(Arising out of SLP (Crl.) No. 23 of 2012.

Date of Decision 22.11.2012

**A. Prevention of Corruption Act, 1988, Sections 7, 13(1)(a) and 13(2)— Recovery of bribe money— Demand and acceptance— No proof of– Held, if accused is acquitted under Section 7, then he cannot be convicted under section 13(2) of the Act— Further held, provision under Section 13(2) is not substantive offence.**

[Paras 7,9 and 13]

**B. Prevention of Corruption Act, 1988, Sections 13(1) and 13(2)— Whether Section 13(2) speaks about punishment of criminal misconduct— Whether in absence of Section 7, conviction under section 13(2) is permissible— Held No.**

[Paras 7 and 9]

## Cases Referred :

Joseph Kurian Philip Jose v. State of Kerala, 1994(3) R.C.R.(Criminal) 668 : (1994)6 SCC 535.

Wakil Yadav v. State of Bihar, (2000)10 SCC 500.

Banarsi Dass v. State of Haryana, 2010(2) RCR (Criminal) 553 : 2010(2) R.A.J. 471: (2010)4 SCC 450.

C.M. Girish Babu v. CBI, 2009(2) R.C.R.(Criminal) 134 : 2009(2) R.A.J. 101 : (2009)3 SCC 779.

Suraj Mal v. State (Delhi Admn.), (1979)4 SCC 725.

---

## Acquittal of Assistant Lineman and Meter Reader from bribe case as to reduce meter reading though they have not received bribe money

***Keshav Dutt v. State of Haryana***

**(From Punjab and Haryana High Court)**

2010(6) Law Herald 4462:2010(9) SCC 286:2011(1) ALT (Crl.) 15:2011(97) AIC 176:2011(6) R.C.R. (Criminal) 2446:2010(4) ECrC 164:2010(3) CalCrilR 678:2010(10) SCR 151:2010(2) W.L.C. 665:2010 (8) Scale 609:2010 Cri. L.R. 921:2010(3) SCC (Cri) 1345:2010(4) Mh.LJ (Crl.) 510:2010(4) GLR 3500:2010(3) L.R.C. 396:2010(4) BBCJ 433:2010(47) Orrisa Cri. R. 483:2011(1) Ori. Law Rev. 37.

**Judges :**— Justice Altamas Kabir.

**Advocates:**

1. For the Appellant: — Mr. Nitin Sangra, Mr. Gaurav Agarwal.
2. For the Respondent: — Mr. Rajeev Gaur, Mr. Naseem, Mr. Nazid K. Hye, Mr. Kamal Mohan Gupta.

Criminal Appeal No. 1560 of 2010.

Date of Decision 19.8.2010.

**A. Prevention of Corruption Act, 1988, Section 7 and 13(1)(d)— Criminal Procedure Code, 1973, Section 293(1)(4)(e)— Charge of bribe— Convection of accused by Special Court— Non-receipt and acceptance of bribe money— Conviction on the basis of proof of meter reading by handwriting type of expert— No opportunity to accused to cross examine handwriting type of— Conviction of accused quashed— Special Leave Petition in Supreme Court— Appeal of acquittal allowed.**

[Paras 2, 8, 9 and 15]

**B. Prevention of Corruption Act, 1988, Sections 7 and 13(1)(d)— Conviction of accused— Appeal in High Court— Peduction of sentence of one accused.**

[Para 6]

**Cases Referred :**

State of Maharashtra v. Damu, 2000 (6) SCC 269.

---

# Acquittal of In-charge of H.P State Civil Supplies on the ground of Presumption of innocence

## Sudershan Kumar v. State of Himachal Pradesh

**(From High Court of Himachal Pradesh)**

2014(14) Scale 276:2015 RajCriC 1:2015 AIR (SCW) 1180:2015(1) Law Herald (SC) 505:2015(1) CCR 112:2015(147) AIC 208:2015(2) JLJR 19:2015(1) AICLR 951:2015(2) CalCriLR 437:2014(15) SCC 666:2015(1) R.C.R. (Criminal) 496:2015(1) Recent Apex Judgements (R.A.J.) 213:2015(88) ACrC 956:2015 All SCR 891:2015(2) Law Herald 1034:2015(1) BBCJ 95:2015(60) Orrissa Cri. R. 419:2015(1) All. Crl. Rulings 953.

**Judges :**— Justice A.K. Sikri and Justice J. Chelameswar.

**Advocates:**

1. For the Appellants :—Mr. Sidharth Luthra, Mr.A. Sharan, Senior Advocates, Mr. S.S. Shamshery, Mr. Bhakti Vardhan Sngh, Mr. Amit Sharma,Ms. Ruchi Kohli, Mr. Narendera M. Sharma, Mr. Abhishek Sharma, Mr. Ankur Sood, Mr. Shubhra Mishra and Mr.Ajay Choudhary,.
2. For the Respondents :— Mr. Suryanarayana Singh and Ms. Pragati Neekhra.

Criminal Appeal No. 1403 of 2011 with Criminal Appeal No. 1404 of 2011. Criminal Appeal Nos. 1445—1446 of 2011 and Criminal Appeal Nos. 1447—1448 of 2011.

Date of Decision 18.12.2014

**A. Criminal Procedure Code, Section 161— Statement of witnesses recorded after a delay of 77 days for which no explanation given— such an abnormal delay tells a lot about the way investigation was carried out— This factor also shakes the credibility of the deposition of the witness— Inthis case accused was acquitted.**

[Para 28]

**B. Criminal procedure Code, Sections 378 and 386—Appeal against order of acquittal—A cardinal principle in criminal jurisprudence that presumption of innocence of the accused is reinforced by an order of the acquittal—The principles curied out in Dhanapal v. State by Public Prosecutor, Madras, 2010 (5) RCR (Crl.) 353 reiterated:—**

1. The accused is presumed to be innocent until proven guilty. The accused possessed this presumption when he was before the trial court. The trial court's acquittal bolsters the presumption that he is innocent.
2. The power of reviewing evidence is wide and the applellate court can re—appreciate the entire evidence on record. It can review the trial court's conclusion with respect to both facts and law, but the Appellate Court must give due weight and consideratin to the decision of the trial court.
3. The appellate court should always keep in mind that the trial court had the distince advantage of watching the demeanour of the witnesses. The trial court is in a better position to evaluate the credibility of the witnesses.
4. The appellate court may only overrule or otherwise disturb the trial court's acquittal if it has "very substantial and compelling reasons" for doing so.
5. If two reasonable or possible views can be reached — one that leads to acquittal, the other to conviction — the High Courts/appellate courts must rule in favour of the accused. 2010(5) RCR (Crl.) 353, relied.

[Paras 29 and 30)

**Cases Referred :**

Dhanapal v. State by Public Prosecutor, Madras, 2010(5) R.C.R.(Criminal) 353 : (2009) 10 SCC 401.

Chandrappa v. State of Karnataka, 2007(2) R.C.R.(Criminal) 92 : 2007(1) Recent Apex Judgments (R.A.J.) 841 : (2007) 4 SCC 415.

---

## Acquittal of Advocate from charge of giving false legal advice to Bank in favour of conspirators

***Central Bureau of Investigation, Hyderabad v. K. Narayana Rao***

**( From High Court of Andhra Pradesh)**

2013(1) ECrC 68:2012(4) Recent Apex Judgements (R.A.J.) 597:2012(4) R.C.R. (Criminal) 601:2012(4) KLT 92:2012 AIR (SCW) 5139:2012(4) MLJ (Criminal 420:2012(9) SCC 512:2012(6) CTC 569:2012 CriLJ 4610:2012(3) CalCriLR 811:2012(4) AICLR 537:2013(1) Cri.CC 219:2012(4) Crimes 181:2012(3) SC-C(Cri) 1183:2013(2) PLR 160:2013 AIR (SC) (Cri) 448:2012(9) SCR 54:2012(9) Scale 228:2013(1) W.L.C. 1:2013(1) J.C.R. 95:2012 Cri. L.R. 1101:2012(9) JT 359:2012(3) SriLJ 288:2013(1) JBCJ 115:2012(30) LCD 2013:2012(3) GujLH 373:2012(4) B.L.Jud. 153:2012(53) Orrisa Cri. R. 806:2013(1) Ori. Law Rev. 74:2018(125) CutLT 436:2018(3) Cal. L.T. 46.

**Judges :—** Justice P. Sathasivam and Justice Ranjan Gogoi.

**Advocates:**

1. For the Appellant :— Mr. H.P. Raval, ASG with him Mr. Rajiv Nanda, Ms. Padmalakshmi Nigam and Mr. Arvind Kumar Sharma.
2. For the Respondent :— Mr. R. Venkataramani, Senior Advocate with him Mr. Ashok Panigrahi, Mr. Aljo Joseph and Mr. Surajit Bhaduri.

Criminal Appeal No. 1460 of 2012 (Arising out of S.L.P. (Crl.) No. 6975 of 2011).

Date of Decision 21.9.2012.

**A. Prevention of Corruption Act, 1988, Sections 13(1)(d) and 13(2)— Indian Penal Code 420, 468 and 471— Loan from bank under Criminal Conspiracy— Legal advice from Accused Advocate— Acquittal of accused Advocate by Apex Court— Held an Advocate giving legal opinion on the basis of documents placed before him by bank cannot be prosecuted on the ground that he gave false advice.**

[Paras 2, 12, 18 20 and 28]

**B. Prevention of Corruption Act, 1988, Sections 13(1)(d) and 13(2)— Indian Penal Code, 1860, 34,35, and 120-B— Charge of Criminal Conspiracy— Absence of proof of Acquittal of accused.**

[Paras 2, 8, 18, 19 and 20]

**Cases Referred:**

Jacob Mathew v. State of Punjab, 2005(3) R.C.R. (Criminal) 836 : 2005(2) Apex Criminal 649 : (2005)6 SCC 1.

Mahavir Prashad Gupta v. State of National Capital Territory of Delhi, 2000(4) R.C.R.(Criminal) 480 : (2000) 8 SCC 115.

P. Vijayan v. State of Kerala, 2010(1) R.C.R.(Criminal) 826 : 2010(1) R.A.J. 502: (2010)2 SCC 398.

Pandurang Dattatraya Khandekar v. Bar Council of Maharashtra, (1984)2 SCC 556.

Rupan Deol Bajaj (Mrs.) v. Kanwar Pal Singh Gill, 1995(3) R.C.R.(Criminal) 700: (1995)6 SCC 194.

Sajjan Kumar v. Central Bureau of Investigation, 2010(4) R.C.R.(Criminal) 382: 2010(5) Recent Apex Judgments (R.A.J.) 350 : (2010)9 SCC 368.

Shivnarayan Laxminarayan Joshi v. State of Maharashtra, (1980)2 SCC 465.

State of Bihar v. Murad Ali Khan, (1988)4 SCC 655.

State of Bihar v. Ramesh Singh, (1977)4 SCC 39.

State of Haryana v. Bhajan Lal, 1991(1) R.C.R.(Criminal) 383 : 1992 Supp (1) SCC 335.

---

## Acquittal of IAS Officer though recovery of huge cash from his house on ground of failure of evidence by prosecution

***D.S.P. Chennai v. K. Inbasagaran***
**(From Madras High Court)**

2006(2) Mh.LJ 399 : 2006(1) RajCriC 107 : 2006(1) Apex Criminal 3 : 2006 AIR (SC) 552 : 2006(1) Cri.CC 586 : 2006(1) AICLR 593 : 2006(1) SCC 420 : 2005(10) Scale 1 : 2005(10) JT 332 : 2006 CriLJ 319 : 2006(1) SCC(Cri) 325 : 2006(1) AIR Jhar R. 400 : 2006(54) ACrC 291 : 2006(1) Crimes 68 : 2005 AIR (SCW) 6208 : 2006(1) RLW 434 : 2006(1) Andh LD (Criminal) 293 : 2006(1) ECrC 222 : 2006(1) W.L.C. 117 : 2006 Cri. L.R. 55 : 2006(1) CalCriLR 304 : 2006 ALL MR(Cri) 304 : 2006(37) AIC 111 : 2006(1) M.P.L.J. 512 : 2006 (282) ITR 435 : 2006(1) BLJR 523 : 2006(200) CurTr 624 : 2006(1) L.R.C. 8 : 2006(1) B.L.Jud. 71 : 2006(1) R.C.R.(Criminal) 107: 2006(33) Orrisa Cri. R. 300 : 2006(1) Cri. App. R (SC) 41.

**Judges :—** Justice B.N. Agrawal & Justice A.K. Mathur.

**Advocates:**

1. For the Appellant :— Mr. Abhay Kumar, Advocate with Mr. Subramonium Prasad.
2. For the Respondent :— Mr. Chinmoy Khaladkar and Mr. Ajit Kumar Sinha.

Criminal Appeal No. 480 of 2002.
Date of Decision 7.12.2005

**A. Prevention of Corruption Act, 1988, Sections 13(2) and 13(1)(e)— Raid in the house of IAS Officer— Recovery of 13 lakhs in cash— Wife of accused is a business person— Accused and his wife stay in same house— Wife contending that the cash recovered was black money— Assessment already done by Income Tax Department— Burden of proof of guilty— Failure of— Contention of wife— Admissibility of— Acquittal by Lower Courts— Order of acquittal upheld by Apex Court.**

[Para 15]

**B. Prevention of Corruption Act, 1947, Section 5(3)— Recovery of unaccounted money and assets from the house of public servant— Burden**

**of proof is on accused person— Acquittal by Lower Courts— Acquittal upheld by Apex Court— Held accused could not be held guilty if he provides satisfactory and plausible explanation of white money.**

[Paras 13, 14, 15 and 16]

C. **Prevention of Corruption Act, 1947, Section 5(3)— Huge amount of cash recovered from house of accused— Burden of proof falls on prosecution— Failure of— Acquittal of accused.**

[Para 13]

## Cases Referred :

C.S.D. Swami v. State, AIR 1960 Supreme Court 7.

State of Maharashtra v. Wasudeo Ramchandra Kaidalwar, (1981)3 SCC 199.

State of Maharashtra v. Pollonji Darabshaw Daruwalla, 1987(2) RCR(Crl.) 697 (SC).

K. Veeraswami v. Union of India, 1991(2) RCR(Crl.) 559 (SC) : (1991)3 SCC 655.

P. Nallammal v. State represented by Inspector of Police, 1999(3) RCR(Crl.) 676 (SC) : (1999)6 SCC 559.

K.C. Builders v. Assistant Commissioner of Income Tax, (2004)2 SCC 731.

State of M.P. v. Awadh Kishore Gupta, 2004(1) RCR(Crl.) 233 : 2004(2) Apex Criminal 158 (SC) : (2004)1 SCC 691.

---

# Acquittal of Lecturer of Pharmaceutical College though tainted money recoverd from him on the ground of other evidences

***State of Kerala v. C.P. Rao***
**(From Kerala High Court)**

2011(2) KLT 812 : 2011(6) SCC 450 : 2011(74) ACrC 551 : 2011(3) AICLR 397 : 2011(2) Crimes 289 : 2011(3) R.C.R.(Criminal) 688 : 2011(4) Recent Apex Judgements (R.A.J.) 183 : 2011(4) MLJ (Criminal) 723 : 2012 AIR (SC) (Cri) 911 : 2011(2) SCC (L&S) 714 : 2011(2) SCC(Cri) 1010 : 2011(3) Cri.CC 135 : 2012 AIR (SCW) 2879 : 2012 CriLJ 2607 : 2011(3) ECrC 117 : 2011(104) AIC 154 : 2011(6) SCR 864 : 2011(6) Scale 358 : 2011(2) W.L.C. 359 : 2011(3) JT 641 : 2011(2) JLJR 299 : 2011(sup) CutLT (Criminal) 1681 : 2011(3) M.P.W.N. 247 : 2011(7) SLT 202 : 2011(4) BBCJ 223 : 2011(49) Orrisa Cri. R. 601 : 2011(2) Apex Court Judgements (SC) 327.

**Judges :—** Justice Asok Kumar Ganguly and Justice Deepak Verma.

**Advocates:**

1. For the Appellant :— Mr. G. Prakash and Mr. Ramesh Babu.
2. For the Respondent :— Mr. P.P. Rao, Senior Advocate, Mr. Guntur Prabhakar.

Criminal Appeal No. 1098 of 2006.

Date of Decision 16.5.2011.

A. **Prevention of Corruption Act, 1988, Sections 7 and 13(1)(d)— Allegation of bribery— Recovery of tainted money from the instance of accused— Demand of bribe not proved— Acquittal— Held, mere recovery by itself could not prove the charge of persecution against the accused —Acquittal by High Court upheld by Apex Court.**

[Para 10]

**Cases Referred :**

1. Panalal Damodar Rathi v. State of Maharashtra, 1979(4) SCC 526.
2. Suraj Mal v. State (Delhi Admn.), 1979(4) SCC 725.
3. A. Subair v. State of Kerala, 2009(3) R.C.R.(Criminal) 370 : 2009(4) R.A.J. 125: 2009(6) SCC 587.
4. Sanwat Singh v. State of Rajasthan, 1961(3) SCR 120.
5. Sheo Swarup's, 1934 L.R. 61 I.A. 398.

---

## Acquittal of a Head Constable in bribery case on the ground that fundamental of prosecution should be maintained

***State of Maharashtra v. Dhyaneshwar Laxman Rao Wankhede***
**(From Bombay High Court)**

2009(15) SCC 200:2009 AIR (SCW) 5411:2009(4) R.C.R. (Criminal) 217:2009(5) Recent Apex Judgements (R.A.J.) 356:2009(4) AICLR 496:2009 CriLJ 4425:2009(5) AIR Bom.R 781:2009 ALL MR(Cri) 3127:2009(10) Scale 355:2009(2) W.L.C. 753:2009(sup) Cri. L.R. 368:2010(2) SCC(Cri) 385:2009(4) L.R.C. 275:2009(4) BBCJ 224:2009(44) Orrisa Cri. R. 425.

**Judges :**— Justice S.B. Sinha and Justice Cyriac Joseph.

**Advocates:–**

1. For the Appellant :— Ms. Madhavi Divan and Mr.Ravindra Keshavrao Adsure.
2. For the Respondent :— Mr. Manish Pitale and Mr. Chander Shekhar Ashri.

Criminal Appeal No. 1350 of 2009 [Arising out of SLP (Crl.) No. 211 of 2006].

Date of Decision 29.07.2009.

**A. Prevention of Corruption Act, 1988, Sections 7 and 13(1)(d)— Bribery— Recovery of bribery money from accused— Death of witness— Still prosecution has to prove demand by accused. Acquittal by Apex Court.**

[Para 17]

**B. Prevention of Corruption Act, 1988, Section 20— Demand of bribe by accused— Recovery of— Foundation fact should be proved by prosecution itself— Proof of innocence beyond reasonable doubt— Acquittal.**

[Paras 6 and 9]

**C. Prevention of Corruption Act, 1988, Sections 7, 13(1)(d)— Criminal Procedure Code, 1973, Section 378— Acquittal of accused— Appeal against— Held even burden is on accused to prove about the recovery money the prosecution must prove fundamental facts.**

[Para 21]

**Cases Referred :**

Shivappa v. State of Karnataka, (2008)11 SCC 337.

State of Maharashtra v. Rashid B. Mulani, 2006(1) RCR(Criminal) 422 : 2006(1) Apex Criminal 127 : (2006)1 SCC 407.

State through Inspector of Police, A.P. v. K. Narasimhachary, 2005(3) Apex Criminal 415 : (2005)8 SCC 364.

Noor Aga v. State of Punjab, 2008(3) RCR(Criminal) 633 : 2008(4) RAJ 381 : 2008(9) SCALE 691.

Jayendra Vishnu Thakur v. State of Maharashtra and Anr., 2009(7) SCALE 757.

Dilip v. State of M.P., 2007(1) RCR(Criminal) 586 : 2007(1) RAJ 235 : (2007)1 SCC 450.

Gagan Kanojia v. State of Punjab, 2007(1) RCR(Criminal) 222 : 2007(1) RAJ 114: (2006)13 SCC 516.

---

## Acquittal of Development Officer of an Insurance Company on the ground of lack of charge of conspiracy and cheating

### *Hanuman Chand v. State Thr. Insp. of Police*

**(From High Court of Madras)**

**Judges:—** Justice Pinaki Chandra Ghose and Justice Amitava Roy.

**Advocates:**

1. For the Appellants :— Ms. Srishti Govil, Balaji Srinivasan.
2. For the Respondents :— Mr. S.N. Terdal, Mr. N.K. Karhail, Mr. M.K. Maroria, Mr. Arvind Kumar Sharma, (N.P.).

Criminal Appeal No. 2416 of 2010.

Date of Decision 10.6.2016

A. **Prevention of Corruption Act, 1988, Sections 13(1)(d) and 13(2)— Indian Penal Code, 1860, Sections 120-B and 420 r/w 511— Acquittal of accused in corruption case— Criminal misconduct— Conspiracy— Lack of evidence of conspiracy— Contradiction between charge against accused person— Ingredients offence— Lack of convincing evidence— Held the accused person untitled to acquittal.**

[Paras 8 and 9]

B. **Prevention of Corruption Act, 1988, Section 20— Presumption under— No presumption attached by— Lack of both direct and convincing evidence— Order for acquittal— Benefit of doubt.**

[Paras 8 and 9]

---

## Acquittal of Income Tax Officer from bribe case due to lack of evidence and cognizability of case

### State of Punjab v. Madan Mohan Lal Verma

**(From Punjab and Haryana High Court)**

2013(4) ECrC 269 : 2013(3) CCR : 2013(3) R.C.R.(Criminal) 972 : 2013(4) Recent Apex Judgements (R.A.J.) 669 : 2013(7) SCR 1130 : 2013(3) MLJ (Criminal) 565: 2013 AIR (SCW) 4757 : 2013(10) Scale 211 : 2013 AIR (SC) (Cri) 1918 : 2013 CriLJ 4050 : 2013(4) AIR Jhar R. 32 : 2013(4) PLJR 109 : 2013 AIR

(SC) 3368: 2013(5) Law Herald (SC) 4080 : 2013(4) Law Herald 3182 : 2014(1) ALT (Crl.) 35 : 2014(1) AICLR 96 : 2013(14) SCC 153 : 2014(4) SCC(Cri) 136 : 2013(3) JLJR 580 : 2013 Cri. L.R. 914 : 2013(4) JBCJ 110 : 2013(2) Andh LD (Criminal) 792 : 2013(3) Apex Court Judgements (SC) 738 : 2013(7) SLT 180 : 2013(3) BBCJ 192 : 2013(4) B.L.Jud. 46 : 2013(56) Orrisa Cri. R. 425.

**Judges:–** Justice B.S. Chauhan and Justice S.A. Bobde.

## Advocates:–

1. For the Appellant :— Mr. Ashok K. Panda, Senior Advocate, Mr. Syed Tanweer Ahmad, Mr. Rajiv Nanda, Mr. B.V. Balram Das and Mr. Arvind Kumar Sharma, Advocates.
2. For the Respondent: — Caveator—In—Person.

Criminal Appeal No. 2052 of 2010.

Date of Decision 12.8.2013.

**A. Prevention of Corruption Act, 1988, Sections 7,13(1)(d) and 13(2)— Charge of illegal gratification against accused— Trap and raid— Arrest of accused— Criminal background of complainant— Defence of by accused— Witness of recovery of amount— No witness of acceptance of bribe money— Conviction by Lower Courts— Acquittal by Apex Court.**

[Paras 1 and 10]

**B. Prevention of Corruption Act, 1988, Section 20— Charge of bribe by public servant— Trap and raid— Demand of illegal gratification— Demand and acceptance— Recovery of tainted money— No witness of acceptance of same— Conviction by Lower Court— Acquittal by Supreme Court— Held, mere recovery of tainted money was not sufficient to convict the accused.**

[Para 7]

**C. Prevention of Corruption Act, 1988, Sections 13(1)(d) and 13(2)— Charge of bribe— Trap and raid— Recovery of tainted money— No evidence of acceptance— Conviction by Lower Court— Acquittal by Apex Court— Held, The Court must look for independent corroboration of evidence of partisan witness and interested witness before convicting the accused.**

[Paras 2 and 7]

## Cases Referred :

Abrar v. State of U.P., 2011(4) R.C.R.(Criminal) 104 : 2011(5) Recent Apex Judgments (R.A.J.) 2.

Rukia Begum v. State of Karnataka, 2011(3) R.C.R.(Criminal) 745 : 2011(4) Recent Apex Judgments (R.A.J.) 306 .

State of Madhya Pradesh v. Dal Singh, 2013(3) R.C.R.(Criminal) 1 : 2013(3) Recent Apex Judgments (R.A.J.) 625 .

Ram Prakash Arora v. State of Punjab, AIR 1973 SC 498.

T. Subramanian v. The State of T.N., 2006(1) Apex Criminal 159 .

State of Kerala v. C.P. Rao, 2011(3) R.C.R.(Criminal) 688 : 2011(4) Recent Apex Judgments (R.A.J.) 183 : (2011) 6 SCC 450.

Mukut Bihari v. State of Rajasthan, 2012(3) R.C.R.(Criminal) 980 : 2012(4) Recent Apex Judgments (R.A.J.) 206 : (2012) 11 SCC 642.

---

# Acquittal of Bill Collector of Panchayat from bribe case for long delay and without valid sanction for prosecution

***Nanjappa v. State of Karnataka***
**(From High Court of Karnataka)**

2015 ALL MR (Cri) 3318 : 2015(3) MLJ (Criminal) 744 : 2015(2) Andh LD (Criminal) 627 : 2015(91) ACrC 306 : 2015(3) ALT (Crl.) 129 : 2015(153) AIC 146 : 2015(3) Air Kar R 801 : 2015(4) Recent Apex Judgements (R.A.J.) 197 : 2015(8) Scale 171 : 2015(3) R.C.R.(Criminal) 862 : 2015 AIR (SCW) 4432 : 2015(2) PLJ (Criminal) 565 : 2015(3) Crimes 125 : 2015 Cri. L.R. 894 : 2015(3) KLT 96 : 2015(4) Law Herald (SC) 2760 : 2015(4) Law Herald 3054 : 2015(3) Cri.CC 716 : 2015 AIR (SC) 3060 : 2015(4) RLW 2746 : 2015 RajCriC 807 : 2015 CriLJ 4012 : 2015(4) ECrC 6 : 2015(4) PLJR 55 : 2015(4) JCC 2409 % 2015(3) JLJR 565 : 2015(4) AICLR 6 : 2015(3) Apex Court Judgements (SC) 89 : 2015(14) SCC 186 : 2016(2) SCC (Cri) 360 : 2016(121) CutLT 320:2015(3) MadWN (Cri) 245 : 2015(62) Orrisa Cri. R. 79 : 2015(3) All. Crl. Rullings 2385.

**Judges:**— Justice T.S. Thakur and Justice Amitava Roy.

**Advocates:–**

1. For the Appellant :— Mr. S.N. Bhat.
2. For the Respondent: —Mr. V.N. Raghupathy.

Criminal Appeal No. 1867 of 2012.

Date of Decision - 24.7.2015.

**A. Prevention of Corruption Act, 1988, Sections 13(2) and 13(3)(i)— Corruption Case— Acquittal by Trial Court— High Court convicting the**

**accused— Delay in trial— Question of speedy trial— Held, there is no reason for order of fresh trial by Apex Court— Acquittal upheld.**

[Para 21]

**B. Prevention of Corruption Act, 1988, Section 19— Criminal Procedure Code, 1973, Section 465— Sanction for prosecution— grant of valid sanction— Necessity of— Stage— of validity of sanction in trial etc.— Invalid sanction entitles accused to be acquitted.**

[Paras 13, 14 and 15]

**C. Prevention of Corruption Act, 1988, Sections 19(3) and 19(4)— Prosecution of Public Servant— Need of valid sanction for prosecution. Acquittal AIR 1949 Pc 264 and AIR 1945 FC 16 relied.**

[Para 7]

## Cases Referred :

Agarwalla's case A.I.R. (32) 1945 F.C. 16.

B. Saha v. M.S. Kochar, (1979) 4 SCC 177.

Baij Nath Tripathi v. The State of Bhopal, AIR 1957 SC 494.

Basdeo Agarwalla v. King Emperor, AIR 1945 Federal Court 16.

Budha Mal v. State of Delhi, Criminal Appeal No. 17 of 1952. D/d. 3.10.1952.

K. Kalimuthu v. State by DSP, 2005(2) R.C.R.(Criminal) 463 : (2005) 4 SCC 512.

Kaliram v. State of Himachal Pradesh, AIR 1973 SC 2773.

Mohammad Safi v. The State of West Bengal, AIR 1966 SC 69.

State of Goa v. Babu Thomas, 2005(4) R.C.R.(Criminal) 349 : (2005) 8 SCC 130.

State of Karnataka v. C. Nagarajaswamy, 2005(4) R.C.R. (Criminal) 511 : (2005) 8 SCC 370.

Yusofalli Mulla v. The King, AIR 1949 PC 264.

---

# Acquittal of Employee of Delhi Electric Supply Undertaking in bribery case and if one accused is acquitted then other accused should get same privilege

***Dashrath Singh Chauhan v.***
***Central Bureau of Investigation***
**(From Delhi High Court)**

2018 AIR (SC) 4720 : 2018(10) JT 8 : 2018 AIR (SCW) 4720 : 2018(13) Scale 705: 2018(4) Law Herald 2767 : 2018 Cri. L.R. 1022 : 2018(4) Law Herald (SC) 2629: 2018(4) Ker L.J. 721.

**Judges:—** Justice Abhay Manohar Sapre and Justice Indu Malhotra.

**Advocates:–**

1. For the Appellants :— Mr. Rishi Malhotra.
2. For the Respondents :— Mr. Mukesh Kumar Maroria.

Criminal Appeal No. 1276 of 2010.

Date of Decision 9.10.2018.

**A. Prevention of Corruption Act, 1988, Sections 7, 13(1)(d) and 13(2)–Indian Penal Code, 1860, Section 120-B–Conspiracy of accused with co—accused–Accused conspirated with co—accused for bribe from complainant–Acceptance of bribe money by co—accused–Lack of evidence that accused directly accepted bribe money from complainant–No proof of charge against both the accused–Acquittal of both co—accused and accused–Principle of *fortiorari*–If one accused is acquitted the other accused must be acquitted from the same charge.**

[Paras 2, 24, 25 and 30]

**B. Indian Penal Code, 1860, Section 120–B–Charge of conspiracy against co—accused—Failure of–Held, if the co—accused is acquitted, the alleged conspirator must be acquitted–Principle of *fortiorari.***

[Para 7]

**Cases Referred :**

Bhagat Ram v. State of Rajasthan, (1972) 2 SCC 466.

M.K. Harshan v. State of Kerala, (1996) 11 SCC 720.

---

# Acquittal of Lower Division Clerk in the Office of S.P., Vigilance on the ground of unintentional embezzlement of government money does not warrant conviction of accused

***N. K. Illiyas v. State of Kerala***

**(From Kerala High Court)**

2012 (4) Recent Apex Judgements (R.A.J.) 86 : 2012 AIR (SCW) 2496 : 2012 CriLJ 2418 : 2012 AIR (SC) (Cri) 872 : 2012 (3) R.C.R.(Criminal) 837 : 2012 (5) Law Herald (SC) 4056 : 2012 AIR (SC) 3790 : 2011 Cri. L.R. 68 : 2012 (12) SCC 748.

**Judges:—** Justice Harjit Singh Bedi and Justice Gyan Sudha Misra

**Advocates:**

1. For the Applicant :— Mr. M.T. George, Adv., Mr. T.G. Narayanan Nair.
2. For the Respondent :— Mr. P.V. Dinesh, Adv., Ms. Sindhu T.P., Adv., Mr. P.V. Vinod, Adv., Mr. K.R. Sasiprabhu.

Criminal Appeal No. 725 of 2006.
Date of Decision 12.7.2011.

**Prevention of Corruption Act, 1988, Sections 13(1)(c) and 13(1)(d) — Indian Penal Code, 1860, Sections 95 and 409, 471 and 477A — Unintentional temporary embezzlement of government money — Accused was with money for telephone dues — Deposit by accused after 21 days — Held accused not guilty of offence under the Act of 1988 and also not under IPC — Benefit of doubt under Section 95 of IPC Conviction of accused set aside — Acquittal of accused.**

[Paras 2 and 3]

# Acquittal of Medical Officer, Head Clerk, Sub-treasury Officer etc., from charge of criminal breach of trust on the ground of absence of mens rea and absence of proof of offence

***Radha Pisharassiar Amma v. State of Kerala***
**(From Kerala High Court)**

2008 (1) R.C.R. (Criminal) 80:2007 (6) Recent Apex Judgements (R.A.J.) 268 : 2008 (1) AICLR 12 : 2007 (13) SCC 410 : 2007 (13) Scale 73 : 2007 (4) Crimes 258 : 2009 (1) SCC (Cri) 200 : 2007 (7) Supreme 649 : 2008 (1) ECrC 116 : 2007 (4) Cri.CC 1005 : 2008 RajCriC 52 : 2008 (1) JLJR 134 : 2998 (1) PLJR 134 : 2007 (4) L.R.C. 446 : 2007 (4) KHC 679 : 2008 (39) Orrisa Cri. R. 116.

**Judges:–** Justice H.K. Sema & Justice Lokeshwar Singh Panta

**Advocates:–**

1. For the Appearing Parties :— Altaf Ahmed, Kailash Vasdev and T.L. Viswanatha Iyer, Senior Advocates with Romy Chacko, B.S. Swathi Kumar, Arjun Harkauli,

M.T. George, C.S. Rajan, T.G. Narayana Nair, Ms. Ratna Kaul, P.V. Dinesh and K.R. Sasiprabhu.

Criminal Appeal No. 1542 of 2007 (Arising out of Special Leave Petition (Crl.) No. 5705 of 2005).

WITH Crl. Appeal Nos. 1543, 1544, 1545, 1546 and 1547 of 2007 (Arising out of SLP(Crl.) Nos. 5744/2005, 5858/2005, 4683/2006, 4687/2006 and 4684/2006)

Date of Decision 14.11.2007

A. **Prevention of Corruption Act, 1988, Sections 13(1)(c) and 13(2) — Indian Penal Code, 1860, Sections 409, 467 and 471 — Criminal breach of trust — Absence of mens rea — Held, for the conviction of accused mens rea or motive must be proved — Acquittal— Order of Lower Courts set aside.**

[Para 16]

B. **Prevention of Corruption Act, 1988, Sections 13(1)(c) and 13(2) — Indian Penal Code, 1860, Sections 409, 467, 471, 477 A and 120—B — For offence under Section 409, accused in committing offence of breach of trust must be entrusted with the property or has dominion over property in his capacity of public servant — Held, persecution must prove dishonest misappropriation of government property by accused — Ground of acquittal proved — Acquittal of accused.**

[Para 16]

---

## Acquittal of Chief Executive Officer from Corruption charges and Order for his retirement benefits

***Yellinedi Sagareswara Rao v. S.K. Jawahar Reddy***
**(From Andhra Pradesh High Court)**

**Judges :**— Justice J. Chelameswar and Justice A.K. Sikri

**Advocates:–**

1. For the Petitioner :— Petitioner-in-person.
2. For the Respondent :— Mr. Guntur Prabhakar and Ms. Prerna Singh, Advocates.

2014(4) S.C.T. 639.

Contempt Petition (C) Nos. 327—328 of 2014 in SLP(C) Nos. 34970—34971 of 2013.

Date of Decision — 9.10.2014.

**A. Prevention of Corruption Act, 1988 charges of corruption against public servant — Acquittal of accused — No charge was proved — Grant of retirement benefit by Apex Court.**

[Paras 2, 9 and 10]

---

# Acquittal of Executive Engineer of PWD from Criminal Charges during service period and Order for fresh trial of other accused in the same offence

***State of Punjab v. Kailash Nath***

**(From Punjab and Haryana High Court)**

1989 (1) CLR 60 : 1989 (1) R.C.R. (Criminal) 139 : 1989 (1) SCC 321 : 1989 AIR (SC) 558 : 1989 (1) SLR 12 : 1989 CriLJ 813 : 1989 (1) AICLR 235 : 1988 (4) JT 502 : 1988 (2) Scale 1464 : 1989 (2) LLJ 209 : 1989 (1) LLN 256 : 1989 SCC (Cri) 128 : 1989 (58) FLR 32 : 1989 (1) Crimes 126 : 1989 (1) UPLBEC 113 : 1989 Cri. L.R. 16 : 1989 BankJ 121 : 1989 Cri. App. (SC) 113.

**Judges :–** Justice B.C. Ray and Justice N.D. Ojha.

**Advocates:**

1. For the Appellants :— Mr. R.S. Suri.
2. For the Respondents :— Mr. M.R. Sharma, Mr. Kapil Sibal, Senior Advocates, Mr. M.C. Dhingra, Mr. T.S. Arora and Miss Kamini Jaiswal.

Criminal Appeal No. 422 of 1988.

Criminal Appeal No. 423—24 of 1988.

Date of Decision 22.11.1988.

**A. Prevention of Corruption Act, 1947, Sections 5(2) and 5(1)— Punjab Civil Services Rules, Volume 15, Rules 2.2,— Commision of offence during service period— FIR filed after 3 year of retirement— Held, no immunity can be granted— Aquittal of one accused— Ground of.**

[Paras 7, 9, 10 and 11]

**B. Constitution of India, Article 309— Punjab Civil Services Rules, Vol. II, Rule 2.2— FIR after 3 years of retirement of government servant— Prayer for quashing of— Held, Punjab Civil Services Rules 2.2 granting immunity to government servant could not framed as is condition of service under Article 309 of Constitution of India.**

[Paras 7, 8,9,10 and 11]

**Cases Referred :**

Des Raj Singhal v. State of Punjab, 1986(1) R.C.R.(Criminal) 66 : 1986 P.L.R. 82.

State of Madhya Pradesh v. Shardul Singh, 1970(3) SCR 302.

I.N. Subba Reddy v. Andhra University, 1976(3) SCR 1013.

M/s Ram Narain Sons Ltd. v. Asst. Commissioner of Sales Tax, 1955(2) SCR 483.

Abdul Jabar Butt v. State of Jammu & Kashmir, 1957 SCR 51.

Ishverlal Thakorelal Almaula v. Motibhai Nagjibhai, 1966(1) SCR 367.

P.V. Venkatavardan v. State of Tamil Nadu by the Deputy Superintendent of Police, Vigilance and Anti—corruption, Vellore, 1979(23) MLJ (Crl) 275.

State of Punjab v. Charan Singh, 1981(2) SCR 989.

Madheshwardhari Singh v. State of Bihar, AIR 1986 Patna 324.

---

## Acquittal of Mutation Clerk in Revenue Department from the charge of bribe for mutation of Revenue Record on ground of failure of prosecution to prove charges

***State of Haryana v. Surjit Singh***
**(From Punjab and Haryana High Court)**

2009(1) R.C.R.(Criminal) 304:2009(1) Recent Apex Judgements (R.A.J.) 43:2009(1) AICLR 344 : 2008(15) Scale 611 : 2009 AIR (SC) 1480 : 2009(1) Crimes 234 : 2009(1) JLJR 326 : 2009(sup) Cri. L.R. 677 : 2008 ALL MR (Cri) 3579 : 2008(17) SCC 196: 2010(4) SCC(Cri) 500 : 2008(72) AIC 100 : 2009 AIR (SCW) 966 : 2009(3) AIR Jhar R. 659 : 2009(1) PLIR 326 : 2009(2) Apex Court Judgements (SC) 285.

**Judges :—** Justice Dr. Arijit Pasayat and Justice Dr. Mukundakam Sharma.

**Advocates:**

1. For the Appellant :— Mr.T.V. George.
2. For the Respondent :— Mr. Ratnakar Dash, Sr. Advocate with Mr. Sahid Ali Rao and Mr. Javed Mahmud Rao.

Criminal Appeal No. 195 of 2002.

Date of Decision 28.11.2008

**A. Prevention of Corruption Act, 1988, Sections 7 and 13(2) — Charge of corruption against government servant — Absence of proof of charge**

**from prosecution side — Acquittal by Trial Court — Appeal by State against acquittal in High Court — Dismissal of appeal by — Acquittal of Trial Court upheld by Apex Court — Held, High Court had to give reason of setting aside of the Order of Trial Court.**

[Paras 2, 5 and 6]

**B. Prevention of Corruption Act, 1988, Sections 7 and 13(2) — Criminal Procedure Code, 1973, Sections 1 and (3) — Charge of corruption against public servant — Speaking Order — Acquittal of accused in Trial Court — Order of Trial Court upheld by Apex Court.**

[Paras 5 and 6]

**Cases Referred :—**

State of U.P. v. Battan, (2001(10) SCC 607).

State of Maharashtra v. Vithal Rao Pritirao Chawan, (AIR 1982 SC 1215).

Jawahar Lal Singh v. Naresh Singh, (1987(2) SCC 222).

Breen v. Amalgamated Engineering Union, (1971(1) All E.R. 1148).

Alexander Machinery (Dudley) Ltd. v. Crabtree, (1974 LCR 120).

State of Himachal Pradesh v. Sardara Singh, 2008(6) RAJ 575 (SC).

---

# Acquittal of accused persons for quashing of criminal proceedings

***Himachal Pradesh Cricket Association v. State of Himachal Pradesh***

**(From Himachal Pradesh High Court)**

2018(14) Scale 816.

**Judges** :— Justice A.K. Sikri and Justice Ashok Bhushan

**Advocates:**

1. For the Appellants :— Mr. P. S. Patwalia, Sr. Adv., Mrs. Bihu Sharma, Ms. Purnima Krishna, Siddharth Garg, Mr. Abhinav Mukerji, Snehasish Mukherjee.
2. For the Respondents :— Manish Kumar, Vijay Kumar, Ajay Marwah, Kunal Verma, Varinder Kumar Sharma, D.K. Thakur, Shariq Ahmed, Parmatma Singh.

Criminal Appeal Nos. 1258—1259 of 2018. With
Writ Petition (Criminal) No. 135 of 2017.

Date of Decision— 2.11.2018

**A. Prevention of Corruption Act, 1988, Section 13(2)— Indian Penal Code, 1860, Sections 120-B, 406 and 420— Prevention of Damage to Public Property Act, 1984, Section 3— Quashing of Criminal Proceedings—Acquittal of accused person— Conviction by High Court— Withdrawal of sanction for prosecution— Lack of Criminal intent of accused person— Proof of proper official act by accused person as per law 0— Quashing of FIR— Conviction by High Court set aside.**

[Paras 35, 37, 42, 44 and 48]

**B. Criminal Procedure Code, 1973, Sections 482— Quashing of Criminal Proceedings— Inherent power of High Court under the Section— Such power is not a rule but is an exception— Application of rule— Wide power of High Court under the Section Gravity of provision under.**

[Para 46]

**Cases Referred:**

A.N. Sharma v. State of Himachal Pradesh, Cr. MMO No. 134 of 2015.

Andhra Pradesh Dairy Development Corporation Federation v. B. Narasimha Reddy, (2011) 9 SCC 286.

C.K. Jaffer Sharief v. State, (2013) 1 SCC 205.

Central Bureau of Investigation v. Duncans Agro Industries Ltd., (1996) 5 SCC 591: 1996 SCC (Cri) 1045.

Commissioner of Income Tax (Central), Ludhiana v. M/s. Rita Mechanical Works, Ludhiana, (2012) 344 ITR 544.

Commissioner of Income Tax, Mumbai v. Texspin Engg. and Mfg. Works, Mumbai, (2003) 263 ITR 345.

Delhi Judicial Service Association, Tis Hazari Court, Delhi v. State of Gujarat, (1991) 4 SCC 406.

Hridaya Ranjan Prasad Verma v. State of Bihar, (2000) 4 SCC 168 : 2000 SCC (Cri) 786.

Indian Oil Corporation v. NEPC India Ltd., (2006) 6 SCC 736.

Lalita Kumari v. Government of Uttar Pradesh, (2014) 2 SCC 1.

M. Krishnan v. Vijay Singh, (2001) 8 SCC 645 : 2002 SCC (Cri) 19.

Madhavrao Jiwajirao Scindia v. Sambhajirao Chandrojirao Angre, (1988) 1 SCC 692: 1988 SCC (Cri) 234.

Medchl Chemicals & Pharma (P) Ltd. v. Biological E. Ltd., (2000) 3 SCC 269 : 2000 SCC (Cri) 615.

Monica Kumar v. State of Uttar Pradesh, (2008) 8 SCC 781.

Naresh Shridhar Mirajkar v. State of Maharashtra, AIR 1967 SC 1.

Northern Corporation v. Union of India, (1990) 4 SCC 239.

R. Balakrishna Pillai v. State of Kerala, (2003) 9 SCC 700.

R. v. Metropolitan Police Commr., (1968) 1 All ER 763 : (1968) 2 WLR 893 : (1968) 2 QB 118.

Rajesh Bajaj v. State NCT of Delhi, (1999) 3 SCC 259 : 1999 SCC (Cri) 401.

Rupan Deol Bajaj v. Kanwar Pal Singh Gill, (1995) 6 SCC 194 : 1995 SCC (Cri) 1059.

State of A.P. v. Golconda Linga Swamy, (2004) 6 SCC 522.

State of Bihar v. P.P. Sharma, 1992 Supp (1) SCC 222.

State of Bihar v. Rajendra Agrawalla, (1996) 8 SCC 164 : 1996 SCC (Cri) 628.

State of Haryana v. Bhajan Lal, 1992 Supp (1) SCC 335 : 1992 SCC (Cri) 426.

State of Himachal Pradesh v. Nishant Sareen, (2010) 14 SCC 527.

State of Karnataka v. M. Devendrappa, (2002) 3 SCC 89 : 2002 SCC (Cri) 539.

State of Tamil Nadu v. K. Shyam Sunder, (2011) 8 SCC 737.

Ujjam Bai v. State of U.P., (1963) 1 SCR 778.

Umesh Kumar v. State of Andhra Pradesh, (2013) 10 SCC 591.

Union of India v. Sushil Kumar Modi, (1997) 4 SCC 770.

Vineet Kumar v. State of Uttar Pradesh, (2017) 13 SCC 369.

Zandu Pharmaceutical Works Ltd. v. Mohd. Sharaful Haque, (2005) 1 SCC 122: 2005 SCC (Cri) 283.

---

# After acquittal of accused from criminal proceeding the dismissal of accused from service is not permitted and also eligible for back wages

***Om Prakash Bhatnagar v. Madhya Pradesh Electricity Board***
**(From High Court of Madhya Pradesh)**

2017 AIR (SC) 2564 : 2017 AIR (SCW) 2564 : 2017(3) S.C.T. 357 : 2017 DNJ 616: 2017 LIC 2946 : 2018(1) RLW 9 : 2017(6) SLR 510.

**Judges:—** Justice Madan N. Lokur and Justice Deepak Gupta

**Advocates:**

1. For the Petitioner :— Rana Mukherjee, Sr. Advocate, Prashant Shukla, Ms. Anushree Mishra, Kush Agrawal, Nikilesh Ramachandran, Advocates.
2. For the Respondents :— Pukhrambam Ramesh Kumar, Vishesh Issar, Abhijeet Rastogi, Advocates.

Civil Appeal No. 3886 of 2017 (Arising out of SLP(C) No. 22554 of 2013.)

Date of Decision— 10.3.2017.

**Prevention of Corruption Act, 1988— Acquittal under— Held, dismisal after acquittal is to be set aside with Order of 50% back wages.**

[Paras 7 and 8]

---

## Acquittal of First Division Assistant in a Treasury office on the basis of statement of hostile witness

***Selvaraj v. State of Karnataka***

**(From Karnataka High Court)**

2015(62) Orrisa Cri. R. 577 : 2015(9) Scale 691 : 2015(4) R.C.R. (Criminal) 285 : 2015(154) AIC 76 : 2015(8) JT 516 : 2015(4) Recent Apex Judgements (R.A.J.) 575: 2015(10) SCC 230 : 2015 AIR (SC) 3834 : 2015 AIR (SCW) 6064 : 2015(4) Law Herald (SC) 3129 : 2015(91) ACrC 687 : 2015(4) ECrC 286 : 2015 ALL MR(Cri) 4941: 2016(1) RLW 19 : 2016(1) CalCriLR 349 : 2016(1) Rajdhani LR 74 : 2015(3) Apex Court Judgements (SC) 672 : 2015(4) BBCJ 3 : 2016(3) Mh.LJ (Crl.) 9 : 2015(3) All Crl. Rulings 3499.

**Judges :**— Justice H.L. Dattu, Justice CJI, Justice Arun Mishra and Justice Amitava Roy

**Advocates:**

1. For the Appellant :— Mr. Kiran Suri, Sr. Adv., Mr. S.J. Amith and Mr. Dr. Vipin Gupta.
2. For the Respondent :— Ms. Anitha Shenoy.

Criminal Appeal No. 1172 of 2008.

Date of Decision 18.8.2015.

A. **Prevention of Corruption Act, 1988, Section 13(1)(d)— Prevention of Corruption Act, 1947, Section 5(1)(d)— Allegation of bribe— Demand and acceptance of— Contradiction in versions of witness in different ways— Acquittal.**

[Paras 11 and 12]

**B. Prevention of Corruption Act, 1988, Section 13(1)(d)— Acquittal of accused by Trial Court— Appeal against— High Court reversed acquittal Order without going through proper testimony of witness— Acquittal by Apex Court.**

[Paras 10, 11 and 12]

**C. Prevention of Corruption Act, 1947, Section 5— Prevention of Corruption Act, 1988, Section13(1)(d)— Criminal Procedure Code, 1973, Section 378 and 386— Appeal against acquittal by State— Held detailed reason should be given in acquitting an accused in bribery case— High Court erring the reasons. Acquittal by Trial Court upheld.**

[Paras 9, 10, 11 and 12]

**D. Prevention of Corruption Act, 1947, Section 5— Prevention of Corruption Act, 1988, Section 13(1)(d)— Bribery case against accused— Onus of proof— Lack of credibility in prosecution witness— Acquittal of accused.**

[Paras 11, 12, 13, 16 and 17]

## Cases Referred:

A. Subair v. State of Kerala, 2009(3) R.C.R.(Criminal) 370 : 2009(4) Recent Apex Judgments (R.A.J.) 125 : 2009 (6) SCC 587.

G.V. Nanjundiah v. State (Delhi Administration), 1987 (Supp) SCC 266.

Jagan M. Seshadri v. State of T.N., 2002(4) R.C.R. (Criminal) 142:2002 (9) SCC 639.

Kanu Ambu Vish v. The State of Maharashtra, 1971 (1) SCC 503.

Sanwat Singh v. State of Rajasthan, 1961 (3) SCR 120.

State of Kerala v. C.P. Rao, 2011(3) R.C.R.(Criminal) 688:2011(4) Recent Apex Judgments (R.A.J.) 183:2011 (6) SCC 450.

State through Inspector of Police, A.P. v. K. Narasimhachary, 2005(3) Apex Criminal 415: 2005 (8) SCC 364.

---

# Acquittal of Lady Assistant Sub-Inspector of Police from charge of illegally sending some persons abroad on ground of hostile witness but does not entitled to re-instatement

***Baljinder Pal Kaur v. State of Punjab***
**(From Punjab and Haryana High Court)**

2015 (4) R.C.R.(Criminal) 510:2015(4) S.C.T. 355:2105(9) Scale 645:2015(147) FLR 888 : 2015(5) Recent Apex Judgements (R.A.J.) 69 : 2015 (8) JT 507 : 2015(4)

Law Herald (SC) 3309 : 2015(6) SLR 333 : 2015 AIR (SCW) 6904 : 2015(6) All WC 5643: 2015 All SCR 3660:2016(1) SCC 671 : 2016(1) SCC (L&S) 217 : 2016(1) CLR 115: 2016(1) LLN 287: 2015(3) Apex Court Judgements (SC) 489 : 2016(1) KCCR 35.

**Judges** :— Justice Dipak Misra and Justice Prafulla C. Pant

**Advocates:**

1. For the Appellant :— Mr. Sibo Sankar Mishra.
2. For the Respondents :— Mr. Sanchar Anand, AAG, Mr. Apoorv Singhal and Mr. Kuldip Singh.

Civil Appeal No. 5142 of 2009.

Date of Decision — 8.9.2015.

**Prevention of Corruption Act, 1988, Sections 13(1)(d) and 13(2)— Punjab Police Rules, Rule 16.3 — Indian Penal Code, 1860, Sections 406 and 420— Dismissal of accused Police Officer from service — Acquittal of accused by Court on ground of hostile witness — Held, acquittal of accused does not give right to be re—instatement.**

[Paras 10, 11, 12 and 13]

**Cases Referred :**

Capt. M. Paul Anthony v. Bharat Gold Mines Ltd., 1999(2) S.C.T. 660:(1999) 3 SCC 679.

Commissioner of Police, New Delhi v. Mehar Singh, 2013(4) S.C.T. 311:(2013) 7 SCC 685.

Deputy Inspector General of Police v. S. Samuthiram, 2013(1) S.C.T. 115 : (2013) 1 SCC 598.

G.M. Tank v. State of Gujarat, 2006(3) R.C.R.(Criminal) 251 : 2006(3) S.C.T. 252: (2006) 5 SCC 446.

Jasbir Singh v. Punjab & Sind Bank, 2007(1) S.C.T. 57 : (2007) 1 SCC 566.

Union of India v. Bihari Lal Sidhana, 1997(3) S.C.T. 318 : (1997) 4 SCC 385.

---

## Acquittal of District Village Officer from charge of bribe on the ground of failure of prosecution to prove beyond reasonable doubt

***State of Kerala v. P. Muhammed Noushad***

**(From Kerala High Court)**

2016 (3) R.C.R. (Criminal) 526 : 2016 (4) Recent Apex Judgements (R.A.J.) 116:2016 (6) JT 260 : 2016 (6) Scale 154 : 2016 ALL MR (Cri) 3101 : 2016 (3) Law Herald (SC) 2198 : 2016 RajCriC 551 : 2016 (165) AIC 132 : 2016 (4) Law Herald 2795: 2016 (96) ACrC 560 : 2016 (3) AICLR 652 : 2017 (1) Crimes 173 : 2016 (sup2) CutLT (Criminal) 749 : 2016 (14) SCC 318 : 2016 Cri. L.R. 690 : 2016 (64) Orrisa Cri. R. 1085.

**Judges :—** Justice Abhay Manohar Sapre and Justice Ashok Bhushan.

**Advocates:**

1. For the Appellants :— Mr. Nikilesh P, Mr. Niraj Jha, Mr. Saurabh Mishra, Ms. Bina Madhavan.
2. For the Respondents :— Mr. V.K. Sidharthan.

Criminal Appeal No. 736 of 2008.

Date of Decision 29.6.2016

**Prevention of Corruption Act, 1988, Sections 7, 13(1)(d) and 13(2)— Allegation of demand and acceptance of bribe money— Recovery of— Conviction of accused by the Trial Court— Acquittal by High Court— Reasonable ground— High Court judgement was not interfered by Apex Court— Acquittal of accused.**

[Paras 15, 16, 17 and 19]

---

## Acquittal of Assistant Executive Engineer in PWD from charge of bribe on the ground of contradiction of testimony of witness

***Duraisami v. State of Tamil Nadu***
**(From Madras High Court)**

2005(10) SCC 233 : 2005 SCC(Cri) 1508 : 2006(2) ECrC 272 : 2005(2) W.L.C. 570: 2005(32) Orrisa Cri. R. 782.

**Judges :—** Justice K.G. Balakrishnan and Justice Dr. A.R. Lakshmanan

Criminal Appeal No.355 of 2000.

Date of Decision - 05.10.2004.

**Prevention of Corruption Act, 1987, Sections 5(1)(d) and 5(2)— Indian Penal Code, 1860, Section 161— Offence of bribery— Receiving of tainted money— Plea of accused was that the amount was for legal due**

**to him— Proof beyond reasonable ground— Acquittal by Trial Court— Conviction of High Court— Apex Court restored the order of acquittal by Trial Court.**

[Paras 3 and 4]

---

# Acquittal of Bank employee from charge of criminal breach of trust and forgery and departmental proceeding and criminal proceeding operate differently and acquittal of one does not relate to others

***General Manager, UCO Bank v. M. Venuranganath***

**(From Andhra Pradesh High Court)**

2008(1) S.C.T. 212 : 2007(6) Recent Apex Judgements (R.A.J.) 701 : 2008 LIC 405: 2008(1) LLJ 913 : 2008(2) SLR 560 : 2008 AIR (SC) 732 : 2007(13) SCC 251: 2007(14) Scale 306 : 2007(13) SCR 367 : 2008(1) RSJ 593 : 2008(2) SCC (l&S) 598: 2008(61) AIC 125 : 2008(116) FLR 501 : 2008(1) LLN 473 : 2007 AIR (SCW) 7878: 2008(4) JLJR 196 : 2008(4) PLJR 196 : 2008(1) CLR 327.

**Judges :—** Justice Dr. Arijit Pasayat and Justice Aftab Alam.

**Advocates:–**

1. For the Appellants :— Mr.U.N. Bhachawat, Senior Advocate with Mr. B.L. Anand, Mr. Alok Bhachawat and Ms. Pratibha Jain.
2. For the Respondent :— Ms. C.K. Sucharita.

Civil Appeal No. 5826 of 2007 (Arising out of SLP(C) No. 23654 of 2004).

Date of Decision 12.12.2007.

A. **Offence of corruption against Bank employee — Manual on Disciplinary Action, Clause 22(8) — United Commercial Bank (Conduct, Discipline and Appeal) Regulations, 1976, Regulations 15(2), 12(1)(b) and 21(9) — Suspension of Bank employee — Circumstances of.**

[Para 8]

B. **Constitution of India, Article 311 —Departmental Proceeding vs. Criminal Proceedings — Different pose of — Held, even the employee is acquittal in Criminal Trial; his Department Proceedings could not be withdrawn.**

---

# Acquittal of Bank Officer from charge of conspiracy and cheating on ground of failure of prosecution to proof of offence

## S.V.L. Murthy v. State Rep. By CBI, Hyderabad

**(From Andhra Pradesh High Court)**

2009(7) JT 385:2009(3) R.C.R. (Criminal) 696:2009(4) Recent Apex Judgements (R.A.J.) 411:2009(6) SCC 77:2009 AIR (SC) 2717:2009(4) AICLR 51:2009 CriLJ 3930:2010(68) ACrC 231:2009 AIR (SCW) 4165:2009(2) Andh LD (Criminal) 478:2009(6) Scale 758:2009(3) Mh.LJ (Crl.) 374:2009(1) CalCriLR 958:2009(2) SCC (Cri) 941:2009(4) Cri.CC 113:2010(6) SLT 506:2009(3) BBCJ 484:2009(2) MadWN (Cri) 420.

**Judges:**— Justice S.B. Sinha and Justice Dr. Mukundakam Sharma

**Advocates:**

1. For the Appellant :— K.T.S. Tusli, M.N. Krishnamani and Ravindra Shrivastava, Sr. Advocates with Radha Rani, Hari Kumar, Kunal Verma, Krishna Kumar, Supriya Jain, Anup Jain, C. Batra, D. Mahesh Babu, Gaurave Bhargava, Raj Kamal, Rishi Malhotra and K.V. Mohan.
2. For the Respondent :— B. Dutta, Additional Solicitor General, Ms. Rajni, P. Narasimha and B. Krishna Prasad.

Criminal Appeal No. 942 of 2009 [Arising out of SLP (Criminal) No. 7125 of 2007].

Criminal Appeal No. 945 of 2009 [Arising out of SLP (Criminal) No. 7145 of 2007

Criminal Appeal Nos. 943—944 of 2009 [Arising out of SLP (Criminal) Nos. 7313—7314 of 2007

Date of Decision . 06.05.2009.

A. **Prevention of Corruption Act, 1988, Section 13(1)— Indian Penal Code, 1860, Sections 409, 415 and 420— Accused being Bank Officer— Alligation of cheque discounting to some customers of Bank— charge of conspiracy— Criminal intention— Failure to prove by prosecution— Prosecution witness fails to establish conspiracy— conviction of Accused by Lower Court— Set aside by Apex Court— Acquittal.**

[Paras 38, 45,47,48 and 51]

B. **Indian Penal Code, 1860, Section 409— Absence of Framing of Charge— Held, accused could not be convicted on the ground of no charge was framed.**

[Paras 41,42,48,49,50 and 51]

**C. Indian Penal Code, 1860, Sections 420 and 415— Original Procedure code, 1973, Sections 216 and 222— Filing of charge sheet— Failure of prosecution to prove offence— Acquittal.**

[Paras 41,42,43,45 and 51]

**Cases Referred :**

Hira Lal Hari Lal Bhagwati v. CBI, 2003(3) RCR(Criminal) 273 : 2004(1) Apex Criminal 274 : [(2003)5 SCC 257]

Indian Oil Corporation v. NEPC India Ltd., 2006(2) Apex Criminal 637 : 2006(3) RCR(Criminal) 740 : [(2006)6 SCC 736].

Vir Prakash Sharma v. Anil Kumar Agarwal, 2007(3) RCR(Criminal) 960 : 2007(4) RAJ 254 : [(2007)7 SCC 373].

All Carogo Movers (I) Pvt. Ltd. v. Dhanesh Badarmal Jain [2007(12) SCALE 391].

R. Kalyani v. Janak C. Mehta [2008(14) SCALE 85].

Sharon Michael v. State of Tamil Nadu, 2009(1) RCR(Criminal) 759 : 2009(1) RAJ 484 : [2009(1) SCALE 627].

Lala Ram v. State of Uttar Pradesh, 1990(1) RCR(Criminal) 436 : (1990)2 SCC 113.

---

## Acquittal of Bank Clerk from charge of conspiracy and cheating with Order of service benefits

***Punjab National Bank v. K.C. Sareen***
**(From Punjab and Haryana High Court)**

2018(2) S.C.T. 185 : 2018 (2) SLR 141.

**Judges:**— Justice S.A. Bobde and Justice Mohan M. Shantanagoudar.

**Advocates:**

1. For the Appellants :— Mr. Rajesh Kumar, Mr Rakesh Chaurasiya, Mr. Gaurav Kumar Singh, Ms. Khushboo Aggarwal, Mr. Aakash Sehrawat, Mr. Anant Gautam For (M/s. Mitter & Mitter Co.).
2. For the Respondents :— Ms. Mahalakshmi Pavani, Sr. Adv., G. Balaji, Ms. Vaishali Jain, Mr.Divakar Anand.

Civil Appeal No. 18838 of 2017 (Arising out of SLP(C) No. 1670 of 2016).

Date of Decision 10.11.2017.

**Prevention of Corruption Act, 1988, Sections 13(1)(d) and 13(2)—Indian Penal Code, 1860, Sections 420 and 120-B— Acquittal of accused—**

**Conviction by Special Judge— Dismissal of accused from service on basis of conviction— Conviction by special judge upheld by High Court– Special leave petition by accused in Apex Court— Acquittal of accused with direction of 50% back wages.**

[Paras 3 and 8]

**Cases Referred :**

State Bank of India v. Mohammed Abdul Rahim, 2013(4) S.C.T. 133 : 2013 (11) SCC 67.

---

# Acquittal of accused in bribery case on ground of failure of prosecution to prove offence

***State of Rajasthan v. Mohan Lal***
**(From Rajasthan High Court)**

2009(12) SCC 515:2009(2) R.C.R. (Criminal) 812:2009(3) Recent Apex Judgements (R.A.J.) 239:2009 AIR (SC) 1872:2009(2) Crimes 201:2009(237) ELT 435:2009 AIR (SCW) 3352:2009(3) RLW 2755:2009(6) Scale 240:2009(1) W.L.C. 754:2009(2) ECrC 240:2010(1) SCC(Cri) 607:2009(3) L.R.C. 15:2009(3) BBCJ 333:2009 (sup) CutLT (Criminal) 1037:2009(43) Orrisa Cri. R. 338.

**Judges :—** Justice Dr. Arijit Pasayat and Justice Asok Kumar Ganguly.

**Advocates:**

1. For the Appellants :— Dr. Manish Singhvi, AAG (Raj.), Mr. Milind Kumar and Mr. Sandeep Bajaj, Advocates.
2. For the Respondents :— Mr. Aruneshwar Gupta, (NP).

Criminal Appeal No. 85 of 2003.

Date of Decision — 16.04.2009.

**A. Prevention of Corruption Act, 1988, Sections 7, 13(1)(d) and 13(2) — Code of Criminal Procedure, 1973, Section 378(1) —Allegation of corruption — Tainted money recovered from almirah of accused — Demand not proved —Absence of evidence that accused had asked to complainant to put money in his almirah —Acquittal upheld by Apex Court.**

[Paras 2 and 4]

**B. Criminal Procedure Code, 1973 — Acquittal by Lower Court — Appeal against Order of Acquittal — Presumption under section — Available**

**to accused — Reasonable grounds — Acquittal of accused — Benefit of doubt.**

[Paras 2, 4 and 8]

## Cases Referred :

Sheo Swarup v. R. Emperor, (1934) 61 IA 398).

Nur Mohd. v. Emperor, (AIR 1945 PC 151).

Prandas v. State, (AIR 1954 SC 36).

Surajpal Singh v. State, (1952 SCR 193).

Ajmer Singh v. State of Punjab, (1953 SCR 418).

Atley v. State of U.P., (AIR 1955 SC 807).

Aher Raja Khima v. State of Saurashtra, (1955)2 SCR 1285.

Sanwat Singh v. State of Rajasthan, (1961)3 SCR 120.

M.G. Agarwal v. State of Maharashtra, (1963)2 SCR 405.

Surajpal Singh v. State, (1952 SCR 193).

Harbans Singh v. State of Punjab, 1962 Supp (1) SCR 104.

Shivaji Sahabrao Bobade v. State of Maharashtra, (1973(2) SCC 793).

K. Gopal Reddy v. State of Andhra Pradesh, (1979)1 SCC 355.

Ramaphupala Reddy v. State of Andhra Pradesh, (AIR 1971 SC 460).

Bhim Singh Rup Singh v. State of Maharashtra, (AIR 1974 SC 286).

Ramesh Babulal Doshi v. State of Gujarat, 1996(3) RCR(Criminal) 188:(1996)9 SCC 225.

Allarakha K. Mansuri v. State of Gujarat, 2002(1) RCR(Criminal) 748:(2002)3 SCC 57.

Bhagwan Singh v. State of Madhya Pradesh, 2002(2) RCR(Criminal) 593 : (2002)4 SCC 85.

Harijana Thirupala v. Public Prosecutor, High Court of A.P., 2002(3) RCR(Criminal) 861:(2002)6 SCC 470.

Ramanand Yadav v. Prabhu Nath Jha, 2004(1) RCR(Criminal) 469 : 2004(2) Apex Criminal 307 : (2003)12 SCC 606.

Kallu v. State of Madhya Pradesh, 2006(1) RCR(Criminal) 427 : 2006(1) Apex Criminal 135: (2006)10 SCC 313.

Chandrappa v. State of Karnataka, 2007(2) RCR(Criminal) 92 : 2007(1) RAJ 841: (2007(4) SCC 415).

State of Uttar Pradesh v. Krishna Gopal, (1988(4) SCC 302).

Krishnan v. State represented by Inspector of Police, 2003(3) RCR(Criminal) 885: 2004(1) Apex Criminal 405 : (2003(7) SCC 56).

---

# Acquittal of Village Patwari on the ground of hostile witness though there was recovery of tainted money

***Banarsi Dass v. State of Haryana***
**(From Punjab and Haryana High Court)**

2010(3) JT 552 : 2010(4) SCC 450 : 2010(2) AICLR 655 : 2010(2) CriLJ 2419 : 2010 AIR (SC) 1589 : 2010(2) Crimes 351 : 2010(3) ALT (Crl.) 330 : 2010(2) R.C.R. (Criminal) 553 : 2010(2) Recent Apex Judgements (R.A.J.) 471 : 2010(89) AIC 65 : 2010(2) RLW 1395 : 2010(2) CalCriLR 1 : 2010 (4) SCR 383 : 2010(1) W.L.C. 654: 2010(3) Scale 531 : 2010(3) ECrC 174 : 2010 Cri. L.R. 339 : 2010 ALL MR (SC) 1608 : 2010 (2) SCC (Cri) 864 : 2010(3) GujLH 196 : 2010(3) MLJ (Criminal) 132: 2010 AIR (SCW) 2282 : 2010(2) Cri.CC 394 : 2010(2) Law Herald (SC) 1201 : 2010(1) Andh LD (Criminal) 924 : 2010(sup) CutLT (Criminal) 901 : 2010(2) BBCJ 426: 2010(46) Orrisa Cri. R. 152 : 2010(2) Ori. Law Rev. 28 : 2010(2) Apex Court Judgements (SC) 192.

**Judges:**— Justice Swatanter Kumar and Justice Aftab Alam.

**Advocates:**

1. For the Appellants :—Mr. Jaspal Singh, Sr. Adv., Ms. Jaspreet Gogia.
2. For the Respondent :— Mr. Ranjit Rao.

Criminal Appeal No. 630 of 2003.

Date of Decision 5.4.2010.

**A. Prevention of Corruption Act, 1988, Sections 7 and 20— Prevention of Corruption Act, 1947, Section 5(2)— Demand of bribe— Tainted money— Recovery of Hostile witness— Claim of complainant as to no demand made by accused— Benefit of doubt— Acquittal of accused.**

[Paras 13, 14, 15, 16 17 and 18]

**B. Prevention of Corruption Act, 1947, Section 5(2)— Indian Penal Code, 1860, Section 161— Demand and acceptance of bribe — Recovery of money from the pocket of accused— Recovery is improper in law— Viability of provision under 161 of IPC— Prosecution has to prove the demand of bribe money— Demand and recovery is sine *qua non* for prosecution— Acquittal of accused.**

It is in this context the courts have cautioned that as a rule of prudence, some corroboration is necessary. In all such type of cases of bribery, two aspects are important. Firstly, there must be a demand and secondly there must be acceptance in the sense that the accused has obtained the illegal gratification. Mere demand by itself is not sufficient to establish the offence. Therefore, the other aspect, namely, acceptance is very important and when the accused has come forward with a plea that the currency notes were put in the drawer without his knowledge, then there must be clinching evidence to show that it was with the tacit approval of the accused that the money had been put in the drawer as an illegal gratification. Unfortunately, on this aspect in the present case we have no other evidence except that of PW—1. Since PW—1's evidence suffers from infirmities, we sought to find some corroboration but in vain. There is no other witness or any other circumstance which supports the evidence of PW—1 that this tainted money as a bribe was put in the drawer, as directed by the accused. Unless we are satisfied on this aspect, it is difficult to hold that the accused tacitly accepted the illegal gratification or obtained the same within the meaning of Section 5(1) (d) of the *Act,* particularly when the version of the accused appears to be probable.

[Para 10 and 11]

**C. Indian Penal Code1860, Section 161— Criminal Procedure Code, 1973, Section 313— No limit of presumption under— Failure of prosecution to establish proof of bribe— Acquittal of accused.**

[Para 15]

**D. Prevention of Corruption Act, 1988, Sections 7 and 20— Demand of bribe— Bribe money recovered from pocket of accused— Witness turned hostile stating that bribe money recovered was not on demand of accused— Acquittal.**

[Paras 13, 14 and 18]

## Cases Referred :

1. C.M. Girish Babu v. CBI, Cochin, High Court of Kerala, 2009(2) R.C.R.(Criminal) 134 : 2009(2) R.A.J. 101 : 2009(3) SCC 779.
2. Aditya Nath Pandey v. State of U.P. 2000(9) SCC 206.
3. M.K. Harshan v. State of Kerala, 1997(2) R.C.R.(Criminal) 16 : 1996(11) SCC 720.
4. Suraj Mal v. State (Delhi Admn.), 1979(4) SCC 725.
5. M. Narsinga Rao v. State of A.P., 2001(1) RCR(Cri) 95 : 2001(1) SCC 691 : SCC (Cri.) 258.
6. Madhukar Bhaskarrao Joshi v. State of Maharashtra, 2000(4) R.C.R.(Criminal) 705: 2000(8) SCC 571.
7. Sita Ram v. State of Rajasthan, 1975(2) SCC 227.

---

# Acquittal of a Clerk of PWD from bribery case though the tainted money recovered from his pocket on the ground of presumption in his favour

***Khaleel Ahmed v. State of Karnataka***

**(From Karnataka High Court)**

2015(6) Recent Apex Judgements (R.A.J.) 546:2016(1) R.C.R. (Criminal) 366:2016(1) JCC 163:2015(12) Scale 571:2016(1) Law Herald (SC) 124:2016 All SCR (Crl.) 291:2016(1) AICLR 546:2015(16) SCC 350:2016(63) Orrisa Cri. R. 150:2016(sup1) Ori. Law Rev. 965.

**Judges :—** Justice H.L. Dattu, CJI and Justice Arun Mishra.

**Advocates:**

1. For the Appellants :— Mr. S.K. Kulkarni, Mr. M. Gireesh Kumar, Mr. Ankur S. Kulkarni (For Vijay Kumar.
2. For the Respondents :— Ms. Anitha Shenoy.

Criminal Appeal No. 746 of 2008.

Date of Decision 8.9.2015.

**A. Prevention of Corruption Act, 1988, Sections 7, 13(1)(d) and 13(2) — Allegation of demand of bribery — Trap case — Tainted money — Recovery of — Conviction by Lower Court and High Court — Appeal against Order of High Court — Apex Court acquittal on the ground of presumption in favour of accused and there was no corroboration of evidences.**

[Paras 2, 19, 20 and 24]

**B. Prevention of Corruption Act, 1988, Sections 13(1)(d) and 20 — Bribery charge — Recovery of tainted money from pocket of accused — Presumption under Section 20 in favour of accused — Acquittal by Apex Court.**

[Para 25]

**Cases Referred:**

B. Jayaraj v. State of Andhra Pradesh, 2014(2) R.C.R.(Criminal) 410 : 2014(2) Recent Apex Judgments (R.A.J.) 570 : (2014)13 SCC 55.

C.M. Girish Babu v. C.B.I. Cochin, High Court of Kerala, 2009(2) R.C.R.(Criminal) 134 : 2009(2) Recent Apex Judgments (R.A.J.) 101 : (2009)3 SCC 779.

State of Maharashtra v. Dnyaneshwar Laxman Rao Wankhede, 2009(4) R.C.R.(Criminal) 217 : 2009(5) Recent Apex Judgments (R.A.J.) 356 : (2009)15 SCC 200.

Sujit Biswas v. State of Assam, 2013(3) R.C.R.(Criminal) 227 : 2013(3) Recent Apex Judgments (R.A.J.) 692 : (2013)12 SCC 406.

V.D. Jhangan v. State of Uttar Pradesh, (1966)3 SCR 736.

---

## Acquittal of Superintendent of Police from charge of possessing disproportionate assets and unearned source of income on ground of failure of prosecution to prove the offence

***Jagan M. Seshadri v. State of Tamil Nadu***

**(From Madras High Court)**

2002(1) ECrC 311:2002(4) R.C.R. (Criminal) 142:2002 CriLJ 2982:2002 AIR (SC) 2399:2002(1) AICLR 486:2002(9) SCC 639:2001(10) JT 227:2003 SCC(Cri) 1494:2002(2) APLJ 55:2002 W.L.C. 31:2003 SCC (L&S) 1494:2002 AIR (SCW) 2613:2003(1) RLW 9:2003(25) Orrisa Cri. R. 503:2002(23) Orrisa Cri. R. 553.

**Judges :**— Justice A.S. Anand, C.J.I., Justice R.C. Lahoti and Justice Ashok Bhan.

Criminal Appeal No. 169 of 1999.

Date of Decision 25.9.2001.

A. **Prevention of Corruption Act, 1988, Sections 13(1)(e), 13(2) and 30 — Prevention of Corruption Act, 1947, sections 5(1)(d) and (e) — Charge under Act—1947 Act Repealed by Act of 1988 — Effect of — Held, charge framed under Act of 1947 could not be substituted by the Act of 1948 — Presumption in favour of accused — Acquittal by Apex court.**

[Paras 2 and 5]

B. **Criminal Procedure Code, 1973, Section 378– Appeal against Order of acquittal– Allegation of unknown source of income– Failure of prosecution to prove– Acquittal byApex court.**

[Paras 2 and 8]

---

## Acquittal of Second Division Surveyor from charge of demand of illegal gratification on the ground that mere recovery of tainted money does not amount to prosecution

***M.R. Purushotham v. State of Karnataka***

**(From Karnataka High Court)**

2014(4) ECrC 226:2015 CriLJ 72:2015(1) PLJ (Criminal) 47: 2014(4) CCR 420:2015(145) AIC 155:2015 (2) Crimes 101:2014(4) CCR 353:2014(4) Crimes 398:2015(1) AICLR 837:2014(5) Recent Apex Judgements (R.A.J.) 457:2014(4) R.C.R. (Criminal) 444:2014(11) Scale 467:2014(4) Law Herald (SC) 3347:2014 AIR (SCW) 5740:2014(4) Bom.C.R. (Cri.) 424:2014(6) KantLJ 32:2014(4) Air Kar R 599:2015 (88) ACrC 341:2015(3) SCC 247:2015(1) Cri.CC 115:2015(1) W.L.N. 168:2015(2) SCC (Cri) 249:2014(3) Apex Court Judgements (SC) 642:2015(61) Orrisa Cri. R.1034.

**Judges:**— Justice Madan B. Lokur and Justice C. Nagappan.

**Advocates:**

1. For the Appellant :— Dr. (Mrs.) Vipin Gupta.
2. For the Respondent :— Mr. V. N. Raghupathy.

Criminal Appeal No. 1578 of 2011.
Date of Decision — 24.9.2014.

**Prevention of Corruption Act, 1988, Sections 7, 13(1)(d) and 13(2)— Allegation of bribe— Recovery of tainted money at the instant— Absence proof— Acquittal. Held, mere possession and recovery of tainted money from the accused without proof of demand could not amount to conviction.**
[Paras 2 and 6]

**Cases Referred:**

B. Jayaraj v. State of Andhra Pradesh, 2014(2) R.C.R. (Criminal) 410 : 2014(2) Recent Apex Judgments (R.A.J.) 570 : 2014(4) Scale 81.

---

# Acquittal of Assistant Engineer in PWD from allegation of misuse of position on ground of misconception of prosecution

***A. Sivaprakash v. State of Kerala***
**(From Kerala High Court)**

2016(3) Recent Apex Judgements (R.A.J.) 296:2016(2) R.C.R. (Criminal) 1002:2016 AIR (SCW) 2287:2016 Cri. L.R. 467:2016 All SCR (Crl.) 885:2016 (5) JT 14:2016 AIR (SC) 2287:2016(94) ACrC 954:2016 RajCriC 335:2016 (162) AIC 116:2016(2) Crimes 249:2016(5) Scale 53:2016(3) MLJ (Criminal) 97:2016(1) SCCriR725:2016(3) Bom.C.R. (Cri.) 140:2016 CriLJ 2654:2016(2) CallJ 143:2016(3) JBCJ 235:2016(3) Ker L.J. 227:2016(3) Ker L.J. 227:2016(3) Cri.CC 524:2016(3) ECrC 113:2016(2) Apex Court Judgements (SC) 739:2016(2) ALT (Crl.) 341:2016(164) AIC 145:2016(2) Andh LD (Criminal) 407:2016(3) KLT 109:2016(3) AICLR 655:2016(2) Law Herald (SC) 1570:2016(3) JLJR 117:2016(4) KCCR 460:2016(3) B.L.Jud. 42:2016(2) MadWN (Cri) 505:2016(12) SCC 273:2016(64) Orrisa Cri. R. 492:2016(2) All. Crl. Rulings 1918.

**Judges :—** Justice A.K. Sikri and Justice Prafulla C. Pant.

**Advocates:**

1. For the Appellant :— Mr. Basant T.R., Sr. Adv., Mr. Adolf Mathew, Karthiku, Mr. Sanjay Jain.
2. For the Respondent :— Mr. R. Sathish.

Criminal Appeal No. 131 of 2007.

Date of Decision 10.5.2016.

**Prevention of Corruption Act, 1988, Sections 13(1)(d) and 13(2)— Scope of— Ingredients of offence under— Allegation of abuse of position of accused is public servant— Absence of proof— Acquittal by Apex Court.** [Paras 2 and 17]

**Cases Referred :**

Abdulla Mohd. Pagarkar v. State (Union Territory of Goa, Daman and Diu), (1980) 3 SCC 110.

C. Chenga Reddy v. State of A.P., 1996(3) R.C.R.(Criminal) 793 : (1996) 10 SCC 193.

---

# Acquittal of Executive Officer of a Temple though tainted money recovered from accused and demand and acceptance of the same was not proved

***T. Subramanian v. State of Tamil Nadu***
**(From Madras High Court)**

2006(1) Apex Criminal 159:2006(1) JT 101:2006(1) SCC 401:2006(1) Cri.CC 410:2006 CriLJ 804:2006 AIR (SC) 836:2006(1) SCC(Cri) 401:2006(1) Scale 116:2006(1) SCR 180:2006(54) ACrC 899:2006 ALL MR(Cri) 620:2006(1) RajCriC 200:2006(1) AIR Jhar R. 666:2006(2) PLJR 100:2006(2) RLW 1152:2006(1) Andh LD (Criminal) 436:2006(2) ECrC 79:2006(1) W.L.C. 448:2006 Cri. L.R. 149:2006(1) CalCriLR 506:2006(38) AIC 114:2006(101) CutLT 516:2006(1) Crimes 75:2006 AIR (SCW) 184:2006(1) Supreme 1:2006(2) JLJR 151:2006(1) L.R.C. 67:2006(2) BBCJ 69:2006(1) B.L.Jud. 429:2006(1) MadWN (Cri) 187:2006(33) Orrisa Cri. R. 338:2006(1) Apex Court Judgements (SC) 339:2006(1) Cri. App. R (SC) 120.

**Judges:**— Justice S.B. Sinha and Justice R.V. Raveendran.

**Advocates:**

1. For the Appellant :— Mr. M.A. Krishnamoorthy andMr. M.A. Chinnasamy.
2. For the Respondent :— Mr. Abhay Kumar and Mr. Subramonium Prasad.

Criminal Appeal No. 186 of 2000.

Date of Decision 4.1.2006.

**A. Prevention of Corruption Act, 1947, Sections 5(1)(d) and 5(2)—Allegation of demand of bribe— Recovery of tainted money from accused— Demand**

**and acceptance— No proved— Enmity with complainant— Aquittal of accused.**

[Paras 2 and 7]

**B. Prevention of Corruption Act, 1947, Sections 5(1)(d) and 5(2)— Criminal Procedure Code, 1973, Section 378— Benefit of doubt available to accused— Acquittal— Failure of prosecution to prove offence beyond reasonable doubt— Acquittal.**

[Paras 2, 7 and 10]

**Cases Referred :**

Punjabrao v. State of Maharashtra, 2002(1) RCR(Crl.) 231 (SC) : 2002(10) SCC 371.

Chaturdas Bhagwandas Patel v. State of Gujarat (AIR 1976 SC 1497).

State through Inspector of Police, Andhra Pradesh v. K. Narasimhachary, 2005(3) Apex Criminal 415 (SC) : [2005(8) SCALE 266].

---

# Acquittal of Surveyor of Merchantile Marine Department in absence of proof of demand and acceptance

***Union of India v. Purnandu Biswas***

**(From Madras High Court)**

2005(4) R.C.R. (Criminal) 517:2005(3) Apex Criminal 442:2006(2) CurLJ 295:2005(4) Cri. CC 715:2005(4) AICLR 705:2005(12) SCC 576:2005(12) JT 505:2005(8) Scale 246:2005(Sup4) SCR 181:2006(1) SCC (Cri) 520:2006(1) RajCriC 59:2006(1) CalCriLR 23:2006(1) ECrC 50:2005(2) W.L.C. 715:2005(36) AIC 379:2005(4) Crimes 176:2005(7) Supreme 256:2005(32) Orrisa Cri. R. 869:2005(2) Cri. App. R (SC) 995.

**Judges :—** Justice S.B. Sinha and Justice R.V. Raveendran.

**Advocates:**

1. For the Appellant :— Mr. A. Sharan, Additional Solicitor General, Ms. Binu Tamta, Ms. Shalini Ranjan, Mr. Amit Anand Tiwari and Mr. P. Parmeswaran.
2. For the Respondent :—Mr. S. Balakrishnan, Sr. Advocate with Mr. Sudarshan Rajan, Mr. K.K. Misra and Mr. P. Narasimhan.

Criminal Appeal No. 471 of 2004.

Date of Decision — 7.10.2005.

**A. Prevention of Corruption Act, 1988, Sections 13(1)(d) and 13(2) — Allegation of bribe and grantification by accused — Demand and**

**acceptance not proved — Held, it was not enough that tainted money handed over to accused amounted to acceptance.**

[Paras 2, 37 and 38]

**B. Prevention of Corruption Act, 1988, Sections 13(1)(d), 13(2) and 20 — Claim of gratification — Demand by accused — Presumption under section 20 in favour of accused — Acquittal.**

[Paras 2, 36 and 37]

**Cases referred:**

State of U.P. v. Zakaullah, 1998(1) RCR(Crl.) 345 (SC) : [(1998)1 SCC 557].

B. Hanumantha Rao v. State of U.P., 1992(3) RCR(Crl.) 188 (SC) : [(1993) Supp. 1 SCC 323].

Habeeb Mohammad v. State of Hyderabad [AIR 1954 SC 51].

M. Narsinga Rao v. State of A.P., 2001(1) RCR(Crl.) 95 (SC) : [(2001)1 SCC 691].

# Acquittal of Mandal Revenue Officer on ground of failure of proof of demand and acceptance and failure of sanction for prosecution

### *V. Venkata Subbarao v. State represented by Inspector of Police, A.P*

**(From Andhra Pradesh High Court)**

2007(1) R.C.R. (Criminal) 519:2007(1) Recent Apex Judgements (R.A.J.) 321:2007 AIR (SC) 489:2007 CriLJ 754:2007(1) AICLR 807:2006(14) Scale 125:2006(13) SCC 305:2006(Sup 10) SCR 729:2007 (3) SCC (Cri) 175:2007(1) Crimes 101:2007(1) Cri.CC 746:2007(1) KantLJ 227:2007(1) Andh LD (Criminal) 209:2007(1) W.L.C. 535:2007(2) J.C.R. 253:2007 ALL MR (Cri) 1201:2007(50) AIC 369:2007 AIR (SCW) 9:2007 (2) AIR Jhar R. 154:2007(2) Air Kar R 18:2007(2) RajCriC 629:2007(2) RLW 1649:2007(1) Apex Court Judgements (SC) 276:2007 NCC 199:2007(1) L.R.C. 274:2007(1) CLR 270:2007(2) CLR 451.

**Judges :—** Justice S.B. Sinha and Justice Markandey Katju, JJ.

**Advocates:**

1. For the Appellant :— Mr. Y. Raja Gopala Rao, Mr. Y. Ramesh and Ms. Y. Vismai Rao.
2. For the Respondent :—Mr. P. Vinay Kumar and Mr. C.H. Leela Sarveswar for Mrs. D. Bharathi Reddy.

Criminal Appeal No. 970 of 2000.
Date of Decision 12.12.2006.

A. **Prevention of Corruption Act, 1988, Section 20— Allegation of demand and acceptance of bribe by accused— Failure of proof of— Presumption under section in favour of accused— Acquittal of.**

[Paras 2, 11, 12 and 13]

B. **Prevention of Corruption Act, 1988, Sections 13(1)(d) and 13(2)— Allegation of demand and acceptance of bribe by accused— Sanction for prosecution— Non—production of vital documents before sanctioning authority— Vitiation of sanction— Acquittal.**

[Para 23]

**Cases referred :**

M.S. Narayana Menon @ Mani v. State of Kerala, 2006(3) RCR(Crl.) 504 : 2006(2) Apex Criminal 531 (SC) : [(2006) 6 SCC 39].

Union of India through Inspector, CBI v. Purnandu Biswas, 2005(4) RCR(Crl.) 517: 2005(3) Apex Criminal 442 (SC) : [(2005) 12 SCC 576].

State through Inspector of Police, A.P. v. K. Narasimhachary, 2005(3) Apex Criminal 415

Kalyan Singh v. State of Maharashtra [2006 (12) SCALE 577].

Samghaji Hariba Patil v. State of Karnataka [2006(10) SCALE 283].

Umrao v. State of Haryana [AIR 2006 SC 2152].

---

## Acquittal of Executive Engineer from charge of bribe on the ground of contradiction of statements of witness

***M.K. Harshan v. State of Kerala***

**(From Kerala High Court)**

1997 (2) R.C.R. (Criminal) 16:1995 AIR (SC) 2178:1995 CriLJ 3978:1996(11) SCC 720:1997 SCC (Cri) 283:1996(1) KLT 88:1995 CalCriLR 365:1995 AIR (SCW) 3385.

**Judges:**— Justice M.M. Punchhi and Justice K. Jayachandra Reddy.

Criminal Appeal No. 121 of 1989.

Date of Decision 8.3.1995

A. **Prevention of Corruption Act, 1947, Section 5(1)(d)— Trap case— Allegation of bribe— Tainted money recovered from drawer of accused— Absence of Corroboration of— Statement of trap witness— Unreliability**

**by Court— Accused stating that tainted money recovered from his draws was kept without his knowledge 'Admissibility of— Acquittal by Apex Court.**

[Paras 2, 8 and 10]

**B. Indian Penal Code, 1860, Section 161— Trap case— Contradiction in statement of witness which does not corroborate with recovery of tainted money from drawer of accused— Acquittal.**

[Paras 2, 7, 8, 9 and 10]

---

## Acquittal of Police Officer from charge of disproportionate assets on ground of marginality of assets and lack of proper framing of charges

***Ashok Tshering Bhutia v. State of Sikkim***
**(From Sikkim High Court)**

2011 AIR (SCW) 1505:2011(4) SCC 402:2011 AIR (SC) (Cri) 686:2011(2) ALT (Cri.) 103:2011(73) ACrC 371:2011 AIR (SC) 1363:2011 CriLJ 1770:2011(2) R.C.R. (Criminal) 99:2011(2) Recent Apex Judgement (R.A.J.) 45:2011 (100) AIC 14:2011(3) Mh.LJ (Crl.) 150:2011(3) SCR 240:2011(2) Scale 735:2011(1) W.L.C. 754:2011 (2) ECrC 155:2011(2) JT 512:2011 ALL MR(Cri) 2003:2011(2) SCC (Cri) 258:2011(2) SCC (L&S) 697:2011(2) Cri.CC 92:2011(1) NCC 861:2011(sup) CutLT (Criminal) 1087:2011(2) B.L.Jud. 93:2011(48) Orrisa Cri. R. 1060:2011(1) Ori. Law Rev. 967:2011(1) Apex Court Judgements (SC) 676.

**Judges:—** Justice P. Sathasivam and Justice B.S. Chauhan.

**Advocates:**

1. For the Appellants :— V.A. Bobde, Senior Advocate, Arunabh Chowdhury, Raktim Gogoi, Ms. G. Panimei and Mrs. Manik Karanjawala.
2. For the Respondents :— P.P. Malhotra A.S.G., A. Mariarputtam, Senior Advocate, P.K. Dey, Gaurav Sharma, Ms. Sonia Malhotra, A.K. Sharma and P. Parmeswaran.

Criminal Appeal No. 945 of 2003.
Date of Decision. 25.2.2011

**A. Prevention of Corruption Act, 1988, Sections 13(1)(e) and 13(2)– Charge of corruption against public servant– Disproportionate assets– Fractional amount know between source of income and unexplained source of income– Conviction by Special Judge and High Court– Conviction Set**

**aside Acquittal of Accused– Held, alleged unexplained income remained merely with marginal sum which any government employee can save every near.**

[Para 32]

B. **Prevention of Corruption Act, 1988, section 13(2)– Service Rules of Public Servants– Submission of return to government about their assets and liabilities on first appointment and then after every near– Question compliance with Rules– Held, a public servant could not be fastened with the criminal liability for want of compliance of the said requirement of the Rules.**

[Para 25]

C. **Prevention of Corruption Act, 1988, Section 13(1)(d)– Criminal Procedure Code, 1973, Sections 161 and 162– Charge of corruption– Evidence– Necessity of corroboration of evidence. Held in absence of any corroboration of evidence it would merely be a case where some witnesses had stated particular fact before and the same remained inadmissible before law.**

[Para 19]

## Cases Referred:

1. Anil Sharma v. State of Jharkhand, 2004(3) R.C.R. (Cri) 774 : 2004(3) Apex Criminal 337 .
2. Bharat Sanchar Nigam Limited v. BPL Mobile Cellular Limited, (2008)13 SCC 597.
3. H.N. Rishbud v. State of Delhi, AIR 1955 Supreme Court 196.
4. Kalpnath Rai v. State (Through CBI), 1997(4) R.C.R.(Criminal) 788 .
5. Khandu Sonu Dhobi v. State of Maharashtra, AIR 1972 Supreme Court 958.
6. M.C. Mehta v. Union of India (Taj Corridor Scam), 2007(1) R.C.R.(Criminal) 266: 2007(1) R.A.J. 99.
7. Munnalal v. State of U.P., AIR 1964 Supreme Court 28.
8. P. Sirajuddin etc. v. State of Madras etc., AIR 1971 Supreme Court 520.
9. Parkash Singh Badal v. State of Punjab, 2007(1) RCR (Criminal) 1:2007(1) R.A.J. 71.
10. Rajeswar Prasad Misra v. State of West Bengal, AIR 1965 Supreme Court 1887.
11. Rambhau v. State of Maharashtra, 2001(2) R.C.R.(Criminal) 721 .
12. Ratilal Bhanji Mithani v. State of Maharashtra, AIR 1971 Supreme Court 1630.
13. Sajjan Singh v. State of Punjab, AIR 1964 Supreme Court 464.

14. Santa Singh v. State of Punjab, AIR 1956 Supreme Court 526.
15. Shankerbhai Laljibhai Rot v. State of Gujarat, (2004)13 SCC 487.
16. Sidhartha Vashisht @ Manu Sharma v. State (NCT of Delhi), 2010(2) R.C.R.(Criminal) 692 : 2010(3) R.A.J. 1.
17. State by Police Inspector v. Sri T. Venkatesh Murthy, 2004(1) R.C.R.(Criminal) 834: 2004(2) Apex Criminal 404 : (2004)7 SCC 763.
18. State Inspector of Police, Vishakhapatnam v. Surya Sankaram Karri, 2006(4) R.C.R.(Criminal) 53 : 2006(3) Apex Criminal 87 : (2006)7 SCC 172.
19. State of Gujarat v. Mohanlal Jitamalji Porwal, AIR 1987 Supreme Court 1321.
20. State of Haryana v. Ch. Bhajan Lal, 1991(1) R.C.R.(Criminal) 383 .
21. State of M.P. v. Bhooraji, 2001(4) R.C.R.(Criminal) 40 .
22. State of M.P. v. Ramesh Chand Sharma, (2005)12 SCC 628.
23. State of M.P. v. Virender Kumar Tripathi, (2009)15 SCC 533.
24. State of Maharashtra v. Kaliar Koil Subramaniam Ramaswamy, AIR 1977 Supreme Court 2091.
25. State of Maharashtra v. Krishnarao Dudhappa Shinde, 2009(3) R.C.R.(Criminal) 378: 2009(4) R.A.J. 134 : (2009)4 SCC 219.
26. State of Maharashtra v. Pollonji Darabshaw Daruwalla, 1987(2) R.C.R.(Criminal) 697.
27. State of Orissa v. Mrutunjaya Panda, AIR 1998 Supreme Court 715.
28. State of Rajasthan v. Bhawani, 2003(3) R.C.R.(Criminal) 875 : 2004(1) Apex Criminal 391 .
29. Tori Singh v. State of Uttar Pradesh, AIR 1962 Supreme Court 399.
30. Zahira Habibulla H. Sheikh v. State of Gujarat, 2004(2) R.C.R.(Criminal) 836: 2004(3) Apex Criminal 46 : (2004)4 SCC 158.

---

## Acquittal of Overseer from charge of disproportionate assets which also leads to reinstatement in service

***G. M. Tank v. State of Gujarat***

**(From Gujarat High Court)**

2006(3) R.C.R. (Criminal) 251:2006(3) S.C.T. 252:2006(2) Apex Criminal 429:2006(3) Cri. CC 397:2006 AIR (SC) 2129:2006(4) SLR 10:2006 (4) AICLR 161:2006(5) SCC 446:2006(5) Scale 582:2006(3) LLJ 1075:2006(11) JT 36:2006 (Sup2) SCR

253:2006(4) Air Kar R 641:2006(4) Supreme 740:2006(3) RLW 2480:2006 AIR (SCW) 2709:2006(3) AIR Jhar R. 312:2006(3) All. C.J. 2151:2006(3) KLT 514:2006(2) WBLR 388:2006(3) J.C.R. 309:2006(2) GujLH 533:2006(3) GLR 2348:2006(3) CTC 494:2006(4) LLN 28:2006 SCC (L&S) 1121:2006(3) L.R.C. 163:2007 M.P.L.S.R. 1:2006(2) Apex Court Judgements (SC) 675:2006(1) Cri. App. R (SC) 494.

**Judges :—** Justice Dr. AR. Lakshmanan and Justice R.V. Raveendran.

**Advocates:—**

1. For the Appellant :— L. Nageshwar Rao, Sr. Advocate, Sanjay Kapur, Rajiv Kapur and Ms. Shubhra Kapur.
2. For the Respondents :— Maulik Nanavati, Ms. Shivangi and Ms. Hemantika Wahi.

Civil Appeal No. 2582 of 2006. (Arising out of S.L.P. (Civil) No. 8910 of 2004).

Date of Decision 10.5.2006

**Prevention of Corruption Act, 1988, Section 13(2)— Prevention of Corruption Act, 1947, Sections 5(1)(e) and 5(2)— Constitution of India, Article 311— Charge of disproportionate assets of public servant— Accused faced both departmental enquiry and criminal trial— Acquittal in Criminal Trial— order of dismissal from service dismissed on the same ground.**

[Paras 2&21)

## Cases Referred :

Capt. M. Paul Anthony v. Bharat Gold Mines Ltd., 1999(2) SCT 660 : (1999) 3 SCC 679.

Union of India v. Jaipal Singh, 2004(1) SCT 108 : (2004) 1 SCC 121.

Commissioner of Police, New Delhi v. Narender Singh, 2006(2) SCT 441 : 2006(4) Scale 161 : 2006(4) JT 328.

R.P. Kapur v. Union of India, AIR 1964 Supreme Court 787.

Corporation of City of Nagpur, Civil Lines, Nagpur v. V. Ramachandra G. Modak, AIR 1984 Supreme Court 626.

Anil Kumar Nag v. General Manager (PJ), Indian Oil Corporation Ltd., Haldia, (2005) 7 SCC 764.

Depot Manager, A.P. State Road Transport Corporation v. Mohd. Yousuf Miya, (1997) 2 SCC 699.

State of Andhra Pradesh v. S. Sree Rama Rao, AIR 1963 Supreme Court 1723.

Krishnakali Tea Estate v. Akhil Bharatiya Chah Mazdoor Sangh, (2004) 8 SCC 200.

# Death of a Lower Division Clerk in Ayurvedic Hospital leads him acquittal from charge of bribery and Order for retirement benefit to family

***Girja Prasad (Dead) By LRs. v. State of Madhya Pradesh***

**(From Madhya Pradesh High Court)**

2007(4) R.C.R.(Criminal) 84 : 2007(4) Recent Apex Judgements (R.A.J.) 683 : 2007(10) JT 421 : 2007(7) SCC 625 : 2007(4) AICLR 497 : 2007 AIR (SC) 3106 : 2007(3) SCC(Cri) 475 : 2007(10) Scale 358 : 2007(9) SCR 483 : 2007(3) Crimes 367 : 2007(sup) ACrC 96 : 2007(4) Cri.CC 90 : 2007 AIR (SCW) 5589 : 2007(6) Supreme 49 : 2007(4) RLW 3311 : 2007(4) ECrC 242 : 2007(2) Andh LD (Criminal) 924 : 2007(4) KLT 99 : 2008(1) Mh.LJ (Crl.) 152 : 2008(1) W.L.C. 73 : 2007(58) AIC 230 : 2007(3) Apex Court Judgements (SC) 249 : 2007(4) BBCJ 378 : 2007(3) CLR 282 : 2007(38) Orrisa Cri. R. 428.

**Judges :—** Justice C.K. Thakker and Justice Tarun Chatterjee.

**Advocates:**

1. For the Appellants :— Mr. Shiv Sagar Tiwari.
2. For the Respondent :— Mr. C.D. Singh, Mr. Merusagar Samantary, Mr. sunny Chowdhary and Ms. Vairagya Vardhar.

Criminal Appeal No. 885 of 2002.

Date of Decision — 27.8.2007

**Prevention of Corruption Act, 1947, Sections 5(1) and 5(2)— Indian Penal Code, 1860, Section 161 repealed by Prevention of Corruption Act, 1988— Charge of bribery— Acceptance by accused– Death of accused during pendency of Trial— Accused found guilty in Trial— Conviction was set aside— Family members entitled to retirement benefit.**

[Paras 2,12,21,22 and 24]

## Cases Referred :

Aher Raja Khima v. State of Saurashtra, AIR 1956 Supreme Court 217.

Tahir v. State (Delhi), (1996)3 SCC 338.

Kunju Muhammed v. State of Kerala, (2004)9 SCC 193 : JT (2003)7 SC 114.

Kashi Ram v. State of M.P., 2001(4) RCR(Criminal) 556 : (2002)1 SCC 71 : JT (2001)8 SC 650.

Meena v. State of Maharashtra, 2000(2) RCR(Criminal) 661 : (2000)5 SCC 21 : JT 2000(4) SC 521.

Shivaji Sahabrao Bobade v. State of Maharashtra, (1973)2 SCC 793.

Chandrappa v. State of Karnataka, 2007(2) RCR(Criminal) 92 : 2007(1) R.A.J. 841: (2007)4 SCC 415 : JT (2007)3 SC 316.

## Acquittal of one Bank Officer in Bank fraud and conviction of other Bank officers being set off for the period of sentence already undergone

*Mir Nagvi Askari v. C.B.I.*

**(From Bombay High Court)**

2009(15) SCC 643 : 2010 AIR (SC) 528 : 2010(5) R.C.R.(Criminal) 425 : 2009(4) BC 243 : 2009 AIR (SCW) 7089 : 2009(4) CCR 146 : 2009(1) Scale 174 : 2010(2) SCC(Cri) 718.

**Judges:—** Justice S. B. Sinha and Justice Cyriac Joseph.

Criminal Appeal No. 1477 of 2004 with Criminal Appeal Nos. 1525, 1526 of 2004, 5 and 121 of 2005.

Date of Decision — 7.8.2009.

**Prevention of Corruption Act, 1988, Sections 13, 13(1)(c), 13(1)(d) and 13(2)— Indian Penal Code, 1860, Sections 120-A, 120-B, 405, 406, 407, 408 and 409, 463 and 464— Accused were Bank Officers— Criminal Breach of trust— Forgery and cheating— Documentary evidence— Proof of— Acquittal of one accused— Lack of evidence— Conviction of other four accused— But their conviction were set off for sentence already undergone.**

[Paras 2,39,139 to 141, 205, 210, 212, 213, 214 to 218, 242 to 247, 233, 254 to 261]

### Cases Referred:

R. Venkatkrishnan v. Central Bureau of Investigation (Criminal Appeal No. 76 of 2004.

Mohammad Usman Mohammad Hussain Maniyar v. State of Maharashtra, 1981 (2) SCC 443.

Kehar Singh v. State (Delhi Administration), 1988(3) SCC 609.

State of Maharashtra v. Som Nath Thapa, 1996(4) SCC 659.

K. R. Purushothaman v. State of Kerala,IV (2005) CCR 168(SC) : VIII(2005) SLT 135 : 2005(12) SCC 631.

Mohmed Amin @ Amin Choteli Rahim Miyan Shaikh v. C.B.I. through its Director, IV(2008) CCR 686 (SC) : X (2008) SCT 100 : IV (2008) DLT (Crl.) 780(SC) : 2008 (14) SCALE 240.

C. Chenga Reddy v. State of A.P., 1996(10) SCC 193.

Dr. Vimla v. Delhi Administration, 1963 Supp 2 SCR 585.

State of Punjab v. Pritam Chand, 2009(2) SCALE 457.

Sharon Michael v. State of Tamil Nadu., 1(2009) SLT 593 : 1 (2009) CCR 261 (SC) : 2009(1) SCALE 627.

Onkar Nath Mishra v. State (NCT of Delhi), I(2008) SLT 329 : I(2008) CCR 81(SC): I (2008) DMC 265 (SC) : I(2008) DLT (Crl.) 311(SC) : 2008(2) SCC 561.

---

## Acquittal of Deputy Tahasildar though tainted money was recovered on the ground that there was no proof of demand

### *N. Sunkanna v. State of Andhra Pradesh*

**(From Andhra Pradesh High Court )**

2015(9) JT 319:2015(5) Recent Apex Judgements (R.A.J.) 299:2015(4) R.C.R. (Criminal) 797:2015(5) Law Herald (SC) 3634:2015(10) Scale 690:2015 Cri. L.R. 1164:2015(4) JLJR 329:2015 ALL MR(Cri) 4551:2015(4) Crimes 308:2015(4) AICLR 768:2015 CriLJ 4927:2015(4) Bom.C.R. (Cri.) 780:2015 AIR (SCW) 6764:2015(4) JBCJ 400:2015(4) PLJR 418:2015(5) Law Herald 4374:2016(157) AIC 73:2016(157) AIC 179:2015 RajCriC 1088:2016(1) SCC 713:2016(1) Apex Court Judgements (SC) 536:2016(92) ACrC 468:2016(1) Cri.CC 507:2016(1) Andh LD (Criminal) 230:2016(1) SCC (Cri) 544:2016(1) ECrC 52:2015(3) M.P.W.N. 217:2016(3) Him. L.R. 1508:2016(1) SCCriR 34:2016 (sup2) CutLT (Criminal) 108:2016(1) B.L.Jud. 72:2015(4) BBCJ 158:2016(4) Mh.LJ (Cri.) 8:2015(62) Orrisa Cri. R. 1129:2016(1) Ori. Law Rev. 8:2016(1) All. Crl. Rulings 789.

**Judges :—** Justice M.Y. Eqbal and Justice C. Nagappan.

**Advocates:**

1. For the Appellants :— Mr. Guntur Prabhakar andMr. G. Pramod Kumar.
2. For the Respondents :—Mr. D. Mahesh Babu.

Criminal Appeal No. 1355 of 2015 [Arising out of SLP (Crl.) No.2958 of 2011].

Date of Decision — 14.10.2015.

A. **Prevention of Corruption Act, 1988, Sections 13(1) and 13(2)– Charge of bribe– Demand and acceptance of– Recovery of tainted money from possession of accused– Demand of bribe not proved– Acquittal of accused– Held, though the tainted money was recovered from the possession of accused the accused would be acquitted as the demand of same was not proved.**

[Paras 2,5 and 6]

**B. Prevention of Corruption Act, 1988, Sections 7 and 20– Charge of bribery– Demand and recovery of same– Acceptance was proved but demand was not proved– Presumption under Section 20 of the Act was in favour of accused– Acquittal of accused.**

[Paras 2,6 and 7]

**Cases Referred :**

B. Jayaraj v. State of Andhra Pradesh, 2014(2) R.C.R.(Criminal) 410 : 2014(2) Recent Apex Judgments (R.A.J.) 570 : (2014) 13 SCC 55.

P. Satyanarayna Murthy v. The District Inspector of Police, 2015(4) R.C.R.(Criminal) 350: 2015(4) Recent Apex Judgments (R.A.J.) 625 : (2015 (9) SCALE 724.

---

# Acquittal of Assistant Director of Commissionerate of Technical Education from bribe case though acceptance was proved and demand was not proved

***P. Satyanarayana Murthy v. Dist. Inspector of Police***
**(From Andhra Pradesh High Court)**

2015(4) Recent Apex Judgements (R.A.J.) 625:2015(9) Scale 724:2015 All SCR 3171:2015(4) Crimes 60:2015(4) KLT 47:2015 AIR (SC) 3549:2015(4) R.C.R. (Criminal) 350:2015(8) JT 255:2015(4) RSJ 1:2015 AIR (SCW) 5263:2015 Cri. L.R. 1047:2015(4) Law Herald (SC) 3111:2015(4) Law Herald 3460:2015 CriLJ 4670:2015(91) ACrC 655:2015(155) AIC 255:2015(3) PLJ (Criminal) 1:2015(4) Bom.C.R. (Cri.) 523:2016(1) SCC (Cri.) 11:2015(10) SCC 152:2015(4) Cri.CC 536:2015(4) AICLR 955:2015(4) ECrC 254:2015(4) JCC 2674:2015(2) Andh LD (Criminal) 883:2016(1) ALT (Crl.) 160:2016(1) RLW 595:2016(1) W.L.N. 215:2015(3) Apex Court Judgements (SC) 538:2017(1) CalCriLR 24:2016(1) BBCJ 101:2016(3) Mh.LJ (Cri.) 450:2015(62) Orrisa Cri. R. 592:2016(1) All. Crl. Rulings 474.

**Judges:**— Justice H.L. Dattu, CJI, justice V. Gopala Gowda and Justice Amitava Roy.

**Advocates:**

1. For the Appellant :— A.T.M. Ranga Ramanujam, Senior Advocate, Amrender Kumar, Hitesh Kumar Sharma, Prakhar Sharma, Dipankar Das and Anu Gupta.
2. For the Respondents :— Prerna Singh, Guntur Prabhakar, and D. Bharathi Reddy (NP).

Criminal Appeal No. 31 of 2009.

Date of Decision 14.9.2015.

**A. Prevention of Corruption Act, 1988, Sections 13(1)(d) and 13(2)– Charge of bribe– Demand and acceptance of– Demand of bribe–Proof of– No evidence of acceptance– Acquittal of accused.**

[Paras 2,20,21 and 22]

**B. Prevention of Corruption Act, 1988, Sections 7, 13(1)(d) and 13(2)– Charge of bribe– Demand of bribe– Recovery of tainted money– Proof of– But no proof of acceptance– Failure of prosecution to charge the accused– Acquittal of accused– Held, in absence of proof of demand, such legal presumption under Section 20 of the Act would also not arise.**

[Paras 2,20,21 and 22]

## Cases Referred :

A. Subair v. State of Kerala, 2009(3) R.C.R.(Criminal) 370 : 2009(4) Recent Apex Judgments (R.A.J.) 125 : (2009)6 SCC 587.

B. Jayaraj v. State of Andhra Pradesh, 2014(2) R.C.R.(Criminal) 410 : 2014(2) Recent Apex Judgments (R.A.J.) 570 : (2014) 13 SCC 55.

State of Kerala v. C.P. Rao, 2011(3) R.C.R.(Criminal) 688 : 2011(4) Recent Apex Judgments (R.A.J.) 183 : (2011) 6 SCC 450.

Sujit Biswas v. State of Assam, 2013(3) R.C.R.(Criminal) 227 : 2013(3) Recent Apex Judgments (R.A.J.) 692 : (2013)12 SCC 406.

---

# Acquittal of a Minister of Madhya Pradesh due to lack of proper procedures by the prosecution

### *State of Madhya Pradesh v. Sheetla Sahai*

**(From Madhya Pradesh High Court)**

2010(1) MLJ (Criminal) 1103:2009(3) R.C.R. (Criminal) 835:2009(5) Recent Apex Judgements (R.A.J.) 110:2009(2) CalCriLR 851:2009(8) SCC 617:2009 CriLJ 4436:2009(3) Ker L.J. 647:2009(4) Cri.CC 378:2009 (Sup) AIR (SC) 1744:2009(10) Scale 632:2009(2) W.L.C. 622:2009 Cri. L.R. 752:2010(1) Mh.LJ (Crl.) 14:2009(3) SCC (Cri) 901:2009 AIR (SCW) 5514:2010(1) JabLJ 185:2009(3) Apex Court Judgements (SC) 623.

**Judges :—** Justice S.B. Sinha and Justice Cyriac Joseph.

**Advocates:**

1. For the Appellants :— K.T.S. Tulsi, Sr. Advocate, Ravinder Singh, Puneet Jain, Sushil Kumar Jain, Ashwin V. Kotemath.

2. For the Respondent :— Vivek K. Tankha, Ajay Mishra, Uday Umesh Lalit, Sr. Advocates, B.K. Salija, Siddharth Gupta, Mohit Nayak, Akshat Shrivastava, P.P. Singh, Inderjeet Yadav.

Criminal Appeal No. 1417 of 2009 [Arising out of SLP (Crl.) No. 4130 of 2006].

Date of Decision — 04.08.2009.

**A. Prevention of Corruption Act, 1988, Sections 13(1)(d) and 19– Criminal Procedure Code, 1973, Section 197– Change of corruption against a Minister of Madhya Pradesh and others including two Secretaries — Absence of Sanction for prosecution– Setting aside of charge sheet– Finding that accused persons acted as part of their official duties.**

[Paras 60,61,62 and 63]

**B. Prevention of Corruption Act, 1988, Section 13(1)(d)– Indian Penal Code, 1860, Section 120—B– Criminal Procedure Code, 1973, Sections 228 and 240– Charge of corruption against a Minister of Madhya Pradesh and six others including two Secretaries– Failure of prosecution– Charge sheet filed against them– Setting aside of Charge Sheet.**

[Paras 46,47,53,54 and 55]

**C. Prevention of Corruption Act, 1988, Section 13(1)(d)– Criminal Procedure Code, 1973, Sections 173(5), 228 and 240– Charges against a Minister and six others– Charge Sheet filed by Police– Framing of charge– Two different views– Failure of charges– Acquittal– Settings aside of Chage Sheet.**

[Para 59]

**D. Prevention of Corruption Act, 1988, Sections 13(1)(d)– Criminal Procedure Code, 1973, Sections 119 and 197– Charges against a Minister and six others– Sanction for prosecution– Opinion of Court–Setting aside of Charge Sheet.**

[Paras 58,59 and 60]

## Cases Referred :

Soma Chakravarty v. State Through CBI [(2007)5 SCC 403].

K.N. Sathyapalan (Dead) by LRs. v. State of Kerala, 2007(1) RCR(Civil) 270 : 2007(1) RAJ 125 : [(2006)12 SCALE 654].

Kehar Singh and Ors. v. State (Delhi Administration) [1988(3) SCC 609.

State (NCT) of Delhi v. Navjot Sandhu @ Afsan Guru, 2005(3) Apex Criminal 49: [(2005)11 SCC 600].

Ram Narayan Popli v. CBI [(2003)3 SCC 641].

Yogesh @ Sachin Jagdish Joshi v. State of Maharashtra, 2008(2) RCR(Criminal) 896 : 2008(3) RAJ 391 : [(2008)6 SCALE 469].

Inspector Prem Chand v. Govt. of N.C.T. of Delhi, 2007(2) SCT 650 : 2007(2) RAJ 565 : [2007 AIR SCW 2532].

State of Punjab v. Ram Singh Ex. Constable, 1992(3) SCT 448 : [1992(4) SCC 54].

Bharat Petroleum Corpn. Ltd. v. T.K. Raju [2006(3) SCC 143].

State of Maharashtra v. Som Nath Thapa, 1996(2) RCR(Criminal) 480 : [(1996)4 SCC 659].

Centre for Public Interest Litigation v. Union of India, 2005(4) RCR(Criminal) 707: 2005(4) SCT 603 : 2005(3) Apex Criminal 711 : [(2005)8 SCC 202].

Sankaran Moitra v. Sadhna Das, 2006(2) RCR(Criminal) 389 : 2006(1) Apex Criminal 551 : [(2006)4 SCC 584].

Matajog Dobey v. H.C. Bhari [AIR 1956 SC 44 : 1955(2) SCR 925].

B. Saha v. M.S. Kochar [(1979)4 SCC 177].

R. Balakrishna Pillai v. State of Kerala, 1996(2) RCR(Criminal) 765 : [(1996)1 SCC 478].

Rakesh Kumar Mishra v. State of Bihar, 2006(1) RCR(Criminal) 456 : 2006(1) Apex Criminal 175 : [(2006)1 SCC 557].

Parkash Singh Badal v. State of Punjab, 2007(1) RCR(Criminal) 1 : 2007(1) RAJ 71 : [(2007)1 SCC 1].

State of Karantaka v. Ameerjan, 2007(4) RCR(Criminal) 375 : 2007(5) RAJ 202: [(2007)11 SCC 273].

---

## Acquittal of a Mandal Revenue Inspector from charge of bribe on the ground of benefit of doubt

### *State Through Inspector of Police, A.P. v. K. Narasimhachary*

**(From Andhra Pradesh High Court)**

2005(3) Apex Criminal 415 : 2006 AIR (SC) 628 : 2006(1) CurLJ 373 : 2005(4) Cri. CC 688 : 2006(1) AICLR 654 : 2005(8) SCC 364 : 2005(8) Scale 266 : 2006 CriLJ 518 : 2005(12) JT 553 : 2005(Sup4) SCR 197 : 2006(1) SCC(Cri) 41 : 2006(1) AIR Jhar R. 395 : 2006(1) ECrC 81 : 2006(1) CalLJ 105 : 2006(1) Andh LD (Criminal) 32 : 2995(2) W.L.C. 723 : 2005(2) CalCriLR 650 : 2005(36) AIC 372 : 2006(1) APLJ 9 : 2005 AIR (SCW) 6275 : 2005(7) Supreme 155 : 2005(4) Crimes 167 : 2006(1) B.L.Jud. 285 : 2005(32) Orrisa Cri. R. 740 : 2005(2) Cri. App. R. (SC) 1003.

**Judges :—** Justice S.B. Sinha & Justice R.V. Raveendran.

**Advocates:**

1. For the Appellant :— Mr. P. Vinay Kumar, Mrs. D. Bharathi Reddy and Ms. Sneha Bhaskaran.
2. For the Respondent :— Mr. Srinivas R. Rao and Ms. Neeru vaid.

Criminal Appeal No. 82 of 2004.
Date of Decision— 7.10.2005

**A. Prevention of Corruption Act, 1988, Sections 13(1)(d) and 20– Charge of corruption– Conviction by Trial Court– Acquittal by High Court– Appeal against the Order of High Court– Held two views could not be subserved that one for conviction and other for acquittal– Benefit of doubt.**

[Paras 2,11,13 and 15]

**B. Prevention of Corruption Act, 1988, Section 19– Evidence Act, 1872, Sections 47 and 67– Sanction for prosecution of public servant– Held, accused not to raise objection at appellate stage that there was non— proof of sanction as per law.**

[Paras 13,14 and 15]

**Cases Referred :**

R.J. Singh Ahuluwalia v. State of Delhi [(1970)3 SCC 451].

Ranvir Singh v. Union of India, 2005(4) RCR(Civil) 277 (SC) : 2005(7) SCALE 238.

Gulzar Ali v. State of H.P., 1998(2) RCR(Crl.) 571 (SC) : [(1998)2 SCC 192].

Mohd. Iqbal Ahmed v. State of Andhra Pradesh [(1979)4 SCC 172].

---

# On acquittal of accused from charge of misappropriation of funds, his property attached before his death can be handed over to his legal representatives

***U. Subhadramma v. State of Andhra Pradesh***

**(From Andhra Pradesh High Court)**

2016(6) JT 242 : 2016(3) R.C.R.(Criminal) 548 : 2016(2) Recent Apex Judgements (R.A.J.) 206 : 2016(6) Scale 180 : 2016 AIR (SCW) 3095 : 2016(3) Law Herald (SC) 1736 : 2016 AIR (SC) 3095 : 2016(2) SCCriR 998 : 2016 All SCR (Cri.) 1206 : 2016(95) ACrC 976 : 2016(164) AIC 241 : 2016 RajCriC 490 : 2016(7) SCC 797 : 2016 CriLJ 3575 : 2016(3) SCC(Cri) 236 : 2016(3) PLJR 368 : 2016(4) Cri. CC 51 : 2016(3) Apex Court Judgements (SC) 213 : 2016(4) MLJ (Criminal) 226

: 2016(4) ECrC 90 : 2016(4) AICLR 5 : 2016(3) JLJR 259 : 2016(4) KCCR 367 : 2017(1) Andh LD (Criminal) 18 : 2017(1) Crimes 184 : 2017(1) HLT (Cri.) 142 : 2016(3) MadWN (Cri) 94 : 2016(6) Mh.LJ (Cri.) 437 : 2017(1) LW (Cri.) 437 : 2017(1) LW (Cri.) 742 : 2016 Cri. L.R. 722 : 2016(65) Orrisa Cri. R. 207 : 2016(2) Ori. Law Rev. 566 : 2016(2) All. Cri. Rulings 2229 : 2018(1) Rajdhani LR 214.

**Judges :—** Justice S.A. Bobde and Justice Amitava Roy.

**Advocates:**

1. For the Appellants :— Mr. D. Mahesh Babu.
2. For Respondents :—Mr. G.N. Reddy.

Criminal Appeal No. 1596 of 2011.

Date of Decision— 4.7.2016.

**A. Prevention of Corruption Act, 1988, Charge of Corruption– Death of accused– Presumption of innosence– Acquittal– Effect on legal heirs– on attachment of property.**

[Paras 2,5,6,7 and 10]

**B. Prevention of Corruption Act, 1988, Charge of corruption and criminal offence– Criminal Laq amendment ordinance, 1944, Clause 4-A—Procurrenment of property by committing criminal offence— Death of accused– Attachment of property before death— Appeal by legal representative— Succeeding of.**

[Paras 2,5,6,7 and 10]

**Case Referred :**

State of Punjab v. Jagbir Singh, Baljit Singh and Karan Singh, AIR 1973 SC 2407.

---

# Acquittal of a Lower Division Clerk in a Transport Office for lack of evidence

***A. Subair v. State of Kerala***

**(From High Court of Kerala)**

2009(8) JT 415 : 2009 CriLJ 3450 : 2010(1) MLJ (Criminal) 995 : 2009(2) CalCriLR 348 : 2009(4) Mh.LJ (Cri.) 465 : 2009(3) R.C.R.(Criminal) 370 : 2009(4) Recent Apex Judgements (R.A.J.) 125 : 2009(6) SCC 587 : 2011(3) ALT (Cri.) 261 : 2009(3) Crimes 1 : 2009(4) Cri.CC 493 : 2009(8) Scale 585 : 2009(sup) Cri. L.R. 635 : 2009(3) L.R.C. 86 : 2009(43) Orrisa Cri. R. 909.

**Judges:—** Justice V.S. Sirpurkar and Justice R.M. Lodha, JJ.

**Advocates:—**

1. For the Appellant :— Mr. V.K. Sidharthan.
2. For the Respondent :— Mr. RAmesh Babu M.R.

Criminal Appeal No. 639 of 2004.

Date of Decision — 26.05.2009

**A. Prevention of Corruption Act, 1988, Sections 13(1)(d) and 13(2) — Recovery of bribe money— Trap Case— Complainant not examined— Conviction set aside— Held, in the absence of examination of the complainant, there is no substantive evidence to prove the factum of demand.**

[Paras 2,4,5,6,7 and 12]

**B. Prevention of Corruption Act, 1988, Sections 7 and 20— Corruption charge— Presumption where Public servant accepts illegal gratification— Held—**

**(1) Court is not bound to draw a presumption under Section 20 where the alleged gratification is too trivial.**

[Paras 2,7,8,9 & 22]

**C. Prevention of Corruption Act, 1988 , Sections 13(1)(d), 13(2) and 7 & 20— Corruption charge — Prosecution has to prove the charge beyond reasonable doubt and the accused should be considered innocent till it is established otherwise by proper proof of demand and acceptance of the illegal gratification, the vital ingredient, necessary to be established to procure a conviction for the offences under consideration.**

[Paras 2,18 and 19]

**Case Referred:**

C.K. Damodaran Nair v. Government of India, (1997) 9 SCC 477.

---

## Acquittal of Inspector General of Police in serious charges of corruption but conviction on minor charges and direction of court to pay retirement benefits to his widow

***A.K.K. Nambiar v. State***

**(From Andhra Pradesh High Court)**

1988(2) Scale 942

**Judges:**— Justice M.P. Thakkar and Justice B.C. Ray, JJ.

In Criminal Appeal No. 191 of 1978.

Date of Decision — 28.9.1988.

**Prevention of Corruption Act, 1988, Sections 5(1)(d) and 15(2)— Criminal Procedure Code, 1973, Section 394 — Income Tax Act, 1961, Section 192— Suspension on ground of many a number of charges Failure of prosecution to prosecute in all charges— Acquittal in serious charges Conviction on minor charges— Death of accused— Direction of Court to pay to widow of accused all and other benefits including salary, pension.**

[Para 2]

---

## Acquittal of officers of Octroi Check Post from charge of illegal gratification

***Amrish bhai Manubhai Brahmbhatt v. State of Gujarat***

**(From Gujarat High Court)**

**Judges:**— Justice C. K. Buch.

**Advocates:—**

1. For the Appellants :— A.D. Shah
2. For the Opponent :— A.J. Desai, Addl. Public Prosecutor.

Criminal Appeal No. 526 of 1993.

Date of Decison — 10.5.2007.

A. **Prevention of Corruption Act, 1988, Section 7— Corruption charge— Illegal gratification — Evidence of accepting of illegal gratification — Held, Mereby because trap in instant case was first trap of the Police Officer, his evidence should not be considered with any discredit, unless the Court is able to reach to such conclusion after evaluating his version individually and also in the background of other evidence on record.**

[Paras 2,3,17]

B. **Prevention of Corruption Act, 1988, Sections 7, 13(1)(d) Corruption charges— Illegal gratification — Proof of accepting illegal gratification—**

**Allegation that the accused who was Senior Clerk at the octroi checkpost demanded bribe for undervaluation of the goods — Valuation was done by accused No. 2 who was Valuation Officer — Police receiving information of corrupt practice being adopted by the persons posted at the octroi checkposts in the entire city and not against the particular two accused — Trap in question was first trap of Police Officer — No allegation that accused No. 2 demanded any bribe for undervaluation of goods — Complainant not proved to have been obliged by assessing less value of his goods — Presence of anthracene powder on the hands of accused No. 1, table, Muddamal receipt etc. found explained — Accused No. 1 not proved to have pocketed currency notes which were smeared with anthracene powder nor placed them on table — It cannot be said that acceptance of notes was against any demand by accused No.1 — Conviction of both accused set aside.**

[Paras 2,17,19,20,21,25 and 28]

**Cases Referred :—**

Dhanvantrai Desai v. State of Maharashtra, AIR 1964 Supreme Court 575.

Kantilal H. Patel v. State of Gujarat, 2007 (1) GLH 736.

---

## Acquittal of Public Servant from charge of corruption as the complaint was by a private person without proper sanction for prosecution

***Anil Kumar v. M.K. Aiyappa***

**(From Karnataka High Court)**

2013(12) Scale 283:2014(1) ECrC 31:2013(4) KLT 125:2014(1) SCC(Cri) 35:2013(4) CCR 262:2013(9) SCR 869:2014(1) J.C.R. 278:2013(4) R.C.R. (Criminal) 586:2013(5) Recent Apex Judgements (R.A.J.) 479:2013 AIR (SCW) 5570:2013(4) Cri.CC 388:2013(6) KantLJ 1:2013(4) AICLR 353:2013 AIR (SC) (Cri) 2202:2013(4) Ker L.J. 370:2013(4) Bom.C.R. (Cri.) 296:2013(6) AIR Bom.R. 895:2013 (132) AIC 237:2013(10) SCC 705:2014(1) Mh.LJ (Cri.) 36:2014(1) AIR Jhar R. 37:2014 CriLJ 1:2014(1) PLJR 4:2013(13) JT 127:2014(1) ALT (Crl.) 317:2014(84) ACrC 695:2013(4) JLJR 601:2014(1) CalCriLR 295:2013 Cri. L.R. 1050:2013(4) JBCJ 225:2013(3) Apex Court Judgements (SC) 436:2013(8) SLT 463:2013(4) BBCJ 110:2013(4) B.L.Jud. 173.

**Judges :—** Justice K.S. Radhakrishnan & Justice A.K. Sikri, JJ.

## Advocates:

1. For the Petitioner :— Mr. Kailash Vasdev, Senior Advocate, Mr. Girish Ananthamurthy, Mr. Preshant Jain and Mr. Umrao Singh Rawat, Advocates, Mrs. Vaijayanthi Girish, Advocate (N.P.).
2. For the Respondent :— Mr. Uday U. Lalit, Senior Advocate, Mr. Sandeep Patil, Mr. Nishant Patil for Mr. Guntur Prabhakar.

Criminal Appeal Nos. 1590—1591 of 2013 (@ Special Leave Petition (Criminal) Nos. 6652—6653 of 2013).

Date of Decison — 1.10.2013.

**A. Criminal Procedure Code 1973, Section 197 — Prevention of Corruption Act, 1988, Sections 13(1)(d), 8 and 19(1) and 19(3)— Criminal Procedure Code, Section 156(3)— Private complaint against a public servant under Prevention of Corruption Act and Indian Penal Code — Complaint not accompanied by a sanction order — Special Judge sent the complaint to Police for further investigation — Order of Special Judge quashed.**

[Paras 2,3,5,6 and 8]

**B. Criminal Procedure Code, 1973, Sections 156(3) and 200— Private Complaint under Section 200 of Criminal Procedure Code— Magistrate directing investigation under Section 156(3) of Criminal Procedure Code— Magistrate, while exercising his powers under Section 156(3) Criminal Procedure Code, could not act in a mechanical or casual manner — Magistrate is required to apply his mind, in such a case — The application of mind by the Magistrate should be reflected in the Order.**

**C. Criminal Procedure Code, Section 156(3) — Criminal Procedure Code, Sections 200 and 204 — Private Criminal Complaint — Magistrate directing investigation under Section 156(3) Criminal Procedure Code — The order directing investigation under Section 156(3) Criminal Procedure Code would not amount to taking cognizance of offence, but it is a pre—cognizance stage.**

[Paras 9 and 10]

**Cases Referred :**

Maksud Saiyed v. State of Gujarat, 2007(4) R.C.R.(Criminal) 406 : 2007(5) Recent Apex Judgments (R.A.J.) 229 : (2008)5 SCC 668.

P.V. Narasimha Rao v. State (CBI/SPE), 1998(4) R.C.R.(Criminal) 260 : (1998)4 SCC 626.

R.S. Nayak v. A.R. Antulay, (1984)2 SCR 495.

Srinivas Gundluri v. SEPCO Electric Power Construction Corporation, 2010(3) R.C.R.(Criminal) 887 : 2010(4) Recent Apex Judgments (R.A.J.) 471 : (2010)8 SCC 206.

State of Uttar Pradesh v. Paras Nath Singh, (2009)6 SCC 372.

State of West Bengal v. Mohd. Khalid, 1995(1) R.C.R.(Criminal) 318 : (1995)1 SCC 684.

Subramanium Swamy v. Manmohan Singh, 2012(1) R.C.R.(Criminal) 720 : 2012(1) Recent Apex Judgments (R.A.J.) 201 : (2012)3 SCC 64.

Tula Ram v. Kishore Singh, (1977)4 SCC 459.

---

## Acquittal of Mandal Revenue Officer from charge of bribe though tainted money recovered on the ground of failure of prosecution to prove other evidences

***B. Jayaraj v. State of Andhra Pradesh***
**(From Andhra Pradesh High Court)**

2014(2) MadWN (Cri) 376:2014(2) AICLR 8:2014(137) AIC 41:2014(2) AIR Jhar R. 727:2014(85) ACrC 1000:2014 CriLJ 2433:2014(2) Cri.CC 500:2014(2) JBCJ 327:2014(13) SCC 55:2014(2) CCR 327:2014(4) SCR 554:2014(2) J.C.R. 301:2014(2) R.C.R. (Criminal) 410:2014(2) Recent Apex Judgements (R.A.J.) 570:2014(4) Scale 81:2014(5) SCC (Cri) 543:2014 All SCR 1619:2014(2) MLJ (Criminal) 358:2014 RajCriC 393:2014 Cri. L.R. 445:2014(7) JT 381:2014 AIR (SCW) 2080:2014(2) UPLBEC 8:2014(3) JCC 1552:2014(2) Andh LD (Criminal) 73:2015 (sup) Cut-LT (Criminal) 159:2014(2) Apex Court Judgements (SC) 131:2014(2) M.P.W.N. 265:2014(2) GujLH 149:2014(2) B.L.Jud. 116:2014(2) BBCJ 313:2014(58) Orrisa Cri. R. 175:2014(1) Ori. Law Rev. 1014.

**Judges :—** Justice P. Sathasivam, CJI, Justice Ranjan Gogoi and Justice N.V. Ramana.

**Advocates:—**

1. For the Appellant :— Guntur Prabhakar.

Criminal Appeal No. 696 of 2014 (Arising Out of SLP (Crl.) No. 2085 of 2012).

Date of Decision — 28.3.2014

**A. Prevention of Corruption Act , 1988, Sections 7, 13(1)(d) and 13(2) and 20— Demand of bribe— Recovery of tainted money from pocket of accused— Demand of bribe not proved— Acquittal of accused— Benefit of doubt.**

[Paras 2,5,6,7,8 and 9]

**B. Prevention of Corruption Act, 1988, Sections 7 and 13(2) Charge bribe— Failure of prosecution to prove charges— Held, demand of illegal gratification is *sine qua* non constitute the said offence and mere recovery of tainted money constituted the offence unless proved beyond reasonable doubt.**

[Paras 6 & 7]

**Cases Referred :**

C.M. Sharma v. State of A.P., 2011(1) R.C.R.(Criminal) 183 : 2010(6) Recent Apex Judgments (R.A.J.) 636 : (2010) 15 SCC 1.

C.M. Girish Babu v. C.B.I., 2009(2) R.C.R.(Criminal) 134 : 2009(2) Recent Apex Judgments (R.A.J.) 101 : (2009) 3 SCC 779.

---

## Acquittal of accused a non-public servant for the lack of evidence that he had taken bribe to induce a public servant

***Babji v. State of Andhra Pradesh***
**(From Andhra Pradesh High Court)**

2018 AIR (SC) 3831 : 2018 AIR (SCW) 3831 : 2018(10) Scale 201 : 2018 CriLJ 4210: 2018(9) JT 12 : 2018(3) JLJR 402 : 2018(3) PLJR 414 : 2018 All SCR (Cri.) 1431: 2018 Cri. L.R. 879 : 2018(72) Orrisa Cri. R. 302 : 2018(4) AICLR 144.

**Judges** :— Justice R. Banumathi and Justice Vineet Saran.

**Advocates:—**

1. For the Appellants :— Anil Kumar Tandale.
2. For the Respondents :— Mukesh Kumar Maroria.

Criminal Appeal No. 2159 of 2009.

Date of Decision — 9.8.2018

**Prevention of Corruption Act, 1988, Section 8— Constitution of India, Article 136— Inducement to public servant by a non-public servant— Conviction by Lower Court— Appeal against conviction— Acquittal on the ground that though receiver of money man not be public servant the prosecution has to establish that money received for inducing to public servant in his official capacity and hence conviction cannot be sustained— Acquittal.**

[Para 6]

---

## Acquittal of Accounts Officer of an Electricity Supply Undertaking on the ground of lack of evidence

***Babu Lal Bajpai v. State of Uttar Pradesh***
**(From Allahabad High Court)**

1994(3) R.C.R. (Criminal) 300:1994 AIR (SC) 1538:1994 CriLJ 1383:1994 All. LJ 296:1994 AIR (SCW) 1149.

**Judges :—** Justice P.B. Sawant and Justice R.M. Sahai.

Criminal Appeal No. 339 of 1980.

Date of Decison — 24.11.1992

**Prevention of Corruption Act, 1947, Section 5(1)(d)— Demand of Bribe money— Defence of accused that complainant tried to thrust money in his pocket— Accused resisted and threw the same on floor— Version of accused supported by independent witness— No motive on part of accused to demand and accept bribe proved— No bill of complainant contractor was pending— Acquittal of accused upheld.**

[Para 6]

---

## Acquittal of Former Railway Minister from corruption charges for to and fro air fare for his travel to London from Railway Money

***C.K. Jaffer Sharief v. State (through CBI)***
**(From Delhi High Court)**

2013(121) AIC 206 : 2012(6) Recent Apex Judgements (R.A.J.) 247 : 2013(1) R.C.R. (Criminal) 187 : 2013(1) CalCriLR 401 : 2012(6) Law Herald (SC) 4917 : 2012 AIR (SCW) 6166 : 2013(1) MLJ (Criminal) 90 : 2013(1) AICLR 148 : 2013 CriLJ 341 : 2013(2) SCC (Cri) 482 : 2013 AIR (SC) 48 : 2013(1) Cri.CC 290 : 2013(1) SCC 205 : 2013(80) ACrC 979 : 2013 AIR (SC) (Cri) 687 : 2013(1) Crimes 43 : 2012(10) SCR 1079 : 2012(11) Scale 71 : 2013(1) J.C.R. 82 : 2012 Cri. L.R. 1951 : 2012(11) JT 283 : 2013(2) Mh.LJ (Crl.) 306 : 2013(1) ECrC 54 : 2013(1) JBCJ 215 : 2013(1) Andh LD (Criminal) 890 : 2012(4) GLR 2931 : 2013(1) Apex Court Judgements (SC) 231 : 2012(8) SLT461 : 2013(1) BBCJ 46 : 2013(1) B.L.Jud. 55 : 2013(54) Orrisa Cri. R. 9: 2013(1) All WC 15.

**Judges :—** Justice P. Sathasivam and Justice Ranjan Gogoi.

**Advocates:—**

1. For the Appellants :— P.P. Rao and Rajiv Datta, Senior Advocates with Gopal Singh.
2. For the Respondents :— Mohan Jain, ASG, D.K. Thakur, M. Tatia, B.V.B. Das and Arvind Kumar Sharma.

Criminal Appeal No. 1804 of 2012 (Arising out of SLP (Crl.) No. 3841 of 2012).

Date of Decision — 9.11.2012

**Cases Referred :**

M. Narayanan Nambiar v. State of Kerala, (1963) Supp. (2) SCR 724.

---

# Acquittal of Executive Engineers and others from charge of illegal clearance of jungle but order for Departmental enquiry

***C. Chenga Reddy v.***
***State of Andhra Pradesh***
**(From Andhra Pradesh High Court)**

1996(3) Crimes 119:1996(3) R.C.R. (Criminal) 793:1996 AIR (SC) 3390:1996 CriLJ 3461:1996(10) SCC 193:1996(6) JT 397:1996 SCC(Cri) 1205:1996(6) JT 739:1996(5) Scale 318:1996 SCR 479:1997 Cri. L.R. 258:1996(2) Andh LD (Criminal) 483:1995 (sup) ACrC 321:1997(1) ECrC 814:1997 MLJ (Criminal) 396:1996 AIR (SCW) 2903:1997 SCCriR 64.

**Judges** :— Justice G.N. Ray and Justice Dr. A.S. Anand.

**Advocates:—**

1. For the Appellants :— Mr. K. Madhava Reddy, Mr. U.R. Lalit, Mr. A.S. Nambiar, Senior Advocates with Mr. D. Prakash Reddy, Mr. Vimal Dave, Mr. Rani Chhabra and Mr. S.C. Patel.
2. For the Respondent :— Ms. K. Amareshwari, Senior Advocate with Mr. N.M. Reddy, Mr. K. Sethu Madhavan and Mr. Guntur Prabhakar.

Criminal Appeal Nos. 52—175 of 1993.

Date of Decison — 12.7.1996

---

## Acquittal of Police Officer as the demand and acceptance of bribe was not proved

### *C. Sukumaran v. State of Kerala*
**(From Kerala High Court)**

2015(1) Bom. C.R. (Cri.) 635:2015(88) ACrC 922:2015(2) R.C.R. (Criminal) 159:2015(1) Scale 751:2015(1) JT 487:2015(2) Recent Apex Judgements (R.A.J.) 169:2015(2) AIR Jhar R. 281:2015 AIR (SCW) 951:2015(1) Crimes 130:2015(1) CCR 356:2015(1) ALT (Cri.) 505:2015(2) Law Herald 1407:2015(147) AIC 58:2015 Cri. L.R. 382:2015(1) Andh LD (Criminal) 717:2015(2) JCC 1322:2015(2) ECrC 27:2015(3) W.L.N. 152:2015(3) AICLR 847:2015 ALL MR (Cri) 1200:2015(1) PLJ (Criminal) 244:2015 RajCriC 155:2015 CriLJ 1715:2015(2) Law Herald (SC) 927:2015(2) BBCJ 45:2015(11) SCC 314:2015(60) Orrisa Cri. R. 708:2015(1) All. Crl. Rulings 1094.

**Judges**:— Justice V. Gopala Gowda and Justice R. Banumathi.

**Advocates:—**

1. For the Petitioner :— Mr. Nishe Rajen Shonker.
2. For the Respondent :— Mr. Ramesh Babu M.R..

Criminal Appeal No. 192 of 2015
(S.L.P (Crl.) No. 9835 of 2014).

Date of Decison 29.1.2015.

**A. Prevention of Corruption Act , 1988, Sections 7, 13(1)(d) read with 13(2) Offence under— Conviction— Appeal against— Unsustainability— Demand and acceptance— Accused was station writer at the fort police station allegedly demanded and accepted ₹1500/— from the complainant for releasing certain articles— Demand not proved— High Court set aside the conviction under Section 7 of the act but confirmed conviction under Section 13(1)(d) read with Section 13(2).**

[Para.]

**B. Prevention of Corruption Act, 1988, Section 13(1)(d) read with 13(2) Conviction— Appeal against— Unsustainability— Demand and acceptance not proved— Held, in the absence of demand of gratification, the charge under Section 13(1)(d) of the Act is wholly unsustainable in law— Conviction under Section 13(1)(d) read with 13(2) of the Act not justified and set aside— Appeal allowed.**

[Para.]

**Cases Referred :**

B. Jayaraj v. State of A.P., 2014(2) R.C.R.(Criminal) 410 : 2014(2) Recent Apex Judgments (R.A.J.) 570 : (2014) 13 SCC 55.

---

# Acquittal of Central Excise Inspector though tainted currency recovered but demand of bribe not proved

***C. M. Girish Babu v. CBI, Cochin***

**(From Kerala High Court)**

2009 (2) R.C.R. (Criminal) 134:2009(2) Recent Apex Judgements (R.A.J.) 101:2009(3) SCC 779:2009 AIR (SC) 2022:2009 (2) JLJR 153:2009(3) Scale 107:2009(1) J.K.J. 3:2008(sup) Cri. L.R. 25:2009(2) Ker L.J. 217:2009(2) SCC(Cri) 1: 2010(1) GujLH 142:2009 AIR (SCW) 1693:2009(1) CalCriLR 865:2009(2) PLJR 209:2009(2) L.R.C. 93:2016(3) AICLR 481:2009 (sup) CutLT (Criminal) 850:2009(43) Orrisa Cri. R.48.

**Judges** :— Justice Lokeshwar Singh Panta and Justice B. Sudershan Reddy.

**Advocates:—**

1. For the Appellant :— U.U. Lalit, K.V. Viswanathan, M. Girish Kumar, B. Raghunath, Avijeet K. Lala and Vijay Kumar.
2. For the Respondent :— Naresh Kaushik, Manish Kaushik and B. Krishna Prasad.

Criminal Appeal No. 377 of 2009 (Arising out of SLP(Crl) No. 578 of 2008).

Date of Decison — 24.02.2009

**A. Prevention of Corruption Act, 1988, Sections 13(1)(d), 13(2) and 13(7)— Charge of bribe— Payment by complainant— Trap and raid— Recovery of tainted money from pocket of accused— Accused proved that the money was towards of loan— Conviction by Lower Courts— Acquittal by Apex Court.**

[Paras 12, 19 and 20]

**B. Prevention of Corruption Act, 1988, Sections 4 and 20— Indian Evidence Act, Sections 102, 103 and 105— Burden of proof on accused does not lie— Held, it was not neccesity from the side of accused to prove his case beyond reasonable doubt— Acquittal of accused.**

[Paras 2 and 20]

**Cases Referred :**

Suraj Mal v. State (Delhi Admn.) [(1979)4 SCC 725].

M. Narsinga Rao v. State of A.P., 2001(1) RCR(Criminal) 95 : (2001)1 SCC 691.

Jhangan v. State, 1966(3) SCR 736.

---

# Quashing of proceedings against Bank Officers on the basis of compromise between the parties

### *CBI, ACB, Mumbai v. Narendra Lal Jain*

**(From Bombay High Court)**

2014 (3) Scale 137:2014(2) CCR 19:2014(2) MLJ (Criminal) 124:2014(3) SCR 444:2014(3) Mh.LJ (Cri.) 606:2014(2) R.C.R. (Criminal) 15:2014(2) Recent Apex Judgements (R.A.J.) 220:2014(136) AIC 1:2014(2) AICLR 296:2014 Cri. L.R. 283:2014 RajCriC 353:2014(2) Law Herald 1418:2014(2) Law Herald (SC) 1135:2014(6) JT 638:2014(5) SCC 364:2014(2) Cri.CC 396:2014(2) SCC (Cri) 579:2014 AIR (SCW) 1603:2014(2) Crimes 1:2014(85) ACrC 346:2014 ALL MR (Cri) 1481:2014(2) CalCriLR 328:2014(2) Bom. C.R. (Cri.) 394:2014(2) JBCJ 9:2014(2) Apex Court Judgements (SC) 15:2014(2) GujLH 1:2014(57) Orrisa Cri. R. 1061:2014(2) AIR Bom. R (Cri) 31.

**Judges**:—Justice P. Sathasivam, Justice C.J.I., Justice Ranjan Gogoi and N.V. Ramana.

**Advocates:—**

1. For the Petitioner :— Mr. P. Parmeswaran, AOR.
2. For the Respondents :— Mr. K.N. Rai, AOR and Mr. Sunil Kumar Verma, AOR.

Criminal Appeal No. 517 of 2014 (Arising out of Special Leave Petition (Crl) No. 6138 of 2006).

Date of Decision — 28.2.2014

**Offence for Section 420 and 120B, I.P.C.— Parties entering into compromise— Offence under Section 420 I.P.C. compoundable, but offence under Section 120-B not compoundable— Proceedings quashed under Section 482, Cr.P.C.**

**Prevention of Corruption Act , 1988 Sections 13(2) and 13(1)(d) Criminal Procedure Code, Section 320 — Indian Penal Code, Sections 420 and 120B — Criminal and Civil proceedings — Compounding of offence — Offence under Section 420 and 120B, I.P.C. — Parties entering into compromise —**

**Offence under Section 420, I.P.C. compoundable, but offence under Section 120-B not compoundable — Proceedings quashed under Section 482, Cr.P.C.**

**ON FACTS**

Accused (two in number) inflated the figure of credit worthiness of their companies in connivance with Bank Officials and secured more advances/loans from the bank than they were entitled to — A case under Section 420/120—B IPC registered against them — A case under Prevention of Corruption Act registered against Bank officials — Bank also instituted suits for recovery of amount due from them — Suits were disposed of in terms of consent decrees — Criminal proceedings rightly quashed against the two accused — Held:—

(i) The bank had been mutually settled between the parties and the accused had accepted the lability in this regard, the High Court had thought it fit to invoke its power under Section 482 Cr.P.C..

(ii) Continuance of a criminal proceeding which is likely to become oppressive or may partake the character of a lame prosecution would be good ground to invoke the extraordinary power under Section 482 Cr.P.C. 2012(4) RCR (Crl.) 543 : 2012(4) Recent Apex Judgment (RAJ) 549, relied.

[Paras 10, 11, 12, 3 and 4]

## Cases Referred:

B.S. Joshi v. State of Haryana, 2003(2) R.C.R.(Criminal) 888 .

Central Bureau of Investigation, SPE, SIU(X), New Delhi v. Duncans Agro Industries Ltd., Calcutta, 1996(3) R.C.R.(Criminal) 60 : (1996)5 SCC 591.

Gian Singh v. State of Punjab, 2012(4) R.C.R.(Criminal) 543 : 2012(4) Recent Apex Judgments (R.A.J.) 549 : (2012)10 SCC 303.

Nikhil Merchant v. Central Bureau of Investigation, 2008(4) R.C.R.(Criminal) 102 : 2008(5) Recent Apex Judgments (R.A.J.) 156 : (2008)9 SCC 677.

---

# Acquittal of Odisha Administrative Service Officer for possesing disproportionate assets on the ground of invalid sanction for prosecution

***Chittaranjan Das v. State of Orissa***

**(From Orissa High Court)**

2011(7) SCC 167:2011 AIR (SC) (Cri) 1656:2011 AIR (SCW) 4281:2011 AIR (SC) 2893:2011(3) AICLR 541:2011(3) R.C.R. (Criminal) 512:2011(4) Recent Apex Judgements (R.A.J.) 64:2011(4) Air Kar R 783:2011 CriLJ 4306:2011(4) AIR Jhar R. 454:2012(110) AIC 162:2012(76) ACrC 612:2012(1) MLJ (Criminal) 407:2011(3) Cri.CC 474:2011(8) JT 504:2011(7) SCR 836:2011(7) Scale 461:2011 Cri. L.R. 62:2012(2) ECrC 77:2011(2) SCC (L & S) 757:2011(3) SCC (Cri) 78:2012(1) Andh LD (Criminal) 271:2011(49) Orrisa Cri. R. 1019:2011(2) Ori. Law Rev. 871.

**Judges** :— Justice G.S. Singhvi and Justice Chandramauli Kr. Prasad.

**Advocates:—**

1. For the Appellant :— Vinod Bhagat.
2. For the Respondent :— Suresh Chandra Tripathy.

Criminal Appeal No. 820 of 2007.

Date of Decision — 4.7.2011.

**A. Corruption case against Public servant— Prosecution not launched as sanction for prosecution refused by Govt.— Retirement of Public Servant— Prosecution cannot be launched even after retirement if the sanction was refused by Govt. before retirement of Public servant.**

**B. Criminal Procedure Code, Section 197— Prevention of Corruption Act, 1988, Section 19— Corruption case against Public Servant— Prosecution not launched as sanction for prosecution refused by Govt.— Retirement of Public Servant— Prosecution cannot be launched even after retirement if the sanction was refused by Govt. before retirement of Public servant.**

## ON FACTS :—

Prosecution of Public servant on the allegation that he possessed assets disproportionate to his known source of income — Sanction for prosecution, however, refused by Govt. — No prosecution launched — Retirement off Public Servant — Prosecution lunched against Public Servant after retirement on the ground that sanction for prosecution was not required after retirement — Catenation repelled — Held :—

In a case in which sanction sought is refused by the competent authority, while the public servant is in service, he cannot be prosecuted later after retirement, notwithstanding the fact that no sanction for prosecution under the Prevention of Corruption Act is necessary after the retirement of Public Servant. 2004(2) R.C.R. (Criminal) 641 : 2004(2) Apex Criminal 707, Distinguished.

[Para 8]

**C. Criminal Procedure Code, Section 197— Prevention of Corruption Act, 1988, Section 19— Prevention of Corruption Act , 1947, Sections 5(1) (e) and 5(2)— Sanction for prosecution of Public Servant— Object of sanction— Held:—**

**Sanction is a devise provided by law to safeguard public servants from vexatious and frivolous prosecution— It is to give them freedom and liberty to perform their duty without fear or favour and not succumb to the pressure of unscrupulous elements— It is a weapon at the hands of the sanctioning authority to protect the innocent public servants from uncalled for prosecution but not intended to shield the guilty.**

[Para 8]

**Case Referred :**

N. Bhargavan Pillai (dead) by LRs. v. State of Kerala, 2004(2) R.C.R.(Criminal) 641: 2004(2) Apex Criminal 707.

---

## Acquittal of one accused in same case of corruption due to lack of sanction for prosecution and sanction should be for each accused

***Dilawar Singh v. Parvinder Singh @ Iqbal Singh***

**(From Punjab and Haryana High Court)**

2005(4) R.C.R. (Criminal) 855:2005(3) Apex Criminal 565:2006 AIR (SC) 389:2006(1) CurLJ 466:2005(4) Cri.CC 670:2005(9) Scale 200:2005(9) JT 476:2006 CriLJ 145:2005(12) SCC 709:2005(Sup5) SCR 83:2006(1) SCC(Cri) 727:2006(54) ACrC 25:2005(7) Supreme 524:2005 AIR (SCW) 6021:2006(1) RLW 186:2006(1) AIR Jhar R. 202:2005(4) Crimes 222:2006(1) PLJR 401:2006(1) RajCriC 22:2006(1) All. LJ 342:2006(1) CalLJ 85:2006(1) AIR Bom. R 373:2006(1) ECrC 171:2006(1) W.L.C. 37:2005 Cri. L.R. 923:2006(1) CalCriLR 61:2006 ALL MR(Cri) 278:2005(36) AIC 16:2005(4) KLT 1029:2006(2) JLJR 14:2006(1) Andh LD (Criminal) 57:2006(1) CLR 94:2006(33) Orrisa Cri. R. 3:2005(2) Apex Court Judgements (SC) 625:2005(2) Cri. App. R (SC) 1021.

**Judges**:— Justice H.K. Sema & Justice G.P. Mathur.

**Advocates:—**

1. For the Appellant :— Sudhir Nandrajog, Sujit K. Singh, Abhishek Agarwal and Gagan Gupta.

2. For the Respondent :— C.L. Sahu.
3. For the State :— A.S. Sohal and Harpreet S. Sandhu, Advocates.

Criminal Appeal Nos. 982—983 of 2003.

Date of Decison — 8.11.2005

**A. Prevention of Corruption Act , 1988 , Section 19— Criminal Procedure Code, Section 319— Prosecution of Public servant in Corruption case— Sanction for prosecution accorded by Competent Authority under Section 19 of Prevention of Corruption— An other public servant added as accused under Section 319 of Criminal Procedure Code— Court cannot take cognizance without sanction for prosecution— Sanction for prosecution has to be granted with respect to a specific accused. AIR 1958 Supreme Court 124 relied.**

[Paras 4, 8]

**B. Interpretation of statutes— If a special provision has been made on a certain matter, that matter is excluded from the general provisions.**

[Para 8]

**Cases Referred:**

Raghubans Dubey v. State of Bihar, AIR 1967 Supreme Court 1167.

State through CBI v. Raj Kumar Jain, 1998(3) RCR(Crl.) 656 (SC):(1998)6 SCC 551.

Jaswant Singh v. State of Punjab, AIR 1958 Supreme Court 124.

State of Goa v. Babu Thomas, 2005(4) RCR(Criminal) 349 (SC) : 2005(3) Apex Criminal 351 (SC).

Venkateshwar Rao v. Govt. of Andhra Pradesh, AIR 1966 Supreme Court 828.

State of Bihar v. Yogendra Singh, AIR 1982 Supreme Court 882.

Maharashtra State Board of Secondary Education v. Paritosh Bhupesh Kumar Sheth, AIR 1984 Supreme Court 1543.

---

## Acquittal of Head Guard of Ashoka Hotel from charge of false medical reimbursement bill as the hotel is not a government department

***State of Karnataka v. M. Muniswamy***

**(From Karnataka High Court)**

2002(10) SCC 546:2004 SCC(Cri) 1151:2000(8) SLT 646:2003(25) Orrisa Cri. R. 728

**Judges**:— Justice K.T. Thomas and Justice R.P.Sethi.

Criminal Appeal No. 6 Of 1996.

Date of Decision - 1.11.2000.

**Indian Penal Code, 1860, Section 21— Prevention of Corruption Act, 1988, Section 2(C)— Public servant— Head Guard in security department of Ashoka Hotel Bangalore concocted some bills for supporting a bogus claim for medical reimbursement— Special Court established under Prevention Corruption Act convicted accused— Evidence insufficient for holding that Ashoka Hotel or Indian Tourism Development corporation was a Government company— Held, whole trial before special court was without Jurisdiction.**

[Paras 4 and 5]

---

## Acquittal of Indian Forest Service Officer from false charge of possessing disproportionate assets and thereby order of ₹10 lakh compensation to him

***Ram Lakhan Singh v. State Government of Uttar Pradesh Through Chief Secretary***

**(From Allahabad High Court)**

2016(4) ADJ 9:2015(12) Scale 479:2015(6) Recent Apex Judgements (R.A.J.) 534:2016(1) R.C.R. (Criminal) 343:2015(5) Law Herald (SC) 3644:2015 AIR (SCW) 6323:2015(8) MLJ 367:2016(114) ALR 179:2016(1) PLJR 83:2016(157) AIC 219:2015(4) JLJR 566:2016(1) All WC 1:2016(1) KLT 5:2016(1) CalLJ 26:2016(1) RSJ 15:2016(1) W.L.N. 25:2016(1) All. LJ 104:2016(1) JBCJ 46:2016(1) J.C.R. 75:2016(1) ALL MR 946:2015(16) SCC 715:2016(2) SCC (L & S) 343:2015(4) BBCJ 417:2016(63) Orrisa Cri. R. 58:2016(1) Ori. Law Rev. 299

**Judges** :— Justice Ranjan Gogoi and Justice N.V. Ramana.

**Advocates:—**

1. For the Petitioner :— In person.
2. For the Respondent :— Dinesh Dwivedi, Gaurav Bhatia, Utkarsh Jaiswal and Abhishek Chaudhary.

Writ Petition (Civil) No. 933 of 2014.

Date of Decision — 17.11.2015

**Prevention of Corruption Act, 1988, Sections 13(1)(a) and 13(2)— Criminal Procedure Code, 1973, Section 357— Malicious Prosecution— FIRs lodged against petitioner (Public Servant) on charge of amassing wealth— No material to support allegation in Court— Discharge of petitioner by Court— Petitioner remained 11 days in jail and fought legal battle for 10 years— State directed to pay compensation of ₹10 lakhs.**

[Paras 9, 11, 12, 13 and 14]

---

# Acquittal of a Special Deputy Commissioner of Land Revenue for absense of mens rea

***Dr. Ramegowda v. State of Karnataka***

**(From Karnataka High Court)**

2017 ALL MR(Cri) 880

**Judges**:— Justice Mr. Ranjan Gogoi and Justice Mr. Ashok Bhushan.

**Advocates:**

1. For the Petitioners :— Mr. Raju Ramachandran, Sr. Adv., Mr. S. Udaya Kumar Sagar, Ms. Bina Madhavan and Ms. Ramandeep Kaur, Advocates for M/s. Lawyer S. Knit & Co.
2. For the Respondents :— Mr. Joseph Aristotle S., Mrs. Priya Aristotle, Ms. K. Priyadarshini, Mr. Shankar Chillarge and Mr. M.P. Shorawala.

Criminal Appeal No.23 of 2017, (Arising out of Special Leave Petition (Criminal) No.1565 of 2016).

Date of Decison — 04.01.2017

**Criminal Procedure Code, 1973, Section 482— Indian Penal Code, 1860, Sections 114, 119, 120B, 167, 218, 420, 464, 468 and 470— Prevention of Corruption Act, 1988, Sections 9, 13(1)(b) and 13(2)— Use of land granted by Govt, for purpose other than the terms of grant— Accused manipulated the Kannada version grant order English Translated copy by inserting "Education purpose" in the grant conditions to obtain land use certificate for education from the Appellant—Special Deputy Commissioner— Appellant without looking the original grant issued certificate to use for education purpose— No criminal intention on the part of Appellant— At the most appellant could be held negligent— Proceedings against appellant quashed.**

[Paras 4 and 5]

---

# Acquittal of Survey Inspector from charge of bribe due to lack of proper evidentiary value

***G. Harinatha Rao v. State of Andhra Pradesh REP. ACB***

**(From Andhra Pradesh High Court)**

2014(13) SCC 44 : 2014(4) Crimes 567 : 2014(2) Scale 253 : 2014(5) SCC(Cri.) 534: 2014(16) R.C.R.(Criminal) 38 : 2016 All SCR (Cri.) 556.

**Judges**:— Justice Chandramauli Kr. Prasad and Justice Pinaki Chandra Ghose.

**Advocates:—**

1. For the Appellant :— Y. Raja Gopala Rao, Y. Vismai Rao, Hitender Nath Rath.
2. For the Respondent :— D. Mahesh Babu, Suchitra Hrangkhawl, Amjid Maqbool, Amit K. Nain, Aditya Jain, Ramakrishna Rao.

Criminal Appeal No. 1378 of 2011.

Date of Decision — 15.1.2014

**Prevention of Corruption Act, 1988, Sections 7 and 13(1)(d) read with 13(2)— Illegal gratification— Appellant, was working as the Survey Inspector— Allegedly demanded illegal gratification for preparing a favourable report— Informant during the course of trial has nowhere stated that any demand was made by the appellant— Trap witness, stating that as the matter was being adjourned on several dates, he thought that the appellant will not do his work unless he bribed him with cash and with this notion, he went to meet the appellant, gave money, which he refused— Held that, merely because this witness has admitted to have given the report alleging demand of bribe by the appellant would not be sufficient to hold that he made a demand.**

[Para 9]

---

# Acquittal of Officer of Revenue Department from charge of bribery due to lack of proper evidentiary value

***Ganapathi Sanya Naik v. State of Karnataka***

**(From Karnataka High Court)**

2007(4) R.C.R. (Criminal) 184:2007(5) Rcenet Apex Judgements (R.A.J.) 132:2007(11) JT 162:2007(8) SCC 309:2007(4) AICLR 724:2007 AIR (SC) 3213:2007 CriLJ 4689:2007(3) SCC (Cri) 541:2007 (11) Scale 94:2007(9) SCR 939:2007(4) Crimes

85:2007 ALL MR (Cri) 2978:2007(4) Cri.CC 139:2007 AIR (SCW) 5824:2007(6) Air Kar R 211:2007(6) Supreme 578:2007(3) RajCriC 982:2007(4) PLJR 182:2008(1) KantLJ 104:2008(1) Mh.LJ (Crl.) 1:2007(2) W.L.C. 730:2007(4) ECrC 211:2007(58) AIC 9:2007(3) GujLH 619:2007(4) JLJR 174:2007(3) Apex Court Judgements (SC) 558:2007(4) L.R.C. 157:2008(sup) CutLT (Criminal) 213:2007(38) Orrisa Crl. R. 631.

**Judges**:— Justice S.B. Sinha and Justice Harjit Singh Bedi.

**Advocates:—**

1. For the Appellant :— Lakshmi Raman Singh.
2. For the Respondent :— Sanjay R. Hegde, Vikrant Yadav, Amit Kumar Chawla and Ramesh S. Jadhav.

Criminal Appeal No. 1218 of 2007 (arising out of SLP(Crl) No. 2906/2007).

Date of Decision — 14.9.2007

**Prevention of Corruption Act, 1988 , Sections 13(1)(d) and 13(2)—Acquittal in corruption case— Prosecution case that accused demanded money from complainant for effecting entry of mutation in revenue record— A trap laid— Currency notes recovered from table of accused beneath office files— Defence version that no demand was made and currency notes had been surreptitiously put on the table while the appellant was otherwise engaged in some activity— Defence version plausible— Accused acquitted.**

[Paras 7 and 8]

---

## Acquittal of IAS Officer from charge of corruption on the ground that his deputation to a Co-operative Society is not a Public Office

***Gopinath v. Superintendent of Police (Karnataka)***

**(From Karnataka High Court)**

2014(2) KantLJ 216 : 2013(32) R.C.R.(Civil) 166.

**Judges**:— Justice Huluvadi G. Ramesh.

**Advocates:—**

1. For the Petitioner :— B. Bapegowda.
2. For the Respondents :— A. Syed Habeeb, Special State Public Prosecutor.

Criminal Petition No. 15932 of 2013.

Date of Decison — 6.12.2013

**A. Karnataka Lokayukta Act, 1984, Section 2(12)— Prevention of Corruption Act, 1988, Section 13(2)— Relief to an IAS Officer— Lokayukta Police registered a case under Section 13(1) (c) and 13(2) of the Prevention of Corruption Act, 1988— Lokayukta— Lokayukta have not jurisdiction to entertain a complaint against the person who does not come within the definition of a public servant under the Act— In present case, accused was serving as Project Manager of Nirmithi Kendra, Bijapur— It was a registered Co-operation Society— Held, petitioner does not fall within definition of Section 2(12) of the Act , thus criminal proceeding quashed.**

[Paras 1, 14, 11 and 12]

**B. Karnataka Societies Registration Act, 1960, Section 8 — Exemption from purview of Lokayukta raids — Held, an IAS Officer working on deputation to the Co—operation Society is not a public servant.**

[Para 5]

**C. Indian Penal Code, 1860, Section 21 "Public Servant"— Who is public servant?— Limitation of Lokayukta Police— Words public servant has been defined under Section 2(12) of the Lokayukta Act— All officers on deputation to registered Co-operative Societies are exempted from purview of Lokayukta Police— Held, petitioner was given benefits and First Information Report registered against him by Lokayukta Police was quashed as not maintainable— Petition allowed.**

[Para 10]

**Cases Referred :**

Sri. M.A. Parthasarathy v. The Special Deputy Commissioner, Bangalore District, 2009 (5) Kar. L.J. 203:ILR 2009 Kar. 1940.

State of Maharashtra v. Laljit Rajshi Shah, AIR 2000 SC 937 : (2000) 2 SCC 699: 2000 SCC (Cri.) 533:2000 Cri. L.J. 1494 (SC).

State of Punjab v. Karnail Singh, (2008) 9 SCC 114 : (2008) 3 SCC (Cri.) 697 : 2008 AIR SCW 7418 : 2009 Cri. L.J. 395 (SC) : AIR 2009 SC 372.

---

## Acquittal of Motor Vehicle Inspector for possessing disproportionate assets but it does not bar departmental proceedings

***Government of Andhra Pradesh v. C. Muralidhar***

**(From Andhra Pradesh High Court)**

1997(3) S.C.T. 636:1997 AIR (SC) 3005:1997(6) SCC 594:1997(5) Scale 57:1997(7) JT 59:1997 LIC 2884:1997(4) SLR 756:1997(3) RSJ 719:1997 SCC (L & S) 1746:1997(7) Supreme 193:1997 AIR (SCW) 3037.

**Judges** :— Justice S.C. Agrawal and Justice G.T. Nanavati.

**Advocates:—**

1. For the Appellants :— Mr. K. Ram Kumar, Ms. Asha, Nair, and C. Balasubramanian.
2. For the Respondent :— Mr. L. Nageshwara Rao, Mr. G.R.K. Prasad, Mr. V.S. Reddy and Mr. Udaya Kumar Sagar.

Civil Appeal No. 4911 of 1997 (Arising out of SLP (C) No. 23943 of 1996).

Date of Decison — 22.7.1997

**Prevention of Corruption Act, 1988, Section 5— Andhra Pradesh Civil Services (Classification, Control and Appeal) Rules, 1963— Charge of possession of disproportionate assets— Lack of proof of evidence against— Acquittal from charge— Departmental proceeding also framed against accused— Held, acquittal from criminal proceeding does not entitle to accused to be free from departmental proceeding.**

[Paras 2, 5 and 6]

---

## Acquittal of a Bench Clerk of a Court from charge of bribe for lack of prosecution evidence

***Gulam Mahmood A. Malek v. State of Gujarat***
**(From Gujarat High Court)**

1980 AIR (SC) 1558:1980 CriLJ 1096:1980 (sup) SCC 684:1980 Cri. L.R. 504:1980 CLJ (Criminal) 141:1980 UJ (SC) 878:1980 SCCriR 404:1981 SCC(Cri) 586:1980 GLR 965.

**Judges:—** Justice R.S. Sarkaria and Justice P.S. Kailasam.

Criminal Appeal No. 47 of 1975.

Date of Decision — 10.6.1980.

A. **Prevention of Corruption Act, 1947, Section 5(1)(d)— Criminal Procedure Code, 1973, Section 161 — Evidence Act, 1872, Section 3 — Conviction for accepting bribe — Appreciation of evidence — Held, that the**

**background of the case should not be lost sight of — The accused could not be convicted for accepting bribe on the corroborating testimony of the panch witness as to recovery of money for want of independent witness.**

[Para 6]

**B. Criminal Procedure Code, 1973, Section 386— Appeal against acquittal— Reversal of order of acquittal— Held, that High Court must have sufficient grounds for holding that appreciation of evidence by trial Court is unsupportable— Further held that the trial Court has given convincing as to why the evidence of panch witness cannot be accepted Trial court on appreciation of evidence has rightly not accepted the testimony of the complaint and the panch witness— Appeal allowed.**

[Para 7]

---

# Acquittal of Bodygurad of D.I.G. Muzaffarpur as he was not competent authority to give a job to relative of complainant

***Hawaldar Nathjee Singh @ Nathjee Singh v. The State Of Bihar***

**(From Patna High Court)**

2013 (1) BBCJ 302

**Judges:**— Justice Smt. Sheema Ali Khan.

**Advocates:—**

1. For the Appellant :— Mr. Ganesh Prasad Singh.
2. For the Respondent :— Ms. Abha Singh, A.P.P.
3. For the Vigilance :— Mr. Ramakant Sharma, Senior.

Criminal Appeal (SJ) No. 358 of 2000(Against The Judgment Of Conviction And The Order Of Sentence Dated 13th September, 2000 Passed By Shri Jitendra Mohan Sharma, Special Judge (Vigilance), North Bihar, Patna In Special Case No. 18 Of 1991 Arising Out Of Mithanpura Police Station Case No. 123 Of 1987).

Date of Decison — 05.10.2012.

**Indian Penal Code, 1860, Section 161— Prevention of Corruption Act, 1988, Section 5(2) read with Sections 7 and 5(1)(d)— Bribery— Demand and acceptance of money to provide job— Accused convicted for—**

**Appeal against conviction— Allegation is of receiving Rs. 8,000/- in order to secure a job for PW 4— Appellant was not in a position of power or authority to get a job for PW 4, rather the allegation is that he took the money and promised to influence the D.I.G., Muzaffarpur and thereby help the nephew of the informant to get a job in the Police Service— The allegation does not come within the purview of Section 7 of Prevention of Corruption Act— Therefore, conviction of appellant would fall on that ground itself— Judgment of conviction against appellant set aside— Appellant acquitted of charges levelled against him— Appeal allowed.**

[Paras 10 to 12]

---

# Acquittal of Officer of Revenue Department with the Order of increment to be payable for his suspension period

***Indra Raj Barupal v. State of Rajasthan***
**(From Rajasthan High Court)**

2011(4) W.L.N. 398:2011(26) S.C.T. 667

**Judges**:— Justice Govind Mathur, J.

**Advocates:—**

1. For the Petitioner :— Mr. Sunil Beniwal.
2. For the Respondents :— I.S. Pareek, Addl. Govt.

S.B. Civil Writ Petition No. 6700 of 2007.
Date of Decision — 25.8.2011.

A. **Rajasthan Service Rules, 1951, Rule 29— Increment for suspension period— Entitlement to— Petitioner suspended due to criminal case under Prevention of Corruption Act, 1988— However, acquitted by Trial Court but appeal pending against acquittal in High Court— As per Rule 29 of the Rules of 1951 annual grade increments are required to be released as right, if not otherwise withheld as a consequent to disciplinary action— In the instant matter, it is the position admitted that no disciplinary action has been taken against the petitioner by the respondent employer— Petitioner held entitled to increment for suspension period unless withheld for any disciplinary action.**

[Para 9]

**B. Rajasthan Service Rule, 1951, Rule 54— Petitioner suspended due to criminal proceeding under Prevention of Corruption Act but acquitted— Claim by petitioner for salary for suspension period— Question to be considered by competent authority as per Rule 54 of 1951 Rules— Question not to be considered by Writ Court.**

[Paras 7 and 9]

---

# Acquittal of Public Servant as demand of bribery not proved though there was recovery of tainted money

***Jhabar Singh v. State of Haryana***
**(From Punjab and Haryana High Court)**

2016 All SCR (Cri.) 1874.

**Judges:**— Justice Mr. Ranjan Gogoi and Justice Mr. Abhay Manohar Sapre.

**Advocates:**—

1. For the Petitioners:— Mr. Gagan Deep Sharma, Mr. M.K. Saroha, Mr. Nikhil Jain.
2. For the Respondents:— Mr. Rahul Verma, Addl. A.G. Mr. Vishwa Pal Singh.

Criminal Appeal No. 987 of 2016 (Arising out of Special Leave Petition (Criminal) No. 1390 of 2016).

Date of Decision — 18.10.2016

**Prevention of Corruption Act , 1988, Sections 7 and 20— Conviction— Complainant and shadow witness turned hostile— Conviction based on presumption following recovery of tainted money— In absence of proof of demand mere recovery not sufficient to attract conviction— Conviction illegal— Appeal allowed.**

[Para 5]

**Cases Referred :**

B. Jayaraj v. State of Andhra Pradesh, (2014) 13 SCC 55.

C.M. Girish Babu v. CBI, (2009) 3 SCC 779.

C.M. Sharma v. State of A.P., (2010) 15 SCC 1.

---

## Quashing of Proceedings against Public Servant as charge sheet had been filed after four years

### *Johnson Alexander v. State by CBI, ACB*

**(From Karnataka High Court)**

2015 All SCR 1803:2015(2) Recent Apex Judgements (R.A.J.) 294:2015(2) R.C.R. (Criminal) 364:2015(2) R.C.R. (Civil) 495:2015(2) Law Herald (SC) 1368:2015(2) Cri. CC 842:2015(3) AICLR 938

**Judges** :— Justice V. Gopala Gowda and Justice C. Nagappan.

**Advocates:—**

1. For the Appellant :— Mr. Amarendra Sharan, Senior Advocate, Mr. S.K. Kulkarni, Mr. M. Gireesh Kumar, Mr. Ankur S. Kulkarni and Mr. Somesh Chandra Jha.
2. For the Respondent :— Mr. Arvind Kumar Sharma, (NP).

Criminal Appeal No. 1478 of 2010.

Date of Decison — 26.2.2015.

**Prevention of Corruption Act, 1988, Section 13(1)(d) and 13(2)— Indian Penal Code, 1860, Section 120B(2)— Accused charged with offence under Section 120B(2) I.P.C. read with Sections 13(1)(d) and 13(2) of Prevention of Corruption Act— Accused not a Govt. servant— Offence under Section 120B(2), I.P.C. punishable with six months S.I.— Limitation to file complaint Section 468, Cr.P.C. is one year but in the instant case, incident took place in the year 1995, FIR lodged in the year 1999 and cognizance taken in the year 2001— Held :—**

**(i) For the reason that the complaint and FIR is registered beyond one year, therefore, the proceedings are not maintainable in law.**

[Para 7]

## Cases Referred:

P. Nallammal & Anr. v. State Rep. by Inspector of Police, 1999(3) R.C.R.(Criminal) 676: (1999) 6 SCC 559.

State of U.P. v. Udai Narayan & Anr., 1999(4) R.C.R.(Criminal) 739 : (1999) 8 SCC 741.

State thr. C.B.I. v. Jitender Kumar Singh, 2014(1) R.C.R.(Criminal) 908 : 2014(1) Recent Apex Judgments (R.A.J.) 628 : (2014) 2 SCALE 65.

# Acquittal of accused on the ground that the sanction for prosecution was not made by Competent Authority

***K. Devassia v. State of Kerala***
**(From Kerala High Court)**

2006(10) SCC 447:2006(3) SCC (Cri) 577.

**Judges** :— Justice B. N. Agrawal and Justice A. K. Mathur.

Criminal Appeal No. 625 of 2000.
Date of Decison — 29.3.2006.

**Prevention of Corruption Act, 1988 , Section 19— Prevention of Corruption Act, 1947, Section 6— Secretary (Vigilance) whether competent to accord sanction for prosecution— As per decision rendered in (2003) 9 SCC 504— Secrevary (Vigilance) was authorised to grant sanction on 23.4.1994— However, in instant case sanction was granted by said authority prior to 23.4.1994— Thus, conviction of appellant not justified— Appellant acquitted.**

[Paras 1 and 2]

**Case Referred :**

Mohandas v. State of Kerala, 2002 (2) KLT 251 (SC).

---

# Acquittal of Co-accused as he had no knowledge of bribe

***K. Subba Reddy v. State of Andhra Pradesh***
**(From Andhra Pradesh High Court)**

2007(4) R.C.R.(Criminal) 505 : 2007(5) Recent Apex Judgements (R.A.J.) 360 : 2007(8) SCC 246 : 2008 AIR(SC) 106 : 2007(4) AICLR 642 : 2007(3) SCC(Cri) 528 : 2007(13) JT 512 : 2007(11) Scale 516 : 2007(10) SCR 419 : 2008 CriLJ 345 : 2007(4) Crimes 102 : 2007(4) PLJR 191 : 2007(6) Supreme 605 : 2008(1) Ori. Law Rev. 38 : 2007(4) ECrC 228 : 2007(4) JLJR 183 : 2008(1) Mh.LJ (Cri.) 410 : 2007 ALL MR(Cri) 3554: 2007(2) SCC (L&S) 875 : 2008(1) Cri.CC 614 : 2007 AIR (SCW) 6205 : 2008(1) Apex Court Judgements (SC) 275 : 2008(1) BBCJ 338 : 2008(sup) CutLT (Criminal) 167 : 2008(2) CLR 382 : 2007(38) Orissa Cri. R. 674.

**Judges**:— Justice Dr. Arijit Pasayat & Justice D.K. Jain.

**Advocates:—**

1. For the Appellant :— C.S.N. Mohan Rao.
2. For the Respondent :— Mrs. D. Bharathi Reddy.

Criminal Appeal No. 1309 of 2007 (Arising out of SLP(Crl.) No. 6306 of 2005).

Date of Decision — 28.9.2007.

**Prevention of Corruption Act , 1988 , Section 7— Accused working as Excise Sub-Inspector— Demanded ₹3000/- from complainant to do a favour— Complainant, however, asked the complainant to pay the money to co-accused who was working as Home Guard— Trap was laid and the bribe money was recovered from co-accused— Co-accused acquitted— There was no material to show that co-accused had knowledge regarding the money being bribe— Moreover co-accused had no role to do favour.**

[Paras 7, 8 and 9]

---

# Acquittal in bribery case due to death of complainant, Conversation on tape records not produced in court and hostileness of shadow witness

***K.M. Mallaiah v. State of Karnataka***

**(From Karnataka High Court)**

2015 All SCR 1799:2015(2) R.C.R. (Criminal) 117:2015(2) Recent Apex Judgements (R.A.J.) 51:2015(2) Law Herald (SC) 1272.

**Judges** :— Justice Madan B. Lokur and Justice R.K. Agrawal.

**Advocates:—**

1. For the Appellant :— Mr. B.P.S. Patil, Senior Advocate, Mr. Amjid Maqbool, Mr. Chinmay Deshpande, Mr. B. Subrahmanya Prasad and Anirudh Sanganeria.
2. For the Respondent :— Mr. Parikshit P. Angadi and Mr. V.N. Raghupathy.

Criminal Appeal No. 260 of 2015 (Arising out of SLP (Crl.) No. 6965 of 2014).

Date of Decision — 10.2.2015

**Prevention of Corruption Act, 1988, Sections 7, 13(1) and 13(1)(d)— Charge of bribery— Trap and raid— Tape Recorder Conversation—**

**Death of accused during pending of trial— Hostility of shadow witness— Non—production of tape records in court— Tainted money lost and not produced in court— Acquittal of accused— Ground of.**

[Paras 2, 11 & 15]

---

# Acquittal of Assistant Commissioner of Cochin, Devaswom Board from the charge of fraudulent misappropriation of temple property for failure of prosecution to prove charge against him

***K.R. Purushothaman v. State of Kerala***

**(From Kerala High Court)**

2006(1) ECrC 43 : 2005(4) R.C.R.(Criminal) 848 : 2005(3) Apex Criminal 553 : 2006 AIR (SC) 35 : 2006(1) Cri.CC 213 : 2006(12) SCC 631 : 2005(8) Scale 618 : 2005(9) JT 38 : 2005 CriLJ 4648 : 2005 SCR 498 : 2006(1) SCC(Cri) 686 : 2005(54) ACrC 255 : 2006(1) CalCriLR 51 : 2006(1) Andh LD (Criminal) 402 : 2005(2) W.L.C. 754: 2005 Cri. L.R. 878 : 2006 ALL MR(Cri) 575 : 2005(4) KLT 842 : 2005(36) AIC 68: 2006(2) Cal. L.T. 78 : 2005 AIR (SCW) 5437 : 2005(4) Crimes 191 : 2005(7) Supreme 323 : 2005(32) Orrisa Cri. r. 897 : 2005(2) Cri. App. R(SC) 1008.

**Judges** :— Justice H.K. Sema and Justice P.P. Naolekar.

**Advocates:—**

1. For the Appellant :— E.M.S. Anam.
2. For the Respondent :— Ms. G. Indira and K.R. Sasiprabhu.

Criminal Appeal No. 495 of 2004.

Date of Decision — 25.10.2005

**A. Indian Penal Code, Sections 409 and 477 & 120B— Conspiracy— Misappropriation by accused— Another person had knowledge that accused was indulging in his misappropriation but no evidence that there was any agreement between the two — The person not guilty of conspiracy and not guilty of offence of misappropriation — In the absence of some positive evidence indicating agreement to that effect, conspiracy could not be inferred.**

[Paras 18 and 19]

**B. Prevention of Corruption Act, 1988, Section 13(1)(c) — Misappropriation by a Public servant — To constitute an offence under Section 13(1)(c) of Prevention of Corruption Act , it is necessary for the prosecution to prove that the accused has dishonestly or fraudulently misappropriated any property entrusted to him or under his control as a public servant or allowed any other person to do so or converts that property for his own use — The entrustment of the property or the control of the property is a necessary ingredient of Section 13(1)(c).**

[Para 20]

**C. Prevention of Corruption Act , 1988 , Section 13(1)(d) — Corruption charge against public servant — For conviction of accused under Section 13(1)(d) of Prevention of Corruption Act , there must be evidence on record that the accused has obtained for himself or for any other person, any valuable thing or pecuniary advantage by corrupt or illegal means or by abusing his position as a public servant obtained for himself, or for any person, any valuable thing, or pecuniary advantage without any public interest.**

[Para 21]

**D. Indian Penal Code, Section 409 & 120B— A public servant carried the gold to expert for melting and converting into a gold bar— Public servant misappropriating the gold— Another person who accompanied the accused cannot be held guilty of conspiracy— Cannot be inferred that there was an agreement entered into between them to misappropriate the gold.**

[Para 18]

**E. Indian Penal Code, Section 120B— Criminal conspiracy— Law reiterated:—**

(1) Criminal conspiracy is an agreement to break law.

(2) Parties to such an agreement will be guilty of criminal conspiracy, though the illegal act agreed to be done has not been done.

(3) It is also not an ingredient of offence that all the parties should agree to do a single illegal act — It may comprise the commission of a number of acts .

(4) To constitute a conspiracy, meeting of mind of two or more persons for doing an illegal act or an act by illegal means is the first and primary condition.

(5) It is not necessary that all the conspirators must know each and every detail of conspiracy — Neither it is necessary that every one of the conspirators takes active part in the commission of each and every conspiratorial acts .

(6) The agreement amongst the conspirators can be inferred by necessary implication.

(7) In most of the cases, the conspiracies are proved by the circumstantial evidence, as the conspiracy is seldom an open affair.

(8) Criminal conspiracy is an independent offence in Indian Penal Code.

(9) Unlawful act is sine qua non for constituting offence under Indian Penal Code and not an accomplishment.

(10) Mere knowledge, even discussion of the plan would not per se constitute conspiracy — The offence of conspiracy shall continue till the termination of agreement.

[Paras 13 and 14]

**Cases Referred :—**

Major EG Barsay v. State of Bombay, AIR 1961 Supreme Court 1762.

State through Superintendent of Police, CBI/SIT v. Nalini, 1999(2) RCR(Crl.) 682 (SC): JT 1999(4) SC 106.

Noor Mohd. v. State of Maharashtra, AIR 1971 Supreme Court 885.

State (NCT of Delhi) v. Navjot Sandhu @ Afsan Guru, 2005(3) Apex Crl. 49 (SC) : JT 2005(7) SC 1.

---

## Acquittal of a Doctor on the basis that demand and acceptance of fee for private practice is not a bribe

***Kanwarjit Singh Kakkar v. State of Punjab***

**(From Punjab and Haryana High Court)**

2011(2) KLT 630 : 2011 AIR (SC) (Cri) 1184 : 2011 AIR (SCW) 2757 : 2011(3) SLR 365 : 2011(2) AICLR 660 : 2011(3) Air Kar R 360 : 2011(3) JCC 1917 : 2011 CriLJ 3360 : 2011(75) ACrC 196 : 2011(2) Crimes 235 : 2011(5) R.C.R.(Criminal) 774 : 2011(5) Recent Apex Judgements (R.A.J.) 29 : 2011(4) R.C.R.(Criminal) 127 : 2011(3) GLR 2645 : 2011(13) SCC 158 : 2011(2) CalCriLR 543 : 2011(6) SCR 895 : 2011(5) Scale 37 : 2011(2) W.L.C. 209 : 2011(4) ADJ 734 : 2011(3) ECrC 85 : 2011(5) JT 214: 2011(2) GujLH 445 : 2011(273) ELT 356 : 2011(106) AIC 99 : 2011(2) Cri.CC 654 : 2011(5) Law Herald 637 : 2011(3) JLJR 100 : 2011(3) PLJR 137 : 2012(1) SCC(Cri) 805 : 2011(2) Andh LD (Criminal) 651 : 2012(113) CutLT 744 : 2011(3) BBCJ 58 : 2011(3) BBCJ 305 : 2011(2) B.L.Jud. 222 : 2011(1) SriLJ 22 : 2011(3) C.G.L.J. 308: 2011(49) Orrisa Cri. R. 327 : 2011(2) Apex Court Judgements (SC) 285.

**Judges** :— Justice Markandey Katju and Justice Gyan Sudhu Misra.

Crl. A. No. 1041 of 2011.

Date of Decision — 28.4.2011

**A. Prevention of Corruption Act, 1988, Sections 13(1)(d) and 13(2)— Indian Penal Code, 1860, Section 168— Illegal Gratification— Demand/receipt of the fee while doing private practice by a Government Doctor cannot be held to be an illegal gratification— No offence under Act, 1988 or Section 168 of Indian Penal Code established.**

[Paras 11 and 15]

**B. Indian Penal Code, 1860, Section 168— Trade— Government doctor indulged in private not amount to indulgence in "trade" while holding post of Government doctor.**

[Para 16]

## Cases Referred :

1. State of Gujarat v. Maheshkumar Dheerajlal Thakkar, (AIR 1980 SC 1167).
2. Raj Rajendra Singh Seth alias R.R.S. Seth v. State of Jharkhand, (2008) 11 SCC 681.
3. B. Noha v. State of Kerala, 2006 (4) KLT SN 64 (C. NO. 88)SC : 2006 (12) SCC 277.
4. Madhukar Bhaskarrao Joshi v. State of Maharashtra, (2000) 8 SCC 571 at 577.
5. M. Narsinga Rao v. State of A.P., 2001 1 SCC 691.

---

# Acquittal of an Assistant Engineer from the charge of possessing disproportionate assests on the ground of failure of proof against him.

***Kedari Lal v. State of Madhya Pradesh***

**(From Madhya Pradesh High Court)**

2015 Cri. L.R. 518:2015(2) Recent Apex Judgements (R.A.J.) 438 : 2015(3) ALT (Cri.) 58 : 2015(4) Scale 175 : 2015(3) JT 419 : 2015(2) Law Herald (SC) 1136: 2015(2) JCC 1182:2015(2) CCR 148 : 2015(149) AIC 79 : 2015(2) Crimes 142: 2015(89) ACrC 633:2015 All SCR 1568 : 2015(2) Law Herald 1634 : 2015(2) ECrC 141 : 2015(2) RajCriC 486:2015(3) AICLR 56 : 2015 AIR (SCW) 4413: 2015 CriLJ 4045 : 2015(2) R.C.R.(Criminal) 477 : 2015(sup) Cri.CC 222 : 2015(2) JabLJ 171:2015(2) Apex Court Judgements (SC) 522 : 2015(14) SCC 505 : 2016(1) SCC (L&S) 841:2016(2) SCC(Cri) 399 : 2015(61) Orissa Cri. R. 733.

**Judges** :— Justice Dipak Misra and Justice Uday Umesh Lalit.

**Advocates:—**

1. For the Appellant :— Mr. Sidharth Luthra, Sr. Adv. Ms. Sopriya Uneja, Adv. Ms. Shradha Karol, Adv. Mr. Vipin Kumar Saxena, Adv. Mr. Rajeev K. Sinha, Adv. Mr. Anoop Kr. Srivastav.
2. For the Respondents :— Mr. C.D. Singh, Adv. Mr. Darpan Bhuyan.

Criminal Appeal No. 782 of 2011.

Date of Decision — 23.3.2015.

**Prevention of Corruption Act, 1988, Sections 13(1)(e) and 13(2)— Allegation that accused (a public servant) was in possession of assets disproportionate to his known sources of income to the tune of ₹4,05,077/-— It was explained by accused that he received various amounts through gifts and inheritance and every time he received the amount department was informed and income was reflected Income Tax returns— Thus fact was proved on record— Conviction of accused set aside— Held, there is no violation of Section 13(1)(e) read with Section 13(2) of the Act . 1992(2) RCR (Crl.) 481, 2006(1) Apex Criminal 3, Relied.**

[Paras 12, 13 and 14]

**Cases Referred :**

D.S.P Chennai v. K. Ibasagarain, 2006(1) Apex Criminal 3 : 2006 (1) SCC 420.

Krishnanand v. State of Madhya Pradesh, 1977 (1) SCC 816.

M. Krishana Reddy v. State, 1992(2) R.C.R.(Criminal) 481 : 1992(4) SCC 49.

N. Ramakrishnaiah (D) through LR's v. State of A.P., 2009(1) R.C.R.(Criminal) 286: 2009(1) Recent Apex Judgments (R.A.J.) 112 : 2008 (17) SCC 83.

---

## Acquittal of Police Officer from charge of bribe as demand was not proved though tainted money was recovered

***Krishan Chander v. State of Delhi***

**(From Delhi High Court)**

2016(63) Orrisa Cri. R. 630 : 2016(1) R.C.R. (Criminal) 806 : 2016(1) Recent Apex Judgements (R.A.J.) 349 : 2016(1) Scale 143 : 2016 Cri. L.R. 1 : 2016(1) ECrC 224: 2016(1) Law Herald (SC) 398 : 2016(1) Law Herald 837 : 2016 AIR(SC) 298 : 2016 RajCriC 32 : 2016(3) SCC 108 : 2016 CriLJ 1079 : 2016(226) DLT 292 : 2016(1) Crimes 29 : 2016(1) JT 263 : 2016 AIR (SCW) 298 : 2016(92) ACrC 941 :

2016(158) AIC 208: 2016(1) JBCJ 190 : 2016(1) JCC 495 : 2016(1) Andh LD (Criminal) 434 : 2016(1) SCC(Cri) 725 : 2016(155) drj 449 : 2016(2) Him. L.R. 1148 : 2016 All SCR (Cri.) 372: 2016(1) AICLR 646 : 2016(2) RLW 1173 : 2016(2) Bom.C.R (Cri.) 756 : 2016(1) SCCriR 1 : 2016(3) KCCR 299 : 2016(sip1) CutLT (Criminal) 550 : 2016(1) B.L.Jud. 212 : 2016(1) MadWN (Cri) 255 : 2016(5) Mh.LJ (Cri.) 578 : 2017(3) CalCriLR 433: 2017(1) Rajdhani LR 495.

**Judges** :— Justice T.S. Thakur, CJI and Justice V. Gopala Gowda.

**Advocates:—**

1. For the Appellant :— Ajay Sharma.
2. For the Respondent :— D.S. Mahra.

Criminal Appeal No. 14 of 2016 (Arising out of SLP (Crl.) No. 703 of 2015).

Date of Decision — 6.1.2016

**A. Criminal Procedure Code, 1973, Section 300— Double Jeopardy— FIR against in a criminal offence— Accused gave false name and address to Investigating— A second FIR under Section 419, 420, Indian Penal Code for giving false application— Charge sheet on first FIR set aside as no case was made— Second FIR commits be quashed on this ground— Second FIR does not form part of first offence.**

[Para ]

**B. Evidence Act, 1872, Section 145— Hostile witness— Whenever a prosecution witness turns hostile his testimony cannot be discarded altogether— (1976) 4 SCC 233 Relied.**

[Para 25]

**C. Prevention of Corruption Act, 1988, Sections 7, 13(1)(d) and 13(2)— Conviction in bribery case — The demand for the bribe money is sine qua non to convict the accused for the offences punishable under Sections 7 and 13(1)(d) read with Section 13(2) of the PC Act — 2004 (2) RCR (Crl.) 410: 2014 (2) RAJ 570 : 2005 (4) RCR (Crl.) 350: 2015 (4) RAJ 625 Relied.**

[Para 34]

**D. Prevention of Corruption Act, 1988, Sections 20 and 13(1)— Tainted currency notes recovered from accused as a result of said, but demand by accused not proved — Conviction set aside —**

[Para 15]

**Cases Referred:**

A. Subair v. State of Kerala, 2009(3) R.C.R.(Criminal) 370 : (2009) 6 SCC 587.

B. Jayaraj v. State of Andhra Pradesh, 2014(2) R.C.R.(Criminal) 410 : 2014(2) Recent Apex Judgments (R.A.J.) 570 : (2014) 13 SCC 55.

P. Satyanarayana Murthy v. The Dist. Inspector of Police, State of Andhra Pradesh, 2015(4) R.C.R.(Criminal) 350 : 2015(4) Recent Apex Judgments (R.A.J.) 625 : (2015) 10 SCC 152.

Rabindra Kumar Dey v. State of Orissa, (1976) 4 SCC 233.

Sat Paul v. Delhi Administration, AIR 1976 SC 294.

Satvir Singh v. State of Delhi, 2014(4) RCR(Criminal) 40 : 2014(5) Recent Apex Judgments (R.A.J.) 20 (SC)

State of Kerala v. C.P. Rao, (2011) 6 SCC 450.

V.K. Mishra v. State of Uttarakhand, 2015(3) R.C.R.(Criminal) 899 : 2015(4) Recent Apex Judgments (R.A.J.) 233 : (2015) 9 SCC 588.

---

# Acquittal of Patwari in bribery case as demand was not proved though tainted money had been recovered

***Kuldeep Singh v. State of Haryana***

**(From Punjab and Haryana High Court)**

2015(3) Law Herald 2486:2015(8) R.C.R. (Criminal) 86:2016(1) AICLR 859

**Judges** :— Justice Raj Mohan Singh.

**Advocates:—**

1. For the Petitioner :— Naresh Kumar.
2. For the Respondent :— Pardeep Parkash Chahar, DAG Haryana.

CRA S 2343—SB of 2003.

Date of Decison — 3.7.2015.

A. **Prevention of Corruption Act, 1988, Sections 7 and 13—Accused convicted under—Appeal against conviction—Assessment of all incriminating facts and circumstances on record—Demand at the instance of appellant is not proved on record—Motive for such demand is also non-existent—Evidence of demand and acceptance are at variance—Prosecution story is found to be untrustworthy on the basis of official record of Revenue Department, shadow witness has not supported the case of prosecution and link evidence is not established on record—Considering all the attending circumstances of the case, benefit should go to the appellant in technical offence—Resultantly, this appeal is allowed—Judgment and order of conviction set aside.**

[Para 33]

**B. Prevention of Corruption Act, 1988, Section 7— Mere possession and recovery of currency notes from the accused without proof of demand will not bring him the offence under Section 7 — Demand of illegal gratification is *sine qua non* to constitute the said offence.**

[Para 30]

**Cases Referred :**

Abdul Rashid Ansari v. State of U.P., 1993 (2) Crimes 261 (Allahabad).

Amrik Singh v. State of Punjab, 2005(4) R.C.R. (Criminal) 310.

B.Jayaraj v. State of Andhra Pradesh, 2014(2) RCR (Criminal) 410.

Banarasi Dass v. State of Haryana, 2010 (2) RCR (Criminal) 553.

Jarnail Singh v. State of Haryana, 1991, Volume I RCR (Criminal) 391.

Karnail Singh v. State of Punjab, 2009 Volume I RCR (Criminal) 403.

Lalita Kumari v. State of U.P., (2014) 2 SCC 1.

M.R. Parshotam v. State of Karnataka, 2015 (Criminal) Law Journal 72.

Vineet Kumar v. State of Punjab, 2015 Volume I RCR (Criminal) 647.

## Acquittal of Former Chief Minister of Sikkim from charge of possession of disproportionate assets

***Kunga Nima Lepcha v. State of Sikkim***

**(From Sikkim High Court)**

2010(3) JT 222:2010(4) SCC 513:2010(2) AICLR 677:2010 CriLJ 2411:2010(2) ICC 835:2010(5) BCR 357:2010 AIR (SC) 1671:2010(80) ALR 741:2010(2) R.C.R. (Criminal) 531:2010(2) Recent Apex Judgements (R.A.J.) 454:2010(89) AIC 152:2010(2) WBLR 470:2010 AIR (SCW) 2245:2010(3) SCR 787:2010(4) Cal. H.C.N. 81:2010(1) W.L.C. 564:2010(3) Scale 309:2010 Cri. L.R. 335:2010(3) ALL MR 439:2010(2) SCC (Cri) 878:2010(3) GauLT 17:2010(sup) CutLT (Criminal) 967:2010(3) L.R.C. 65:2010(46) Orrisa Cri. R. 94.

**Judges** :— Justice K.G. Balakrishnan, Justice CJ., Justice P. Sathasivam and Justice J.M. Panchal.

**Advocates:—**

1. For the Petitioners :— Mr. Annam D.N. Rao, Adv. Mr. Vinod Bobde, Sr. Adv. Mr. Anupam Lal Das.
2. For the Respondents :— MR. K.K. Venugopal, Sr. Adv. Mr. Altaf Ahmed, Sr. Adv. Mr. A. Mariaputham, Adv. Mrs. Aruna Mathur, Adv. For M/s. Arputham, Aruna & Co., Advs. Mr. Mohan Parasaran, ASG Mr. P. Parmeswaran, Adv. Mr. Ram Jethmalani, Sr. Adv. Ms. V. Mohana.

Writ Petition (Civil) No.(s) 353 of 2006.

Date of Decision — 25.03.2010

**Prevention of Corruption Act, 1988, Section 13(2)— Constitution of India, Articles 32 and 142, Articles 227 and 226— Public Interest Litigation— Allegation of corruption against Cheif Minister of a State— PIL before Supreme Court praying for investigation of allegations by CBI— PIL dismissed— Held:**

**(1) The alleged acts come within the Prevention of Corruption Act — Writ jurisdiction may not be used as a matter of due course where statutory remedies are available — Court cannot sit in judgment over whether investigations should be launched against politicians for alleged acts of corruption — Petitioners to approach the investigative agencies directly with the incriminating materials and it is for the investigative agencies to decide on the further course of action.**

**(2) In the past, writ jurisdiction has been used to monitor the progress of ongoing investigations or to transfer ongoing investigations from one investigating agency to another. Such directions have been given when a specific violation of fundamental rights is shown.**

**(3) Writ court can only play a corrective role to ensure that the integrity of the investigation is not compromised.**

**(4) Court cannot sit in judgment over whether investigations should be launched against politicians for alleged acts of corruption.**

[Paras 9, 10 and 11]

**Case Referred :**

Vineet Narain v. Union of India, 1998(1) R.C.R.(Criminal) 357 : (1998) 1 SCC 226.

---

# Acquittal of the Chief Minister of Bihar from charge of disproportionate assets on the ground that lack of power of State if offence has been investigated under Delhi Special Police Establishment Act

***Lalu Prasad Yadav v. State of Bihar***

**(From Patna High Court)**

2010(3) JT 433:2010(5) SCC 1:2010(2) AICLR 610:2010(2) CriLJ 2427:2010 AIR (SC) 1561:2010(2) Crimes 328:2010(2) MLJ (Criminal) 621:2010(2) Recent Apex Judgements (R.A.J.) 421:2010(2) R.C.R. (Criminal) 480:2010(89) AIC 222:2010(2)

Bom.C.R. (Cri.) 4:2010(2) SCC (Cri) 1215:2010(2) KCCR 1477:2010(2) CalCriLR 52:2010(4) SCR 334:2010(1) W.L.C. 633:2010(3) Scale 443:2010(2) ECrC 183:2010 Cri. L.R. 394:2010 AIR (SCW) 2291:2010(4) AIR Jhar R. 451:2010(2) KLT 42:2010(3) RLW 2619:2010(3) Mh.LJ (Cri.) 387:2010(2) JLJR 97:2010(sup) CutLT (Criminal) 910:2010(2) SLT 774:2010(2) BBCJ 275:2010(2) MadWN (Cri) 179:2010(46) Orrisa Cri. R. 120.

**Judges** :— Justice K.G. Balakrishnan, Justice CJ., Justice R.M. Lodha and Justice B.S. Chauhan.

**Advocates:—**

1. For the Appearing Parties :— Ram Jethmalani, Pravin H. Parekh, Chitranjan Sinha, A. Mariarputham, L. Nageshwar Rao, Sr. Advs., M/s. Lata Krishnamurti, P.R. Mala, E.R. Kumar, Sameer Parekh, Saurabh Ajay Gupta, Somanadri Gaud, Pranav Diesh (for M/s. Parekh &. Co.), M/s. T. A. Khan, Devadatt Kamat, Arvind K. Sharma, P.K. Dey (for B. Krishna Prasad), Vishwajit Singh, Mrs. Veera Kaul Singh, Ritesh Agarwal, Siddharth Sengar, Abhindra Maheshwari.

Criminal Appeal No. 662 of 2010 [Arising out of SLP (Crl.) No. 6563 of 2007.

WITH Criminal Appeal No. 670 of 2010 [Arising out of SLP (Crl.) No. 6821 of 2007].

Date of Decision — 01.04.2010.

A. **Prevention of Corruption Act, 1988, Sections 13(1)(e) and 13(2)— Delhi Special Police Investigation Act— Appeal against acquittal— Case investigated by CBI and filing of charge sheet— Acquittal of Accused in CBI Special Court— Criminal Procedure Code, 1973, Section 378— Held, State of Bihar has no competence to file appeal as case was investigated by CBI.**

[Paras 3,27,31,34,3738 and 39]

**Cases Referred :**

1. Eknath Shankarrao Mukkawar v. State of Maharashtra, (1977)3 SCC 25.
2. Khemraj v. State of M.P. (1976)1 SCC 385.
3. Robert Mitchell v. Soren Torup, (1766) Parker 227.
4. Becke v. Smith, (1836)2 Meeson and Welsby 191.
5. Union of India v. Hansoli Devi, 2003(2) R.C.R.(Civil) 734 : (2002)7 SCC 273.
6. Kirkness v. John Hudson & Co. Ltd., (1955)2 All ER 345.
7. Aswini Kumar Ghose v. Arabinda Bose, AIR 1952 Supreme Court 369.
8. Quebec Railway, Light Heat & Power Co. Ltd. v. Vandry, AIR 1920 PC 181.

9. Williams v. Milotin, 97 C.L.R. 465.
10. Bengal Immunity Company Limited v. The State of Bihar, (1955) 2 SCR 603.
11. D.R. Fraser & Co. Ltd. v. The Minister of National Revenue, AIR 1949 PC 120.
12. Stone v. Yeovil Corp., (1875—76) L.R. 1 CPD 691.
13. Salmon v. Duncombe, (1886)11 AC 627.
14. State of Orissa v. Sudhansu Sekhar Misra, AIR 1968 Supreme Court 647.

---

# Quashing of Proceeding against Deputy Commissioner of Pallamu for lack of sanction for prosecution

***Louis Peter Surin v. State of Jharkhand***
**(From Jharkhand High Court)**

2010(4) AICLR 129:2010(12) SCC 497:2011(3) AIR Jhar R. 29:2010(3) R.C.R. (Criminal) 932:2010(4) Recent Apex Judgements (R.A.J.) 519:2011(75) ACrC 961:2011(108) AIC 271:2012 AIR (SC) (Cri) 157:2010(8) SCR 1115:2010(7) Scale 748:2011 Cri. L.R. 620:2011(1) SCC (Cri) 578:2010(4) PLJR 221:2011 (sup) CutLT (Criminal) 495:2010(3) L.R.C. 192:2011(1) Ori. Law Rev. 125.

**Judges** :— Justice Harjit Singh Bedi & Justice C.K.Prasad.

**Advocates:—**

1. For the Appellant :— Vikas Singh, Sr. Adv., Yunus Malik, Ravi Kishore, Samir Malik, Amrita Narayan, Shiva Lakshmi, Udita Singh and Prashant Chaudhary.
2. For the Respondent :— Gopal Prasad.

Criminal Appeal No. 498 of 2006.

Date of Decision — 27.7.2010

**Criminal Procedure Code, Section 197— Prevention of Corruption Act, 1988, Sections 13(1)(e) and (2) and 19— Sanction for prosecution— Corruption case registered against a Public Servant in the year 1984— Sanction to prosecute rejected by Competent Authority twice— Accused retired in the year 1997— Charge sheet filed in the Court in the year 2001 as sanction of Authority was not required after retirement of accused— Held;-**
**In view of these peculiar facts the initiation of proceedings against the appellant was not justified— Proceedings quashed. 2001(4) RCR (Crl) 589, 1994(2) RCR (Crl) 491 relied.**

[Paras 4, 5 and 6]

**Cases Referred :**

Mahendra Lal Dua v. State of Bihar, 2001(4) R.C.R.(Criminal) 589:(2002) 1 SCC 149.

Ramanand Chaudhary v. State of Bihar, 1994(2) R.C.R.(Criminal) 491:(2002) 1 SCC 153.

---

# Acquittal of accused from charge of possessing disproportionate asset for lack of proper evidence

## *M. Krishna Reddy v. State Deputy Superintendent of Police*

**(From Andhra Pradesh High Court)**

1992 (2) R.C.R. (Criminal) 481:1993 AIR (SC) 313:1993 CriLJ 308:1992(2) Crimes 1197:1992(4) SCC 45:1992(4) JT 436:1993(1) KLT 8:1993(1) SimLJ 605:1992(3) RSJ 593:1992(2) Scale 120:1992 Cri. L.R. 613:1992 SCC (Cri) 801:1992AIR (SCW) 3204:1992(2) UJ (SC) 613.

**Judges**:— Justice S. Ratnavel Pandian and Justice R.M. Sahai.

Criminal Appeal No. 354 of 1990.

Date of Decision — 17.7.1992.

A. **Prevention of Corruption Act, 1947, Section 5(1)(e)— Possession of assets by Government servant disproportionate to known sources of income— Mere acquisition of property does not constitute offence— Failure to satisfactorily account for such possessions is offending to law.**

[Para 7]

B. **Prevention of Corruption Act, 1947, Section 5(1)(e)— Assets possessed by Public Servant disproportionate to his known sources of income— Prosecution should first prove the known sources of income and property in possession of Public Servant— Only after the prosecution has proved the ingredients, burden to satisfactorily account for possession of resources or property shifts to the accused.**

[Paras 6 and 7]

C. **Prevention of Corruption Act, 1947, Section 5(1)(e)— Benami owner— Allegation of prosecution that accused was owner of certain amount which was lying in the account of another person— Burden to prove Benami lies on prosecution AIR 1977 SC 796 relied.**

[Para 19]

**D. Prevention of Corruption Act, 1988, Section 5(1)(e)— Possession of assets by Public servant disproportionate to his known sources of income— Memo of Govt No. D/88—4 dated 13.2.1989 giving guidelines to Anti Corruption Bureau to give allowance of 20% on the total income of Government servant while computing his income— These are guidelines and cannot be laid down as proposition of law.**

[Para 23]

**Cases Referred :**

S. Thiremolaiah v. State of A.P. Inspector of Police II A.C.B., Karnool, Criminal Appeal No. 459 of 1989, Andhra Pradesh High Court.

Krishnanand Agnihotri v. State of M.P., AIR 1977 Supreme Court 796:1977(1) SCC816.

---

## Acquittal of Sub-Registrar of Registration Department in Maharashtra for lack of evidence

***Mahmood Khan Pathan v. State of Maharashtra***

**(From Bombay High Court)**

1998(4) ALL MR 78 : 1998 AIR (SC) 2360 : 1998 CriLJ 3635 : 1997(1) Crimes 186: 1997(1) AICLR 621 : 1997(10) SCC 600 : 1997 SCC(Cri) 894 : 1997(2) JT 232: 1997(1) Scale 689 : 1997(1) SCR 830 : 1998 CRiLJ 3635 : 1997(2) Supreme 414: 1998 AIR (SCW) 2334 : 1997(34) ACrC 558 : 1999 Cri. L.R. 46 : 1997 Cri. L.R. 231: 1997(1) ALT (Cri.) 505:1997 SCCriR 782:1997(2) B.L.Jud. 203:1997(1) CLR309.

**Judges** :— Justice M.M. Punchhi and Justice K.T. Thomas.

**Advocates:—**

1. For the Appellant :— Dr. R.B. Masookar and K.L. Taneja.
2. For the Respondent :— S.M. Jadhav.

Criminal Appeal No. 381 of 1990.

Date of Decision — 3.2.1997

**Case Referred:**

Dhanvantrai Balwantrai Desai v. State of Maharashtra, AIR 1964 Supreme Court 575.

---

## Acquittal of Public Servant for lack of Sanction for Prosecution by Competent Authority

***Mohandas v. State of Kerala***

**(From Kerala High Court)**

2003(9) SCC 504:2004 SCC(Cri) 1176:2002(2) KLT 251:2003(3) All. C.J. 2238:2005(30) Orrisa Cri. R. 355.

**Judges**:— Justice G.B. Pattanaik and Justice Brijesh Kumar.

**Prevention of Corruption Act, 1988, Section 19— Sanction for prosecution— Jurisdiction of competent authority— Grant of sanction on the date when competent authority was having no jurisdiction amounts to sanction without jurisdiction— Conducting prosecution of appellant— Secretary (Vigilance) authorised for granting sanction only on specified date— Sanction was given by said authority prior to that date— Date on which the sanction for prosecution have been given, the authority concerned had no jurisdiction— Absence of any order of State Government making the Secretary (Vigilance) competent to accord sanction prior to the said date— There is an embargo on court's power to take cognizance for non-compliance of provisions of Section 19— Proceeding against appellant are liable to be quashed.**

[Para 3]

---

## Acquittal of C.M. Mayawati, Uttar Pradesh from charge of possessing disproportionate assets on the ground that CBI exceeded its duty and power

***Mayawati v. Union of India***

**(From Allahabad High Court)**

2012(3) SCC (Cri) 801:2012(3) Recent Apex Judgements (R.A.J.) 413:2012(3) R.C.R. (Criminal) 622:2012(4) CTC 322:2012 AIR (SCW) 4110:2012(8) SCC 106:2012 CriLJ 4282:2012 AIR (SC) (Cri) 1428:2012 AIR (SC) 3765:2012(116) AIC 111:2013(2) ALT (Cri.) 216:2012(7) SCR 33:2012(6) Scale 239:2012(2) W.L.C. 185:2012 Cri. L.R. 675:2012(3) ECrC 283:2012(6) JT 49:2012(3) JLJR 297:2012(5) SLT 193:2012(52) Orrisa Cri. R. 799.

**Judges** :— Justice P. Sathasivam and Justice Dipak Misra.

**Advocates:—**

1. For the Appearing :— Mohan Parasaran, ASG, Kapil Mishra, Abhinav Shrivastava, D.L. Chidananda, T.A. Khan, Arvind Kumar Sharma, Ms. Anupam Bharti, Shashank Singh, Pyloli Swatija, Akhilesh Karla Rohit Kr. singh, Mr. S.C. Mishra, Senior Advocate, Mr. Shail Kumar Dwivedi, Mr. Arvind Kumar Sharma, Mr. B. Krisha Prasad, Mr. Kamini Jaiswal and P. Narasimhan.

Writ Petition (Criminal) No. 135 of 2008.

Date of Decision — 6.7.2012.

**A. Prevention of Corruption Act , 1988 , Sections 13(1)(e) and 13(2)— Taj Heritage Corridor Case— Charge of misappreprlation of funds— Charges also against officers of U.P. Government— Disproportionate assets of accused persons not founded against misappreprlation of funds in Taj Heritage Case— F.I.R. quashed by Apex Court.**

[Paras 17,18,19,20,21 and 22]

**B. Prevention of Corruption Act, 1988, Section 13(1)(e) and 13(2)— Criminal Procedure Code, 1973, Sections 157 and 156— Delhi Special Police Establishment Act, 1946, Section 6— Loading of F.I.R. without consent of state government— Held, F.I.R. not sustainable— Constitution of India, Article 21— Public Interest Litigation— Third Party not empowered— F.I.R. Quashed.**

[Paras 17 to 22]

## Cases Referred:

Janata Dal v. H.S. Chowdhary, (1991)3 SCC 756.

M.C Mehta v. Union of India, (2003)8 SCC 711.

M.C. Mehta (Taj Corridor Scam) v. Union of India, 2007(4) R.C.R.(Criminal) 613: 2007(5) R.A.J. 524 : (2007)1 SCC 110.

M.C. Mehta (Taj Trapezium Matter) v. Union of India, (1997)2 SCC 353.

M.C. Mehta v. Union of India, (2003)8 SCC 706.

M.C. Mehta v. Union of India, (2003)8 SCC 696.

M.C. Mehta v. Union of India, (2007)1 SCC 136.

M.C. Mehta v. Union of India, I.A. No. 387 of 2003 in Writ Petition (C) No. 13381 of 1984, D/d. 16.7.2003.

M.C. Mehta v. Union of India, W.P. No. 13381 of 1984, D/d. 18.9.2003.

PIL (Union of India v. W.N. Chadha, 1993 (Supp) 4 SCC 260.

State of West Bengal v. Committee for Protection of Democratic Rights, West Bengal, 2010(2) R.C.R.(Criminal) 141 : 2010(1) Recent Apex Judgments (R.A.J.) 664 : (2010)3 SCC 571.

# Acquittal of Police Officer (since dead) from charge of bribery due to failure of proper evidence to support prosecution

***Mukhtiar Singh (Since Dead) v. State of Punjab***

**(From Punjab and Haryana High Court)**

2017(3) R.C.R.(Criminal) 694 : 2017(4) Recent Apex Judgements (R.A.J.) 395 : 2017 AIR (SC) 3382 : 2017(7) Scale 702 : 2017 Cri. L.R. 641 : 2017(7) JT 257 : 2017 AIR (SCW) 3382 : 2017 All SCR (Cri.) 1270 : 2017(68) Orrisa Cri. R. 81 : 2017(8) SCC 136 : 2017(3) JCC 1978 : 2017(4) JBCJ 40 : 2017(4) AICLR 50 : 2017(2) SCCriR 1168.

**Judges**:— Justice Arun Mishra and Justice Amitava Roy.

**Advocate:—**

1. For the Appellant :— Mr. O.P. Bhadani.
2. For the Respondent :— Mr. Kuldip Singh.

Criminal Appeal No. 1163 of 2017 (Arising Out of S.L.P (Criminal) No. 207 of 2016).

Date of Decision — 14.7.2017.

**Prevention of Corruption Act, 1988, Sections 7 and 13(2)— Charge of bribe— Death of accused— Conviction by Lower Court— Acquittal by Apex Court on the ground that prosecution failed to prove the offence.**

**Cases Referred :**

A. Subair v. State of Kerala, 2009(3) R.C.R.(Criminal) 370 : 2009(4) Recent Apex Judgments (R.A.J.) 125 : (2009) 6 SCC 587.

B. Jayaraj v. State of A.P., 2014(2) R.C.R.(Criminal) 410 : 2014(2) Recent Apex Judgments (R.A.J.) 570 : (2014) 13 SCC 55.

Mukhtiar Singh v. State of Punjab, 2016(3) R.C.R.(Criminal) 558 : 2016(4) Recent Apex Judgments (R.A.J.) 215 : (2016) 11 SCC 357.

P. Satyanarayana Murthy v. District Inspector of Police, State of Andhra Pradesh, 2015(4) R.C.R.(Criminal) 350 : 2015(4) Recent Apex Judgments (R.A.J.) 625 : (2015) 10 SCC 152.

Somabhai Gopalbhai Patel v. State of Gujarat, 2014(4) R.C.R.(Criminal) 441 : 2014(5) Recent Apex Judgments (R.A.J.) 453 : (2014) 15 SCC 103.

State of Kerala v. C.P. Rao, 2011(3) R.C.R.(Criminal) 688 : 2011(4) Recent Apex Judgments (R.A.J.) 183 : (2011) 6 SCC 450.

---

## Acquittal of accused from the charge of criminal breach of trust in respect of Mutual Fund Scam

### *S. Mohan v. Central Bureau of Investigation*

**(From Bombay High Court)**

2008(7) SCC 1:2008(8) Scale 66:2008(9) SCR 46:2008(2) Crimes 304:2008(3) Cri. CC 696:2008(2) CalCriLR 499:2008(2) Andh LD (Criminal) 25:2009(4) ECrC 184:2008(106) CutLT 360:2008(66) AIC 246:2008(2) APLJ 159:2008(3) SCC (Cri) 1:2008(4) AIR Bom.R 332:2008(sup) AIR (SC) 1831:2008 AIR (SCW) 3557.

**Judges:—** Justice R. Raveendran, J. and Justice K.G. Balakrishnan, CJI.

Criminal Appeal No. 910 of 1998.

Date of Decision — 16.5.2008.

**Case Referred:**

Canbank Financial Services Ltd. v. Custodian (2004) 8 SCC 355.

---

## Quashing of charges of posessing disproportionate assets on the death of accused during pendency of trial and order made for participant of children in auction

### *N. Naveen Kumar v. State of Andhra Pradesh*

**(From Andhra Pradesh High Court)**

2008(4) R.C.R. (Criminal) 818:2008(6) Recent Apex Judgements (R.A.J.) 145:2008(9) SCC 800:2009 AIR (SC) 241:2009(1) AICLR 135:2009 CriLJ 382:2008(3) SCC (Cri) 880:2008(11) JT 362:2008(13) Scale 447:2009(2) AIR Jhar R. 121:2008(71) AIC 25:2009(1) W.L.C. 752:2009 ALL MR(Cri) 250:2009(1) Mh.LJ (Crl.) 316:2008 AIR (SCW) 7201:2008(4) Cri.CC 782:2008(4) L.R.C. 289:2009(sup) CutLT (Criminal) 96:2008(41) Orrisa Cri. R. 843.

**Judges :—** Justice Dr. Arijit Pasayat and Justice P. Sathasivam.

**Advocates:—**

1. For the Appellants :— Sarvesh Bisaria and Anil Nag.
2. For the Respondent :— Ms. Altaf Fathima and Mrs. D. Bharathi Reddy.

Criminal Appeal No. 1627 of 2008 Arising out of SLP (Crl) No. 5252 of 2006.

Date of Decision — 17.10.2008.

---

## Quashing of charges of corruption and forgery after compromise between the parties

### *Nikhil Merchant v. Central Bureau of Investigation*
**(From Bombay High Court)**

2009(1) CalCriLR 19:2008(4) R.C.R. (Criminal) 102:2008(5) Recent Apex Judgements (R.A.J.) 156:2008(9) SCC 677:2009 AIR (SC) 428:2008(4) AICLR 237:2008(9) JT 192:2008(11) Scale 379:2008(3) SCC(Cri) 858:2008(3) Crimes 377:2009(1) AIR Bom.R 197:2008 AIR (SCW) 7501:2009(1) RLW 185:2008(69) AIC 34:2008(2) Andh LD (Criminal) 591:2009(1) W.L.C. 581:2009(3) ECrC 209:2008 Cri. L.R. 746:2008(3) KLT 769:2009(1) GujLH 31:2008(12) SCR 236:2008(2) Cri.CC 299:2008(2) GLD 529:2008 RajCriC 790:2008 NCC 901:2008(4) L.R.C. 10:2008(3) KHC 955:2008(4) BBCJ 96:2008(sup) CutLT (Criminal) 1226:2008(41) Orrisa Cri. R. 427.

**Judges** :— Judges Altamas Kabir and Judges Markandey Katju.

**Advocates:—**

1. For the Appellant :— R.F. Nariman and Ranjit Kumar, Senior Advocates with M.P. Bharucha, Manu Nair, Mark D'Souza and Vivek Vashi for M/s Suresh A. Shroff & Co..
2. For the Respondent :— A. Sharan, ASG with B.B. Singh, Senior Advocate with Ms. Ranjana Narayan, B.K. Prasad, P. Parmeswaran and Ravindra Keshavrao Adsure.

Criminal Appeal No. 1302 of 2008 (@ S.L.P. (Crl) No. 6355 of 2005).
Date of Decision — 20.08.2008.

**Cases Referred :**

Central Bureau of Investigation v. Duncans Agro Industries Ltd., 1996(3) RCR(Criminal) 60 : 1996(5) SCC 591.

B.S. Joshi v. State of Haryana, 2003(2) RCR(Criminal) 888 : 2004(1) Apex Criminal 197 : 2003(4) SCC 675.

State of Haryana v. Bhajan Lal, 1991(1) RCR(Crl.) 383 : 1992 Suppl. (1) SCC 335.

Supreme Court Bar Association v. Union of India, (1998)4 SCC 409.

---

## Acquittal of Senior Accountant in absence of proof of demand and acceptance by accused

### *N. Raja Kantham v. State*
**(From Andhra Pradesh and Telangana High Court)**

2009(17) SCC 415 : 2011(5) R.C.R.(Criminal) 739 : 2011 AIR (SC) (Cri) 2041 : 2009(13) Scale 98 : 2011(1) SCC(Cri) 1045 : 2010(1) OriLR 39 : 2009(44) Orrisa Cri. R. 977 : 2010(1) Ori. Law Rev. 39.

**Judges** :— Justice H.S. Bedi and Justice Dr. B.S. Chauhan.

Criminal Appeal No. 817 of 2006.

Date of Decision - 23.7.2009.

**A. Prevention of Corruption Act, 1988, Sections 13(1)(d) and 13(2)— Allegation of illegal gratification— Absence of proof—Acquittal by trial court— Conviction by High Court— Acquittal by Apex Court. Held, trial court had given very good reasons as to why the prosecution story could not inspire confidence.**

[Paras 2,8 and 14]

**B. Prevention of Corruption Act, 1988, Section 5(1)(d)— Indian Penal Code, 1860, Section 161— Demand of bribe— Recovery of tainted money— Demand was not proved— Complainant turning hostile— Acquittal of accused.**

[Paras 2,3 and 4]

---

## Acquittal of Public Servant from Corruption Charge due to lack of proper sanction for prosecution

***Om Kr. Dhankar v. State of Haryana***

**(From Punjab and Haryana High Court)**

2012(1) Recent Apex Judgements (R.A.J.) 429:2012(2) R.C.R. (Criminal) 209:2012(2) KLT 106:2012(1) ALT (Crl.) 407:2012(77) ACrC 243:2012(2) CTC 871:2012(2) Cri. CC 508:2012(2) PLJR 175:2012(2) Law Herald (SC) 1216:2012(3) PLR 120:2012(3) MLJ (Criminal) 563:2012(2) AICLR 745:2013(1) SCC (Cri) 493:2012(1) Ori. Law Rev.849:2012(1) CalCriLR 883:2012(1) SCR 1160:2012(3) Scale 363:2012(1) W.L.C. 667:2012 Cri. L.R. 364:2012(3) J.K.J. 59:2012(2) CalLJ 111:2012(2) ECrC 121:2012(3) JT 485:2012 ALL MR(Cri) 1358:2012(11) SCC 252:2012(2) JLJR 16:2012(Sup) CutLT (Criminal) 1299:2012(2) M.P.W.N. 141:2012(4) SLT 289:2012(2) BBCJ 422:2012(2) B.L.Jud. 191:2012(2) Ker L.J. 453:2012(52) Orrisa Cri. R. 63:2012(1) Apex Court Judgements (SC) 720.

**Judges** :— Justice R.M. Lodha and Justice H.L. Gokhale.

**Advocates:—**

1. For the Appellants :— Dr. Sushil Balwada.
2. For the Respondents :— Anis Ahmed Khan, Shoaib Ahmed Khan, S.P. Singh, chowdhari, Ramesh Kumar, Kamal Mohan Gupta.

Criminal Appeal No. 464 of 2012 (Arising Out of S.L.P. (Crl) No. 6908 of 2008).

Date of Decision — 28.2.2012.

**Cases Referred :**

Amar Nath v. State of Haryana, (1977) 4 SCC 137.

K.M. Mathew v. State of Kerala, 1992(1) R.C.R.(Criminal) 232 : (1992) 1 SCC 217.

Madhu Limaye v. State of Maharashtra, (1977) 4 SCC 551.

Prakash Singh Badal v. State of Punjab, 2007(1) R.C.R. (Criminal) 1 : 2007(1) R.A.J. 71: (2007) 1 SCC 1.

Rajendra Kumar Sitaram Pande v. Uttam, 1999(1) R.C.R. (Criminal) 800 : (1999) 3 SCC 134.

Rakesh Kumar Mishra v. State of Bihar, 2006(1) R.C.R. (Criminal) 456 : 2006(1) Apex Criminal 175 : (2006) 1 SCC 557.

V.C. Shukla v. State, 1980 Supp. SCC 92.

---

## Acquittal of Police Inspector for lack of prosecution evidence

### *Om Parkash v. State of Haryana*

**(From Punjab and Haryana High Court)**

2006(2) ECrC 29 : 2006(1) Apex Criminal 345 : 2006(1) R.C.R.(Criminal) 820: 2006(1) JT 343 : 2006(2) SCC 250 : 2006(1) Cri.CC 851 : 2006(2) AICLR 150: 2006 CriLJ 972 : 2006 AIR (SC) 894 : 2006(1) SCC(Cri) 493 : 2006(1) Scale 290: 2006(1) SCR 423 : 2006(54) ACrC 526 : 2006 AIR (SCW) 368 : 2006(1) Crimes 179 : 2006(2) AIR (Jharkhand) 81 : 2006(1) Supreme 275 : 2006(2) OLJR 90 : 2006(2) CalLJ 147 : 2006(1) W.L.C. 259 : 2006 Cri. L.R. 103 : 2006(1) CalCriLR 314 : 2006 ALL R(Cri) 930 : 2006(38) AIC 1 : 2006(1) Law Herald (SC) 437 : 2006(2) JLJR 141 : 2006(1) Andh LD (Criminal) 269 : 2006(2) M.P.W.N. 1 : 2006(1) L.R.C. 142 : 2006(2) B.L.Jud. 637 : 2006(1) CLR 506 : 2006(33) Orrisa Cri. R. 529 : 2006(1) Apex Court Judgements(SC) 250 : 2006(1) Cri. App. R.(SC) 203.

**Judges** :— Justice S.B. Sinha and Justice P.K. Balasubramanyan.

**Advocates:—**

1. For the Appellant :— Uday Umesh Lalit, Sr. Advocate, Jasbir Singh Malik, D.K. Sharma, Arun Kumar Singh and S.K. Sabharwal.
2. For the Respondent :— Rajeev Gaur Naseem and T.V. George.

Criminal Appeal No. 110 of 2006 [Arising out of SLP (Crl.) No. 4709 of 2005].

Date of Decison - 17.1.2006.

**Cases referred :**

Union of India v. Purnandu Biswas, 2005(3) Apex Criminal 442 : 2005(4) RCR(-Criminal) 517 : 2005(8) SCALE 246.

T. Subramanian v. State of Tamil Nadu, 2006(1) Apex Criminal 159 : (2006(1) SCALE 116).

---

## Acquittal of Mandal Development Officer in case of demand of bribe due to contradiction in witness evidence

### *P. Parasurami Reddy v. State of Andhra Pradesh*

2011(74) ACrC 959:2011(105) AIC 46:2011(4) MLJ (Criminal) 85:2011(3) R.C.R. (Criminal) 863:2011(4) Recent Apex Judgements (R.A.J.) 458:2012(1) ALT (Crl.) 65:2011(12) SCC 294:2011(3) CalCriLR 475:2011(3) W.L.N. 64:2011(9) SCR 656:2011(8) Scale 625:2011(2) W.L.C. 368:2011(4) ECrC 230:2011 Cri. L.R. 623:2011(4) J.C.R. 250:2011 ALL MR(Cri) 2952:2011(4) Cri.CC 240:2012(1) SCC(Cri) 552:2012 (Sup) CutLT 502:2011(8) SLT 673:2011(4) B.L.Jud. 35:2011(50) Orrisa Cri. R. 232:2011(2) Ori. Law Rev. 618.

**Judges:**— Justice V.S. Sirpurkar and Justice T.S. Thakur.

**Advocates:**

1. For the Appellant :— R. Sundervardhan, Senior Advocate, Ms. T. Anamika.
2. For the Respondents :— I. Venkatanarayana, Senior Advocate, D. Mahesh Babu, Ramesh Allanki, V. Pattabhi Ram and Ms. Savita Dhanda.

Criminal Appeal No. 462 of 2003.

Date of Decision — 2.8.2011

**Prevention of Corruption Act, 1988, Sections 7,13(1)(C) and 13(2)— Charge of demand of bribe— Tainted money thrusted into pocket of accused— Accused threw same towards Public— Failure of raid party to recover— Conviction**

**by Lower Court and High Court— Conviction Set aside by Supreme Court— Acquittal on the ground of faiture of prosecution to prove guilty of accused.**
[Paras 2,9,10 and 12]

---

## Acquittal of Doctor from charge of bribery due to absence of evidence that he had voluntarily accepted bribe

***Prabhat Kumar Gupta v. State of Jharkhand***
**(From Jharkhand High Court)**

2005(1) SCC(Cri) 427 : 2014(14) SCC 516 : 2010(10) Scale 48 : 2011(111) CutLT 296: 2010(47) Orrisa Cri. R. 865

**Judges** :— Justice Harjit Singh Bedi And Justice Chandramauli Kr. Prasad.

Crl.A. No. 1386 of 2003.

Date of Decision - 7.9.2010.

**Prevention of Corruption Act, 1988, Sections 7 and 13(1) read with 13(1) (d)— Demand and acceptance of bribe— Trap case— Witnesses turning hostile—Appellant asked for payment of Rs. 100/- for plaster— Amount was not paid to him but was paid to the compounder— Even if we assume that the currency note was recovered from his possession there is no evidence that he had voluntarily accepted the same— Conviction set aside.**
[Para 9]

**Cases Referred:**

C.M. Girish Babu v. CBI, Cochin, High Court of Kerala, 2009 (3) SCC 779.

Suraj Mal v. State (Delhi Admn.) 1979 4 SCC 725.

State of U.P. v. Dr. G.K Ghosh, 1984 (1) SCC 254.

Subbu Singh v. State By Public Prosecutor, 2009 (6) SCC 462.

---

## Acquittal of Director General of Indian Council of Medical Research due to absence of Sanction for Prosecution from Competent Authority

***Prof. N.K. Ganguly v. CBI, New Delhi***
**(From Delhi High Court)**

2015(12) Scale 500:2015(5) Law Herald (SC) 3497:2016(1) R.C.R. (Criminal) 98:2015(6) Recent Apex Judgements (R.A.J.) 237:2015 AIR (SCW) 6372:2015(4) Crimes 372:2015(4) MLJ (Criminal) 605:2015 All SCR 3717:2016(1) PLJR 71:2016 (157) AIC 186:2016(1) Cal. L.T. 1:2015 RajCriC 1101:2016(1) JCC 243:2016(1) Apex Court Judgements (SC) 541:2016(1) SCC 290:2016(1) AIR Jhar R. 339:2015(4) JLJR 554:2016(92) ACrC 470:2016 CriLJ 371:2016(1) All. LJ 315:2016(2) SCC 143:2016(1) SCC (Cri) 478:2016(1) JBCJ 14:2016(1) AI-CLR 270:2016(2) ECrC 125:2016(3) JCC 1523:2016(3) Rajdhani LR 299:2016 (sup 2) CutLT (Criminal) 449:2016(63) Orrisa Cri. R. 44:2016(1) Ori. Law Rev. 338:2016(1) All. Cri. Rulings 460.

Criminal Appeal No. 799 of 2015, Criminal Appeal No. 800 of 2015, Criminal Appeal No. 801 of 2015, Criminal Appeal No. 930 of 2015 and Criminal Appeal No. 1537 of 2015 (Arising out of SLP (Crl.) No. 9838 of 2015)(@ Slp (Crl).... Crl. M.P. No. 9612 of 2015).

**Judges**:— Justice V. Gopala Gowda and Justice Amitava Roy.

**Advocates:—**

1. For the Appellants :— P.P. Khurana, Senior Advocate, Arun K. Sinha, Rajesh Singh Chauhan, Mr. Sachin Sood, Mr. Jetendra Singh, Ms. Kalpana Sabharwal, Ms. Priyanka Singh, Ms. Manju Jetley, Mr. Kumar Kaushik, Mr. Bhupesh Sharma, Mr. Shiv Ram Pandey, Mr. S.D. Singh, Mr. Vijay Kumar, Mr. J. Singh, Ms. Bharti Tyagi, Mr. T. Srinivasa Murthy, Ms. Shruti Iyer, Mr. T. Rahman, Mr. Kushagra Pandey and Mr. Senthil Jagadeesan.
2. For the Respondent :— B.V. Balaram Das.

Criminal Appeal No. 798 of 2015.

Date of Decision - 19.11.2015.

**Indian Penal Code, 1860 Section 120(B) Criminal Procedure Code, 1973 Section 197 Prevention of Corruption Act , 1988 Section 13(1)(d) and 13(2)**

**(i) Offence under Section 120B I.P.C. (Criminal Conspiracy) committed by a Public Servant — Sanction for prosecution of competent Authority under Section 197 Cr.P.C. whether required ? — In the facts of case, held that sanction was required which was not obtained and proceedings quashed.**

## ON FACTS

**Prosecution version that accused were officers and officials of Registered Co—operative Society wholly funded by Govt. — They entered into conspiracy and transferred a plot of land of society to a Private Housing Society of which they were members at drastically low price and dishonestly obtained an undue**

**pecuniary advantage to the tune of L 13.14 crores for themselves — A charge—sheet under Section 120B I.P.C. and Sections 13(1)(d) and 13(2) of Prevention of Corruption filed — No sanction of prosecution obtained from Competent Authority — It was contended that illegal acts committed by accused cannot be said to have been carried out in discharge of official duty and thus no sanction was required — Contention not tenable — Held :—**

**(i) In the charge—sheet filed before court it was submitted that the alleged offences were committed by accused in discharge of their official duty — In such a case sanction for prosecution was required which was not obtained — Criminal proceedings and order of Special Magistrate taking cognizance set aside in absence of sanction for prosecution.**

[Paras 24, 25, 26 and 17]

## Cases Referred :

Abdul Wahab Ansari v. State of Bihar, 2000(4) R.C.R.(Criminal) 572 : (2000) 8 SCC 500.

Amrik Singh v. State of Pepsu, AIR 1955 SC 309.

B. Saha v. M.S Kochar, (1979) 4 SCC 177.

Baijnath Gupta v. State of Madhya Pradesh, AIR 1966 SC 220 : 1966 (1) SCR 210.

Dr. Hori Ram Singh v. Emperor, AIR 1939 Federal Court 43.

H.H.B. Gill v. The King, AIR 1948 PC 128.

M.P v. Sheetla Sahai, 2009(3) R.C.R.(Criminal) 835 : 2009(5) Recent Apex Judgments (R.A.J.) 110 : (2009) 8 SCC 617.

Matajog Dobey v. H.C. Bhari, AIR 1956 SC 44.

Prakash Singh Badal v. Union of India, 2007(1) R.C.R.(Criminal) 1 : 2007(1) Recent Apex Judgments (R.A.J.) 71 : (2007) 1 SCC 1.

R. Balakrishna Pillai v. State of Kerala, 1996(2) R.C.R.(Criminal) 765 : (1996) 1 SCC 478.

R.R. Chari v. State of Uttar Pradesh, AIR 1951 SC 207.

R.S Nayak v. A.R Antulay, (1984) 2 SCC 183.

Satwant Singh v. State of Punjab, AIR 1960 SC 266.

Shankaran Moitra v. Sadhna Das, 2006(2) R.C.R.(Criminal) 389 : (2006) 4 SCC 584.

Shreekantiah Ramayya Munipalli v. State of Bombay, AIR 1955 SC 287.

Superintendent and Remembrance of Legal Affairs, West Bengal v. Abhani Kumar Bannerjee, AIR 1950 Calcutta 437.

## Acquittal of Patwari from charge of bribery due to failure of prosecution to establish offence

***Punjabrao v. State of Maharashtra***
**(From Bombay High Court)**

2002(1) R.C.R. (Criminal) 231:2002 AIR (SC) 486:2002(1) Cri. CC 93:2001(3) AICLR 776:2002(10) SCC 371:2001(5) JT 532:2004 SCC (Cri) 1130:2001(43) ACrC 372:2001(3) Crimes 309:2001(5) Supreme 231:2002 AIR (SCW) 16:2001(2) Apex Court Journal 143:2002(1) APLJ 50:2003(25) Orrisa Cri. R. 824.

**Judges :**— Justice G.B. Pattanaik and Justice U.C. Banerjee.

Criminal Appeal No. 1749 of 2001.

Date of Decision — 14.2.2001.

---

## Acquittal of Special Officer of a Sanskrit University, Ernakullam due to lack of invalid sanction for prosecution and charge sheet being filed after 8½ years.

***R. Ramachandran Nair v. Deputy Superintendent Vigilance Police***

2011(4) SCC 395:2011(2) KLT 135:2011 AIR (SC) (Cri) 992:2011 (74) ACrC 985:2011(2) Crimes 95:2011(2) R.C.R. (Criminal) 564:2011(2) Recent Apex Judgements (R.A.J.) 377:2011(4) MLJ (Criminal) 687:2011(2) Cri.CC 470:2011(2) ECrC 227:2011(3) SCR 1054:2011(4) Scale 14:2011(2) W.L.C. 482:2011(4) JT 500:2011(2) SCC (Cri) 251:2011(2) SCC (L&S) 691:2011(106) AIC 136:2011 ALL MR (Cri) 2911:2012(Sup) CutLT (Criminal) 385:2011(2) B.L.Jud. 207:2011(49) Orrisa Cri. R. 188.

**Judges** :— Justice P. Sathasivam and Justice B.S. Chauhan.

**Advocates:—**

1. For the Appellant :— K.V. Viswanathan, Senior Advocate, Nikhil Goel, Marsook Bafaki, Rajesh B. and A. Venayagam Balan.
2. For the Respondent :— Jayadeep Gupta, Senior Advocate, G. Prakesh and Ms. Beena Prakash.

Criminal Appeal No. 792 of 2011 (Arising out of S.L.P. (Crl.) No. 9818 of 2010).

Date of Decision — 28.3.2011

**Indian Penal Code, Section 409 — Prevention of Corruption Act , 1988 , Sections 13(2) and 13(1)(d) — Sree Sankarachaya University of Sanskrit**

**Act , 1994, Section 50(2) — Charge sheet filed against a Vice Chancellor of University on charge of corruption — Sanction of Syndicate University not obtained as required under the Act — Vice Chancellor is a public servant — Moreover charge sheet filed after 8½ years of registration case — Even on merits the respondents are not justified in continuing the criminal proceedings — Accused discharged.**

[Paras 9 and 10]

---

## Acquittal of an Employee of MCD for absence of proof that the tainted money was handed over to him as bribe

***R.P.S. Yadav v. C.B.I.***

**(From Delhi High Court)**

2015 AIR (SCW) 2828 : 2015 All SCR 1827 : 2015(2) R.C.R.(Criminal) 91 : 2015(2) Recent Apex Judgements (R.A.J.) 25 : 2015(2) Law Herald (SC) 1244 : 2015(148) AIC 103 : 2015(3) AIR Jhar R. 320 : 2015(3) Law Herald 1915 : 2015(2) ECrC 82: 2015(2) CalCriLR 467 : 2015 Cri. L.R. 849 : 2015(89) ACrC 666 : 2015(3) AICLR 852:2015(11) SCC 642 : 2015(61) Orrisa Cri. R. 1028 : 2015(1) All. Cri. Rulings 1098.

**Judges**:— Justice Fakkir Mohamed Ibrahim Kalifulla and Justice Abhay Manohar Sapre.

**Advocates:—**

1. For the Appellant :— Brajesh Kumar Singh and Anil Kumar Tandale.
2. For the Respondent :— Vibha Dutta Makhija, Senior Advocate, Ms. Rashmi Malhotra, Disha Vaish and Arvind Kumar Sharma.

Criminal Appeal No. 9 of 2012.

Date of Decision — 28.1.2015.

---

## Quashing of prosecution against Circle Inspector of Revenue Department in Bihar for lack of evidence and lack of proper sanction for prosecution

***Ramanand Chaudhary v. State of Bihar***

**(From Patna High Court)**

1994(2) R.C.R.(Criminal) 491:1994 AIR (SC) 948:1994 CriLJ 1221:2002(1) SCC 153:2004(3) Scale 266:2002 SCC(Cri) 114:1994 AIR (SCW) 1033:1994(2) B.L.Jud. 324.

**Judges**:— Justice Kuldip Singh and Justice N.M. Kasliwal.

Criminal Appeal No. 198 of 1992.

Date of Decision — 7.8.1992.

---

## Acquittal of Police Officer due to lack of valid sanction for prosecution

***Romesh Lal Jain v. Naginder Singh Rana***

**(From Punjab and Haryana High Court)**

2005(4) R.C.R. (Criminal) 835:2005(3) Apex Criminal 533:2006 AIR(SC) 336:2006(1) SCC 294:2006(1) Cri. CC 363:2005(8) Scale 810:2005(9) JT 393:2005 (Sup4) SCR 868:2006(2) SCC (Cri) 593:2006(54) ACrC 850:2006(1) RajCriC 138:2005(3) JCC 1937:2006(1) W.L.C. 57:2006 ALL MR (Cri) 1783:2005 CriLJ 5068:2005(36) AIC 108:2005(8) Supreme 106:2005(4) Crimes 290:2005 AIR (SCW) 5875:2006 (1) B.L.Jud. 482:2006(2) CLR 132:2006(33) Orrisa Cri. R. 90:2006(1) Apex Court Judgements (SC) 537:2005(2) Cri. App. R (SC) 1055.

**Judges**:— Justice S.B. Sinha & Justice R.V. Raveendran.

**Advocates:—**

1. For the Appellant :— Neeraj Kumar Jain, Aditya Kr. Chaudhary, Bharat Singh, Sanjay Singh and Ugra Shankar Prasad.
2. For the Respondents :— K.T.S. Tulsi, Sr. Advocate with Rishi Malhotra, Prem Malhotra, Sanjay Jain, Vinay Arora, Adolf Mathew and Bimal Roy Jad.

Criminal Appeal No. 691 of 2003.

Date of Decision — 28—10—2005

**Prevention of Corruption Act, 1988, Sections 19 and 13(2)— Criminal Procedure Code, 1973, Section 197— Indian Penal Code, 1860, Sections 409, 167, 218, 419, 420, 465, 468 and 471— Charge of corruption against accused Police Officer— Rank of Sub—Inspector— Quetion of Sanctioning authority— Acquittal of accused due to lack of sanction for prosecution by competent authority.**

[Paras 13,14,17,18,19,37 and 47]

**Cases referred:**

Shreekantiah Ramayya Munipalli v. State of Bombay [1955(1) SCR 1177].

P.K. Pradhan v. State of Sikkim represented by Central Bureau of Investigation, 2001(3) RCR(Crl.) 835 (SC) : [(2001)6 SCC 704].

State of U.P. v. M.P. Gupta [(2004)2 SCC 349].

Amrik Singh v. State of Pepsu [(1955)1 SCR 1302].

N. Bhargavan Pillai (dead) by LRs. v. State of Kerala, 2004(2) RCR(Crl.) 641 (SC): [AIR 2004 SC 2317].

State of H.P. v. M.P. Gupta, 2004(1) RCR(Crl.) 197 (SC) : (JT 2003(10) SC 32).

State of Orissa through Kumar Raghvendra Singh v. Ganesh Chandra Jew, 2004(2) RCR(Crl.) 663 (SC) : [(2004)8 SCC 40].

Matajog Dobey v. H.C. Bhari, (AIR 1956 SC 44).

S.K. Zutshi v. Bimal Debnath, 2004(3) RCR(Crl.) 813 (SC) : [(2004)8 SCC 31].

K. Kalimuthu v. State by DSP, 2005(2) RCR(Crl.) 463 (SC) : 2005(2) Apex Criminal 58 (SC) : (2005)4 SCC 512.

B.S. Sambhau v. T.S. Krishnaswamy [(1983)1 SCC 11].

Om Prakash Gupta v. State of U.P. [1957 SCR 423].

Manohar Nath Kaul v. State of Jammu & Kashmir [(1983)3 SCC 429].

B. Saha v. M.S. Kochar [(1979)4 SCC 177].

Dr. Hori Ram v. Emperor [1939 FCR 159 : AIR 1939 Federal Court 43].

State of Maharashtra v. Atma Ram [AIR 1966 SC 1786].

Baijnath Gupta v. State of Madhya Pradesh [1966(1) SCR 210].

Harihar Prasad, etc. v. State of Bihar [(1972)3 SCC 89].

State v. Gulab Singh, AIR (1954) Raj. 211.

Abdul Wahab Ansari v. State of Bihar, 2000(4) RCR(Crl.) 572 (SC) : [(2000)8 SCC 500].

State of Karnataka through CBI v. C. Nagarajaswamy, 2005(4) RCR(Criminal) 511 (SC) : 2005(3) Apex Criminal 406 (SC) : JT 2005(12) SC 349].

Raj Kishore Roy v. Kamleshwar Pandey, 2002(3) RCR(Crl.) 873 (SC):(2002)6 SCC 543.

---

## Acquittal of Police Constables from charge of bribery for the lack of evidence

***Sadashiv Mahadeo Yavaluje and Gajnan Shripatrao Solokhe***
***v. State of Maharashtra***
**(From Bombay High Court)**

1990(1) R.C.R.(Criminal) 174 : 1990(1) SCC 299 : 1990 AIR (SC) 287 : 1990 CriLJ 600 : 1990(1) AICLR 399 : 1989(4) JT 569 : 1989(2) Scale 1253 : 1990 SCC(Cri) 104 : 1990(40) DLT 272 : 1990(1) Crimes 46.

**Judges** :— Justice G.L. Oza and Justice M. Fathima Beevi.

Criminal Appeal Nos. 622 and 623 of 1979.

Date of Decision — 6.12.1989.

---

## Acquittal of Police Officer due to inaudible condition of electronic voice record.

***Sanjaysinh Ramrao Chavan v. Dattatray Gulabrao Phalke***
**(From Bombay High Court)**

2015(1) MLJ (Criminal) 308:2015(1) Bom. C.R. (Cri.) 593:2015(1) Law Herald 822:2015(1) R.C.R. (Criminal) 570:2015(1) Recent Apex Judgements (R.A.J.) 326:2015(1) Scale 457:2015(1) JT 365:2015(1) Crimes 90:2015(1) PLJ (Criminal) 1:2015(1) Law Herald (SC) 204:2015 AIR (SCW) 784:2015 RajCriC 75:2015 Cri. L.R. 160:2015(3) SCC 123:2015(148) AIC 204:2015(2) SCC (Cri) 19:2015(2) PLJR 185:2015(2) ALT (Crl.) 119:2015(1) CCR 267:2015(2) JLJR 96:2015(2) JBCJ 8:2015(1) AICLR 962:2015(2) CalCriLR 268:2015(1) ECrC 333:2016(2) Rajdhani LR 406:2015(1) AIR Bom. R (Cri) 637:2015 All SCR 851:2015 CriLJ 1259:2015(89) ACrC 309:2015(2) JCC 930:2015(1) Apex Court Judgements (SC) 775:2015(1) B.L.Jud. 195:2015(4) Mh.LJ (Crl.) 1:2015(60) Orrisa Cri. R. 784:2015(2) All. Crl. Rulings 1818.

**Judges** :— Justice Kurian Joseph and Justice Abhay Manohar Sapre.

**Advocates:—**

1. For the Appellants :— Harin Raval, Senior Advocate, Ravindra Keshavrao Adsure and Siddeshwar Biradar.
2. For the Respondents :— Arun Pedneker, Sunil Kumar Verma, Aniruddha P. Mayee, Charudatta Mahindrakar and A. Selvin Raja.

Criminal Appeal No. 97 of 2015 (Arising out of S.L.P. (Criminal) No. 6927 of 2013).

Date of Decision — 16.1.2015

**NUTSHELL**

Corruption Case— Demand of bribe recorded by voice recorder— Voice not audible— No case made out.

**A. Prevention of Corruption Act, 1988, Sections 7, 13(1)(d) and 13(2)— Evidence Act, Section 65— Electronic evidence— Prosecution that accused made a demand for bribe— Allegation supported by conversation recorded by voice recorder— According to report of Forensic Science Laboratory conversation is not in audible condition and, hence, the same is not considered for spectrographic analysis— Conversation could not be take in evidence— Held:—**

**(i) Magistrate rightly accepted the closure report. 2014(4) RCR (Civil) 504 : 2014(5) Recent Apex Judgment (RAJ) 459, relied.**

[Paras 16 and 17]

**B. Criminal Procedure Code, 1973, Sections 173(2), 140 and 204— Police submitting report under Section 173(2) Cr.P.C. — At the stage of taking cognizance of a case what is to be seen is whether there is sufficient ground for taking judicial notice of an offence with a view to initiate further proceedings.**

**(i) The court is not bound by the report submitted by the police under Section 173(2) of Cr.P.C. — If the report is that no case is made out, the Magistrate is still free, nay, bound, if a case according to him is made out, to reject and take cognizance — It is also open to him to order further investigation under Section 173(8) of Cr.P.C. 2008(2) RCR (Crl.) 38 : 2008(2) Recent Apex Judgment (RAJ) 20 : 2012(2) RCR (Crl.) 794 : 2012(2) Recent Apex Judgment (RAJ) 425, relied.**

[Paras 11 and 14]

**C. Criminal Procedure Code, Section 204 — Criminal trial — Summoning of an accused in a criminal case is a serious matter — Criminal law cannot be set into motion as a matter of course — The process of the criminal court shall not be permitted to be used as a weapon of harassment. 1997(4) RCR (Crl.) 761, relied.**

[Para 17]

**D. Criminal Procedure Code, Section 173(2) — Police submitting its report under Section 173(2) after investigation of offence — Magistrate went through the entire records of the case, not limiting to the report filed by the police and has passed a reasoned order holding that it is not a fit case to take cognizance for the purpose of issuing process**

**(i) Unless the order passed by the Magistrate is perverse or the view taken by the court is wholly unreasonable or there is non—consideration of any relevant material or there is palpable misreading of records, the revision court is not justified in setting aside the order, merely because another**

**view is possible — The revisional court is not meant to act as an appellate Court.**

[Para 14]

**E. Criminal Procedure Code, 1973 Sections 397 to 401 Order of conviction by trial Court — Unless the finding of the Court, whose decision is sought to be revised, is shown to be perverse or untenable in law or is grossly erroneous or glaringly unreasonable or where the decision is based on no material or where the material facts are wholly ignored or where the judicial discretion is exercised arbitrarily or capriciously, the courts may not interfere with decision in exercise of their revisional jurisdiction.**

[Para 14]

**F. Criminal Procedure Code, Section 197 — Prosecution of Public Servant in Corruption Case — No Court can issue a positive direction to an authority to give sanction for prosecution. 1997(4) RCR (Crl.) 236, relied.**

[Para 18]

## Cases Referred :

Anvar P.V. v. P.K. Basheer, 2014(4) R.C.R.(Civil) 504 : 2014(5) Recent Apex Judgments (R.A.J.) 459 : 2014 (10) SCALE 660.

Bhushan Kumar v. State (NCT of Delhi), 2012(2) R.C.R.(Criminal) 794 : 2012(2) Recent Apex Judgments (R.A.J.) 425 : (2012) 5 SCC 424.

Mansukhlal Vithaldas Chauhan v. State of Gujarat, 1997(4) R.C.R.(Criminal) 236 : (1997) 7 SCC 622.

Pepsi Foods Limited v. Special Judicial Magistrate, 1997(4) R.C.R.(Criminal) 761 : (1998) 5 SCC 749.

S.K. Sinha, Chief Enforcement Officer v. Videocon International Ltd., 2008(2) R.C.R.(Criminal) 38 : 2008(2) Recent Apex Judgments (R.A.J.) 20 : (2008) 2 SCC 492.

Smt. Nagawwa v. Veeranna Shivalingappa Kinjalgi, (1976) 3 SCC 736.

State of Bihar v. P.P. Sharma, 1991(2) S.C.T. 397 : IAS, 1992 Supp (1) SCC 222.

State of Karnataka v. L. Muniswamy, (1977) 2 SCC 699

State of Maharashtra Through CBI v. Mahesh G. Jain, 2013(3) R.C.R.(Criminal) 263 : 2013(3) Recent Apex Judgments (R.A.J.) 725 : Criminal Appeal No. 2345 of 2009. D/d. 28.5.2013.

Vasanti Dubey v. State of Madhya Pradesh, 2012(1) R.C.R.(Criminal) 588 : 2012(1) Recent Apex Judgments (R.A.J.) 93 : (2012)2 SCC 731.

## Acquittal of Bank Manager due to lack of evidence and with order of reinstatement and back salary with pension

***State Bank of Patiala v. Vijay Garg***

**(From Punjab and Haryana High Court)**

2015(3) SLR 386 : 2014(5) Scale 434 : 2014(4) S.C.T. 197 : 2014(4) RSJ 754.

**Judges:**— Justice H.L. Gokhale and Justice Dipak Misra.

**Advocates:—**

1. For the Appellant :— C.U. Singh, Sr. Adv., Sanjay Kapur, Anmol Chandan, Priyanka Das, Shubhra Kapur.
2. For the Respondent :— Respondent—In—Person.

Civil Appeal No. 872 of 2014 (Arising out of SLP (C) No. 12554 of 2013).

Date of Decision - 17.1.2014.

**Constitution of India, Article 32— Prevention of Corruption Act, 1988 Sections 7 and 13(1)(d) Salary and Pension— Conviction for accepting illegal gratification— Bank discharging Respondent from service— High Court setting aside conviction and order of discharge from service also set aside— Respondent held entitled to salary only for period after order of conviction was set aside— Also entitled to pension.**

[Para 6]

**Cases Referred :**

State Bank of India. v. Mohammed Abdul Rahim, 2013(4) S.C.T. 133 : C.A. No. 5472 of 2013. D/d. 15.6.2013.

---

## Acquittal of Assistant Station Master, South Eastern Railway on ground of invalid sanction for prosecution

***State Inspector of Police v. Surya Sankaram Karri***

**(From Andhra Pradesh High Court)**

2006(3) Crimes 316:2006(4) R.C.R. (Criminal) 53:2006(3) Apex Criminal 87:2006(7) SCC 172:2006(4) Cri. CC 231:2007(1) AICLR 206:2006 CriLJ 4598:2006(8) JT 177:2006(8) Scale 451:2006(Sup5) SCR 229:2006(3) SCC(Cri) 225:2006(2) W.L.C. 549:2006 AIR (SCW) 4576:2006(6) Supreme 560:2006(3) All. C.J. 2079:2006(2) Ori.

Law Rev. 536:2006(4) PLJR 73:2007 (sup) AIR (SC) 1860:2006(46) AIC 716:2006(2) CalCriLR 516:2007(1) CalLJ 138:2007(1) Bom.C.R. (Cri.) 942:2006(4) ECrC 148:2006 Cri. L.R. 762:2007 ALL MR(Cri) 555:2007(1) APLJ 9:2007(1) AIR Jhar R. 73:2006 RajCriC 695:2006(4) JLJR 81:2006(2) Andh LD (Criminal) 564:2006(4) L.R.C. 218:2006(2) MadWN (Cri) 208:2006(35) Orrisa Cri. R. 318:2006(3) Apex Court Judgements (SC) 68.

**Judges** :— Justice S.B. Sinha & Justice Dalveer Bhandari.

**Advocates:—**

1. For the Appellant :— A. Sharan, A.S.G., Amit Anand Tiwari and W.A. Qadri.
2. For the Respondent :— A.T.M. Ranga Ramanujam, Sr. Advocate, Mrs. Gaouri Karuna Das, Ms. Anu Gupta, Rajesh Singh, K. Uma Shanker for Ms. Rnai Jethmalani (N.P.).

Criminal Appeal No. 1335 of 2004.

Date of Decision - 24.8.2006.

**IMPORTANT**

Corruption case investigated by Police Authority without written sanction of Superintendent of Police — It was mandatory — Conviction set aside.

A. **Prevention of Corruption Act , 1988 , Sections 19 and 13(2) — Prosecution of Public Servant in corruption case — Sanction for Prosecution of Public Servant accorded by Authority who was not appointing Authority, but power of appointment had been delegated to him — Order of delegation not brought on record — Conviction set aside — When a sanction is granted by a person not authorised in law, the same being without jurisdiction, would be a nullity. 2005(4) RCR(Crl.) 511 : 2005(3) Apex Criminal 406 relied.**

[Paras 23 and 24]

B. **Prevention of Corruption Act , 1988 , Sections 17 and 13(1)(e)— Corruption case against Public Servant— Section 17 of Prevention of Corruption Act provides that an offence under Section 13(1)(e) shall not be investigated without the order of Police Officer not below the rank of Superintendent of Police— It is mandatory provision— In the instant case investigation conducted by Police Officer who could not produce written sanction of S.P.— It caused prejudice to accused— Conviction of set aside.**

[Paras 13, 16 and 17]

C. **Criminal Procedure Code, Section 156 — Defective Investigation — Investigation conducted by Police Officer who was not specifically authorised — Only on the basis of the illegal investigation a proceeding may not be quashed unless miscarriage of justice is shown.**

[Para 20]

**D. Evidence Act, Section 114 — Adverse inference — When a document being in possession of a public functionary, who is under a statutory obligation to produce the same before the court of law, fails and/or neglects to produce the same, an adverse inference may be drawn against him.**

[Para 18]

**Cases referred :**

State of Andhra Pradesh v. P.V. Narayana [(1971) 1 SCC 483 ].

Sailendra Nath Bose v. State of Bihar [AIR 1968 SC 1292].

State of Karnataka through CBI v. C. Nagarajaswamy, 2005(4) RCR(Crl.) 511 : 2005(3) Apex Criminal 406 : [(2005) 8 SCC 370].

---

# Acquittal of Assistant Commercial Tax Officer on the ground of benefit of doubt

***State of Andhra Pradesh v. Kesavapatnam China Swamy***

**(From Andhra Pradesh High Court)**

2015(3) ALT (Crl.) 45:2015(3) Recent Apex Judgements (R.A.J.) 346:2015(2) CCR 525:2015(4) JT 410:2015(6) Scale 90:2015(151) AIC 245:2015 AIR (SCW) 3353:2015(3) Law Herald (SC) 2016:2015 CriLJ 3126:2015 All SCR 2197:2015(3) AICLR 208:2015(3) Crimes 44:2015(90) ACrC 324:2015(2) Andh LD (Criminal) 408:2015(2) R.C.R. (Criminal) 945:2015(14) SCC 9:2016(2) SCC(Cri) 355:2015(61) Orrisa Cri. R. 426:2015(2) All. Crl. Rulings 2013.

**Judges** :— Justice Pinaki Chandra Ghose and Justice Uday Umesh Lalit.

**Advocates:—**

For the Appellant :— Guntur Pramod Kumar, Guntur Prabhakar.

For the Respondent :— Ms. T. Anamika.

Criminal Appeal No. 89 of 2009.

Date of Decision — 6.5.2015.

---

# Acquittal of Revenue Divisional Officer from the charge of possessing disproportionate assets

***State of Andhra Pradesh v. J. Satyanarayana***

**(From Andhra Pradesh High Court)**

2000(4) AICLR 44:2000(10) JT 430:2000(3) All. Crl. Rulings 2450:2000(3) ECrC 1116:2000(41) ACrC 733:2000(7) SLT 43:2000 CalCriLR 508:2017(6) SCC 628:2017(3) SCC (Cri) 340:2017(2) SCC (L&S) 544.

**Judges**:— Justice Dr. A.S. Anand, Justice R.C. Lahoti and Justice K.G. Balakrishnan.

Criminal Appeal No. 596 of 1994.

Date of Decision — 19.7.2000.

**Prevention of Corruption Act, 1988, Sections 5(1)(e) and 5(2)— Charge of possession of disproportionate assets— Marginal difference from total assets— Loan transaction and Income Tax Returns— Filing of before raid and registration of Case— Proof of House Property belongs to wife— Acquittal of accused.**

[Para 2, 6 & 7]

---

## Quashing of charge of bribery and other corruption cases against I.A.S. Officer due to absence of time bound Inquiry Order

***State of Bihar v. Ashok Kumar Singh***

**(From Patna High Court)**

2014(3) ECrC 400:2014(sup) Crl. L.R. 172:2015(1) SCC (L & S) 304:2014(13) SCC 81:2014(3) CCR 372:2014(5) SCC(Cri) 566:2014(3) JLJR 344:2014(8) Scale 490:2014(4) Recent Apex Judgements (R.A.J.) 565:2014(3) R.C.R. (Criminal) 883:2014 All SCR2618:2014(3) Law Herald (SC) 2154:2014 (140) AIC 1:2014 AIR (SCW) 4230:2014(3) PLJR 330:2014(2) RajCriC 722:2014(3) AIR Jhar R. 776:2014(86) ACrC 617:2014(3) AICLR 680:2014(3) JBCJ 404:2014(3) BBCJ 393:2014(3) B.L.Jud. 151.

**Judges**:— Justice Sudhansu Jyoti Mukhopadhaya and Justice V. Gopala Gowda.

**Advocates:—**

For the Appearing Parties :— Sunil Kumar, Armerndra Sharan, Sr. Advs., S.K. Bagaria, ASG, Sandeep Singh, Manish Kumar, Chandan Kumar, Gopal Singh, Anil Kumar Jha, Shreekant N. Terdal, C.D. Singh and Sakshi Kakkar.

Criminal Appeal No. 1615 of 2013.

Date of Decision — 9.7.2014.

**A. Prevention of Corruption Act, 1988, Sections 13(1)(d) and 13(2)— Bihar Reorganisation Act, 2000— Sections 76 and 96— Indian Penal Code, 1860, Sections 420, 467 and 471— Vigilance inquiry against Accused I.A.S. Officer— High Court directions to complete inquiry within & months— Enquiry not completed— F.I.R. quashed.**

[Paras 10,11,14,19,21,23,24,29,30 and 31]

---

## Acquittal of Drug Inspector for lack of proper sanction for prosecution.

***State of Himachal Pradesh v. Nishant Sareen***
**(From Himachal Pradesh High Court)**

2011(1) JCC 36:2011 AIR (SC) 404:2011(1) KLT 2:2011(1) RLW 287:2011(1) ALT (Crl.) 394:2011(1) Crimes 47:2011(72) ACrC 423:2011 AIR (SC) (Cri) 265:2011 AIR (SCW) 3699:2011(1) R.C.R. (Criminal) 193:2010(6) Recent Apex Judgements (R.A.J.) 646:2011(98) AIC 193:2010(14) SCC 527:2011(1) CalCriLR 287:2010(13) SCR 1200:2010(13) Scale 245:2011(3) SCC(Cri) 836:2011(2) Andh LD (Criminal) 895:2011(1) Him. L.R. 433:2012 (sup) CutLT (Criminal) 116:2011(48) Orrisa Cri. R. 384:2011(1) Apex Court Judgements (SC) 165.

**Judges**:— Justice Aftab Alam and Justice R.M. Lodha.

**Advocates:—**

1. For the Appellant :— Mr. Naresh K. Sharma.
2. For the Respondent :— Mr. K.T.S. Tulsi, Senior Advocate with Niraj Gupta.

Criminal Appeal No. 2353 of 2010 (Arising out of SLP (Criminal) No. 2239 of 2010).

Date of Decision — 9.12.2010.

**Cases Referred :**

1. Gopikant Choudhary v. State of Bihar, (2000)9 SCC 53.
2. Mansukhlal Vithaldas Chauhan v. State of Gujarat, 1997(4) R.C.R.(Criminal) 236 : (1997)7 SCC 622.
3. Romesh Lal Jain v. Naginder Singh Rana, 2005(4) R.C.R.(Criminal) 835 : 2005(3) Apex Criminal 533:: (2006)1 SCC 294.
4. State of Punjab v. Mohammed Iqbal Bhatti, 2009(3) R.C.R.(Criminal) 861 : 2009(4) R.A.J. 605 : JT 2009(13) SC 180.

---

# Acquittal of an Employee of a Co-operative Society due to lack of invalid and improper sanction for prosecution

***State of Karnataka v. Ameer Jan***

**(From Karnataka High Court)**

2007(4) R.C.R. (Criminal) 375:2007(5) Recent Apex Judgements (R.A.J.) 202:2007 (11) JT 183:2008 AIR (SC) 108:2007(11) SCC 273:2007(11) Scale 207:2007(9) SCR 1105:2008(1) SCC (Cri) 130:2008 CriLJ 347:2007(4) Crimes 22:2007(59) AIC 133:2007(3) GujLH 614:2007(6) Supreme 341:2007 AIR (SCW) 6217:2007(3) RajCriC 963:2007(6) Air Kar R 484:2007(2) CalCriLR 693:2008(1) KantLJ 33:2008(1) W.L.C. 173:2007(4) ECrC 198:2007 Cri. L.R. 880:2007(4) Cri.CC 467:2007(3) Apex Court Judgements (SC) 493:2007(4) L.R.C. 118:2008(1) B.L.Jud. 75:2007(2) SriLJ 482:2007(38) Orrisa Cri. R. 568.

**Judges** :— Justice S.B. Sinha & Justice Harjit Singh Bedi.

**Advocates:—**

1. For the Appellant :— Sanjay H. Hegde and Ramesh S. Jadhav.
2. For the Respondent :— Sanjay Parikh, A.M. Singh and Jitin Sahni.

Criminal Appeal No. 766 of 2001.

Date of Decision — 18.9.2007.

**Cases referred :**

Gokulchand Dwarkadas Morarka v. King [AIR 1948 PC 82].

Jaswant Singh v. State of Punjab [AIR 1958 SC 124].

Mohd. Iqbal Ahmed v. State of Andhra Pradesh [(1979)4 SCC 172].

R.S. Nayak v. A.R. Antulay [(1984)2 SCC 183].

Mansukhlal Vithaldas Chauhan v. State of Gujarat, 1997(4) RCR(Criminal) 236 : (1997)7 SCC 622.

State of T.N. v. M.M. Rajendran, (1998)9 SCC 268.

Prakash Singh Badal v. State of Punjab, 2007(1) RCR(Criminal) 1 : 2007(1) R.A.J. 71: [(2007)1 SCC 1].

Sankaran Moitra v. Sadhna Das, 2006(2) RCR(Criminal) 389 : 2006(1) Apex Criminal 551: [(2006)4 SCC 584 : JT 2006(4) SC 34].

# Acquittal of Public Servant from corruption charge due to lack of evidence

***State of Madhya Pradesh v. Rakesh Gandhi***

**(From Madhya Pradesh High Court)**

**Judges**:— Justice Harjit Singh Bedi & Justice Gyan Sudha Misra.

Criminal Appeal No. 22 of 2009.

Date of Decision — 12.07.2011.

**Prevention of Corruption Act, 1988, Section 13(2)— Charge of corruption against Public Servant— Conviction by Trial Court— Acquittal by High Court— Reasonable order— Absence of evidence— Apex Court upheld the acquittal of by HIgh Court.**

---

# Acquittal of Police Officer from charge of bribery though there was recovery of tainted money

***State of Madhya Pradesh v. J.B. Singh***

**(From Madhya Pradesh High Court)**

2000(4) Crimes 162:2000 AIR (SC) 3562:2000 CriLJ 4591:2000(7) JT 539:2000(3) AICLR 377:2000 SCC (Cri) 1507:2000 AIR (SCW) 3557:2000(7) Supreme 198:2001(1) Andh LD (Criminal) 124:2000(3) ECrC 814:2000(3) All. Crl. Rulings 1901:2000(41) ACrC 339:2000 ALL MR(Cri) 1719:2001(1) JLJR 735:2000(2) Apex Court Journal 606:2000(3) CTC 249:2000(7) SLT 412:2000(3) MadWN (Cri) 323.

**Judges** :— Justice G.B. Pattanaik and Justice S.N. Variava.

Criminal Appeal No. 293 of 1996.

Date of Decision — 27.4.2000.

**Prevention of Corruption Act, 1988 , Section 5(1)(d)— Allegation of demanding money for release of complainant— Money paid and recovered from the rest room— Conviction set aside by High Court in appeal— Appreciation of evidence— Demand made not established— Complainant turns hostile— Acquittal justified.**

[Para 4]

---

# Acquittal of Sub-Engineer due to refusal of State to issue sanction for prosecution

***State of M.P. v. Ram Manohar Pandey***
**(From Madhya Pradesh High Court)**

2015(12) SCC 726:2014(13) Scale 744:2015(1) JCC 492:2015(2) AICLR 275:2014(6) Recent Apex Judgements (R.A.J.) 669:2015(1) R.C.R. (Criminal) 252:2016(1) SCC (Cri) 332:2015(1) Cri. CC 406:2015(1) Apex Court Judgements (SC) 221.

**Judges**:- Justice Sudhansu Jyoti Mukhopadhaya and Justice Prafulla C. Pant.

**Advocates:—**

1. With Criminal Appeal No. 2548 of 2014 (Arising out of SLP (Crl.) No. 9976 of 2013).
2. For the Appellants :— Ms. Musharra Chaudhary, Ms. Ayesha Chaudhary, C.D. Singh.
3. For the Respondents :— Sushil Kumar Jain, Senior Advocate, Abhinav Gupta, Ms. Ankita Gupta and Ms. Pratibha Jain.

Criminal Appeal No. 2547 of 2014 (Arising out of SLP (Crl.) No. 9809 of 2013).

Date of Decision — 09.12.2014.

**A. Prevention of Corruption Act, 1988, Section 19— Criminal Procedure Code, Section 197— Prosecution of Public Servant— State refused to grant sanction for prosecution— Accused discharged by the Court— A fresh Challan cannot be filed after superannuation of accused from service. 2011(3) RCR (Crl.) 512 : 2011(4) Recent Apex Judgment (RAJ) 64, relied.**

[Paras 22, 25 to 27]

**B. Prevention of Corruption Act, 1988, Section 19— Criminal Procedure Code, Section 197— Prosecution of public servant in a corruption case— No time limit is fixed for grant of sanction— State asked to introduce a time—limit in Section 19 of the Prevention of Corruption Act , 1988 for its working in a reasonable manner.**

[Para 25]

## Cases Referred:

Chittaranjan Das v. State of Orissa, 2011(3) R.C.R.(Criminal) 512 : 2011(4) Recent Apex Judgments (R.A.J.) 64 : (2011)7 SCC 167, etc.

D.L. Rangotha v. State of M.P., Criminal Appeal No. 1213 of 2013.

Maneka Gandhi v. Union of India, (1978)1 SCC 248.

State of Madhya Pradesh v. Sheetla Sahai, 2009(3) R.C.R.(Criminal) 835 : 2009(5) Recent Apex Judgments (R.A.J.) 110 : (2009)8 SCC 617.

Subramanian Swamy v. Manmohan Singh, 2012(1) R.C.R.(Criminal) 720 : 2012(1) Recent Apex Judgments (R.A.J.) 201 : (2012) 3 SCC 64.

---

# Acquittal of Road Transport Inspector due to non production of relevant documents by Police during trial

***State of Madhya Pradesh v. Mohan Lal Soni***
**(From Madhya Pradesh High Court)**

2000(3) Crimes 105:2000(3) R.C.R. (Criminal) 452:2000 AIR (SC) 2583:2000 CriLJ 3504:2000(6) SCC 338:2000(5) Scale 197:2000(8) JT 333:2000(3) AICLR 771:2000 SCC (Cri) 1110:2000(3) MPHT 467:2001 (sup) ACrC 632:2000(3) All. Crl. Rulings 2123:2000 Cri. L.R. 603:2000(3) ECrC 945:2000 ALL MR (Cri) 1570:2000 AIR (SCW) 2674:2000(5) Supreme 139:2000(4) PLJR 90:2000(3) BBCJ 215:2000(3) B.L.Jud. 684:2001(2) MadWN (Cri) 83:2000(2) CLR 426:2000(19) Orrisa Cri. R. 475.

**Judges**:- Justice S. Rajendra Babu and Justice Shivaraj V. Patil.

**Advocates:—**

1. For the Petitioner :— Mr. K.N. Shukla, Sr. Advocate with Ms. Sushila Shukla and Mr. Uma Nath Singh.
2. For the Respondent :— Mr. Gopal Subramanium, Sr. Advocate with Mr. Ashok Kumar Singh.

Special Leave Petition (Crl.) No. 593 of 1999.

Date of Decision — 19.7.2000

**A. Criminal Procedure Code, 1973, Sections 173, 228 and 227 — Framing of charge — Material to be taken into consideration at the time of framing of charge :—**

**i. Court has to prima facie consider whether there is sufficient ground for proceeding against the accused — Court is not required to appreciate evidence to conclude whether materials produced are sufficient or not for convicting the accused.**

**ii. Court is required to evaluate the material and documents on record with a view of finding out if the facts emerging therefrom taken at their face value disclose existence of all the ingredients constituting the offence.**

**iii. Court may for this limited purpose sift the evidence as it cannot be expected even at initial stage to accept all that the prosecution states as gospel truth even if it is opposed to common sense or broad probabilities of the case. 1990(4) SCC 76.**

**iv. Sessions Judge is not expected to hold a roving enquiry into the pros and cons of the case at the stage of framing charges by weighing the evidence as if he was conducting the trial. 1996(3) R.C.R. (Crl.) 411 (SC).**

**v. If the evidence which the prosecution possesses to prove the guilt, even if fully accepted without rebuttal, cannot show that accused committed the particular offence, then the charge can be quashed.**

[Paras 7 to 11]

**B. Criminal Procedure Code, 1973, Sections 227, 228 and 173 — Prevention of Corruption Act, 1988 , Section 13(1)(e) and 13(2) — Offence under Prevention of Corruption Act — Charge sheet submitted by Police under Section 173 Criminal Procedure Code — Documents such as Income—tax return, assessment orders taken into possession by Police but not produced alongwith charge—sheet — Court can consider these documents, though not submitted by Police.**

[Paras 11, 12 and 13]

## Cases referred :

State of M.P. v. S.B. Johari and others, 2000(1) Scale 138.

Satish Mehra v. Delhi Administration and another, 1996(3) RCR (Crl.) 411.

Anand Bezbaruah v. Union of India, 1994 Cr.L.J. 12.

Niranjan Singh Karam Singh Punjabi v. Jitendra Bhimraj Bijjaya and others, 1990(4) SCC 76.

State of Bihar v. Ramesh Singh, (1977)4 SCC 39.

Union of India v. Prafulla Kumar Samal, (1979)3 SCC 4.

Supdt. & Remembrancer of Legal Affairs, West Bengal v. Anil Kumar Bhunja, (1979)4 SCC 274.

---

# Quashing of proceedings against the accused not being a Public Servant who was running a coaching centre on the ground that she was not holding a public office

***State of Punjab v. Nirmal Kaur***

**(From Punjab and Haryana High Court)**

2009(13) SCC 418:2009(sup) AIR (SC) 2187:2009(2) CalLJ 254:2012(5) R.C.R. (Criminal) 648:2009(6) Scale 653:2009(66) ACrC 943:2009(3) ECrC 312:2009(81) AIC 152:2010(1) SCC (Cri) 1040:2009(3) L.R.C. 236.

**Judges**:- Justice Arijit Pasayat and Justice A.K. Ganguly.

**Advocates:—**

1. For the Appellants:— Ranjit Kapoor, Add. Sonia Kapoor, S.N. Mehrotra, Falak Momd. and Kuldip Singh.
2. For the Respondent:— Sant Pal Singh Sidhu, Dinesh Verma, A.P. Mohanty and Dr. Kailash Chand.

Criminal Appeal No. 866 Of 2009.

Date of Decision — 28.4.2009.

**Prevention of Corruption Act, 1988, Section 2(c)(viii)— Applicability of— Respondent running a coaching centre— Charges under Section 13(1)(d) read with Section 13(2) framed against respondent— Respondent contending that since she was not a public servant, charges cannot be framed against her under Prevention of Corruption Act— Stand of appellant State that in any event by running a coaching centre, respondent was performing public duty— Held, stand of appellant not sustainable— It is nobody's case that respondent was holding an office by virture of which she was authorised to perform any public duty— Appeal dismissed.**

[Para 5]

---

## Acquittal of Junior Engineer in Electricity Board in bribery case due to lack of evidence

### *State of Punjab v. Sohan Singh*

**(From Punjab and Haryana High Court)**

2009(7) JT 355:2009(3) R.C.R. (Criminal) 971:2009(4) Recent Apex Judgements (R.A.J.) 585:2009 AIR (SC) 1887:2009(6) SCC 444:2009(65) ACrC 909:2009(78) AIC 53:2009(2) SCC (Cri) 1080:2009(1) CalCriLR 941:2009(8) Scale 260:2009(2) W.L.C. 552:2009(4) Mh.LJ (Crl.) 363:2009 AIR (SCW) 3386:2009(3) L.R.C. 38:2009(43) Orrisa Cri. R. 807.

**Judges** :— Justice S.B. Sinha and Justice Dr. Mukundakam Sharma.

**Advocates:—**

For the Appellant :— Gagandeep Sharma and Ajay Pal for Kuldip Singh.

For the Respondent :— Rajiv Dutta, Sr. Advocate with Ms. M.F. Humayunisa Kumar, Dushyant Singh and R. Ndumaran.

Criminal Appeal No. 792 of 2006.
Date of Decision — 15.05.2009.

**Prevention of Corruption Act, 1988, Section 2 and 13(1)— Demand of bribe to release of electric connection out of turn— Trap and Raid— Recovery of tainted money— Accused was not proper authority for the work— Independence witness not examined— Absence of relevant question during trial— Acquittal of accused.**

[Paras 2,20,21,22,23,24 and 25]

**Cases referred :**

John K. John v. Tom Varghese, 2007(4) RCR(Crl.) 807 : 2007(4) RCR(Civil) 724 : [(2007)12 SCC 714].

State of Punjab v. Gurnam Kaur, 2009(2) RCR(Crl.) 309 : 2009(2) RAJ 344 : 2009(4) SCALE 343.

---

## Acquittal of Special Temporary Assistant in Taluk Office from charge of bribe for issue of Patta Certificate on ground of lack of evidence

***State of Tamil Nadu v. S. Krishnamurthy***
**(From Madras High Court)**

2002(4) Crimes 295 : 2002(9) SCC 530 : 2002(2) Jr. 173 : 2003 SCC(Cri) 1236 : 2002(2) W.L.C. 118 : 2002(6) Supreme 490 : 2002(3) B.L.Jud. 393 : 2003(25) Orrisa Cri. R. 485 : 2002(2) Apex Court Judgements (SC) 546.

**Judges** :— Justice N. Santosh Hegde And Justice Doraiswamy Raju.

Criminal Appeal No. 653 of 1996.
Date of Decision — 29.1.2002.

**Prevention of Corruption Act, 1988, Section 13(2) read with Section 13(1)(d)(ii)— Bribe for issuing patta certificate by accused in Taluk Office— Trap— Money recovered from pocket of accused—Respondent— Defence that he received money as donation for Teachers' Day— Trial Court finding respondent guilty— Held, that prevalence of the practice in the office in question of collecting the Flag Day fund and the Teachers' Day fund seems to have been an authorised practice, though we do not approve of such practice— Defence taken by the accused is in conformity with such practice, we are**

**in agreement with the High Court that the mere fact that the respondent received a sum of Rs. 300 would not ipso facto lead to the conclusion that the money in question was received by him as a bribe.**

[Para 6]

---

# Acquittal of Transport Inspector due to non-recovery of tainted money and lack of other evidences

***State of Uttar Pradesh v. Jagdish Singh Malhotra***
**(From Allahabad High Court)**

2001(1) Crimes 322:2000(4) AICLR 791:2001(10) SCC 215:2000(sup 1) JT 559:2003 SCC (Cri) 1008:2001(1) Andh LD (Criminal) 520:2000(2) CLJ (Criminal) 378:2000(3) All. Crl. Rulings 2650:2000(41) ACrC 951:2001 All. LJ 1629:2001 AIR (SCW) 2392:2001(2) Supreme 261:2000(4) All WC 3387:2001 CalCriLR 49:2000(7) SLT 289:2001(20) Orrisa Cri. R. 507

**Judges**:— Justice Dr. A.S. Anand, Justice CJI, Justice N. Santosh Hegde and Justice Shivaraj V. Patil.

Criminal Appeal No. 709 of 1991.

Date of Decision — 20.9.2000.

**Prevention of Corruption Act, 1988, section 5— Indian Penal Code, 1860, Section 161— Demand of illegal gratification— Absence of evidence for payment of bribe— Acquittal.**

[Paras 2,5,6,7,8 and 9]

---

# Acquittal of Non-Public Servants when the Public Servant dies during trial of same offence

***State through CBI, New Delhi v. Jitender Kumar Singh***
**(From Delhi High Court)**

2014(1) Recent Apex Judgements (R.A.J.) 628:2014(207) DLT 323:2014(2) Scale 65:2014(1) MLJ (Criminal) 566:2014(3) AIR Jhar R. 154:2014(1) CCR 419:2014(11) SCC 724:2014(2) SCR 621:2014(2) ECrC 292:2014(1) R.C.R. (Criminal) 908:2014(3) JT 182:2014(1) KLT 666:2014 RajCriC 193:2014 AIR (SC) 1169:2014(2) Ker L.J. 117:2014 All SCR 867:2014 CriLJ 1394:2014(136) AIC 186:2014(2) Law Herald (SC) 1075:2014 AIR (SCW) 1153:2014(85) ACrC 253:2014(2) JCC 1172:2014(2)

Cri.CC 200:2014(1) NCC 450:2014(2) Andh LD (Criminal) 106:2014(3) SCC (Cri) 512:2014(2) AICLR 666:2014(1) Apex Court Judgements (SC) 612:2014(2) B.L.Jud. 64:2014 Cri. L.R. 432:2014(57) Orrisa Cri. R. 874:2014(1) AIR Bom.R (Cri) 746.

**Judges**:— Justice K. S. Radhakrishnan & Justice A.K. Sikri.

**Advocates:—**

For the Appearing Parties :— Mr. V. Giri, Mr. Basanth R., Mr. K. Radhakrishnan, Mr. Uday U. Lalit and Mr. Guru Krishna Kumar, Senior Advocates, Mr. P.P. Malhotra, ASG, Mr. Mohammed Sadique T.A., Mr Shivaji M. Jadhav, Mr. Anish R. Shah, Dr. Ahsok Dhamija, Mr. T.A. Khan, Mr. Yasir Rauf, Ms. Sharika Bhanot, Ms. Sonia Dhamija, Mr. Hari Shankar K., Mr. Kawal Nain, Mr. Vikas Singh Jangra, Mr. Aditya Verma and Mr. Lakshmi, Advocates, Ms. Asha G. Nair, (NP).

Criminal Appeal No. 943 of 2008.

WITH Criminal Appeal No. 161 of 2011.

Date of Decision - 5.2.2014.

**A. Prevention of Corruption Act, 1988, Sections 7, 13(1)(d) and 13(2)— Peculiar case— Trial of Public Servant along with non-public servants— Death of Public Servant— Abatement of charge— Held, under section 4(3) of Act Special Judge could try cases against non-public servants.**

[Paras 24,25,26,27 and 46]

**B. Prevention of Corruption Act, 1988, Sections 4(3), 13(1) and (13)(2)— Indian Penal Code 1860, sections 420, 471 and 120-B— Scope of— Question of power of special Judge— Held, special judge has no jurisdiction to try remaining non public servants on death of public servant.**

[Paras 23, 24 & 25]

## Cases Referred :

Ajay Aggarwal v. Union of India, 1993(3) R.C.R.(Criminal) 34 : (1993)3 SCC 609.

Carona Ltd. v. Parvathy Swaminathan & Sons, 2007(2) R.C.R.(Rent) 490 : 2007(5) Recent Apex Judgments (R.A.J.) 429 : (2007)8 SCC 559.

Kartongen Kemi Ochforvaltning AB v. State through CBI, (2004)1 JCC 218.

Mohd. Arif v. State (NCT of Delhi), 2012(6) R.C.R.(Criminal) 895 : (2011)13 SCC 621.

Ramesh Chandra Sankla v. Vikram Cement, (2008)14 SCC 58.

Ratilal Bhanji Mithani v. State of Maharashtra, (1979)2 SCC 179.

Sanichar Sahni v. State of Bihar, (2009)7 SCC 198.

Vivek Gupta v. CBI, 2003(4) R.C.R.(Criminal) 549 : (2003)8 SCC 628.

# Acquittal from charge of corruption for want of prosecution witness

***Subash Parbat Sonvane v. State of Gujarat***

**(From Gujarat High Court)**

2003(2) R.C.R.(Criminal) 541 : 2003(2) Cri.CC 632 : 2002(2) Crimes 267 : 2002(3) SCR 359 : 2002(2) AICLR 783 : 2002 CriLJ 2787 : 2002(4) JT 348 : 2002(4) Scale 40:2002(3) Supreme 418 : 2002(4) Cal. H.C.N. 81 : 2002(2) GujLH 654 : 2003 AIR (SC) 2169 : 2002 SCC(Cri) 954 : 2002(2) RajCriC 552 : 2002 AIR (SCW) 1952 : 2002(3) RLW 476 : 2002(3) GLR 2245 : 2002(3) R.C.R.(Criminal) 188 : 2002(5) SCC 86:2002 W.L.C. 618 : 2002 CalCriLR 785 : 2003(1) CLR 68 : 2003(3) CLR 379: 2002(22) Orrisa Cri. R. 817 : 2003(1) Apex Court Judgements (SC) 255.

**Judges**:- Justice M.B. Shah, Justice Bisheshwar Prasad Singh and Justice H.K. Sema.

**Advocates:—**

1. For the Appellant :— Mahendra Anand, Sr. Advocate, Rajiv Mehta, Ms. Anita Pandey.
2. For the Respondent :— S.K. Dholakia, Sr. Advocate, Ms. Hemantika and Ms. Aruna Gupta.

Criminal Appeal No. 3688 of 2001.

Date of Decision - 24.4.2002.

**A. Prevention of Corruption Act , 1988, Section 13(1)(d)(i)— Evidence to the effect that complainant gave something which accused put in his pocket— No evidence of demand by accused— Conviction under Section 13(1)(d)(i) set aside.**

[Para 10]

**B. Prevention of Corruption Act, 1988, Section 13(1)(d)(i)— Corruption case— For convicting the person under Section 13(1)(d), there must be evidence on record that accused 'obtained' for himself or for any other person any valuable thing or pecuniary advantage by either corrupt or illegal means or by abusing his position as a public servant or he obtained for any person any valuable thing or pecuniary advantage without any public interest.**

[Para 6]

**Cases referred :**

Ram Krishan & anr. v. State of Delhi, 1956 SCR 183.

M.W. Mohiuddin v. State of Maharashtra, 1995(3) SCC 567.

C.M. Damodaran Nair v. Government of India, 1997(2) RCR(Crl.) 70 (SC): 1997(9) SCC477.

———

## Acquittal of Land Revenue Department Officer from charge of bribery as demand was not proved and though tainted money recovered from co-accused

***Sukhwant Singh v. State of Punjab***
**(From Punjab and Haryana High Court)**

**Judges** :— Justice Ranjan Gogoi and Justice Prafulla C. Pant.

**Advocates:—**

1. For the Appellants :— R.S.Cheema, Sr. Adv., S.S. Behl, Samar Vijay Singh, Ms. Taranum Cheema.
2. For the Respondents :— Devendra Singh, (Not Present).

Criminal Appeal No.603 of 2016 (Arising out of SLP (Crl.) No.3255 of 2016).

Date of Decision — 11.7.2016.

**Prevention of Corruption Act, 1988, Sections 7 and 13(1)(d) Illegal Gratification— Proof— Both complainant and shadow witness have turned hostile— Demand of bribe by appellant had not been proved— Money allegedly offered was recovered from co-accused and not from appellant— That apart, the mutation of land for which bribe was allegedly demanded and received had been completed on 24.11.2006 whereas the incident is of 29.11.2006— Held, there is doubt with regard to correctness of conviction— Judgement of conviction set aside— Appeal allowed.**

[Para 4]

## Acquittal of some Medical Officers from the charge of manipulation of official records on the ground of lack of evidence

***Surinder Kaur v. State of Haryana***
**(From Punjab and Haryana High Court)**

2015(1) CCR 223:2015 ALL MR (Cri) 2924:2014(15) SCC 109:2014(4) R.C.R. (Criminal) 819:2014(6) Recent Apex Judgements (R.A.J.) 124:2014(10) Scale 716:2015(1) JCC 586:2014 (sup) Cri.CC 558.

**Judges** :— Justice V. Gopala Gowda and Justice Adarsh Kumar Goel.

**Advocates:—**

1. For the Appellants :— Rishi Malhotra, Prem Malhotra, R.K. Kapoor, Ms. Shiwani Mahipal, Anis Ahmed Khan, Sudhir Walia, Ms. Niharika Ahluwalia, Dr. Abhishek Atrey, Rajat Sharma (for Dr. Kailash Chand).
2. For the Respondents :— Manjit Singh, AAG, Tarjit Singh and Kamal Mohan Gupta.

Criminal Appeal No. 1195 of 2010.

Date of Decision — 18.9.2014.

**Prevention of Corruption Act , 1988 Sections 13(1)(d) and 13(2) Indian Penal Code, Sections 474 and 406— Accused a public servant manipulating official record to help a person— No evidence that accused had taken some pecuniary advantage— Accused could not be convicted under Prevention of Corruption Act.**

**Cases Referred :**

Bhagwan Kaur v. Maharaj Krishan Sharma, (1973)4 SCC 46.

---

# Acquittal of only co-accused who was a Deputy Commissioner in Department of Prohibition and Excise from charge of corruption due to delay in trial and age being above 80 years

***Seeta Hemchandra Shashittal v. State of Maharashtra***
**(From Bombay High Court)**

2001(5) BCR 323:2001(1) R.C.R. (Criminal) 838:2001 AIR (SC) 1246:2001 CriLJ 1242:2001(1) Crimes 248:2001(1) AICLR 647:2001(4) SCC 525:2001 SCC (Cri) 787:2001(2) JT 558:2001(2) Scale 8:2001 (1) SCR 990:2001 (2) RLW 297:2001(1) Andh LD (Criminal)559:2001(5) Bom.C.R. (Cri.) 323:2001 (42) ACrC 617:2001 Cri. L.R. 256:2001 ALL MR (Cri) 582:2001 CalCriLR 197:2001 AIR (SCW) 795:2001(1) Supreme 661:2001(2) BomLR 978:2001(1) JLJR 505.

**Judges :—** Justice K.T. Thomas and Justice R.P. Sethi.

**Advocates:—**

1. For the Appellants :— Dr. Rajeev Dhawan, Sr. Advocate with Mr. Markand D. Adkar, Mr. S.D. Singh and Mr. Vishwajit Singh.
2. For the Respondent :— Mr. Shridhar Y. Chitale and Mr. S.V. Deshpande.

Criminal Appeal No. 176 of 2001 (Arising out of S.L.P. (Crl.) No. 2311 of 2000).
Date of Decision — 13.2.2001.

**Cases referred :**

Hussaiara Khatoon and ors. v. Home Secretary, State of Bihar, 1980(1) SCC 81.

State of Andhra Pradesh v. P.V. Pavithran, 1990(2) SCC 340.

A.R. Antulay v. R.S. Nayak, 1992(1) SCC 225.

Rajdeo Sharma v. State of Bihar, 1998(7) SCC 507.

---

## Acquittal of Public Servant from charge of bribe due to non-corroboration of evidence

***State of Gujarat v. Kumudchandra Pranjivan Shah***
**(From Gujarat High Court)**

1995 CriLJ 3623:1997 SCC (Cri) 750:1998(1) GLR 74:1996(1) RLW 48:1995 AIR (SCW) 3073.

**Judges:—** Justice G.N. Ray and Justice Faizan Uddin.

Criminal Appeal No. 408 of 1984.
Date of Decision — 22.3.1995.

---

## Quashing of charges against a Deputy Commissioner of Police and others as Lokayukta is not competent to investigate the allegation of disproportionate assets in an administrative action

***State of Karnataka v. Kemaiah***
**(From Karnataka High Court)**

1998(3) R.C.R. (Criminal) 756:1998 AIR (SC) 3047:1998 CriLJ 4070:1998(3) Crimes 77:1998(3) SCR 910:1998(6) SCC 103:1998(4) Scale 290:1998(5) JT 181:1998(4) AICLR 309:1998 SCC (Cri) 1417:1998 AIR (SCW) 2907:1998(2) Andh LD (Criminal) 435:1998 Cri. L.R. 553:1999(1) ECrC 82:1998 (6) Supreme 122.

**Judges :—** Justice M.K. Mukherjee and Justice S.S. Mohammed Quadri.

**Advocates:—**

1. For the Appellants :— Mr. K.R. Nagaraja and Mr. K.K. Tyagi.
2. For the Respondent :— Mr. Ashok K. Srivastava and Mr. T.V. Ratnam.

Criminal Appeal Nos. 722—723 of 1998 (Arising out of SLP (C) Nos. 1380-81/97).

Date of Decision — 27.7.1998.

---

## Acquittal of an Inspector of the Regional Transport Office from the charge of possessing disproportionate assets due to lack of evidence

***State of Maharashtra v. Kaliar Koil Subramaniam Ramaswamy***

**(From Bombay High Court)**

1977 AIR (SC) 2091:1978(1) SCR 274:1977 CriLJ 1740:1977(3) SCC 525:1977 SCC (Cri) 528:1978 M.L.W. (Cri.) 11:1977 SerLC 197:1977 CLJ (Criminal) 219:1977 UJ (SC) 597:1977 SCCriR 336:1977 Cri. L.R. 372:1977 Cri. App. R (SC) 309:1978(1) SCWR 90.

**Judges :—** Justice N.L. Untwalia and Justice P.N. Shinghal.

**Advocates:—**

1. For the Appellant :— M.N. Phadke, Sr. Advocate M.N. Shroff, Advocate.
2. For the Respondent :— V.S. Desai, Sr. Advocate S.B. Wad and Jayashree Wad.

Criminal Appeal No. 6 of 1972.

Date of Decision — 8.8.1977.

**Cases referred :**

Ramanand Pundlik Kamat v. State, Criminal Appeal No. 1436 of 1968 decided on 26/27th August, 1971 (SC).

Sajjan Singh v. State of Punjab. (1964)4 SCR 630.

C.S.D. Swamy v. State, (1960)1 SCR 461.

Surajpal Singh v. State of U.P. (1961)2 SCR 971.

---

## Acquittal of Police Officer in a false charge against him

***State of Tamil Nadu v. Krishnan***

**(From Madras High Court)**

2001 AIR (SCW) 2415:2002(9) SCC 521:2003 SCC (Cri) 1231:2007(7) SLT 266:2003 (25) Orrisa Cri. R. 481

**Judges :—** Justice A.S. Anand, C.J. N. Santosh Hegdea and Justice Shivaraj V. Patil.

Criminal Appeal No. 393 of 1993.

Date of Decision — 20.9.2000.

---

## Acquittal of Assistant Iron & Steel Controller from charge of corrupt and illegal means for making allotment of steel

***State (Delhi Administration) v. N.S. Giani***

**(From Delhi High Court)**

1990(2) R.C.R. (Criminal) 32:1990(3) SCC 325:1990 AIR (SC) 1190:1990 CriLJ 1207:1990(1) CurLJ 677:1990(1) AICLR 964:1990(2) JT 76:1990(3) Crimes 254:1990(41) DLT 1:1990(1) Scale 654:1990 Cri. L.R. 285:1991 SCC (Cri) 16:1990(2) APLJ 6:1990 CalCriLR 159:1990 Cri. App. R. (SC) 164.

**Judges :—** Justice S. Ratnavel Pandian And Justice K. Jayachandra Reddy.

**Advocates:—**

Counsel for the Parties :— Ms. A. Subhashini, Mr. R.P. Ramasesh, K.C. Dua.

Criminal Appeal No. 383 of 1975.

Date of Decision — 4.4.1990.

A. **Prevention of Corruption Act, 1947, Section 5(1)(d)— Accused working as Assistant Iron and Steel Controller—Accused making allotment of huge quantity of steel— Allegation that accused used corrupt and illegal means and abused official capacity in making allotment— Case based on circumstantial evidence— From circumstances it was difficult to infer any dishonest intention to obtain benefit— Further, evidence did not necessarily lead to the only inference that accused acted dishonestly— Acquittal upheld.**

[Para 5]

B. **Prevention of Corruption Act, 1947, Section 5(1)(d) — Corruption case against accused — Evidence against accused did not necessarily lead to the only inference that accused acted dishonestly — Acquittal upheld.**

[Para 5]

---

## Acquittal of Public Servant on the ground of lack of evidence

### *T.K. Ramesh Kumar v. State Through Police Inspector, Bangalore*

**(From Karnataka High Court)**

2015(2) Recent Apex Judgements (R.A.J.) 426:2015(2) R.C.R. (Criminal) 464:2015 All SCR 2863:2015(2) Law Herald (SC) 1483:2015(3) AICLR 143:2015(3) Law Herald 2096:2015(2) Cri. CC 614:2015(3) Scale 248:2015(2) Apex Court Judgements (SC) 103:2016(3) SCC (Cri) 316:2015(15) SCC 629.

**Judges** :— Justice V. Gopala Gowda and Justice C. Nagappan.

**Advocates:—**

1. For the Appellant :— Mr. V. Giri, Senior Advocate, Ms. T.S. Shanthi, Mr. Prashant S. Kenjale, Mr. Mohd. Sadique T.A. and Mr. Narendra Kumar.
2. For the Respondent :— Mr. V.N. Raghupathy.

Criminal Appeal No. 331 of 2015 (Arising out of S.L.P. (Crl.) No. 3565 of 2012).

Date of Decision — 18.2.2015.

**A. Prevention of Corruption Act, 1988, Sections 7, 13(1)(d) and 13(2)— Complainant stated that accused demanded ₹2000/- for doing an official favour in presence of his father — Father not examined and his statement not recorded by Investigating Officer during investigation — It is fatal — Held, demand not proved conviction set aside:—**

**(i) It has been held in C.M. Sharma v. State of A.P., 2011(1) RCR (Crl.) 183:2010(6) Recent Apex Judgment (RAJ) 636 that mere recovery of currency notes itself does not constitute the offence under the Act, unless it is proved beyond all reasonable doubt that the accused voluntarily accepted the money knowing it to be bribe. 2012(3) RCR (Crl.) 980:2012(4) Recent Apex Judgment (RAJ) 206, 2011(1) RCR (Crl.) 183:2010(6) Recent Apex Judgment (RAJ) 636, relied.**

[Paras 8, 9 and 10]

**B. Prevention of Corruption Act, 1988, Sections 19, 7, 13(1)(d) and 13(2) Prosecution of Public Servant in corruption— Sanction for prosecution issued by Authority without application of mind— Conviction set aside.**

[Para 11]

**Cases Referred :**

Mukut Bihari v. State of Rajasthan, 2012(3) R.C.R. (Criminal) 980 : 2012(4) Recent Apex Judgments (R.A.J.) 206 : (2012)11 SCC 642.

B. Jayaraj v. State of A.P., 2014(2) R.C.R.(Criminal) 410 : 2014(2) Recent Apex Judgments (R.A.J.) 570 : (2014) 13 SCC 55.

C.M. Sharma v. State of A.P., 2011(1) R.C.R.(Criminal) 183 : 2010(6) Recent Apex Judgments (R.A.J.) 636 : (2010) 15 SCC 1.

Mansukhlal Vithaldas Chauhan v. State ofGujarat, 1997(4) R.C.R.(Criminal) 236 : (1997)7 SCC 622.

---

## Acquittal of a Lower Division Clerk in Punjab Electricity Board in trap and raid case though Investigation Officer supported the case

***Tarlok Chand v. State of Punjab***

**(From Punjab and Haryana High Court)**

2015(2) CCR 215:2014(5) Law Herald (SC) 4126:2015(2) AICLR 567:2014(6) Recent Apex Judgements (R.A.J.) 618:2015(1) R.C.R. (Criminal) 69:2015(1) Cri.CC 513.

**Judges:**— Justice T.S. Thakur, Justice Adarsh Kumar Goel and Justice R. Banumathi.

**Advocates:—**

For the Appellant :— Mr. Nidesh Gupta, Senior Advocate, Mr. Tarun Gupta and Ms. S. Janani.

For the Respondent :— Mr. Jayant K. Sud, AAG, Ms. Jasleen Chahal, Mr. Ajay P. Tushir and Mr. Kuldip Singh.

Criminal Appeal No. 594 of 2012.
Date of Decision — 26.11.2014.

**Prevention of Corruption Act , 1988, Sections 13(2) and 7— Acquittal in corruption case— Prosecution version that accused demanded bribe money of ₹1000/- from complainant in presence of two shadow witnesses — A raid was conducted and bribe money recovered from table of accused — Both the shadow witnesses and complainant resiled from their statements — Conviction of accused set aside — Accused could not be convicted on basis of statement of Investigating Officer.**

[Paras 3 to 5]

---

# Acquittal of Mandal Revenue Officer from charge of bribe as prosecution failed to prove offencc beyond reasonable doubt

## *V. Venkata Subbarao v. State represented by Inspector of Police, A.P.*

**(From Andhra Pradseh High Court)**

2007(1) R.C.R. (Criminal) 519:2007(1) Recent Apex Judgements (R.A.J.) 321:2007 AIR (SC) 489:2007 CriLJ 754:2007(1) AICLR 807:2006(14) Scale 125:2006(13) SCC 305:2006 (Sup10) SCR 729:2007(3) SCC (Cri) 175:2007(1) Crimes 101:2007(1) Cri.CC 746:2007(1) KantLJ 227:2007(1) Andh LD (Criminal) 209:2007(1) W.L.C. 535:2007(2) J.C.R. 253:2007 ALL MR(Cri) 1201:2007(50) AIC 369:2007 AIR (SCW) 9:2007(2) AIR Jhar R. 154:2007(2) Air Kar R 18:2007(2) RajCriC 629:2007(2) RLW 1649:2007(1) Apex Court Judgements (SC) 276:2007 NCC 199:2007(1) L.R.C. 274:2007(1) CLR 270:2007(2) CLR 451.

**Judges** :— Justice S.B. Sinha and Justice Markandey Katju.

**Advocate:—**

1. For the Appellant :— Y. Raja Gopala Rao, Y. Ramesh and Ms. Y. Vismai Rao.
2. For the Respondent :— P. Vinay Kumar and C.H. Leela Sarveswar for Mrs. D. Bharathi Reddy.

Criminal Appeal No. 970 of 2000.
Date of Decision - 12.12.2006

**A. Prevention of Corruption Act , 1988 , Section 20— Complaint made to Police after a period of 15 days from original demand by accused— Prosecution did not explain as to why the complaint had been made after 15 days— Demand also not proved— In absence of a proof of demand, the question of raising the presumption would not arise— Conviction set aside. 2005(4) RCR(Crl.) 517 (SC) : 2005(3) Apex Criminal 442 (SC) relied.**

[Paras 12 and 23]

**B. Prevention of Corruption Act , 1988 , Sections 13(1)(d) and 13(2) — Sanction for prosecution of public servant — Vital document showing involvement of accused not produced before Sanctioning Authority — Sanctioning Authority, therefore, did not have any occasion to apply their mind to the entire materials on record and in that view of the matter, the sanction is vitiated in law — Conviction set aside.**

[Para 23]

**Cases referred :**

M.S. Narayana Menon @ Mani v. State of Kerala, 2006(3) RCR(Crl.) 504 : 2006(2) Apex Criminal 531 (SC) : [(2006) 6 SCC 39].

Union of India through Inspector, CBI v. Purnandu Biswas, 2005(4) RCR(Crl.) 517: 2005(3) Apex Criminal 442 (SC) : [(2005) 12 SCC 576].

State through Inspector of Police, A.P. v. K. Narasimhachary, 2005(3) Apex Criminal 415 (SC) : [(2005) 8 SCC 364].

Kalyan Singh v. State of Maharashtra [2006 (12) SCALE 577].

Samghaji Hariba Patil v. State of Karnataka [2006(10) SCALE 283].

Umrao v. State of Haryana [AIR 2006 SC 2152].

---

# Quashing of charges of corruption against Assistant Engineer for delay in filing of Charge Sheet after 27 years though the court has directed to dispose of case within 3 months

***Vakil Prasad Singh v. State of Bihar***

**(From Patna High Court)**

2009(1) R.C.R. (Criminal) 802:2009(1) Recent Apex Judgements (R.A.J.) 648:2009(3) SCC 355:2009(2) AICLR 14:2009(2) JT 113:2009(2) Scale 22:2009 CriLJ 1731:2009 AIR (SC) 1822:2009(1) CalCriLR 628:2009(3) Cri.CC 669:2009(1) OriLR 555:2009 AIR (SCW) 1418:2009(1) JLJR 277:2009(1) W.L.N. 83:2009(1) W.L.C. 565:2009 Cri. L.R. 372:2009(2) ECrC 187:2010(2) Mh.LJ (Crl.) 493:2009(2) SCC (Cri) 95:2009(1) PLJR 277:2009(2) L.R.C. 81:2009(1) KHC 783:2009(2) BBCJ 140:2009(42) Orrisa Cri. R. 680.

**Judges:**— Justice D.K. Jain and Justice R.M. Lodha.

**Advocates:—**

1. For the Appellant :— Akhilesh Kumar Pandey and Ms. Shalni Chandra.
2. For the Respondent :— Manish Kumar and Gopal Singh.

Criminal Appeal No. 138 Of 2009 (Arising out of S.L.P. (Criminal) No. 6887 of 2007).

Date of Decision — 23.01.2009.

**A. Prevention of Corruption Act, 1988, Section 13(2)— Criminal Procedure Code, Section 482— Constitution of India, Article 21— Prevention of Corruption Act, 1947, Section 5(2)— Speedy trial— Corruption case—**

**Charge-sheet submitted after 27 years despite the direction of High Court that investigation should in completed within 3 months— Delay not attributable to accused— Proceedings quashed despite the fact that allegation against accused were serious— Held:—**

**Right to speedy trial in all criminal persecutions is an inalienable right under Article 21 of the Constitution. 2002(2) RCR(Criminal) 553 (SC) relied.**

[Paras 15 and 16]

B. **Criminal Procedure Code, Section 482— Power of High Court under Section 482, Criminal Procedure Code is very wide but it has to be exercised in appropriate cases, ex debito justitiae to do real and substantial justice for the administration of which alone the courts exist— The inherent powers do not confer an arbitrary jurisdiction on the High Court to act according to whim or caprice— Said powers however have to be exercised. 1992(4) SCC 305 and 1991(1) RCR(Criminal) 383 (SC) relied.**

[Para 9]

## Cases referred :

Kurukshetra University v. State of Haryana, (1977)4 SCC 451.

Janata Dal v. H.S. Chowdhary, (1992)4 SCC 305.

State of Haryana v. Bhajan Lal, 1991(1) RCR(Crl.) 383 : 1992 Supp (1) SCC 335.

Maneka Gandhi v. Union of India, (1978)1 SCC 248.

Hussainara Khatoon v. Home Secretary, State of Bihar, (1980)1 SCC 81.

Abdul Rehman Antulay v. R.S. Nayak, (1992)1 SCC 225.

Common Cause" A Registered Society v. Union of India (UOI), 1996(2) RCR(Criminal) 419 : (1996)4 SCC 33.

Common Cause", A Registered Society v. Union of India, (1996) 6 SCC 775.

Raj Deo Sharma v. State of Bihar, 1998(4) RCR(Criminal) 396 : (1998)7 SCC 507.

Raj Deo Sharma v. State of Bihar, 1999(4) RCR(Criminal) 206 : (1999)7 SCC 604.

P. Ramachandra Rao v. State of Karnataka, 2002(2) RCR(Criminal) 553 : (2002)4 SCC 578.

---

# Acquittal of a Sub-Engineer from charge of possessing disproportionate assets for failure of Evidence

***Vasant Rao Guhe v. State of Madhya Pradesh***

**(From Madhya Pradesh High Court)**

2017(8) Scale 594:2017(4) B.L.Jud. 23:2017(3) R.C.R. (Criminal) 1024:2017 AIR (SC) 3713:2017(7) JT 586:2017(4) Recent Apex Judgements (R.A.J.) 703:2017 AIR (SCW) 3713:2017(3) Crimes 180:2017(3) AIR Jhar R. 825:2017(3) ALT (Crl.) 38:2017(3) MLJ (Criminal) 698:2017 All SCR (Crl.) 1455:2017 Cri. L.R. 894:2017(177) AIC 42:2017(100) ACrC 985:2017(3) JLJR 389:2017(3) Law Herald (SC) 2335:2017(4) PLJR 4:2017(3) JCC 2125:2017(2) PCCR 489:2017(4) JBCJ 232:2017(2) Andh LD (Criminal) 733:2017(2) SCCriR 1285:2017(4) AICLR 509:2017 RajCriC 767:2017(3) All. Crl. Rulings 2789:2017(4) Cri.CC 419:2017(3) Apex Court Judgements (SC) 569:2017(68) Orrisa Cri. R. 1047:2017(3) BBCJ 510:2017(2) Ori. Law Rev. 717:2018 (sup1) CutLT (Criminal) 75:2018(1) JabLJ 388:2018(1) LW (Crl.) 795.

**Judges**:— Justice Dipak Misra, Justice Amitava Roy and Justice A.M. Khanwilkar.

**Advocates:—**

1. For the Appellant :— Harsh Parashar.
2. For the Respondent :— C.D. Singh.

Criminal Appeal No. 1279 of 2017 (Arising Out of S.L.P.(Crl.) No. 3595 of 2014).

Date of Decision — 9.8.2017.

**A. Prevention of Corruption Act, 1988, Sections 13(1)(e) and 13(2)— Possession of property by a Public servant beyond his known sources of income— A public servant charged of criminal misconduct under the Act has to be proved by the prosecution to be in possession of pecuniary resources or property disproportionate to his known sources of income, at any time during the period of his office—**

**(1) The public servant would be held to be guilty of such offence of criminal misconduct, if he cannot satisfactorily account such disproportionate pecuniary resources or property.**

**(2) The explanation to Section 13(1)(e) elucidates the words "known sources of income" to mean income received from any lawful source and that such receipt has been intimated in accordance with the provisions of law, rules, orders for the time being applicable to a public servant.**

[Para 20]

**B. Prevention of Corruption Act, 1988, Sections 13(1)(e) and 13(2)— Criminal Procedure Code, 1973, Sections 227 and 228 Charge sheet filed against accused but accused convicted on different Charges— Conviction set aside— Charge sheet filed in the court that accused possessed assets disproportionate to his known sources of income but the charge for which the accused finally was convicted wears a new complexion different**

**from the one with which he had been arraigned at the initiation of the trial — The accused thus for all practical purposes was subjected to a trial involving fleeting frames of accusations of which he was denied prior notice — This is clearly opposed to the fundamental precepts of a criminal prosecution.**

[Para 17]

C. **Prevention of Corruption Act , 1988 Sections 13(1)(e) and 13(2)— Public servant in possession of property beyond his known sources of income— Burden of proof is a prosecution— In case the prosecution fails to prove that the public servant either by himself or through anyone else had at any time during the period of his office been in possession of pecuniary resources or property disproportionate to his known sources of income, he would not be required in law to offer any explanation to satisfactorily account therefor—**

(1) **A public servant facing such charge, cannot be comprehended to furnish any explanation in absence of the proof of the allegation of being in possession by himself or through someone else, pecuniary resources or property disproportionate to his known sources of income — 2009(4) RCR (Crl.) 217 : 2009(5) Recent Apex Judgments (RAJ) 356 Relied.**

[Paras 21 and 22]

**Cases Referred :**

State of Maharashtra v. Dnyaneshwar Laxman Rao Wankhede, 2009(4) R.C.R.(Criminal) 217 : 2009(5) Recent Apex Judgments (R.A.J.) 356 : (2009) 15 SCC 200.

---

# Acquittal of I.A.S. Officer who had delegated his power to other Officers who face charge of corruption

***Vinod Chandra Semwal v.***
***Special Police Establishment, Ujjain***
**(From Madhya Pradesh High Court)**

2015 ALL MR (Cri) 3276:2015 CriLJ 3606:2015(8) SCC 383:2015(2) R.C.R. (Criminal) 242:2015(2) Recent Apex Judgements (R.A.J.) 207:2015(2) Law Herald (SC) 1381:2015(2) CCR 128:2015(2) Cri.CC 356:2015 AIR (SCW) 3960:2015(2) AICLR 601:2015(3) SCC(Cri) 614:2015 Cri. L.R. 1314:2015(3) Scale 537:2015(2) Apex Court Judgements (SC) 28:2016(5) JT 518:2016 RajCriC 387:2016(3) Mh.LJ (Crl.) 102:2015(61) Orrisa Cri. R. 544:2015(2) All. Crl. Rulings 1240.

**Judges** :— Justice Sudhansu Jyoti Mukhopadhaya and Justice N.V. Ramana.

**Advocates:—**

1. For the Appellant :— Dr. Rajeev Dhavan, Sr. Adv. Mr. S.N. Jha, Sr. Adv. Mr. Manish Kumar, Adv. Mr. Rakesh Mishra,Adv. Mr. Piyush Kaushik, Adv. Mr. Sukani Vikram.

2. For the Respondent :— Mr. S.K. Dubey, Sr Adv. Mr. C. D. Singh,Adv. Mr. Yogesh Tiwari, Adv. Mr. Darpan.

Criminal Appeal No. 2129 of 2011.

Date of Decision — 24.2.2015.

**NUTSHELL**

A public servant delegating some power to subordinate officer — Delegatee indulged in corruption — Delegator not guilty of offence committed by delegatee.

Prevention of Corruption Act , 1988 Sections 13(1)(d), 13(2) and 19 A public servant delegating some power to subordinate officer — Allegation that delegatee indulged in corruption — Delegator not guilty of offence committed by delegatee.

**ON FACTS:**

Sanction for prosecution of Public Servant — Appellant who was an IAS officer was appointed as Collector Ratlam — Appellant was also appointed ex—officio Chairman of Improvement Trust — Appellant delegated certain power to Chief Executive Officer of Improvement Trust — The delegatee executed an Exchange deed on behalf of Chairman (Appellant) transferring certain land to accused without consideration thereby causing loss of Rs. 1.34 crores to State Exchequer — Held, if the delegatee has not acted in terms of the delegated powers the delegator cannot be held guilty of offence under Sections 13(1)(d) and 13(2) of P.C. Act — Sanction for prosecution rightly refused by Govt. 2007(1) RCR (Crl.) 1 : 2007(1) Recent Apex Judgment (RAJ) 71, relied.

[Paras 12, 13 and 14]

**Cases Referred :**

Prakash Singh Badal v. State of Punjab, 2007(1) R.C.R. (Criminal) 1 : 2007(1) Recent Apex Judgments (R.A.J.) 71 : (2007)1 SCC 1.

---

## Acquittal of co-accused on the basis of failure of prosecution to prove guilty and on the ground of benefit of doubt

***Virendranath v. State of Maharashtra***

**(From Bombay High Court)**

1996 AIR (SC) 490:1996(11) SCC 688:1997 SCC(Cri) 264:1995 AIR (SCW) 4382.

**Judges**:— Justice M.M. Punchhi and Justice K. Jayachandra Reddy.

Criminal Appeal No. 402 of 1994 with Cri A. No. - of 1995
(arising out of SLP (Cri) No. 2859 of 1992).

Date of Decision — 29.3.1995.

A. **Prevention of Corruption Act, 1988, Section 7— Acceptance of bribe— Proof— Co-accused taking tainted money on the asking of accused— Beforehand there was a talk between complainant and accused only— Bribe money with complainant was meant to pass on the accused at restaurant of Co-accused as it was convenient place for him— Acceptance of money by accused must be held to have been established— Accused cannot be held to have been not guilty on ground that he did not actually receive money— Conviction of accused is confirmed, however his sentence is reduced to the minimum possible.**

[Para 4]

B. **Prevention of Corruption Act, 1988, Section 7— Bribe— Acceptance of tainted money from complainant by accused at instance of another person— Tainted money actually was to pass on to such other person— No evidence was led by the prosecution to prove that accused was habitual go—between in facilitating acceptance of bribe by that person— Single instance in question would not reveal regularity of conduct of such nature— Thus exists an area of doubt— Accused should be given benefit of such doubt and acquitted.**

[Para 5]

---

# Acquittal of Public Servant in a corruption case under some sections of the Act of 1988 and conviction under other sections

***P. Subramanian v. State of Tamil Nadu***

**(From Madras High Court)**

2009(2) AICLR 618

**Judges**:— Justice B.N. Agrawal and Justice G.S. Singhvi.

Criminal Appeal No. 1325 of 2002.

Date of Decision - 19.3.2009.

---

# SUBJECT INDEX